BY THE SAME AUTHOR

INORGANIC AND THEORETICAL CHEMISTRY
ORGANIC CHEMISTRY
SHORTER ORGANIC CHEMISTRY
FIRST-YEAR-RESEARCH METHODS OF CHEMISTRY

THE
WORLD
OF SCIENCE

THE
WORLD
OF SCIENCE

BY

F. SHERWOOD TAYLOR
Ph.D., M.A., B.Sc.

LONDON
WILLIAM HEINEMANN LTD

FIRST PUBLISHED 1936

PRINTED IN GREAT BRITAIN
AT THE WINDMILL PRESS, KINGSWOOD, SURREY

To
MY WIFE

PREFACE

The purpose of this book is to answer in simple terms the questions which the ordinary man and woman ask about living creatures, the world and the mechanical devices daily encountered by all.

The book is neither a text-book of the Sciences nor a history of scientific thought and progress. The precision of language required for the former would be useless and irritating to the reader: the latter could not be adequately treated without increasing the book to twice its present size.

I have pleasure in thanking, on pages 1059–1063, a great many persons and corporate bodies for their help, without which this book could not have been written.

11, *Grays Inn Square,*
London, W.C. 1936.

TABLE OF CONTENTS

PART I

THE STATES OF MATTER

PART II

POWER

PART IV

CHEMISTRY

PART V

THE EARTH AND HEAVENS

PART VI

LIFE

INDEX NOTATION AND DECIMAL NUMBERS.

INDEX NOTATION

Very large and very small numbers are written on the index system which is sufficiently explained by the examples given below:

$$10^{10} = 10,000,000,000 \qquad 10^{-10} = \frac{1}{10,000,000,000} = 0.000,000,000,1$$

$$10^{9} = 1000,000,000 \qquad 10^{-6} = \frac{1}{1000,000} = 0.000,001$$

$$10^{2} = 100 \qquad 10^{-2} = \frac{1}{100} = 0.01$$

$$10^{1} = 10 \qquad 10^{-1} = \frac{1}{10} = 0.1$$

$$3 \times 10^{6} = 3 \times 1000,000 = 3000,000$$
$$2.2 \times 10^{5} = 2.2 \times 100,000 = 220,000$$
$$0.3 \times 10^{-7} = 0.3 \times \frac{1}{10,000,000} = 0.000,000,03$$

DECIMAL MEASURES OF LENGTH.

1 Angstrom Unit (A.U.) = 10^{-8} centimetres (cm.)
1 millimu ($m\mu$) = 10^{-7} centimetres
1 mu. (μ) = 10^{-4} centimetres
1 millimetre (mm.) = $\frac{1}{10}$ centimetre ($\frac{1}{25}$ inch)
1 centimetre ($\frac{2}{5}$ inch)
1 metre = 100 centimetres ($1\frac{1}{12}$ yard)
1 kilometre = 100,000 centimetres ($\frac{5}{8}$ mile)

DECIMAL MEASURES OF CAPACITY.

1 cubic millimetre (cu. mm.) = $\frac{1}{1000}$ cubic centimetre
1 cubic centimetre (cc.) (about 15 drops)
1 litre = 1000 cc. (about a quart)
1 cubic metre = 1000,000 cc. (about $1\frac{1}{3}$ cubic yards.)

DECIMAL MEASURES OF WEIGHT

1 milligram (mg.) = $\frac{1}{1000}$ gram
1 gram (g.) (about $\frac{1}{30}$ oz. or 15 grains)
1 kilogram (kg.) = 1000 grams ($2\frac{1}{4}$ lbs.)
1 metric ton = 1000,000 grams (roughly 1 English ton)

PART I

THE STATES OF MATTER

CHAPTER I

INTRODUCTION

SCIENCE AND SCIENTISTS

THE man in the street has a very fair idea of the meaning of the word Science. It includes, he feels, such pursuits as Astronomy, Chemistry, Biology. He is not so sure whether engineering or medicine is Science and is quite certain that Politics, History, Art, Religion and the like are not.

The Scientist is more interested in doing scientific research than in defining it. He sometimes says that a piece of work or a book is "unscientific" and he usually means by the phrase that it is inexact; that it is badly arranged; that it jumps to conclusions without sufficient evidence or that the author has allowed his personal prejudices to influence his report. By scientific work, then, we mean that which is as exact as is possible, orderly in arrangement and based on sound and sufficient evidence. Moreover it must have no object except to find out the truth.

Perhaps Science is most clearly defined by saying that it is firstly a vast collection of facts expressed in exact and unambiguous language in such a manner that anyone who cares to take the trouble can test their truth; and secondly a collection of rules or laws which express the connection between these facts. This does not sound very interesting, but it is extremely important. As long as men hunted for knowledge in a random sort of way and believed each other's assertions without testing them, knowledge made negligible progress. Once they began to make sure that their facts were right by doing experiments for themselves, Science began to grow.

An example of modern scientific work is not easy to give because it all depends on enormous masses of work which has gone before, and of which the reader may know nothing. Let us imagine, then, that Mr. Smith has noticed for the first time that a rod of iron gets very slightly longer when it is heated. This is a random observation such as anyone might have made since iron

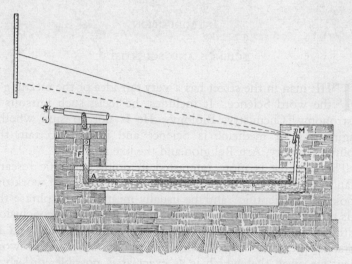

Fig. 1.—Measurement of the expansion of a solid rod.

was first known. Smith is not content to notice the fact: he is going to investigate it according to the methods of Science. The first thing required is an *exact* knowledge of the expansion of iron when heated. Our investigator therefore sets to work to make an instrument to measure the very small increase of length.

The instrument he devises[1] is shown in Figure 1.
An iron rod A B of measured length, say 1 metre, lies in a trough of water, the temperature of which is measured by a ther-

[1] Actually the apparatus described was evolved and perfected over a period of 100 years or so. The need to measure the expansion of iron exactly arose from the alteration noticed in the length of surveying rods in the eighteenth century. The apparatus shown is not the most modern, which depends on Newton's rings (Chapter xv).

mometer. The temperature of the water is (if a sufficient time has elapsed) the same as that of the iron. One end of the iron rod touches a fixed rod F. This end will, therefore, not move if the iron expands. The iron rod is supported on two glass rods so that it slides easily over them. Its right-hand end B touches a lever which has on it a small mirror M.

If the rod expands the lever will be turned on its pivot anti-clockwise, and the mirror will turn with it. Now a telescope is focused on the mirror so that a scale is seen by the observer, reflected in the mirror. The telescope has two crossed wires in its eyepiece so that the observer can note what part of the scale comes exactly opposite the cross wires. Now suppose that Smith packs the trough with ice and water: the iron rod will be at 0°C., and when he looks through the telescope he sees the 10.5 cm. mark of the scale opposite the crosswires. Next he fills the trough with water, kept, say, at 50° C. precisely.[1]

The rod expands, the mirror is turned, and a different part of the scale, say the 22.7 cm. mark, now appears opposite the crosswires. There is a rule which tells him the direction in which rays of light are reflected from mirrors (p. 453) and it is easy to see that a little geometry will enable him to calculate the angle through which the mirror M (and therefore also the lever) has moved. From this he can calculate the distance the end of the rod has moved when being heated from 0° C. to 50° C.

Let us suppose that Smith finds by these measurements that his bar of iron has a length of

1.0000	metre	at	0° C.
1.00011	,,	at	10° C.
1.00055	,,	at	50° C.
1.0011	,,	at	100° C.

It does not take much examination of these results to see that for each degree of temperature it has been heated, it has expanded 0.000011 metres. The next thing to see is whether other bars of

---

[1] The idea of "temperature" and "degrees" is not at all simple. We can feel "hotness and coldness." The way we measure it is taken up again on page 104.

iron behave in the same way. A bar of iron 2 metres long at 0° C. is next taken and the figures for its length are

2.0000	metres	at	0° C.
2.00033	,,	at	15° C.
2.000165	,,	at	75° C.
2.0022	,,	at	100° C.

It expands 0.000022 metres for every degree through which it has been heated. Several more experiments with iron bars of different length are then tried, and our imaginary Smith deduces from these some statement or rule that is *true for all of them*. It is quite easy to find one. "When a piece of iron is heated, it expands by eleven millionths of its length for each degree centigrade through which it is heated."

Smith's knowledge is now much more wide and exact, but is still rather narrow, for his deductions refer only to the metal iron. The next experiment that he does is to repeat the work he has done for iron with other materials, such as copper, glass, etc. He finds that the same sort of rule applies in these cases. Thus, "a piece of copper expands by seventeen millionths for each degree centigrade through which it is heated." "A piece of glass expands by nine millionths of its length for each degree (C.) through which it is heated." Smith tries all the substances that he can get hold of in large enough pieces, and finally gets at this General Law:

"Every solid when heated through one degree centigrade increases in length by a fraction of its length which is always the same for a given solid, but which is different for different solids." He calls this fraction (which is 0.000011 for iron, 0.000017 for copper, 0.000009 for glass, &c.) the *coefficient of expansion*. His next step is to put his law mathematically, because mathematics (to those who understand them) afford the simplest and least ambiguous way of expressing a truth. Accordingly, he says, "If l_0 is the length of a solid at a temperature t_0, and l_1 its length at temperature t_1, then

$$l_1 = l_0 \left[1 + a \left(t_1 - t_0 \right) \right]$$

where a is a constant for the given solid." Those of my readers who solve simple equations may work out the length which a railway line 30 metres long at 10° C. (a cool day), reaches when heated to 30° C. (a hot day). The coefficient of expansion a is .000011.

The procedure for scientific work is first to make accurate observations; then to try to deduce a law or explanation which includes them all; and finally to publish full details and let the world criticize. This last is the surest test of truth. An author may give a too fatherly eye to his discovery: the world assuredly will not. The universally accepted parts of Science have all been tested in this way and though some errors escape notice, they are inconsiderable beside the mass of good work.

The feature then that distinguishes the statements accepted by Science from most others is that *they can be relied on*: they are true according to the only sound criterion of truth, which is, that they have been tested by qualified people and can be, at any time, tested by anyone who doubts them. The facts of Science are tested by the repeating of the experiments which lead to them. Scientific Laws are continually subjected to an even more severe test: they are used to predict what will happen under certain circumstances. If the law is sound, the prediction will come true; if the prediction does not come true, the law must be altered.

Newton's law of gravitation which states that "two masses attract each other with a force which varies inversely as the square of the distance between them" enabled us to predict quite exactly (as it seemed at first), where any planet would appear at any date. Then, as measurements became more accurate, it was noted that the planet Mercury was a little off the astronomer's timetable. The law fitted so well with the other planets that no one wanted to reject it, and it was believed that in the measurements of the orbit there was some undiscovered error that would later be found out. Then Einstein brought forward his theory of relativity which indicated that, in Newton's Law, the word "distance" in the sense of "the length of the straight line connecting the masses" cannot be given an exact meaning, unless their relative motions are taken into account. He showed that a body moved in space, so that its course in "space-time" was a line of the shortest possible "length." Calculations showed that near large masses, "space-time" was appreciably curved, and the attractions and courses of the planets, based on Einstein's theory, gave a slightly different result from those based on the Newtonian theory: the test of experiment then showed that within our experimental error, the motions of all the planets agreed with Einstein's prediction. So, Newton's Law was modified: astronomers recognised that it was so nearly true where great masses or intense forces were not concerned that it might be used for all ordinary purposes; but that where enormous masses or great intensities of energy have to be reckoned with, they would have to make allowance for Einstein's correction.

The readiness of scientific men to change their beliefs and fit them to the facts is in marked contrast to the unwillingness of the politicians to do so. The politician who changes his ideas is called a turncoat or a renegade. To be unconvinced by argument is supposed to be a merit in politics and religion. If Einstein's discovery had been a political matter, there would have been a pro-Einstein and anti-Einstein party, calling each other names and scoffing at each other's arguments. The Scientists waited to see the result of the deciding experiments, then quietly changed their ideas.

It is small wonder that politicians are arguing the same problems as were argued in Greece two thousand years ago, while Science has grown out of all recognition.

THE BEGINNINGS OF SCIENCE

It is interesting to glance back over the centuries and see how Science came into being. The first germ of Science was the wish of man to gain some knowledge of the working of the world about him. We know almost nothing of the thoughts of pre-historic men who for many centuries of centuries inhabited the world before civilisation began, only some five or six thousand years ago. Their graves and their drawings on the rocks suggest to us that they had some simple religion. Probably they believed the stars, the earth, the sky and sea were in some sense alive or animated by gods or spirits. The earliest civilisations we know of were those of Eridu (later Babylon) and of Egypt. These ancient peoples believed in Gods and seem to have thought that the workings of nature were controlled by them.

The Babylonians believed that the stars and planets had a controlling effect on human affairs—an unproved and most improbable belief which has survived till to-day as astrology. Be this as it may, the consequence was that the Babylonians observed the positions of the moon, sun and planets with very great care: they mapped the constellations and recorded the time of eclipses. Their greatest discovery was the Saros, a period of 223 lunar months (18 years, 11 days) after which the sun, moon and earth have almost the same relative positions as they had before it. As an eclipse occurs in certain definite positions of the sun, moon and earth (p. 431), any observed eclipse will recur after the lapse of one Saros. They later found out other similar periods for each of the planets, and thus could predict the state of the sky at any future date. Naturally, the prediction of so alarming an event as an eclipse gained for the Babylonian priests the highest respect and reputation. The Egyptians, whose civilisation began at least as early as 4000 B.C., were by no means such good astronomers as the Babylonians. They excelled in practical arts. They invented simple arithmetic and geometry, and must have had considerable skill in engineering. The pyramids are typical of the spirit of Egypt. They are stern and geometrical in figure; erected by a vast expenditure of slave labour, and directed to a religious object—for they are tombs of kings. The Egyptians had some knowledge of medicine, and in their embalming evidently gained a fair notion of anatomy.

Both Egyptians and Babylonians were applied scientists. They wanted knowledge for its usefulness, not for itself. They needed astronomy (as they thought) to foretell the future, arithmetic for

buying and selling, geometry to measure land and build temples,
medicine to heal the sick.

The Greeks were the first people who sought knowledge for
its own sake. They came into prominence from about 600 B.C.
Their knowledge certainly came in part from Egypt and Babylon,
but their reasoning powers reached far higher levels than those of
any people before them. In art and literature, the Greeks have
never been surpassed. In Philosophy, their work is a living
foundation of all that has come after, but in Science they were
hindered by their unpractical nature. They must be honoured
as the first people who were interested in pure Science, but
although they were very ready to argue about the origins of
things, they could not be bothered to experiment in order to find
out if their conclusions were true.

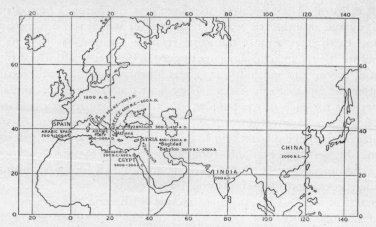

Fig. 2.—Illustrating the centres of scientific thought at successive stages
in the world's history.

Accordingly they made enormous progress in philosophy
and geometry, for which nothing but intellect is required: but
comparatively small advances in Science which must be based on
observation of the behaviour of material things. The name
which stands out as the first great man of Science, is that of
Aristotle (384–322 B.C.) who practically founded the study of

biology, who first tried to classify living creatures and to understand how their bodies worked. For 1,500 years after him, his works remained the greatest textbook of Science.

In somewhat later times, Archimedes (287–212 B.C.) discovered many of the simple principles of physics and Ptolemy (*c.* A.D. 140) and others made some advances in astronomy. Then, after the civilisation of Greece had been absorbed by that of Rome, progress slowed down. A few centuries later barbarians overwhelmed the civilisation of Rome and for a thousand years Science was almost dead. From A.D. 300–1100 Europe was under the shadow of the Dark Ages: only in Byzantium did the Greeks keep knowledge alive. Even there, progress had stopped, though the lamp of learning still burned. The Arabs, too, who rose to prominence from about A.D. 700, kept alive the learning they had gained from the Greeks and inhabitants of Syria. They had a certain genius for mathematics and, indeed, science in general; and when, in the thirteenth century, translations of Arabic works were made in Spain and passed on to Europe, learning began to increase. After the sack of Byzantium by the Turks in 1453, manuscripts of Greek authors and a knowledge of Greek found their way into Europe. The effect was remarkable. Learning ceased to be a monopoly of the priesthood; it became the equipment of gentlemen and even of princes.

The science of Aristotle was eagerly studied, was questioned and was superseded. In 1620, Francis Bacon laid the foundation stone of modern science by his book, the *Novum Organum*, which dealt with the scientific method.

From that date modern science begins. To recount its progress from 1600 to 1936 would be to tell much of what follows in this book. Suffice it to say, that the need for testing knowledge by experiment was only slowly learned; but as men grew ever more scientific in spirit, so discoveries became more rapid, till the nineteenth century was one great triumphal progress of Science. Between 1800 and 1900, the world was altered out of all recognition. The population of the world almost doubled itself between 1845 and 1925. The average life of man is now more than twice as long as it was in 1750. The ends of the earth were brought from six months' distance to six weeks': the period 1900–1936 has reduced this to three days. Beliefs unquestioned for centuries have vanished like smoke. Man, to-day, has far more knowledge, power, health and wealth than he had in 1800, but he has no more brains and very little more wisdom. The war of 1914–1918 showed us what the power of Science in the hands of folly and ambition could do. Science can never recede; if its weapons are not to destroy us we must make ourselves fit to handle them.

SCIENCE AND THE MODERN WORLD

To show ourselves what Science has done, it is only necessary to sit in a modern room and look round. There is nothing to be seen which the hand of Science has left untouched.

The carpet and curtains are dyed in a shade which no plant could have given: the chemists have coaxed out of black and sticky coal tar the queer network of atoms which gives that soft jade green. From the same coal tar comes my bakelite fountain-pen and the ink in it. The artificial silk fabric of the chair-covers was made from wood pulp by a process not thirty years old. The paint on the walls is made from titanium-white, unheard of 20 years ago. The chromium-plated door fittings, the gas that burns in the fire, the electric light bulb, the artificial graphite in my pencil, are all novel. And even the things apparently made by older crafts have been shaped by elaborate machinery. The wood of the table was cut, planed and polished by machines representing the latest discoveries of engineering, driven probably by electricity generated in vast stations which are triumphs of applied science.

We may perhaps regret the passing of the slow and beautiful old ways of craftsmanship, but the fact remains that the world of to-day is created and maintained by Science. Your own existence you probably owe to Science. In 1750 there were six and a half million people in England; to-day, there are forty-five million. This increase was only possible in consequence of scientific discoveries. One English baby in eighteen now dies before it is a year old; in 1860, one baby in six died and in earlier times, for which no figures are available, matters were far worse. Not only does Science allow more babies to grow up, but the vast population can only be fed because engineering has made possible the transport of food from distant lands.

Thus thirty-nine million people in England alone owe their existence to Science.

Impersonally and quietly, Science will go on growing. It will cure more diseases; it will bring about quicker transport; it will perfect our means of pleasure; it will make our way of living still less natural; it will put terrible weapons of death in our hands. Only an utter breakdown of all civilisation is likely to stop it.

Science, then, is by far the most important factor influencing our material lives—and also, perhaps, our spiritual lives. We no longer expect to die in the twenties and thirties—a life of seventy years is looked on almost as a right. In the middle ages, death was always at hand; the thought of death dominated religion. To-day, we all look forward to a long life; early death is an exception and we do not think about it. Our notions of Truth also have been changed by Science. We can no longer passionately argue whether God the Son was *created* by the Father or *is of one substance with* the Father. Controversy on this point shook the world for forty years in the days of the Arian heresy (A.D. 325–364). Such things we are now content to regard as unknowable. Less and less do we concern ourselves with points which can be argued but cannot be proved; and more and more readily do we confess the impossibility of deciding on matters of pure opinion.

The whole of Science is of course infinitely beyond the knowledge of any man. No one tries to know even the whole of his own department of Science. Let us take as an example a fairly well-known physicist—the type of man who might be a Lecturer in Physics at a University. What does he know? First of all, he will almost certainly specialise in a certain department of physics: let us suppose this is Optics—the behaviour of light. He will be doing original work on some smaller portion of this portion of physics, and about this part of Optics he will know all that there is to know. He will know enough about the rest of Optics to read and at once understand any one else's work, but he will not try and remember this. Of the rest of Physics he will have a lesser knowledge, but a few weeks' work will enable him to read up and understand any part of it.

Of the rest of Science he will know much less. He will understand Chemistry much better than the man in the street, though he probably will not be able to write the formulæ for more than a couple of dozen chemical compounds. He will probably know a fair amount about Astronomy, for this science is a good deal concerned with Optics. Finally, he will probably know no more about Geology and Biology than does any ordinary intelligent man.

THE DEPARTMENTS OF SCIENCE

Science is really a single unity, but for convenience is divided into departments. The five chief sciences are:

Physics, which deals with the behaviour which is common to all or most kinds of matter. Any kind of substance falls if dropped[1] or expands when heated. The study of such a falling or expansion is, therefore, Physics.

Chemistry deals with the kind of material of which things are made, and the way in which different materials are transformed into each other. The burning of a candle or the making of petrol from coal is a matter for chemistry.

Astronomy consists of the whole of our knowledge about the "heavenly bodies" and the earth considered as one of them.

Geology deals with the structure of the earth and the different kinds of rocks.

Biology is the science of life.

No one can hope to study the whole of any one of these in a lifetime, so minor divisions are made. Below is a list of the most important of these.

[1] In a vacuum.

The Divisions of Pure Science

Main divisions.	Subdivisions.	What the subdivisions deal with.
	Properties of matter	Behaviour which all matter has in common.
	Acoustics	Sounds.
	Optics	Light and other radiations.
PHYSICS	The study of heat	
	Magnetism	
	Electricity	
	Atomics	The behaviour and structure of atoms.
	Crystallography	The study of crystals.
	Physical chemistry	The borderland of physics and chemistry.
	Inorganic chemistry	The chemistry of elements other than carbon.
CHEMISTRY	Organic chemistry	The chemistry of carbon.
	Geochemistry	The chemistry of the earth.
	Biochemistry	The chemistry of living things.
ASTRONOMY	Astrophysics	What the stars are.
	Astrometry	The mapping of the sky.
	Cosmogony	The origin of the universe.
	Geography	The study of the earth.
	Physical geology	The study of the shape of rocks, mountains, seas, etc.
GEOLOGY	Petrology	What rocks are made of.
	Palaeontology	The study of fossils of extinct animals and plants.
	Stratigraphical geology	Deducing the history of the earth from its rocks.
	Morphology	The forms of animals and plants.
	Taxonomy	Their classification.
	Physiology	How living creatures work.
BIOLOGY	Botany · Ecology	How living creatures are affected by surroundings.
	Zoology · Embryology	How animals reproduce their kind and develop.
	Aetiology	The evolution of the race and individual.
	Psychology	The study of mind.

(SCIENCE is the over-arching main division bracketing PHYSICS, CHEMISTRY, ASTRONOMY, GEOLOGY, BIOLOGY.)

The departments of Science set out in the above list are all *pure* sciences: that is to say they are concerned only with knowing, not with use. The pure Scientist simply finds out how things behave. Applied Science and its workers put the discoveries of the pure scientist to men's use. The kinds of mind needed for pure and applied science are very different. The pure scientist spends his time saying, "Is this true?" "Why does this behave in this peculiar way?" "How does this work?"

The Applied Scientist has to bother about people. He is always asking, "How can I make a thing to do this job?" "Can I make this thing at a price people will pay?" "Is this process of practical value?" "Is this drug pleasanter in use than that?" "Is this operation likely to kill my patient?"

The chief Applied Sciences are:

Applied Physics..	..	Engineering.
Applied Chemistry	..	Chemical Engineering, Pharmacy, etc.
Applied Geology & Astronomy	..	Meteorology, Cartography, Tide prediction, etc.
Applied Biology	..	Agricultural Science, Medicine, Hygiene.

Pure Science must not be thought of as superior to Applied Science. Both are necessary: they require different types of mind. The pure Scientist provides the material which the Applied Scientist shapes to the use of mankind. For these tasks, very different minds are required, and it is rare to find anyone who has been prominent both in pure Science and Applied Science. The perfect example of an Applied Scientist is Edison, with an incredible list of more than a thousand patents for inventions, but almost no discoveries of scientific principles.

The finest example of a pure Scientist is perhaps Clerk Maxwell, whose work in physics is the foundation of a great part of electrical and other engineering, to which he contributed nothing directly himself. Most remarkable, perhaps, is his prediction by reasoning, of the existence of the electromagnetic waves which 40 years afterwards have made possible wireless telegraphy and broadcasting.

CHAPTER II

MATTER AND ENERGY

MASS AND INERTIA

IN our survey of Science, the first ideas to be understood are those of MATTER and ENERGY. These terms are so wide, they include so much, that they are a little difficult to grasp.

By matter we mean roughly what the man in the street means by the word "stuff," as distinguished from "forces" or "ideas." The scientific definition of matter is "that which has mass and inertia." Translating this into common speech, we may say that matter includes everything which, first of all, is attracted by the

FIG. 3.—It takes force to start matter moving and to stop it.

earth or other heavenly body. Now it is the attraction of the
earth which gives a thing weight, so on this definition anything
which has weight while it is near the earth's surface is *matter*.
Secondly, by saying a thing has "inertia", we mean that it takes
force to set it moving, or, if it is moving already it takes force to
stop it. This is true of all "stuff" we come across. If we define
matter as anything with mass or inertia, it is quite clear that all
solids like iron, wood, glass, wax, etc., are matter, and so are
all liquids like treacle, water, petrol, and all gases like air,
hydrogen, etc.

No one who has carried a sack of coals or a bucket of water
needs to be convinced that solids and liquids have mass. No one
who has shovelled sand, rowed a boat or blown a pair of bellows
can doubt that solids, liquids and gases have inertia.

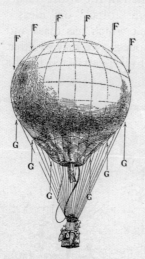

FIG. 4.—The balloon rises
because its weight and the
pressure F on top of it are
less than the pressure G
on the bottom of it.

Ah, but you say, what about
the mass of gases? If hydrogen
is attracted by the earth, why does a
balloon full of it rise? The answer, put
rather crudely, is that the hydrogen is
attracted by the earth but that the air
round and just above the balloon is
attracted still more and, by being pulled
towards the earth, elbows the balloon
away from it. Just in the same way a
cork is attracted by the earth, but it rises
in water because the water is attracted
still more.

The explanation in Fig. 4 is another
way of saying the same thing. For reasons
like these, we conclude that all the
"things" we meet with in the world are
Matter.

What else is there in the world beside
Matter? The answer of Science to this
question is—Energy.

ENERGY

A battered rifle bullet lies on my table. It is obviously Matter. It has mass, for if I drop it it is attracted by the earth and falls ever more quickly to it. It has inertia, for, to set it moving, I have to give it a forcible tap with my finger-nail. After this bullet was fired from a German rifle and before it buried itself in the sand of the parapet beside my head, it was in some way different. It could kill a man, smash a hole in an iron plate. It had a tre-

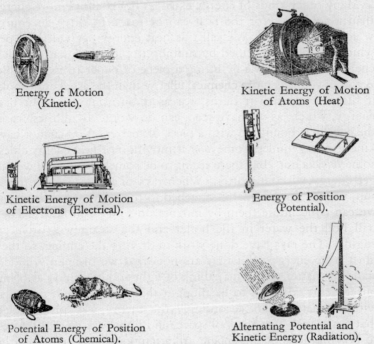

Energy of Motion (Kinetic).

Kinetic Energy of Motion of Atoms (Heat)

Kinetic Energy of Motion of Electrons (Electrical).

Energy of Position (Potential).

Potential Energy of Position of Atoms (Chemical).

Alternating Potential and Kinetic Energy (Radiation).

Fig. 5.—Some forms of energy.

mendous *power of doing work*, and this power we call Energy. The moving rifle bullet is different from the stationary one, because it has more energy. Energy of motion, such as the bullet possessed, we call kinetic energy.

Has it any energy as it lies still on the edge of the table?

Certainly. Knock it off the edge and it drops on to my tea-cup which I left on the floor and smashes it. It has done more work. As it lies on the floor it cannot do that piece of work again, so it evidently had energy because of its distance from the earth which attracts it. This we call potential energy, by which we mean a capacity for doing work which a piece of matter possesses in virtue of its position. Water at the top of a waterfall has potential energy, so has a wound up clock weight, a coiled spring, etc.

Many other kinds of energy exist. A hot coal has more energy than a cold one, for the heat can be made to drive an engine which will *do work*. We call this heat energy. A vulcanite pen which has been electrified by rubbing it with cloth has electrical energy; it can *do work* by lifting a piece of paper from the table. A ton of coal has more chemical energy than the ashes and smoke it turns into when it burns, for as it burns it gives out heat energy, which, as we have seen, can do work. In all these cases the energy is bound up with a piece of matter. You cannot have kinetic energy unless some *thing* is moving nor heat energy unless some *thing* is hot. But there seems to be some cases where we can get energy without matter. When rays of light come from the sun, we can find no matter attached to them. When they arrive, we can concentrate them by mirrors on to a small boiler. They will boil the water in the boiler and the steam will drive an engine. The rays have done work in driving the engine, so they must have energy. But they are not what we ordinarily understand by matter, so we may think of light and other rays as being pure energy. It used to be thought that energy could not exist without matter, and accordingly the theory was propounded that a material *ether* filled all space, and light rays were supposed to be vibrations of this ether. All attempts to find out what the ether was like led to no result, or worse, to contradictions; and nowadays we see no reason why this ether should be invented simply because we feel there ought to be some stuff to be waggled by light vibrations; the modern physicist finds it possible to believe that light waves are energy without matter—*radiant energy*.

Very accurate work has now shown that energy has some mass,

and in that sense may be thought of as a kind of matter. Its mass is so extremely small that we can only detect it if the energy is highly concentrated. A rifle bullet travelling 3,000 feet a second is a minute amount heavier than a bullet when it is still. An electron travelling at 18,000 miles a second—no other piece of matter goes so fast—weighs about one per cent. more than it would when stationary. The fastest moving things we know of are certain electrons shot out of exploding atoms. Some of these move at about 186,000 miles a second, 99.8 per cent. of the velocity of light, and they then weigh nearly seventeen times as much as they would when at rest. In the same way, it has been shown that matter can be changed into energy. We have reason to believe that the matter in the hottest stars is being slowly changed into energy, and that the torrents of energy in the form of the light-rays and heat-rays which flow from them have been produced by changing the actual matter of these stars into energy.

A rule, which was discovered by Einstein, tells us how much energy corresponds to how much matter. The rule is

$$m = E/c^2$$

where m is the mass of the matter in grams, E is the energy which corresponds to it in dynes[1] and c is the velocity of light, 30,000,000,000 centimetres a second.

English people do not think in grams and dynes, but in pounds and horse-power-hours. So, we may put the equation quite simply thus:

"If a pound of matter could be turned into energy, it would give 15,230,000,000 h.p. for an hour." The whole electric power of Great Britain is about 12,000,000,000 units a year, and it is easy to work out that just over a pound of any kind of matter, if we could turn it into energy, would supply the whole of Great Britain with energy enough to drive its electrical generators for a year.

The world has got plenty of matter for its needs, but it is always crying out for energy, so that, if Science can find a way of turning matter into energy, infinite labour will be saved. We

---

[1] The energy needed to set a gram of matter going 1 cm. a second faster than it was moving before.

shall not need to bother about coal, oil wind-power, water-power, etc., for any bit of dirt from the streets will heat our houses and drive our engines. But though the energy is there, we cannot get at it. Inside the stars, where matter is turning into energy, the temperature may be about 20,000,000° C. If we could make matter as hot as that, it might break up into energy. But at present the greatest temperature reached by man is about 4,000° C., so that we have a long road to travel. But let us remember the things that seemed impossible in 1800 are common-places in 1936, and then let us be very careful what we say about what the Scientists will not have done by the year 2100. There is nothing impossible about getting our energy by destroying matter. Science may find the trick next year, or may find it in five hundred years' time. But if I could have half-a-day's trip to the year A.D. 2500 I should be very surprised and disappointed if I found the world still burning coal and oil and harnessing water, wind and tide to get its power.

SCIENCE AND THOUGHT

Matter and energy—is this all? The men of Science have found them enough to explain their world. But there are a few things they have not been able to study by the scientific method, and the chief of these is Thought.

Is thought matter? If I picture a rose, what is that picture in my mind? I call it a picture because it "looks" like one. When I think of a rose, I get something of the same sensation as I experience when I see one. But is a picture there at all? A man who has once been able to see but has had both his eyes removed can still picture a rose, so the picture cannot be in the eyes. As far as we know, sufficiently extensive damage to the brain stops all conscious thought or imagination; accordingly we think that a thought is a happening in the brain.

Possibly, when I *think* of a rose, I make the same thing happen to my brain as has happened before when I have *seen* roses—but as the brain is so little understood by anyone, this is only guess-work. The essential difficulty is that we have only thought to use when we try to make out what thought is. Perhaps thought can no more explain thought than I can pick myself up by the waist-belt and carry myself round the room.

At present no really scientific opinion is possible about thought. There are four chief beliefs held by men about the question, and Science will not serve to decide between them. The religious view is that there is in man a Soul which is neither matter nor energy. This Soul uses the brain as an instrument by which it directs the body. A common philosophical view is that the brain is the instrument which perceives the outside world, knows, thinks, and directs the body, while a soul, spirit, consciousness or what you will, follows what the brain is doing and is the mind and consciousness of which we are aware in ourselves. The scientific opinions do not take much account of the Soul, which is not the sort of affair Science can argue about with any prospect of success. The Vitalists believe that there is a principle of Life which cannot be explained by matter and energy alone, and that thought is a process in the brain which depends on and cannot take place without this principle of Life. Finally, the Mechanists believe that matter and energy are the only things in the world: that the body is an extremely complicated machine, and that thought is a sort of motion or change in the substance of the brain.

Since these four theories are all widely held, there is evidently at present no deciding between them. Scientists have a rule, laid down as long ago as the fourteenth century, which tells them not to assume anything needlessly. This rule has been found to be a good one; accordingly, men of Science will push on with their work and continue to assume that matter and energy are enough to explain everything, until they come up against a set of facts which they *cannot* explain by the notions of matter and energy alone, and *can* explain by assuming a Life-force or Spirit to exist.

It is a great mistake to think that, because scientific men in their work never use the ideas of God and the Soul, they deny their existence. Science concerns itself with things it can understand and test and experiment with. For the rest it minds its own business and leaves everyone to decide on his own religious views.

CHAPTER III

The States of Matter

SOLIDS, LIQUIDS AND GASES

WE have divided all the world which Science can study into Matter and Energy. The plan of Study adopted in Science is to classify things: that is to say, divide them up into sets, all the members of any one of which are more like each other in some respects than they are like the members of the other sets. The simplest classification of Matter is into its three *States*, the solid, liquid and gaseous. Almost everything falls into one of these classes. Everyone thinks he knows a solid, liquid or gas when he meets one, but as there are a few doubtful cases, it is a good thing to have a definite rule laid down by which we can place anything in its right class.

A solid has a fixed volume and shape. A liquid has a fixed volume but no fixed shape. A gas has neither fixed volume nor fixed shape.

These definitions are clear and, though they are not quite true, we cannot make much mistake about them. As a typical solid, we may take a piece of gold, say, a coin. It has a fixed volume, say, 0.1056 cubic centimetres. If we leave it for a thousand years this volume will be the same. It will expand a little if heated, but will return to the same size on cooling. Even enormous pressure will only make it the tiniest bit smaller. Enormous pressures may make it flow like a liquid, but it will not flow under the influence of small forces.

A liquid, say water, has a fixed volume. You can put a pint of water in a quart pot, but it will remain a pint. Even huge pressures will compress it very little; the greatest pressures man can apply

22

will not squeeze a pint of water down to ¾ of a pint. Its volume is fixed but its shape is not. The very smallest force is enough to alter its shape. You can pour your pint into a teapot or a dish and it will at once take the form of either; you can soak it into a

A solid has a fixed shape and a fixed volume.

A liquid has no fixed shape but has a fixed volume.

A gas has no fixed shape nor fixed volume and fills the whole of every space in which it is set free.

FIG. 6.—Solids, liquids and gases.

sponge—it will take any complicated shape, but it won't take up more than a pint of space.

Lastly, a gas has no fixed volume or shape. Allow a cubic inch of chlorine to escape in a room and you will smell it in every corner. The cubic inch fills the whole room. Take a flask from which all the air has been pumped out and allow the smallest whiff of air to enter through a tap. The air expands and fills the whole flask evenly and takes its shape. A gas never has any *surface* except that of the vessel that contains it.

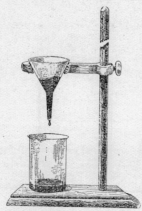

FIG. 7.—Pitch, though apparently solid, is really a liquid and will flow through a funnel. Note the drop, quite hard yet having the shape of a drop of water.

Now what about the doubtful cases? A piece of pitch feels quite solid; you cannot dent it by pressing it with your thumb, but if you leave a lump of it in a box for a year, you will find it has flowed like a liquid and taken the shape of the box.

Fig. 7 shows the result of putting a lump of pitch in a glass funnel. In the course of months it flows exactly like a liquid, though it feels perfectly hard and solid to the touch. On the other hand, butter is a solid. A lump of butter is soft, but if left even for a year it will not flow of its own accord like pitch.

What about mud, froth, smoke, and things of that kind? Are they solids, liquids or gases, for in some ways they resemble two of these? The answer to this difficulty is that they are mixtures. A mixture of big bits of solid with liquid—like pebbles and water—is simple enough to understand, but when the bits of solid are very small indeed, and very numerous indeed, we get curious materials called "colloidal solutions." Let us see what we get if we make very close and fine mixtures of solids, liquids and gases.

(1) Very fine particles of solid surrounded by liquids are MUDS or SLIMES.

(2)   Very fine particles of solid floating in a gas are a SMOKE.

(3)   Very fine particles of liquid floating in a gas are a FOG or MIST.

(4)   Very fine particles of a gas in a liquid are a FOAM.

(5)   Very fine particles of a gas in a solid are a SOLID FOAM.

The rather odd behaviour of these mixtures cannot really be understood until we know a little about what solids, liquids and gases really are.

ATOMS AND MOLECULES

The really fundamental thing about matter is that it is made up of tiny separate particles called atoms and molecules. The reasons for believing this are very good ones, but require some knowledge of Science for their comprehension: it is simplest, therefore, to give a picture of what Matter is believed to be made of without trying to give the evidence. As you read this book you will find a good deal of evidence throughout Parts I—IV.

The simplest sort of matter is an "element," which contains only one sort of matter. Silver is a good example. Suppose we take a little cube of silver the size of a lump of sugar and cut it in half. Cut both the halves in half, then cut the quarters into eighths and so go on cutting the silver into tinier and tinier bits. When the bits of silver are about $\frac{1}{1000}$ inch in diameter they will be too small to see, but let us imagine ourselves reduced to the size of microscopic dwarfs, still cutting and cutting. Finally, when the bits of silver are only about one hundred-millionth of an inch across, we find we can cut no more. Each particle is now an *atom* of silver. It cannot be cut up or split apart by any reasonable force, and if it is split up into smaller bits, lo and behold they are no longer bits of silver but of some other substance such as copper or carbon. Finally, if we were capable of splitting up the atom of silver into the tiniest fragments possible, we should probably get nothing from it but a little hydrogen and a great many electrons which are particles of electricity. These have never been split up.

Of course it is quite impossible to cut up solid silver in this way. No knife could be small enough to cut such tiny particles, nor could they be seen when they were smaller than about a twenty-thousandth of an inch in diameter. But the description may perhaps give a picture of a lump of silver as a mass of extraordinarily tiny particles called atoms of silver. The atom of silver is the smallest portion of silver that can be obtained. If the atom of silver is cut up or split or broken, it ceases to be silver and becomes something else.

Suppose that instead of silver, which is made up of silver and nothing else, we had tried to cut up a drop of water, which is made of hydrogen and oxygen. We know this because the action of electricity will turn nine grams of water into one gram of the gas hydrogen and eight grams of the gas oxygen and nothing else. Every drop, droplet or speck of water is just the same as every other, so every bit, however small, must contain hydrogen and oxygen. If we imagine ourselves dividing up a drop of water as we divided the cube of silver, we should have to stop when we had obtained a piece about one fifty-millionth of a centimetre in diameter. This bit would be the smallest piece of water possible. It would have two atoms of hydrogen and an atom of oxygen in it. If it were further split up—not a difficult task—it would not be water but separate atoms of oxygen and hydrogen.

The smallest piece of a *compound* substance like water is called a molecule. A molecule is made up of several atoms, which are each the smallest possible pieces of some element. It is very necessary to understand what molecules and atoms are, for we cannot explain the world without continually referring to them. So, if you have not a clear notion of them, read pages 25–26 again.

Once it is understood that an atom or a molecule is the smallest bit of any particular kind of stuff which can possibly be obtained, we can ask a few questions about them. What do they look like? What size are they? What shape are they? Do they move? Are they arranged neatly or are they all higgledy-piggledy? Do they touch or have they spaces between them?

WHAT ATOMS ARE LIKE

All these questions have been answered.

What does an atom look like? The answer is quite definite though a little puzzling. It doesn't look like anything at all! If a thing is to be seen, it must shape the rays of light which come from it so as to form a pattern of light which is received on the sensitive curtain at the back of the eye. But an atom is far smaller than a wave of light: a single atom will deflect the course of a light wave as little as a speck of dust will deflect a wave of the sea. The smallest thing the most perfect microscope could show as a speck is several thousands of times bigger than an atom. It is true that an atom when thrown into violent convulsions may send out light. In the glow of a neon sign, atoms of neon are altering their interior arrangements and sending out red light. This light, however, will not tell us what shape the atom is. A rifle bullet fired into water starts a ring of ripples, but no one could tell from the ripples what shape the bullet was. The atom, then, does not look like anything, because it is too small; but it is legitimate to ask what a model of it as big as a house would resemble. This is a more difficult question. Somewhere in the centre there would be something very heavy and about as big as a dust speck. This tiny "nucleus" would have a big positive electrical charge. The rest of the "house" would contain from one to ninety-three minute light particles of negative electricity about as large as full stops racing about at enormous speed—probably revolving in orbits round the heavy positive nucleus. The atom is practically all empty space! Even if our big model had its model nucleus and electrons made of something you could see, say, lead, you would not notice the model if you stood a few yards away.

The atom, then, is nearly all empty space, and it seems very peculiar that an atom with so little of anything in it should behave almost as if it was as solid and hard as a marble. For it certainly seems to be hard. Only the most violent treatment can break it up, and it is impossible to force one atom to enter another. At first sight it would seem that two of these very empty atoms, made up of a few electrons moving about in a space a hundred thousand times bigger than themselves, could perfectly well occupy the same space, just as two flights of birds could occupy a space ordinarily filled by one flight. But in actual fact if we try to compress, say, some iron, it will get a little smaller, but the most enormous pressures we can apply will not drive one of its atoms to occupy the territory contained in another such atom.

Why is it, then, that an atom seems to be only a collection of a few scattered electrons and yet has an almost impenetrable boundary? I say almost impenetrable because if we shoot an electron, moving at the rate of thousands of miles a second, at a collection of atoms—say a bit of tin foil—it will usually go right through the atoms without disturbing them appreciably. Why, then, is the atom impenetrable by another atom, while a single electron goes through it easily? The matter is not so difficult to understand if we realise what the electrons in the atom are and in what fashion they are moving. In the first place the electrons in the atom are moving at tremendous speeds not much less than that of light. Some of them have speeds up to about twenty thousand miles per second and their orbit is only about one thousand-millionth of an inch long.[1] So they get round their orbit about 10^{19} or 10,000,000,000,000,000,000 times every second! Now think of an aeroplane propeller when stationary. You can easily poke your arm between the blades. Set it spinning at the rate of, say, 15 turns a second and you will get your arm cut off if you try to push it through the propeller. Well, if an aeroplane propeller feels solid at fifteen turns a second, what hope has anything of getting inside an atom with, say, fifty electrons each rotating round the central nucleus as often as ten million, million, million times a second? The only thing that

---

[1] Our knowledge about the structure of the atom is by no means definite or fixed. The explanation I have given is a rather crude simplification of one theory: it is perhaps as near to the truth as is possible in a brief popular exposition. It is not really legitimate to treat electrons as if they were little bullets: they behave in many ways as waves, not particles; and they cannot be said to have any *exactly* definable position.

can get through such a barrage is something very small that is going as fast as the electrons themselves. Just as a machine-gun bullet may be fired through the circle of the rotating propeller without striking the blade, so, as we shall see later, it is possible to shoot high speed electrons or alpha-particles, which are much heavier, through the middle of the atom.

There is another and even better reason why the atom behaves like a solid—why it will not let another atom go through it or even come near it.

All atoms have a nucleus of positive electricity in the middle

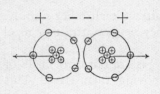

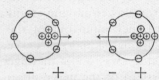

FIG. 8.—When atoms are near their negative exteriors repel each other: when they are more distant the positive end of one atom attracts the negative end of another.

and a set of "shells" of negative electrons outside. And so we can look on an atom as being like a cherry of which the stone is positive electricity and the flesh negative electricity. There is just as much positive electricity as negative electricity, so the *whole* atom is *neutral*, neither positive nor negative. But, when two atoms approach each other closely, their outsides are much nearer than their insides. Electrical experiments show us that, first, negative electricity repels negative electricity and positive electricity repels positive electricity, but positive electricity attracts negative electricity; and, secondly, that the nearer the electrical charges are, the greater is the attraction or repulsion. Accordingly, when two atoms approach each other very closely, the two negative outsides of the atoms repel each other and force the atoms apart again. For this reason, it is impossible to make two atoms actually enter each other—at least with the strongest forces that man can use.

Atoms only repel each other when they are very near. When they are several times their diameter apart, they attract each other, though rather feebly. This is because the positive part of the

atom does not stay exactly central in the middle of the atom.
Consequently, the atom, looked at as a whole, has a positive end
and a negative end, and the positive end of one atom attracts the
negative end of the next. Fig. 8 gives an idea of this attraction
and repulsion.

We must remember about an atom, then:

(1) It is a tiny particle made up of negative electrons with a
far tinier "kernel" of positive electricity.

(2) Atoms, when they get very near to each other, repel each
other so strongly that we can never make them enter each
other.

(3) Atoms at some distance apart attract each other slightly.
There is one distance where they neither attract or repel
each other.

The atoms in a solid, a liquid or a gas are not only made of
moving electrons but are actually moving themselves. This
motion never stops and is very familiar to all of us as *heat*.
If you burn your finger by putting it on a hot gas-ring, the atoms
of iron, moving speedily, collide with the slower-moving atoms
of your skin and speed them up until they jump out of the
complex pattern of atoms which is a normal skin. The nerve
ends are damaged by their atoms breaking away and a message
(probably a disturbance in the atom-pattern of the nerve fibre)
goes to the spinal cord, which, by the way, instantly sends a
signal to the arm-muscles to withdraw the finger and another
to the brain, which feels the burn. Heat will be mentioned many
times in subsequent chapters. At present it is enough to realise
that all atoms are always moving and that the faster they move
the hotter they are.

Everyone realises that atoms are very small indeed and it
seems extraordinary to the scientific amateur that things so tiny
can be measured at all. All the same, there are five or six reliable
ways of measuring them, and all give results fairly near to each
other. The different kinds of atoms are not very different in size.
The largest is not more than about four times the size of the
smallest, though the heaviest is 238 times as heavy as the lightest.

The size and weight of the oxygen atom are about as accurately known as any, and afford a good example.

The weight of an oxygen atom is about 27×10^{-24} grams, which means that it takes 1,080,000,000,000,000,000,000,000

FIG. 9.—Twenty of these rectangles would contain a million dots.

oxygen atoms to weigh an ounce. Its diameter is about 2×10^{-8} cm., which means that 125,000,000 oxygen atoms would have to be laid, end to end, to make an inch.

Well, no one can hope to picture these huge numbers, but you can get just a notion of the vast number and the minute size of these atoms by one or two comparisons. Fig. 9, p. 31, contains 50,000 or a twentieth of a million dots. If you took a hundred and thirty libraries (as big as the British Museum library) each with 8,000,000 books of a thousand pages covered with these dots, there would be about as many dots as there are atoms in a bubble of oxygen, the size of a mustard seed.

Take the smallest speck of soot you can see by straining your eyes. It might be $\frac{1}{250}$th inch across. If this speck was shared up between all the people in London (8,000,000) and each of them counted the atoms in their share at the rate of four a second for eight hours a day, they would finish the job in about 150 years. Another comparison is shown in Fig. 10. If you took

FIG. 10.—This bin, the size of which is apparent from that of the Nelson column beside it, holds as many grains of very fine sand as one such grain contains atoms.

as many grains of very fine sand (with grains about $\frac{1}{300}$th inch in diameter) as there are atoms in one grain, they would fill a bin 100 yards high, 100 yards broad, and 100 yards long.

WHAT SOLIDS, LIQUIDS AND GASES REALLY ARE

Now we know enough about atoms to understand what solids, liquids and gases are. Every substance, we realise, is a mass of separate atoms or molecules—little groups of two, three or more atoms. These atoms are moving and the hotter they are, the quicker they move. They can't be forced to touch each other; if they are a little way apart, they repel each other; if they are some distance apart, they attract each other rather feebly.

In a gas, the molecules are a long way apart—a long way, at least, compared to the size of an atom. In the air of a room, the molecules of oxygen and nitrogen are, on the average, about eight times their length apart—a distance of about $\frac{3}{10000000}$ centimetres. A gas is, therefore, mostly empty space. It is only the average distance apart that can be given, because the molecules are moving. We know how many there are in a given volume of gas, so we can work out the distance there would be between them if they were still and were evenly distributed. If a tiny volume of the gas were magnified till the atoms were as large as tennis balls, a room as big as a rather small bedroom would contain about fifty of these tennis balls travelling at a pace which would make a tennis champion's smash shots look like drifting toy balloons. You can easily convince yourself that a gas is nearly all empty space by considering the fact, well known to engineers, that a cubic inch of water makes 1700 cubic inches of steam. The water turns into the gas, steam, and nothing else, so 1700 cubic inches of steam must contain at least 1699 cubic inches of emptiness and not more than one cubic inch of atoms.

Are the atoms in a gas arranged at all? Do they move in an orderly manner? The answer is—No! An atom simply crashes straight along at several hundred miles an hour, till it hits another atom: it bounces off, hits another atom and so goes on, taking about eight thousand million knocks a second. At ordinary temperatures the knocks do not damage the atoms a bit. But at higher temperatures, above a red heat, some of the outside electrons may get knocked off. The damaged atom, however, soon picks up another electron to replace the missing one, and is then as good as ever. In the interior of the stars where incredible temperatures prevail and the atoms are hurled against each other at speeds which make rifle-bullets look like snails, almost the whole of the electrons may get knocked off the atom and very little except the heavy but very tiny nuclei remain. This very curious state of matter will be talked of again in Chapter XXXVI. Summing up, then, a gas is a collection of atoms or molecules, fairly far apart from each other, dashing about at high speeds and continually colliding.

A liquid obviously contains far less empty space than a gas.

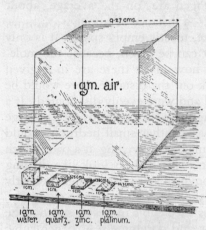

FIG. 11.—Showing the volume of a gram of air as compared with that of a gram of a liquid or solid.

In a liquid, like water, the molecules are only about their own breadth apart. They are moving just as fast as the gas molecules would be at the same temperature and they are not arranged in any way (or if any patterns are formed, they break up almost as once). A liquid is a violently jostling mass of molecules with no elbow room to jostle. If we magnify our liquid till the atoms are as big as tennis balls, the balls would be on the average about three inches apart and would be banging backwards and forwards and sideways with great violence, bouncing off each other. Why is there this difference between a liquid and a gas? If a substance is a gas, it is because its molecules are not sufficiently attracted by each other to make them stay within the distance at which atoms attract each other fairly strongly; this may either be because they are the sort of molecules that do not attract each other much or because the molecules are dashing about very fast—i.e., because the material is very hot. In a liquid, on the other hand, the molecules attract each other so much that they cannot easily dash off into space; if we heat a liquid, the molecules speed up; finally, the attraction can no longer hold them and the liquid boils—that is to say, it turns into a gas. Liquids and gases flow easily because their molecules are not strongly attracted to each other but are always moving. Thus, they can ooze through any hole which will let a molecule through, and that is a pretty small one!

Solids are quite different from gases and liquids in that their

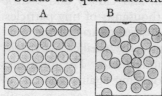

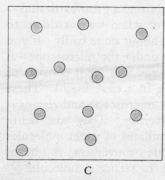

Fig. 12.—Imaginary section of (A) a solid with regular and close packing of molecules, (B) a liquid with irregular, shifting but close arrangement of molecules, and (C) a gas with irregular, shifting and very open arrangement of atoms.

molecules, though always in motion, remain in a fixed pattern. Imagine a great pile of bricks neatly stacked. Imagine a billiard ball in the centre of each brick. Now take the bricks away, and leave the billiard balls. You ought now to be imagining something like Fig. 16, p. 47.

Now set all these balls vibrating an inch each way like pendulum bobs (only doing millions of swings a second instead of one or two) and you have a picture of a solid. Beautifully regular rows of molecules or atoms, each vibrating on its own little beat, but not interfering with the next one. What happens if we heat a solid? The molecules, as always, speed up: the swings of the vibrations become longer until the atoms begin to swing so far out of position that no pattern at all remains. The pattern is destroyed and we just have a jostling crowd of atoms—a liquid—the solid has melted!

A COLLOIDAL SOLUTION

The mixtures of solids, liquids and gases, froths, muds, etc., are now easier to understand. Let us consider a mixture of a solid and a liquid, say, some muddy water. Take a spoonful of mud and stir it into a glass of water. Little stones and sand sink to the bottom at once. In half an hour no bits of solid big enough to see are left in the liquid—they have all sunk to the bottom—but the liquid itself is thick and cloudy and a drop examined under a microscope shows thousands of tiny particles. Leave it a day or two and it will be quite clear—all the mud having sunk to the bottom. Evidently the smaller a particle, the slower it sinks. This is easy to understand. The molecules of the water are darting about and bouncing against the bits of mud. They cannot slow up a sand-grain much, for a molecule hitting a sand-grain is like a rifle-bullet hitting a great battleship—it does not slow it up noticeably. But when we get down to really tiny particles, these get bounced about quite badly. If you look at a drop of diluted Indian ink under the microscope—it must be a pretty good one ($\times$ 1000)—you will see it consists of tiny particles of carbon (soot) floating in a clear liquid. These particles are only just visible with the microscope and *they never stop moving*—rolling about and quivering. They are being battered and shaken by the blows of millions of water molecules and that queer trembling (the Brownian movement) is one of the nearest approaches you will make to seeing a molecule.

The black particles in Indian ink settle out only very slowly—the more so since it is thickened by gum—but if it is left for a year or so untouched, almost all the black settles to the bottom. A mixture of particles of a solid with a liquid is called a suspension. Coarse suspensions settle out, but there are a few suspensions which never settle out at all ! If the particles have an electric charge—suppose they are negatively and the water positively charged—the particles will repel each other and as long as they keep their charges they can never get together at the bottom. These electrically charged suspensions are called colloidal solutions or sols. A *sol* of silver particles swimming in water (thickened with certain chemicals) is a deep brown liquid looking not at all like silver but more like tincture of iodine. Doctors use it as a mild disinfectant for delicate parts of the body.

Tiny droplets of a liquid like oil floating in a liquid in which they don't dissolve make another kind of suspension which is called an *emulsion*. Milk is the most familiar emulsion—it is made up of droplets of butter fat floating in "whey," a weak solution of casein, sugar and other things. When milk is violently shaken, the oil-drops meet, stick together and form butter.

SMOKE AND FOG

Smokes and fogs are like suspensions: they are, in fact, suspensions of solids or liquids in a gas. Ordinary smoke is a suspension of tiny soot particles in air. It isn't very easy to look at some under a microscope, but when it is done, you see tiny particles darting in every direction as the gas molecules hit them. Smokes only settle out very slowly, for the air is always on the move, even when it seems to be still, but the soot gradually deposits, particularly on anything that is moist. Thus, it sticks to the inside of our noses, and the lungs of a townsman are a dirty grey instead of the natural pink colour seen in the lungs of a baby. All air we breathe is really a very thin smoke, that is to say, it is full of dust particles. On a fine day—slightly hazy —there may be 100 to 200 particles of dust in every cubic centimetre; some thousands in every breath we draw. In a London fog, there may be 20,000 particles in every cubic centimetre. The dust particles are very tiny, from $\frac{1}{25000}$ to $\frac{1}{5000}$ of an inch in diameter. You cannot see any of the many thousand dust particles now between your eyes and the book. But let a ray of sun peer through the curtains into a darkened room. The larger dust particles catch and scatter the light and we see them as "motes." If we coat the floor of a glass box with the sticky liquid, glycerine, and leave it for a day or two, all the dust particles will stick to the glycerine and the most brilliant beam of light, projected through the glass, will be invisible as it passes through the dust-free air.

Fogs are either mists—drops of pure water suspended in air— or true fogs of the London type, where each water droplet is surrounded by a film of tarry smoke which causes it to soil everything it touches, and also prevents it from evaporating as does a clean country mist. The droplets in a mist are as large as $\frac{1}{1200}$ of an inch in diameter and can often be seen by the naked eye—in fact, mist, cloud and rain pass into each other without any sharp dividing line.

You have now got a picture of the three states of matter and can see in your minds the darting scattered molecules in a gas, the crowded jostling molecules in a liquid and the orderly pattern of vibrating molecules in a solid. It is now easy to understand something about the behaviour of the ordinary solid things we meet, and explain why they behave as they do.

CHAPTER IV

SOLIDS

THE PATTERNS OF ATOMS IN SOLIDS

WE have arrived at the notion that a solid is made of atoms or molecules, set out in a regular pattern, vibrating a certain distance in each direction but never leaving the pattern. This pattern may be perfectly regular and go from end to end of the solid, in which case we call it a single crystal. More often the pattern persists for a stretch of a few million atoms and then breaks off and starts again. This is the state of affairs in most solids, which are made up of little crystals arranged higgledy-piggledy but firmly stuck together. Plate III shows a photograph of a piece of steel magnified a thousand times. Each of the little compartments is a crystal with a regular pattern of atoms; but at the boundary between them the pattern breaks and is started again with the rows of atoms pointing another way.

At one time it was thought that some solids were not crystalline at all—that their molecules were arranged just anyhow like the molecules of a liquid. Chief of these solids were glass and flint and things like glue and rubber. We are still not very certain about glass and flint; there is probably some sort of pattern in the arrangement of the molecules, but not at all a regular or definite one: things like glue and rubber have such enormous molecules (comparatively speaking) that they can't form neat regular patterns. But generally speaking, every solid is a mass of crystals—neat little mosaics of atoms stuck together.

CRYSTALS

Since most of the solids, of which all the things we touch and handle every day are made, are masses of these crystals, it is important to have a few ideas about crystals in general. If we let a liquid or a gas turn slowly into a solid, or in any way deposit a solid slowly, the molecules have time to arrange themselves in a perfect pattern and we get crystals which are big enough to see or handle.

We can easily see this happening of its own accord, or if we prefer we can do experiments about it ourselves. Buy an ounce of alum at the chemist's, put it in a teacup and pour on it a quarter of a pint of boiling water. Stir it, best with a bit of wood, until the alum has disappeared. Stand the teacup on a folded duster; cover the cup with two or three dusters and let it cool slowly all night. Next morning look at it; the alum will be found as well-formed crystals. A quarter of a pint of boiling water will dissolve an ounce of alum and more, but a quarter of a pint of cold water will dissolve only half an ounce of alum, so the remaining half of the ounce comes slowly out of the water as it cools, and the alum molecules form a regular

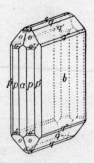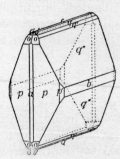

FIG. 13.—Two crystals of potassium sulphate. Their angles between corresponding faces (indicated by the same letter) are identical. If they are set so that a pair of corresponding faces are parallel, all the other pairs will be parallel. (Courtesy of Messrs. Macmillan and Co., Ltd., and Prof. R. H. Tutton, from the latter's *Crystallography and Practical Crystal Measurement*.)

pattern. You will see that the resulting crystals have flat sides and sharp angles; and that they are of much the same shape. Crystals of the same kind do not have exactly the same shape, but they do have the same angles between their faces. Fig. 13 shows two quite different looking crystals of potassium sulphate with the corresponding faces lettered. It shows very clearly how the angles between the faces remain the same for a given crystal, though the sizes of the faces may differ and thus make the crystal appear to be of quite a different shape.

Try another substance. Take a spoonful of salt (cooking salt is better than table salt) and stir it with six spoonfuls of water. Pour a little of the liquid on to a piece of glass (say the bottom of an inverted tumbler), let it dry up of its own accord. There is no harm in putting it near the fire. Minute crystals of salt will appear. A magnifying glass or a microscope will show them to be little transparent cubes. Like the alum crystals, all their sides are flat; and the corresponding angles of every salt crystal are the same, in this case right angles.

One more experiment: Put a lump of camphor in a dry medicine bottle, cork it and stand it on the window sill. In a day or two, little brilliant crystals of camphor will deposit on the cooler side of the bottle. In this case the vapour of camphor has arranged its molecules in a regular pattern and formed crystals. The lump of camphor you start with is a mass of tiny crystals all set anyhow; if you break it, you will see them. The slow depositing of the camphor from its vapour gives the opportunity to make bigger crystals.

What we call "natural processes" make much finer crystals than men can. Nature has unlimited materials and some of her crystals have taken centuries to make.

Plate II shows two beautifully regular crystals, the first fluorspar, or blue-john, the second, beryl, a beautiful blue-green gemstone. Neither of these could at present be made by man. Some of nature's finest crystals are made with water. When water solidifies to ice, it forms "hexagonal" crystals with angles of 60° and 120°. These for some reason show a remarkable tendency to branch. Most people have poured out a half-frozen bucket of water and found in it clear blades of ice, notched like fernleaves. These are water crystals. But the most beautiful productions are found when water-vapour, of which the air usually contains 1% or more, solidifies to ice. Everyone has seen frost

2*

crystals on the window pane: look at them again next time and think how they are all made up of water molecules set together in ever-repeating variations of the six-sided star-pattern. But it is in the snowflake that the most extraordinary regularities are found. As the snowflake forms in the cloud it is surrounded with water vapour which freezes on to it equally and regularly on every side; and, if the flakes are slowly formed, the sort of delicate lacework of crystals is developed, which is illustrated in Plate II. They are a little difficult to observe for oneself, because they melt so quickly, but by catching them on a black sleeve and looking at them with a strong lens, much can be seen.

The crystals are finest when the snowfall is not too heavy, when the air is still and when the weather is pretty cold.

Francis Thompson perfectly described the delicate beauty of crystals of ice and snow in his poem, *To a Snowflake:*

What heart could have thought you?—
Past our devisal
(O filigree petal)
Fashioned so purely,
Fragilely, surely,
From what Paradisal
Imagineless metal
Too costly for cost?
Who hammered you, wrought you,
From argentine vapour?—
God was my shaper
Passing surmisal,
He hammered, He wrought me,
From curled silver vapour,
To lust of His mind:—
Thou coulds't not have thought me!
So purely, so palely,
Mightily, fraily,
Insculped and embossed,
With His hammer of wind,
And His graver of frost.

Beautifully expressed, his thought is wholly sundered from that of the modern man of Science, who, if he looks to God as a Creator, thinks of Him, not as separately fashioning forms of beauty, but as putting forth the supreme marvels of proton, neutron and electron and space-time, which of themselves have, without guidance, created every grace of form and action.

The most obvious and showy thing about crystals is their lovely shape; but even if a crystal had no shape, we should know it for a crystal. Because a crystal is a regular pattern of atoms, it has a *grain* to it, so to speak, and it will behave differently if things are done to it *with* the grain or *across* the grain.

Look at a handkerchief. That is a sort of lattice with its thread-crossings repeating themselves in every direction. If you wanted to tear it up, you could only do it *along* the line of one set of threads or the other. It will easily tear in two directions at right angles to each other but not in others. Now look at a pattern of atoms like Figure 16. It is obviously likely that it will "tear" or split along the spaces between the atoms, much more easily than it will split in a direction which goes through the layers of pattern. Accordingly, we find that most crystals "cleave" easily. A light tap with a knife blade, in the right direction, will split them in two. Plate II shows first the cleaving of a piece of crystalline of calcite, a very pure form of marble. You will see that the pieces have split along two directions at an angle of 74° 55' and 105° 5' to each other and parallel to the original cleavage faces. This cleavage is of some practical use. The diamond is so hard that to cut it a very skilled and slow process of rubbing down with diamond dust and oil on revolving wheels is needed. But find the right angle for cleavage—not a very easy task, it is true—and a tap with a hammer and knife-blade will split it.

The third thing worth noting about crystals is that they behave differently in different directions. If you cut a plate of rock-crystal lengthways from point to point of the crystal, coat it with wax and put a hot point on it, the heat will go more easily up and down the crystal than across it and instead of a circle of melted wax spreading out from the hot point, we shall have an oval.

Most ordinary solids, like steel or marble, do not show these properties of regular shape, cleavage, etc., because they are made of a tremendous number of tiny crystals all set anyhow. If one crystal is cleaved by a tap, the split goes no further, because the next tiny crystal is facing the wrong way to be cleaved. The different appearance of solids in big crystals and little crystals is fairly well illustrated by sugar. Sugar candy is made of a few big crystals of sugar. Coffee sugar, too, is made of single crystals. Their crystal form is shown in Fig. 14. Lump sugar is a mass of small crystals quite easy to see. In foreign loaf or in icing sugar, the crystals are much smaller, while in barley sugar there probably are not any crystals at all but just a mass of sugar

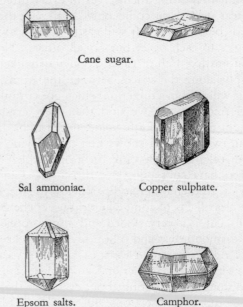

Cane sugar.

Sal ammoniac.   Copper sulphate.

Epsom salts.   Camphor.

FIG. 14.—Crystals of some common substances.

molecules hanging together and not arranged. (Break a bit; you will see no flat crystal faces, only a shiny rounded surface.)

LATTICES

The patterns of molecules we find in solids are those which go on repeating themselves in every direction till we come to the edge of the crystal. A pattern which goes on repeating itself so that every point in it is surrounded by an exactly similar set of neighbouring points is called a space-lattice. The simplest sort of lattice to understand is a flat one as shown in Fig. 15. The point A and the points B and C have in Fig. 15 (*a*) four neighbours

FIG. 15.—Two-dimensional lattices.

0.56 cm. away and set at the corners of a square, and four neighbours 0.4 cm. away and set at the middles of the sides of the same square. The pattern can go on for ever in every direction and each point is indistinguishable from the next. Fig. 15 (*b*) shows another flat (two-dimensional) lattice. Here, every point has six neighbours 0.33 cm. away and equally spaced around it.

Now if a crystal had its atoms in patterns like these, it would only be one atom thick and you couldn't see it. The lattices in which the atoms of a crystal are arranged are three-dimensional, that is to say the pattern goes up and down, left and right and forwards and backwards as well. Fig. 16 gives a picture of one such lattice. It shows the pattern in which the atoms of common salt are arranged: this is like Fig. 15 (*a*) repeated like a pile of sandwiches.

This picture gives you the pattern. To get a clearer notion you should think of the atoms as vibrating back and forth, so that there is not much space in the crystal which is not at least part of the time invaded by one of the neighbouring atoms, and also you must think of the pattern going on almost endlessly in every direction. Suppose a tiny crystal (say a grain of table salt) were magnified till the atoms were as big as tennis balls, the regular pattern of balls arranged as in Fig. 16 would be thirty miles broad, thirty miles long and thirty miles high.

Of course, there are a great many different atoms and molecules which can be formed into these patterns, and the different sizes and attractions of these make each kind of crystal just a little different from any other. The differences between one crystal and another are not only differences in shape. Some of the greatest differences are due to the fact that molecules may be bound into the crystal by very strong forces or quite feeble ones.

At one extreme, take the camphor crystals you made. They are so soft that you can crush them with your thumbnail, and the camphor molecules are held in their lattice so feebly that if you put a camphor crystal on the mantelpiece it will all evaporate away into vapour before many weeks have gone.

Each camphor molecule is held to the next by the feeble attraction that every atom or molecule has for another one a little way from it. The vibrations of the molecules are enough to send the outside ones out of range of the attraction of the rest and they sail off in the air. Camphor smells simply because its molecules sail away and enter one's nose. Suppose a bit of camphor the size of a pea disappears altogether in a year. This means that it is losing about ten million million molecules a second for all that time!

Next look at a crystal of salt. It is a cube harder than the camphor but not difficult to crush, whereupon it splits up into smaller pieces with square edges such as it originally had But weigh it, leave it for a year, and the most delicate balance won't show that any of the salt molecules have gone off into the air. It has to be heated bright red-hot before the molecules are moving fast enough to go off on their own. They stick to each other, because the crystal is held together by strong electrical attractions. The reason why this is so is a little difficult to follow unless you know a little chemistry. Common salt is a combination of the soft inflammable metal sodium and the green poisonous gaseous element chlorine. If you put a bit of sodium in chlorine, it catches alight and burns, giving out a white smoke which finally settles out as a white powder—sodium chloride or common salt. Now, the real thing which happens is that the sodium atom has an electron *too many* to make the stable or "favourite" pattern of eight outer electrons: chlorine has an electron *too few* to make

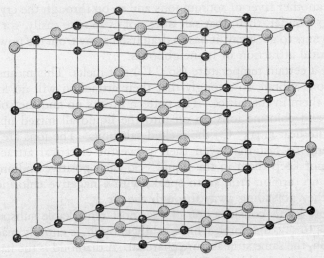

FIG. 16.—The arrangement of ions (electrically charged atoms) in common salt, magnified 70,000,000 times. The spheres indicate the positions of the centres and *relative* sizes of the sodium ions (black) and chlorine ions (grey). Actually these almost touch: they are drawn to a smaller scale to allow the arrangement to be seen.

this pattern; so the sodium hands its electron to the chlorine. Now, the sodium atom started with just as many positive charges (protons) as it had negative electrons, so now it has one positive charge not balanced by a negative one; while the chlorine atom has got a negative charge not balanced by a positive one. So, after the change, the positively charged sodium atom (now called an ion) is strongly attracted to the negatively charged chlorine ion. So when salt crystallises, instead of a set of molecules rather flabbily clinging together (as in camphor) we have a crowd of electrically charged "ions" all pulling on each other. Now, if any sodium ion pulls a chlorine ion to itself, it has to pull it away from the other sodium ions which are pulling it just as hard; so the crowd of ions settles down to a balance like equally matched tug-of-war teams and sort themselves out as a sort of sandwich, first a layer of sodium ions, then a layer of chlorine ions, then another layer of sodium ions and so on through the crystal.

No wonder, then, that salt does not evaporate easily, for if an ion wants to get away, it has to drag itself away from the powerful electrical attraction of its neighbours.

At a certain temperature (804° C.) salt melts. This means that the ions vibrate so strongly that their attraction will no longer hold them in the lattice. The pattern breaks up and the sodium ions and chlorine ions go off into the liquid all mixed up. At a white heat (1413° C.) the melted salt boils. The ions are now moving so fast that even their powerful electrical attractions will not keep them in the liquid. So each positive sodium ion links up (arm-in-arm, so to speak) with a negative chlorine ion and they go sailing away through the air.

Now let us consider one of the most remarkable substances, that is to say, diamond, which, oddly enough, is entirely made of carbon, the same stuff as pure charcoal. A diamond is the hardest thing in the world. Nothing we can do to it will make it melt or turn into vapour. A diamond is a single *giant molecule*, made up of countless carbon atoms. Every carbon atom (Fig. 344) has four outer electrons. If it *lends* a share of one electron to each of its four neighbours and *borrows* a share of an electron from each of them, it gets a share of eight electrons. But since every outer electron is now shared between two carbon atoms these atoms are, so to speak, interlaced and tremendously tightly

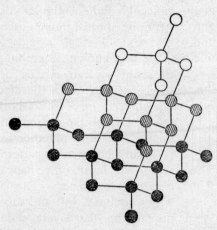

FIG. 17.—The structure of diamond. The circles represent carbon atoms: the different shadings mark out the planes along which a diamond can be cleaved.

bound to each other. This is why a diamond is so hard and why it will not evaporate. If you want to get a piece of diamond away from another piece, you have to make the carbon atoms disgorge each other's electrons, a thing that they will not do unless you apply a great deal of energy to them.

Most very hard things are giant molecules. Carborundum, the next hardest thing after diamond (used for whetstones and grinding wheels), is just like diamond except that instead of having a pattern all of carbon atoms it has a pattern of carbon and silicon atoms all bound together by electrons. Rubies and sapphires (both very hard stones) are made of aluminium and oxygen atoms, all bound together in this way. Nearly as hard as these gemstones is steel, and we shall see that it is a little difficult to make out why it is so hard. It seems that a crystal of pure iron is a giant molecule of iron atoms, bound together by sharing electrons; this giant molecule is not very hard, because the atoms can unship their electron cables (so to speak), slip a certain distance and then hitch on to other atoms. Steel contains a little carbon which seems to fill up the spaces between the iron atoms and stop the slipping in much the same way as sand on a frosty pavement.

There are three kinds of giant molecule altogether. First the solid (or 3-dimensional) one like the diamond we have just talked about; secondly the 2-dimensional or larger ones, which are piles of flat layers of atoms firmly bound to each other but only feebly hanging on to the next layer; thirdly the thread-like 1-dimensional giant molecules where the atoms are strongly bound together into a string like beads, though each string is not very firmly bound to the next.

Of the solids with layer-molecules the best known is graphite, the stuff in lead pencils or stove polishes. Like the diamond, it is made of carbon atoms and nothing else, but these are strung together in layers in a honeycomb pattern and each layer only hangs feebly on to the next. This is why graphite is soft and slippery. The flat layers slide over each other without any difficulty like a pack of cards because they are not bound together by any powerful

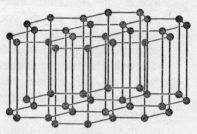

FIG. 18.—Structure of graphite. The black circles are carbon atoms. The short horizontal lines indicate firm linkages by sharing of electrons: the long vertical lines indicate weak linkage by electrical attraction of the atoms.

attractions. Mica, the stuff of which the transparent doors to anthracite stoves are made, is another giant layer molecule (Fig. 378). You can split mica into the thinnest flakes because it is simply a pile of extremely thin layers each of which is an elaborate pattern of silicon, oxygen and magnesium atoms. French chalk is powdered mica and its smooth slippery feel is caused by its being a mass of these tiny thin flakes.

Finally, the giant thread-molecules are important because they make *fibres* and the modern world finds thousands of uses for fibres. Paper, cardboard, cotton, wool, silk, hair, wood, asbestos, are a few of the fibrous materials we use.

Just look round the house and you will see that most common domestic objects are made of fibres. Clothes, carpets, chairs, upholstery stuffing, books, wall paper, are all made of fibrous material. If we look at cotton under the microscope, we see it is made up of hundreds of tiny fibres (Plate XXVIII). These fibres are of course absolutely enormous when compared to molecules, but if they are examined by X-ray photography (pp. 518 *ff*) it appears that each fibre contains thousands and thousands of much smaller fibres laid side by side—rather like sticks in a bundle. Each of these smallest fibres is a giant molecule fashioned rather like a watch-chain, the links being rings of carbon, hydrogen and oxygen atoms. Silk and hair have also long thread-like giant molecules. These fibres are not exactly crystals but they resemble crystals in having a repeating pattern of atoms. Part of a thread molecule from an asbestos fibre is shown in Fig. 378.

HARDNESS AND STRENGTH

If one was asked what was the chief thing that made solids different from liquids one might answer—the fact that they are hard and strong. They keep their shape. From the point of view of the engineer or the builder, the most important question to answer about a solid material is, "What will it stand?" The points to know about a material you are going to use to make a machine, a house, a ship, a railway line, are:

Is it hard or soft?

Is it tough or brittle?

Is it strong or weak?

Something has already been said about hardness and softness, and it will be realised that a hard substance is one which has its molecules firmly bound together and a soft one the opposite. Pure hardness is not very often wanted by the engineer. A material like glass or rock-crystal which is hard (difficult to scratch or dent) but brittle (easily broken when bent) is not a great deal of use. Diamond is, as I have said, the hardest stuff in the world: it is not very brittle but fairly so. A diamond is shattered at once if hit by a hammer, but you can rub it and grind it with anything else but another diamond and will not even be scratched. Diamonds are so expensive that engineers can't afford to use them much, but two very important uses have been found for diamonds which are discoloured and therefore useless as gems.

When a deep hole is being drilled in rock, a heavy cylindrical drill (Fig. 19 B) is twisted round in the hole and slowly cuts out a long cylinder of rock. A steel drill is very soon blunted, for almost all rocks are full of particles of silica (sand or quartz) which is just as hard as steel. So, in the cutting face of the drill the engineer sets a dozen or so strong lumpy diamonds: the dark kind called "bort" are the best. The diamonds cut through the rock enormously quicker than could steel. Such a drill may be worth a couple of thousand pounds and naturally there is a good deal of excitement if it breaks off at the bottom of a hole a thousand feet deep! Another job where hardness— freedom from wear—rather than strength is needed is wire-drawing. To make a wire, a rod of metal is pointed and then pulled through a hole just a little smaller than itself. It is then pulled through a hole a little smaller still and so on, until it is reduced to as small a diameter as may be wanted. These holes

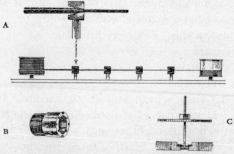

Fig. 19.—(a) Diagram illustrating the method of drawing wire; (b) a diamond drill; (c) a jewelled bearing in a watch.

are very quickly worn out because of the miles of wire hauled through them; the best way to make them is to drill a hole through a diamond, with the help of a rotating bit fed with diamond dust and oil, and set the diamond in a steel ring.

You often see advertisements of watches "with nineteen jewels." The wheels of a watch go round for a lifetime and are not often oiled. The accuracy of the watch depends on their turning very easily without looseness or shaking. Accordingly the bearings (Fig. 19 C) in which the spindles ("arbors") of a watch wheel fits are made of a jewel, usually a small ruby or sapphire, drilled with a fine hole. The end of the spindle, in the best watches, rests on a second jewel.

But, for most purposes, a material has got to stand shocks, A rod of rock crystal will stand as much wear as a rod of steel and will stand very nearly as strong a pull, but it won't stand a sudden shock. The materials which will stand the sort of treatment which a hammer-head, a tramline or the buffers of a train get are only of one kind—metals. It is very difficult to break metals. They bend before they break, whereas most other things like glass, salt, stone, brick, etc., break before they bend. We distinguish, then, things like metals which are *tough* from things like glass which are *brittle*.

Just think of what you would have to do to break, first, a tin can or copper kettle, then a china cup or glass jug, and you will see the difference.

Scientists have been puzzled for a long time as to why metals are so different from anything else. Think of a silver shilling. It has an odd shiny look about it which is shared only by other metals like steel, mercury, nickel and so on. It is absolutely opaque to light. Only the thinnest leaves of silver—fifty or a hundred atoms thick, let any light at all through. It is very tough and strong—try to break it or bend it. It conducts heat mar-vellously—hold one edge in your fingers and the other in a match-flame. It conducts electricity hundreds of times better than anything which is not a metal. There is still a great deal of argument going on as to why metals are so different from other things. The most probable answer is that the hardish ones like iron, copper, silver, chromium, etc. are giant molecules and every atom is bound to every other as, for example, they are in diamond. This makes them hard. But the difference between a metal and a thing like diamond or rock-crystal is that once you do break the bonds between the atoms in a diamond they are broken for ever, while in a metal the *binding electrons can shift from one atom to another*. If you bend a copper rod, the layers of atoms in the copper crystals slide over each other (bend a book or a pile of sheets of paper and see how they slip) and when the bending is done, the atoms link up to each other again and are as strong as before. If the bending is too violent, the layers may be pulled out of reach of each other and can't, so to speak, heal up again. This theory of shifting electrons accounts for the remarkable way in which metals conduct electricity. A current of electricity is just a mad rush of electrons. In a metal, the electrons shift along from one atom to the next quite easily; in a diamond or a ruby they cannot shift at all and not a trace of electricity can get through. The fact that metals do not let light through depends on these free electrons too. Light is made of waves of magnetic and electrical force, as is explained in Ch. XV. Electrons, being electricity, are moved by electrical and magnetic forces and so these forces which make up the light are totally expended in setting loose electrons in the metal moving; thus the light is used up.

The other things which are tough but not hard are the fibrous things mentioned a short way back. In these, the long threadlike molecules are flexible and, since they are not bound to each other at all firmly, they can all bend together without damaging each other.

Tough materials are wanted for a great many engineering purposes. The toughest of all are wanted for pieces of machinery which take violent shocks. Take, for example, the chain links which couple together the trucks of a goods-train. When the engine sets off, each link comes tight with a bang and a jerk. Steel would snap after a time, so a material not as strong as steel but even tougher—wrought iron—is used. Metals are tough and fibres are tough: wrought iron is hammered and rolled in such a way that it is a mass of fibres of nearly pure iron and is the toughest thing in the world. Copper is very tough but very soft as well, but a mixture of copper with about an eighth of its weight of tin gives the alloy, bronze, which is supremely tough and strong though not very hard. Bronze is used for ship's propellers. If a liner's vast propeller weighing 35 tons and turning 250 times a minute hits a sunken log or some such obstruction, it receives a fearful shock; a steel propeller would probably break and leave the ship crippled or helpless, but a bronze propeller will bend before it breaks.

The last but by no means least important quality needed in an engineering material is strength—tenacity—the ability to stand a pull without breaking. The finest steel here stands alone. A rod of steel an inch square will stand a pull of eighty tons, the weight

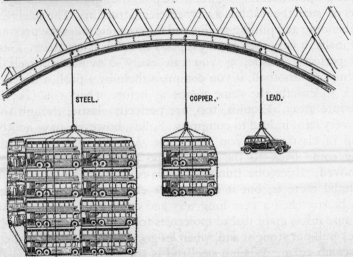

STEEL.   COPPER.   LEAD.

Fig. 20.—A steel rod of 1 in. cross section (the size of the black square) would be at breaking point when supporting eleven motor-buses. A copper rod of the same size would support two buses: a lead rod would support a saloon car.

of nearly a dozen large motor buses. "Mild steel" is less strong but much cheaper: a rod an inch square, made of the mild steel from which girders, etc., are made, will stand a pull of some twenty tons. Mild steel costs only about £8 10s. a ton, and is by far the strongest material at the price. It is not as strong as fine hardened steel, but it is tougher: though it is not as tough as wrought iron, it can be cast in moulds, while wrought iron has to be forged. It is the material *par excellence* for engineering jobs in general.

A great many materials which will not stand a pull will stand a push. All kinds of stony materials like bricks, stone, concrete and so on, will bear a tremendous weight on top of them, but will not stand pulling or bending. The importance of ferro-concrete follows from this. A building of concrete alone would stand a very great weight as long as the strains (such as wind-pressure) did not bend it sideways. Steel is much too heavy and expensive to make a whole building of, but if we pour the liquid concrete round bars of steel the result is a very efficient structure. The steel takes the bending and pulling strains and the concrete takes the pressure.

Finally, a very important property of solids is elasticity. Gases are perfectly elastic, as you can easily convince yourself by sitting on a football; if you compress them by a push, they come back to exactly the same *volume* as before when you take the pressure away. Liquids, too, are perfectly elastic, though they are very hard indeed to compress. Solids, however, have another kind of elasticity: if you alter their *shape* by applying a force, they come back to the same shape again when the force is removed. Everyone thinks of india-rubber as the most elastic material there is, but it is no more elastic than steel. Rubber can be stretched a very long way and come back again. This is because it has giant thread molecules folded like a tangle of rope. They pull out straight and, when let go, snap back and fold themselves up again. When a steel rod is stretched, the atoms in the lattice are pulled a little farther apart. Every atom is hitched to the next by electrons (probably going in an orbit round both) and to stretch the orbit you make the electrons go further and do more work. Each electron is very small and feeble, but the collection of millions of millions puts up a good pull. An elastic metal like steel just stretches these orbits when it is pulled on or bent and, when it is let go, they spring back and the material returns to its former shape. The poorly elastic metal (like lead or copper) when pulled on strongly, just unlinks its atoms and links them up again in the new position. In other words, it stretches. The only important elastic material (beside rubber) is steel, and it must be hardened steel. If steel is made red-hot and suddenly cooled in water, it becomes very hard, very elastic and rather brittle. The process is called tempering. If the tempered steel is then gently heated up, it becomes softer, less elastic but much tougher. Springs, which of course must be very elastic but which must bend a long way without breaking, are almost always made of steel which has been tempered and reheated. It is hard to make a good spring out of anything but steel.

If a steel spring is stretched, it extends, and the *extra* length is proportional to the load: if a one pound weight makes a spring two inches longer, then a 2 lb. weight makes it four inches longer, and so on. But after a time, the *elastic limit* is reached and the spring begins to stretch much more for every pound put on, and if the weight is taken off the spring will no longer go back again. What has happened here? It seems that a sufficient weight makes the links between the atoms give way at the weakest points, which are where the tiny crystals of metal join: these crystals slip past each other and the shape of the spring is altered; a little more weight makes the crystals separate, whereupon the spring breaks.

The engineers are naturally very interested to know how strong a piece of material is. If a bridge is to be erected, a plan is made showing where every rod and girder is to go. Then comes the question, how big have these girders got to be? If they are made too big, the bridge will be very heavy and expensive and someone who can do it cheaper will get the contract; if too small, the bridge may break, lives may be lost and the reputation of the firm may be ruined. So engineers must ascertain how much force their girders can stand before they break and then make sure they will never have more than about a quarter of this force to bear. The usual thing to do is to take test pieces of the actual steel used in the girders and see how many tons pull is needed to break them.

The machinery used for the purpose is illustrated in Fig. 21. The piece of steel P is strained between two cross-heads C, C. The lower one (C) is slowly pulled down by an electric motor M (or handwheel) working a screw (L). The top one (C) is con-

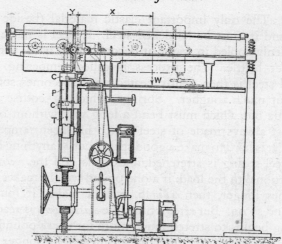

FIG. 21.—Testing machine. The test piece P supports the
pull of the weight W multiplied by X/Y. Y is a fixed
distance. X is read off by a scale marked in tons.
(Courtesy of Messrs. W. & T. Avery, Ltd.)

nected to the beam of a large weighing machine, in principle
like those used for weighing luggage at stations but of course
more powerful. This actually weighs the pull of the screw L
on the test piece. The big weight W, is so heavy that it
is moved along by gearing operated by a handwheel. A
scale enables the user to read off the pull when the test piece breaks.

For many purposes, engineers need a hard material and so
they also require some way of telling how hard a thing is. Now
hardness is not nearly as simple an idea as breaking strain; how
are we to tell if glass is harder than rock crystal or gold harder
than silver? The original test was to see which material scratched
which. A diamond will scratch anything, a ruby won't scratch
a diamond but will scratch steel, steel won't scratch ruby but will
scratch copper, and so on. This test gives a notion as to which
of two things is the harder; but it does not *measure* the hardness
as a figure or number. A simple way is to number ten materials
in order of hardness calling Diamond 10; Corundum (colourless
ruby or sapphire), 9; Topaz, 8; Quartz (rock-crystal), 7; Felspar

(the big whitish crystals you see in polished granite), 6; Apatite, 5; Fluorspar (the ornamental "blue-john" used for vases, etc.), 4; Calcite (marble), 3; Gypsum (alabaster as used for the bowl-reflector electric fittings), 2; Talc (used for the fronts of stoves), 1. Then, if the substance we are testing (say steel) is scratched by rock-crystal but scratches felspar, we say its hardness is between 7 and 6; and we call its hardness 6.5. A rough rule is that things of hardness 1 and 2 can be scratched with a finger-nail, 3, 4, 5, 6 with a knife, and 7—10 not with a knife. Engineers often use a form of the Brinell hardness tester which forces a steel ball into the metal to be tested with a measured force. The

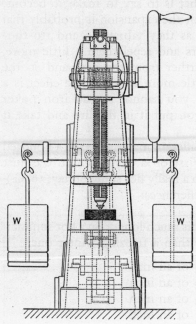

width of the dent it makes is measured and the hardness is calculated from it. Fig. 22 shows the machine. The ball is forced by a screw into the specimen (which is mounted on the platform of a weighing machine) until the weights (W, W) lift, which happens at a pressure of 3000 kilograms (about 3 tons).

This machine is used for metals, but of course is no good for things like glass. Glass is about as hard as ordinary steel, but if you try to dent it, it promptly breaks and you cannot get a measurement.

Finally, the toughness of a material is most difficult to measure. Engineers often test the toughness of steel by finding out how many times it can be doubled on itself like

Fig. 22.—Brinell hardness tester. The screw drives the ball into the test piece (black) until the force applied is enough to lift the weights. The size of the dent in the test piece is then measured. (Courtesy of Messrs. W. & T. Avery, Ltd.)

a folded foot-rule and straightened again without breaking. This is a very severe test and only a tough steel will stand it at all. Copper comes out of it very well. Things like stone are not worth testing for toughness, because no one ever thinks of using them for a job where toughness is required.

HEAT-EXPANSION OF SOLIDS

The effect of heat on solids is the same as its effect on everything else—it speeds up their molecules. The first effect of this is to make the solid expand—that is to say to make it become larger every way. The reason for the expansion is probably that the molecules move faster and as they vibrate to and fro they come nearer to their neighbours and repel them a little more. Every molecule gets a little further from the next and so the lattice becomes spaced out a little more widely. The effect is a very small one: as you know, you cannot see an iron poker getting longer and shorter as you put it in the fire and take it out again.

Actually, if you took bars of different materials, each a hundred feet long, and measured them first on a day when it was just freezing (0° C.) and then again on a really hot summer day (30° C.), you would find the following differences:

A bar 100 feet long made of this material	is this much longer on a hot summer day than a freezing winter one.
Aluminium	$\frac{4}{5}$ of an inch
Copper	$\frac{5}{8}$ of an inch
Cast iron	$\frac{1}{3}$ of an inch
Glass	$\frac{1}{4}$ of an inch
Rock crystal	$\frac{1}{16}$ of an inch

The expansion is very small, but it is exceedingly powerful. Suppose we take a cube of iron with each edge an inch long and hold it between absolutely fixed supports so that it cannot expand in any direction and then heat it from 0° C. (temperature of ice) to 100 °C. (temperature of boiling water). The iron would expand by just about a thousandth of an inch if it was free. But, as we have fixed it, it can't expand; so, in effect, we have compressed our hot piece of iron to $\frac{999}{1000}$ of its length, and, if we measure the force needed to do this, we find it is no less than 35 tons weight. In other words, the iron cube would be straining to expand with a force equal to a weight of about thirty-five tons.

We can see from this that solids expand very little, but (if they are strong and difficult to compress) very forcibly. This expansion has to be taken account of in engineering work. If you have any big metal object of which the temperature is likely to alter, it is essential to give it room to expand and contract. A railway line may be as hot as 40° C. in summer: the line might be laid in winter when the temperature is (say) about 5° C. Steel expands about eleven-millionths of its length for each degree centigrade it is heated; so, on a hot day, a rail 60 feet long would be $\frac{720 \times 11 \times 35}{1,000,000}$ inches (more than a quarter of an inch) longer than when it was laid. Well, suppose the men had laid the rails so that each rail touched the next two. All the rails would get $\frac{1}{4}$ inch longer and the force would make them bend like a bow. When the rail had lifted, so that its middle was six inches above the ground, it would be $\frac{1}{4}$ inch longer and quite comfortable again, but the next train coming along would be wrecked! So railwaymen lay their rails with a gap of a quarter of an inch between each. Big bridges give even more trouble, for the steel girders used are far longer than railway lines. The girders of the Forth Bridge are mounted on rollers so that they can expand and contract (as much as a foot!) on hot and cold days. Steam pipes are a source of trouble too. When superheated steam is going through them, they are not much less than red-hot, but when the machine is not working, they are cold. You can't put gaps in a steam pipe, so the engineers allow for expansion by putting in curved spring sections which are easily bent. Very large pipes require great force to bend them; in Plate I is shown a very large expansion joint made by Messrs. Aiton, Ltd. This is corrugated like a concertina to make it at once strong and springy.

These are some of the troubles the expansion of solids makes: now for a few of its advantages. It gives us a good way of fixing a ring of metal round a disc of metal. As an example, take the flanged "tyres" on railway wheels. The tyres are made a little *smaller* than the centres they have to fit over and are then made hot. They expand, and the cold centre can be slipped in. When the wheel cools, they contract and grip it so that they will not come off again in a hurry! Fig. 23 shows how this is done. The process of "shrinking" one piece of metal over another is quite often used; the outer casings of big guns are often shrunk over the inner ones. The disadvantage of the method is the tremendous strain it may put on the material. If the sizes of the two bits and their temperatures are not very carefully worked out it may well happen that the outer bit is nearly breaking with the pull. Consequently, the tyre of a railway wheel and the centre to fit it are most carefully machined so that the former is only larger than the latter by $\frac{1}{800}$ to $\frac{1}{1000}$ of the diameter of the wheel (say $\frac{1}{12}$ to $\frac{1}{16}$ inch). The amount of the expansion of

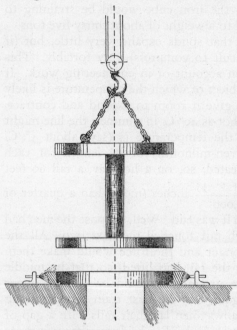

Fig. 23.—Fitting centre to railway tyre. (Courtesy of London, Midland and Scottish Ry. Co., Ltd.)

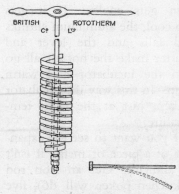

FIG. 24.—A Rototherm bimetallic thermometer operated by a spiral bimetallic strip. Inset, bimetallic strip. The upper of the two metals is the more expansible: the dotted line shows the position taken up when the strip is heated. (Courtesy of British Rototherm Co., Ltd.)

a solid can be used to measure how hot a thing is. The expansion of liquids is used in ordinary thermometers, but for a few kinds of thermometers the expansion of a piece of metal is used. Now a reasonable-sized bit of metal expands so little for each degree that it is not easy to make any gadget which will enable us to see the change, but one rather useful trick has been thought of. Aluminium expands much more than iron, for every degree their expansions are twenty-five millionths and eleven millionths of their length respectively. If we rivet a bit of aluminium to a bit of iron, as in Fig. 24 (inset), and heat the strips, something will have to go. The aluminium gets longer than the iron, but still has to touch it all the way along. The only way in which the strain can be relieved is by the aluminium bending over the iron. A little bit of geometry will show that a very small difference of length in the two metals will cause a biggish curve in the strip. Thermometers are now made from these bimetallic strips. The Rototherm type are very nearly as accurate as mercury thermometers and—as they read on a dial—much more convenient. Fig. 24 shows how the "bimetallic" strips are mounted. The unequal expansion of the spiral strips can only be compensated by the spiral rolling up or unrolling, so moving the pointer. Modern incubators are worked much in this way. A strong bit of steel has a bit of aluminium riveted to it at each end *only*. When the two get warmer, the aluminium is too weak to bend the steel, so it rises up into an arc (just like the rail on p. 61). The regulator is set so that as the incubator gets hotter the aluminium pushes up a lever and lets the hot air from the lamp go outside the incubator, which

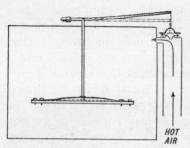

FIG. 25.—Illustrating the principle of the regulating system of an incubator.

then gets cooler. If it gets too cool, the aluminium shrinks and falls and the lever and shutter make the hot air all go into the incubator and warm it up. In this way the incubator is kept just at the right temperature.

If you want to see the expansion of a piece of metal, it isn't too difficult. Get an iron rod (a kitchen poker will do), five bricks, a bit of broken glass, a knitting needle, a straw and a bit of sealing wax. Hold one end of the poker down with the bricks and under the other end put the needle with the bit of glass under it. Fasten the straw on to the needle with a blob of hot sealing wax. Stand a bootbox behind it and mark the position of the end of the straw with a pencil. Now heat the poker with a blow lamp or a tin saucer of methylated spirit. It will expand about a hundredth of an inch. The needle will *roll* a hundredth of an inch, and this will move it about a twentieth of a complete turn, which again will turn the straw through two or three inches. For success, you want a rather smooth bar pressing hard on the needle. Brass is rather better than iron.

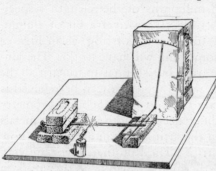

FIG. 26.—A simple way of demonstrating the expansion of a solid when heated.

And now take a flight of fancy from straws and kitchen pokers to the great earth itself. The earth is hot inside. On the average a mine gets hotter by about 1° F. for every hundred feet it descends. We see hot springs coming from the earth. Volcanoes

PLATE I

Roman water wheel, used for pumping water from a copper mine, probably dating from 240 B.C. to A.D. 411. (By courtesy of the Rio Tinto Co., Ltd.)

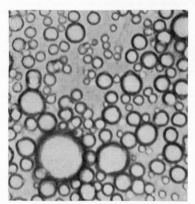

Milk, an emulsion, magnified 850 times.

A large steam pipe. The U-shaped corrugated bend allows for expansion and contraction. (By courtesy of the Aiton Pipe Company, Derby.)

PLATE II

A piece of Iceland spar (left) cleaved by taps with a knife-blade into four fragments with sides and edges at the same angle.

Hexagonal crystal of beryl.
(By courtesy of the Director of the Natural History Museum, London.)

Cubic crystals of fluorspar ("Blue-John").
(By courtesy of the Director of the Natural History Museum, London.)

Microphotographs of snow crystals. All angles are multiples of 60°
(By courtesy of the McGraw Hill Company, from Bentley's *Snow Crystals*.)

belch out glowing lava. As far as we know there is not much heat being produced in the earth and as the inside is hotter than the outside, heat must be gently leaking out of it all the time. This and a good many other reasons make us think that the earth is slowly cooling down. Now suppose the whole earth got cooler by one degree centigrade—not a great deal—and suppose it only contracted as much as a piece of glass would—a low estimate.

The earth is 8000 miles in diameter. On our estimate it would decrease in "length" by about eight millionths for each degree centigrade, so that its diameter would get $\dfrac{8 \times 8000 \times 1760}{1,000,000}$ yards or about a hundred and twelve yards less. Well, if the earth shrank evenly, no one would notice it. But suppose, while the inside cooled, the outside which remains open to the sun and sky stayed at much the same temperature; from the fossil animals and plants found in ancient rocks, we know the temperature cannot have altered much in many million years. The inside will have got smaller while the outside remained much the same size. The interior of the earth must fit the crust, so the outer crust crumples, and these crinkles have been thought to be mountain ranges like the Alps. The crumpling is better understood if you look at an old man's face. The flesh has shrunk but the skin remains the same size, so it has to wrinkle. The mountain ranges of the earth were thought to be the wrinkles on its aged face. This theory is by some considered to be insufficient to account for mountain formation. For reasons, further written of in Chapter XXXIII, they are inclined to think that a gradual drifting of whole continents has raised the Alps and Himalaya.

CONDUCTION OF HEAT

We have already taken for granted the fact that solids conduct heat; that is to say, if you heat one bit, it passes its heat on to the next. It is obvious that this will be so. The molecules of the hot part are moving quicker than the molecules of the cool part.

The speedy molecule will have more kinetic energy and will vibrate in wider swings and, therefore, will swing nearer the next molecules. It will attract and repel these and set them swinging more strongly and itself less strongly and this will go on till every molecule is vibrating just a bit more briskly than before. The heat has spread evenly all over the solid. Cool a corner of the solid: the molecules are slowed down. The quicker moving molecules of the rest of the solid repel and attract these and so speed them up again somewhat. To speed the others up, they must slow themselves down. All the molecules finally go a bit slower and the whole solid gets colder.

This is fairly easy to understand, but the difficulty is to explain why some solids conduct heat much worse than others. You cannot hold a metal cup of freshly poured hot tea in your hand without wrapping it in a handkerchief: a bakelite cup can be held quite comfortably. Why is it that the hot tea can pass on heat only very slowly through bakelite or earthenware and very quickly indeed through aluminium? The answer is that we are not sure. It is pretty certain that metals have some loose electrons in them: these, being very small, are speeded up very easily and run in between the metal atoms, colliding with them and speeding them up. The trouble about this is that the electrons do not seem to be heavy enough to do the job.

Another theory is that the motion of the atoms in a metal is not just handed from one atom of metal to the next, but that the whole metal is moved by the heat and the motion travels on like a wobble in jelly. Physicists are still arguing this with the help of horribly complicated mathematics. They find it pretty easy to show that none of the theories about conduction in metals is quite right, but they haven't yet found out the whole truth of the matter.

In engineering and ordinary domestic life, good conductors of heat—things that let heat through easily—and also bad conductors—things that let heat through only very slowly—are in demand. The best conductors of heat are metals, so we use metal for pots and pans and boilers and radiators, all of which are things through which we want heat to go. Pots and pans are also made of metal because metal does not crack when suddenly heated, whereas glass, china and many bad conductors do. If you pour boiling water into a thick tumbler, the inside of the tumbler expands at once. The outside is still cold and so the inside *forces* it to become larger. Glass does not stand forcing, so the molecules lose their grip of each other and the glass cracks. Very thin glass stands rapid cooling and heating because the inside is so near the outside that the heat gets through almost instantly: for this reason, chemical apparatus is made of thin glass. Metals do not crack in this way, first because the heat spreads and evens itself out so quickly, secondly because strains bend them rather than break them.

In domestic jobs we need bad conductors to enclose things which we want to keep hot or cold. Ordinary solids like china, stone or glass are not very efficient; they do not let nearly as much heat through as metal does, but they still pass a good deal. The worst conductor of heat is a gas, if it is prevented in any way from moving about. Look at Figs. 11–12. A given amount of gas has only about one molecule where the same volume of a solid has a thousand, and the gas molecules carry no more energy than those of the solid. Accordingly, a gas will not carry much heat. If a hot object stands in a gas, the hot gas flows up from it and new cold gas comes in from below. This cools it rather quickly; and so if we want to keep a thing hot, we surround it with a gas tangled up in a solid, and therefore unable to move far. If we pack a hot saucepan round with flannel or cotton wool or hay or crumpled newspaper, we are really packing it in the still air which these things entangle. "Hay-box" cookery was a good deal practised in the war of 1914—1918, when fuel was scarce. The food was heated to boiling and the saucepan was then put in a "nest" of hay and covered with a cloth, on top of which was more hay. The heat escaped so slowly that the food was cooked through before the water became too cool to cook it.

Engineers are always trying to save heat. They spend good money on coal to turn water into steam to drive their engines and, since economical working is required, the heat must be used for power and not allowed to leak away into the air. So engineers cover up their boilers and pipes with something that does not conduct heat well. Things like cotton-wool or felt or flannel are inflammable, so they don't use them but prefer asbestos fibre, which they mix with plaster of paris into a soft porous cement which can be packed round boilers, pipes or anything else. This non-conducting coating they call "lagging." The most remarkable kind of lagging is crumpled aluminium foil, which most people call "silver paper." The air-spaces in between the folds transmit hardly any heat. The aluminium itself is an excellent conductor, but the heat has to travel along its folds for such a long way and through such a very narrow passage, that hardly any gets away.

Just as we use lagging to keep heat in things, we use it to keep heat out. If you want to keep ice from melting you wrap it in a blanket. A blanket stops your heat from getting *out* of the bed; it stops the air's heat from getting *in* to the ice. Refrigerators are usually packed round with some porous material to keep the air's heat out. One of the best things for keeping heat in or out is slag-wool—very odd stuff. Slag is chiefly the part of the iron ore which isn't iron; it comes out of the furnace as a molten liquid which solidifies to a kind of opaque glass. If a jet of air is blown through the molten slag, it cools, becomes treacly, and blows out into long threads which when cool look rather like wool. It is very cheap, light, and non-inflammable, moths and bugs won't eat it, and it doesn't go mouldy. It is greatly used for a non-conducting packing. The very worst conductor of heat is a vacuum. If a space was really empty of gas molecules (it is never quite so) there would be nothing to carry the heat at all. A thermos flask is a double-walled vessel with a vacuum between the walls. A hot liquid in a thermos flask would never cool if it were not that, first, a little heat goes up the inside of the neck and also through the cork; secondly, that a little heat goes out as rays which cross a vacuum as well or better than any other space; and thirdly, that even the best vacuum has a little gas left in it.

The silver on the thermos flask reflects most of the rays back into the liquid and emits very few of them. Consequently, the liquid in a thermos flask cools about twenty times as slowly as it would in an ordinary bottle.

MELTING

The first effect of heat on a solid, then, is to make it expand. But the speeding up of the molecules may have other effects too. The usual effect of heating a solid is to make it melt. The molecules vibrate more and more rapidly and in wider and wider arcs as the material gets hotter. After a time, they vibrate so violently that they can no longer stay in the pattern of the lattice of the crystals of which the solid is made up and instead of a solid there appears a liquid. The solid is said to melt or fuse.

Now, there are several odd things about melting. In the first place, a pure substance, like ice or soda, melts at an absolutely definite temperature. At a thousandth of a degree below 0° C. ice is perfectly hard and solid; at a thousandth of a degree above 0° C. it completely liquefies to water. It does not gradually soften like a candle in hot weather, but melts completely at one temperature. This is why we can speak of "freezing-point." The temperature at which water freezes really is a *point* on the scale, not a range of two or three or more degrees. Of course all this does not mean that as soon as the thermometer (which shows the air temperature) gets above freezing-point all the ice suddenly melts. It *begins* to melt as soon as the surrounding air rises above 0° C. and begins to warm it up. The unmelted ice stays at or below freezing point; as the air heats each successive portion above freezing-point, it melts to water.

Now it is common knowledge that many things do not melt as sharply as ice. Butter when warmed gets gradually sloppier and sloppier till it becomes liquid; it does not melt at any particular temperature. The reason of this is (roughly speaking) that butter is a mixture of quite a number of different fats and oils, all of which melt at different temperatures; consequently the lowest melting ones get liquid first; sloppy butter is a mixture of liquid and solid fats. The matter is complicated by the fact that the solid unmelted fats dissolve in the liquid melted ones as sugar dissolves in tea. The rule about melting points is that pure substances with only one kind of stuff in them melt suddenly and sharply as ice does. Substances made of several different materials usually melt gradually. The plumber takes advantage of this when he "wipes" a joint. A joint in a lead pipe (look in the bathroom) is made by putting the two ends together and wiping a pasty mass of half-melted plumber's solder into a barrel-shaped lump around them. Now it would not be possible to use pure lead as a solder, for this is a thin liquid at 328° C. and quite solid at 327° C. Nor could tin be used, for this is liquid at 232° C. and solid at 231° C. But the wily plumber mixes equal parts of lead and tin. This metal, "plumber's solder," when melted begins to solidify at 220° C. and is not hard till it has cooled to 180° C.; so that the plumber has lots of time to finish wiping the metal into shape before it hardens.

The melting-point and freezing-point of a pure substance is the same. Water is solid ice below 0° C. and liquid water above 0° C. At 0° C. itself both ice and water can exist. Accordingly a mixture of ice and water stays exactly at 0° C. If you try to warm it, it gets no hotter, for the heat is all used up in melting the ice; if you try to cool it, the heat which leaves the mixture is obtained by freezing some of the water. A mixture of ice and water is at a *fixed* temperature and if you want to test a thermometer you can stir crushed ice and a little water together for about ten minutes till they have had time to even up their temperatures. Your thermometer if stuck into this mixture should mark exactly 0° C. or 32° F.

A mixed substance like butter or solder has no true melting point. The best figure to take is the temperature when the *last* bit of solid turns into liquid.

Solids melt at extremely different temperatures. The table which follows gives a chart of a few melting and boiling points. Starting at the bottom, we see helium. Helium atoms are very

A SCALE OF TEMPERATURES.

Temperature in Degrees.			Melts.	Boils.
Centigrade.	Fahrenheit.			
3800	6872		Carbon	
3600	6512			Carbon
3500	6332	Arc Flame		
3360	6080		Tungsten	
2500	4532	A Tungsten Lamp Filament		
2450	4432			Iron
2400	4350	An Oxy-Acetylene Torch		
2204	4000	Bessemer Furnace		
1955	3582			Silver
1755	3190		Platinum	
1750	3180	Carbon Lamp Filament		
1540	2790		Chromium	
1120	2052			Magnesium
1062	1944		Gold	
961	1762		Silver	
905	1660			Zinc
804	1480		Salt	
600	1112	A Bright Coal Fire		
445	833			Sulphur
419	784		Zinc	
357	677			Mercury
327	621		Lead	
218	400			Naphthalene
112	239	Hottest Room in Turkish Bath	Sulphur	
100	212			Water
63	145		Beeswax	
15	60	Average Room		
0	32		Ice	
−34	−29			Chlorine
−100	−148	Coldest Siberia		
−118	−180		Alcohol Freezes	
−185	−303			Argon
−218	−361		Oxygen	
−253	−423			Hydrogen
−272	−458		Helium	
−273	−459	No Heat		

light in weight, and so the motion they derive from their heat-energy makes them go very fast. What is more, helium has a beautifully balanced atom with the positive nucleus almost exactly centred in between its two outside electrons. The result is that one end of a helium atom is hardly at all more positive or negative than the other and so one helium atom hardly attracts the next at all. It follows that the helium atoms jostle about more rapidly than others and attract each other less. Consequently, there is very little to keep them in their lattice and the slightest heat motion jogs them out. Solid helium melts at the extraordinarily low temperature of −272° C., less than one degree above the absolute zero where there is no heat—that is to say, every atom and molecule is motionless. Absolute zero has never been reached, and it does not seem that we shall ever do better than approach it more and more closely. The lowest temperatures have been reached by utilising the fact that certain substances become warmer when they are magnetised and become cooler again when the magnetic field is switched off. By cooling these substances in boiling helium while they are in the field of a magnet and then switching the magnet off, the temperature is made to drop still further, and recently a new low record of only 0.0044—about one two-hundredth—of a degree above the temperature where there is no heat at all, has been reached. Turning to the other end of the melting-point table, we can see carbon with small atoms closely bound together by electrons. We have already discussed the diamond on p. 48, so let us see why tungsten, the next thing on the list, melts at such a tremendous temperature. The reason is probably that, first its atoms are very heavy (46 times as heavy as a helium atom) and are therefore not so much jogged about by heat; secondly, its atoms are small and so get close together and attract each other strongly; thirdly, it has an unsymmetrical arrangement of electrons and so some parts have more positive charge and others more negative charge, which makes the atoms attract each other; and finally that a piece of tungsten is probably a giant molecule like diamond, though not such a strongly built one. All these reasons taken together show why tungsten melts at about 3360° C., and also why it does not release its atoms and turn into vapour at all easily. This high melting-point and small tendency to turn into vapour gives us our electric light bulbs. The hotter you make a thing, the less of the power you use to heat it comes out again as heat and the more comes out as light. An old-fashioned carbon filament bulb had its filament at about 1750° C., a perceptibly "yellow" heat. It turned 99.44% of its electricity into unwanted heat and only 0.56% into light. The tungsten lamp with a filament at 2500° C. gives 1.84% of its energy as light and 98.16% as heat. There is still room for improvement!

You will say that carbon melts at 3800° C. while tungsten melts at only 3360° C., why not therefore heat the carbon filament say to 3500° C.? The reason is, that the carbon atom is light and though carbon will not melt, its atoms fly off as vapour at temperatures above about 1800° C. If a 100-volt carbon lamp is put on a 220-volt circuit, the temperature of the filament goes above 2000° C. It gives a brilliant light and (if the fuse does not blow first) the filament evaporates, depositing black carbon on the glass. As it evaporates it gets thinner and in ten minutes or so breaks. Tungsten filaments, particularly in lamps filled with some gas like argon (which does not affect tungsten) hardly evaporate at all. If anyone could find a lamp which turned all the electrical energy put into it into visible light, it would divide everybody's lighting bill by 55. He would make a gigantic fortune into the bargain. A few very efficient lamps have been made, but they all give light of a horrid colour. In the mercury-vapour arc lamp, the current passes through a glass tube full of mercury vapour and makes it glow with a dazzling blue-green light which makes everyone's face look a revolting and deathly colour. It gives four times as much light for the money as a filament lamp, but it cannot be used for interior lighting. Many arterial roads, railway stations, etc., are lighted by it and they are being rapidly developed and may soon rival the filament lamps. These and other electric lamps are discussed in Chapter XV.

Tungsten is rather rare and expensive to make. If we want to make large things, such as furnace linings, which will stand high temperatures without melting, we use fireclay, which does not melt below 1500° C.—near the melting-point of nickel. For higher temperatures still, we line furnaces with magnesium oxide stuck together with a little tar, which in the furnace turns to carbon and then burns away. Carbon itself (as charcoal, coke or gas carbon) would be a perfect material for furnaces, for it is cheap and impossible to melt in any furnace. The trouble is that it burns away very quickly and it can only be used in a few electric furnaces where air can be kept out.

CASTINGS

Metals melt at all sorts of different temperatures and one of the chief ways they are worked into shape is by casting them. Not every kind of metal is suitable for casting. Some like nickel flow rather sluggishly and do not fill the mould well, some like

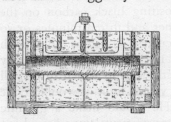

FIG. 27.—A section of a mould arranged for the casting of a flanged pipe. (Courtesy, American Technical Society, Chicago.)

platinum or pure soft iron need too high a temperature to melt them. Both pure metals and alloys —mixtures of metals—are used for castings. Of pure metals, that which is most used for casting lead—employed for ornamental gutters and cisterns and small statues and also for apparatus used for chemical work. Very big castings are not made of lead because it is rather heavy, rather expensive, and so soft that it bends with its own weight.

Aluminium is very widely used. It melts at 657° C. and so is easy to cast. It is so light that it is very much used where neither great strength nor great cheapness is more important than lightness. Aluminium is cast into crank-cases for motor cars; it is also used as sheets for motor car bodies and also very greatly for aeroplane parts.

Copper is not much used as castings, but is chiefly employed as sheet or wire. Pure iron melts at such a high temperature that it is never cast—wrought iron is always forged, for casting would destroy the fibres (p. 54) which make it so tough. Cast iron and mild steel are the two metals most used for castings. Supposing a man wants to have a number of flanged pipes of a particular pattern made in cast-iron. He makes exact drawings of them and sends them to a pattern maker, who cuts out a full-sized model of the pipe in wood. The pattern goes to the moulders, who make a mould of the pipe by ramming round it a particular kind of sand containing some clay and often also some flour or treacle to make it bind. The mould is made in two halves which, fitted together, leave a hollow the exact shape of the pattern. The hollow centre of the pipe is arranged for, by a "core," a cylinder of sand mixed with a little flour and baked hard. The whole thing is set up as shown in Fig. 27. A hole is left through which the molten metal is poured and several air holes are left to allow air and steam to get away. It is usual to pour in a little more metal than is needed and the projecting piece this leaves has to be cut off. The casting, when the mould is taken off, is rather rough. If the metal is to be painted, it may be smooth enough; if not, it is machined, that is to say turned to true and even shape by a lathe or milling-machine.

Cast iron has the great advantage of expanding when it solidifies. The solid iron just after it has set is a tiny bit larger than the mould and so it forces itself into the smallest crevices and gives a very faithful impression. There are not many other metals which do this; the most important one is the rather odd metal antimony. You probably know the Japanese cigarette boxes of a grey silvery metal, cast with elaborate dragons and so on, in high relief. These are made of antimony. Antimony itself is of very little use except for making ornaments because, unlike most metals, it is brittle and a good knock cracks a casting in half. But, if we mix, say, 30% antimony with 55% lead and 15% tin, a white metal is obtained which is quite hard, melts to a very thin liquid and—like antimony itself—expands when it solidifies. This alloy is called type-metal and it is used for casting the types from which this and all other books are

printed. It takes such a fine impression, that a piece the size of
a capital E in this book, bearing an impression of the whole of
the Lord's Prayer, can be cast from a mould.

SUBLIMATION

Besides melting, there are two other things that can happen
to a solid when it is heated. Instead of the molecules speeding
up till they strike each other and knock down the regular pattern
of the atoms of the solid, they may speed up until the attraction
of the neighbouring molecules will not hold the outside molecules
in their places.

If you look at Fig. 28 you will see that the outlying molecules at

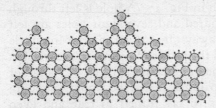

the surface of a solid are
attracted by fewer molecules
than attract those in the
middle of the solid. If
these outer ones waggle hard
enough, they may pull themselves out of range of the
Fig. 28.—Showing that the outermost
atoms of a solid are held by fewer bonds
of attraction than the inner ones.
attraction of the others and
sail away.

Not many substances turn
into vapour like this before they melt; the best known ones
are sal-ammoniac and white arsenic. Camphor and iodine
too turn into vapour very easily. If the vapour is allowed
to get cold, it turns back into the solid, which often forms
glittering crystals. This gives us a very good way of purifying
these things. If sal-ammoniac is mixed with any sort of dirt
which does not turn into vapour, we can put it in a covered
pot and heat it up. The sal-ammoniac turns into vapour and
leaves the dirt behind in the pot. When the vapour touches
the cold lid, it turns back to a mass of pure white sal-ammoniac
crystals. If you want to try a sublimation, put a little sal-ammoniac
in a shallow round tin and stand this on a low gas-flame. The
sal-ammoniac will soon give out a dense white smoke. Put a

saucer of water on the top of the tin, and the vapour will solidify ("condense") on the saucer as a solid white cake. If you try this with camphor, use only a tiny flame, for camphor is inflammable.

DECOMPOSITION BY HEAT

There is one more possibility when a solid is heated. Its molecules may not stand the violent vibration and may split up into atoms or smaller molecules.

A model of the molecule of glucose (a very useful kind of sugar) is drawn in Fig. 29 magnified about sixty million times. You can see it is made of six carbon atoms (black balls), twelve hydrogen atoms (white balls), some of which are out of sight at the back, and six oxygen atoms (grey balls). Of course, as was explained on p. 27, you could not possibly *see* the atoms, but the model shows you the shape and size and how the atoms are put together.

This big molecule is not made for shaking about. When glucose is heated, it melts; the liquid when made still hotter becomes brown and then black and finally emits quantities of steam and leaves a black cindery mass of charcoal (carbon). What has happened is that the molecule has been shaken to bits: the hydrogen atoms and oxygen atoms have struck up partnerships and gone off as steam molecules, and the carbon atoms have been left behind probably linked together in a vague sort of honeycomb pattern. Now glucose melts at 146° C. and later "decomposes" as the chemists call it.

FIG. 29.—A model of a glucose molecule, magnified about 60,000,000 times. (Courtesy of Messrs. Edward Arnold and Prof. Haworth, from the latter's *Constitution of the Sugars.*

But cellulose, the stuff in the cotton fibre, has a molecule like some 150 glucose molecules strung together. Cellulose cannot melt. Its molecule, a thirtieth part of which appears in Fig. 370, is far too large to jostle about in the flippant style suitable to a glucose molecule. So, when we heat cotton, it does not melt or turn into vapour but just decomposes. It goes brown, then black, and its molecules turn into a whole selection of smaller molecules with unpleasant smoky smells and leaves behind some carbon. Most substances with very big molecules do this. Wool, silk, the "keratin" of our hair and toenails, "albumen" of white of egg, all when heated turn brown and break up into simpler things, but do not melt or boil.

You often hear people talk about sugar melting in tea or soda melting in water. This, to the scientist's way of thinking, is incorrect. He keeps the word "melting" for a solid turning into a liquid when heated. He calls the thing which happens when a solid is mixed with a liquid and disappears into it "dissolving." Dissolving is quite a remarkable business and it is discussed on pp. 82–86.

CHAPTER V

LIQUIDS

THE FLUID STATE

THE obvious difference between a solid and a liquid is that
a solid resists attempts to change either its shape or its size,
while a liquid only resists attempts to change its size. Try and
push a well-fitting cork into a completely full bottle of water
and you will quickly see that any attempt to make a liquid smaller
in bulk will need a great deal of force; but the lightest touch of
a hair is enough to move it through the water, so changing the
water's shape. Mind you, a liquid will not change its shape
instantaneously. Dive flat off the 18-foot platform and you will
at once see that water puts up a vigorous temporary resistance
to an attempt to change its shape. But no liquid puts up a
permanent resistance to a distorting force. Even a thick liquid
like treacle will yield to the weight of the tiniest grain of sand
and let it sink to the bottom in the course of minutes or hours.
The reason of this is fairly obvious. A liquid, as we know, is a
crowd of random jostling molecules: if anything presses steadily
in one direction, however gently, it will elbow its way through
the press.

It is because the molecules in a liquid are moving that two
liquids can mix. One of the first facts which struck the ancient
scientific men of Greece as odd was that wine and water could be
mixed. If a pint of wine and a pint of water were stirred together,
the wine and the water each seemed to occupy the whole quart.
This was one of the first reasons for believing things were made
of tiny particles—atoms or molecules. Anyone could see that a

79

pint of peas and a pint of beans can be mixed, so it was natural to suppose that other things which could be mixed—such as wine and water—were also made of little separate bits.

DIFFUSION

It was not found out till a good deal later that two liquids will mix even if they are not stirred. Suppose you put a bottle of motor-oil in a jam jar, carefully filled this up with petrol,

put a screw-cap on to stop it evaporating, and kept the whole thing in a cellar where no differences of warmth could cause currents in the liquids and thus make them mix. The oil is heavier than the petrol; one might think it would stay in its bottle. Not at all. Very, very slowly the oil finds its way into the petrol and the petrol into the oil, until in about a year the whole thing becomes the same all through, a perfectly even mixture of oil and petrol.

FIG. 30—Illustrating the diffusion of one liquid into another against the force of gravitation.

This process of spontaneous mixing is called diffusion. If we think of the petrol as a set of aimlessly moving petrol molecules and the oil as a set of aimlessly moving oil molecules, neither of which has any stronger attraction for their own kind of molecule than for the other kind, it is clear that they will soon mix, just as a crowd of dogs with white collars let go at one end of a field would mix up with a crowd of dogs with black collars released at the other end.

But suppose one of the liquids has molecules which attract each other but do not attract those of the other liquid. Suppose, that we had put water in the inner bottle instead of motor-oil. Now water molecules attract each other (because one side has a different electric charge from the other side), and petrol molecules, lumbering but well-balanced affairs, do not attract each other much, nor are they attracted by water-molecules. Accordingly, if a water molecule begins to go into the petrol, nothing pulls it on and the other water molecules pull it back. So water will not mix with petrol.

Now suppose both liquids had molecules which attracted each other. Imagine we had put water in the inner bottle and alcohol outside. A water molecule venturing out would be pulled back by its fellows but pulled on by the alcohol molecules, with the result that its motion would carry it on and it would wander off into the alcohol. Thus they would mix. The rule then is:

If liquids A and B have molecules which attract their own kind and the other kind but feebly, they mix.

If liquids A and B have molecules which attract their own kind and the other kind strongly, they mix.

If either liquid A or B has molecules which attract their own kind much more strongly than the other kind, they do not mix.

You might think from this, since oil and water form two layers which won't mix, we might put together a dozen different liquids each of which preferred its own molecules to any others and get a vessel with a dozen different layers of liquid like a pile of biscuits. Well, we can't. The best that can be done is four liquids that will not mix, and you can do that yourself. Take an ounce each of petrol and water in a corked medicine bottle and add crystals of carbolic acid (phenol) a little at a time until, after shaking, the liquid settles into three layers. Pour in a little mercury, if you have it, and you will have four liquids, the top one petrol, the second water with a certain amount of phenol and a little petrol dissolved in it, the third liquid phenol with a little water and petrol dissolved in it, and the fourth mercury. Cork the bottle and shake it till the whole thing looks like a single milky liquid, and the separate droplets cannot be seen. Leave it a few hours and the four layers will sort themselves out again! (Plate V.) There are three main classes of liquid from the point of view of mixing.

The first contains the all-important water, and some less important liquids like prussic acid. These all mix with each other, for they attract both their own and other molecules rather strongly.

The second class contains liquids like petrol, chloroform,

ether, benzol, oils, etc. These all mix with each other because they neither attract their own molecules nor any other liquids with any vigour.

But the first class will not mix with the second. A few liquids can mix with both classes: these have molecules with moderate attractions for each other: alcohol and glycerine are good examples.

In the third class are liquid metals. Mercury will not mix with any liquid except a molten metal. Some molten metals will not mix. If you melt some lead and zinc together and let the liquid cool slowly, the zinc will all float to the top and the lead will go to the bottom. On the other hand, gold and silver, or copper and zinc, mix perfectly.

SOLUTIONS

Something of the same notion applies to the dissolving of a solid in a liquid. Everyone knows that if you put a piece of sugar in a glass of water and stir it, the sugar disappears. It is still there, however, because the liquid weighs as much as the sugar and water did before, because it tastes like sugar and because, if we let the water dry up, the solid sugar is left behind. Everyone also knows that if you drop into water a piece of flint or wax, it will stay there for ever without any change. If we had a glass of petrol, the sugar would not dissolve—most motorists know of the dirty trick of putting a car out of order by putting sugar in the petrol tank in order to choke the jets. On the other hand, the wax would dissolve easily. If we imagine (and it is true in a certain sense) that solids turn into liquids when they dissolve, we find that much the same rules as apply to the mixing of liquids apply to the dissolving of solids. There are the same three classes: first, water which dissolves "salts" (compounds of metals and acids, like soda, table-salt, copper sulphate, Epsom salts, silver nitrate and so on), and many things which have in their molecules some group of atoms which attracts water-molecules (caustic soda, cane sugar, glucose, gums, white of egg).

The second class of liquids—things like petrol, ether or benzol —do not dissolve the above things at all, but they do dissolve things like waxes, naphthalene, camphor, sulphur, which water does not dissolve at all.

In the third class is mercury, which dissolves almost all metals, but nothing else.

The dissolving of solids and mixing of liquids is of course of tremendous importance. To start with, we couldn't live without it. We convert all our food into simple substances which *dissolve* or mix with the blood which carries them to the part of the body where they are wanted. The whole working of the tiny cells of which the body is made up is an affair of solutions. The most perfect way of mixing two things is to dissolve them in the same lot of liquid, and chemists, who are always making new things by making something influence something else, almost always dissolve the things which they want to affect each other in the same lot of liquid. A very homely example is found in Fruit Salts. These are a mixture of a harmless acid (say tartaric acid) with sodium bicarbonate and something with medicinal properties, say, magnesium sulphate. Now a bit of solid tartaric acid, however tiny, is made up of tartaric acid molecules all arranged in a regular pattern. Sodium bicarbonate is also a regular arrangement of sodium, hydrogen, carbon and oxygen atoms. These also stick firmly together in their lattice and so the tartaric acid molecules and sodium bicarbonate molecules remain separate and cannot touch each other. Two grains in a powder never really touch: there is always a film of air keeping them apart and so they do not affect each other unless they turn into liquid or vapour.

Now stir the fruit-salt into water; the tartaric acid molecules are attracted out of their lattices by the water molecules and so are the sodium bicarbonate molecules. They all move freely about among the water-molecules and very soon meet and collide. The two molecules then re-assort their atoms and produce a molecule of a new substance, sodium tartrate, which remains dissolved in the water, and a molecule of the gas carbon dioxide. Water-molecules do not attract carbon dioxide molecules much; so they go off, meet their fellows and appear as bubbles of gas. In the same sort of way, thousands of kinds of stuff, which do not affect each other while solid, produce all sorts of new materials when they are mixed as liquids (i.e., either dissolved or melted), or as gases or vapours, the molecules of which, like those of liquids, continually collide.

Another use of solutions is to give an easy way of measuring very small quantities accurately. A doctor wants to put one two-thousandth of a gram of the very poisonous atropine in an eye. Now it is not easy to weigh out $\frac{1}{2000}$ of a gram (it is about a hundredth of the weight of a drop of water), so he weighs out a gram of atropine and dissolves it in 100 c.c. of water and stirs it well to mix it. Now, he knows that 20 drops of water make up 1 c.c.; his gram of atropine is evenly distributed over 2000 drops, so each drop gives him $\frac{1}{2000}$ of a gram. Drops are not quite the same size, but even if the eye got two drops instead of one, it would not be perceptibly the worse.

Finally, by dissolving a thing in a liquid we easily separate it from the things that do not dissolve, and this is the chief method that the chemist uses to separate the drugs he requires from the crude materials which contain them.

Take as an example the substance caffein, used in headache powders, etc. Tea contains about 4% of caffein, and so we make the drug from tea-dust, which has no value for drinking purposes. This tea-dust is boiled with alcohol. This dissolves the caffein and also the tannin—the stuff which gives "stewed" tea its harsh taste—but leaves the fibre of the leaf behind. Next, we strain off the alcohol with the caffein and tannin in it and add to it a chemical—lead acetate—which turns the tannin into something which will *not* dissolve in alcohol, and which therefore appears as a solid "precipitate" or mud. The muddy liquid is filtered—i.e., strained through a sort of fine blotting paper—and a solution of caffein in alcohol is left. This is evaporated and as the alcohol departs the caffein turns into crystals. These crystals are not quite pure, so we treat them as alum was treated on p. 40. We dissolve them in a little boiling water and let the water cool. The water when cold dissolves hardly any caffein, which therefore comes out as crystals. The impurities remain dissolved in the water. This process is a very common one for making chemicals from plants. Quinine is extracted from cinchona-bark and morphine from opium, by variations of this process.

Finally, almost everything is cleaned by dissolving out the dirt or the sticky or greasy stuff that holds the dirt on. If the dirt is just adhering to the material, any liquid will wash it away by friction, but it often sticks to a patch of grease or a sticky (sugary) patch. If grease holds the dirt, petrol or much better a non-inflammable liquid of the same class as grease will dissolve it away (chloroform or carbon tetrachloride will do very well: "Thawpit" is a liquid of this type). If sugar sticks the dirt on, petrol is useless and water is the thing. The use of soap as a cleaner is discussed on p. 631.

An odd thing about dissolving a solid in a liquid is that you can only dissolve so much and no more in a given quantity of liquid. Thus a pint of water at the temperature of a very hot bath (112° F.) dissolves four and a quarter pounds of sugar and no more; a pint of cold water (50° F.) will dissolve only two pounds five ounces.

The reason seems to be that a solid substance dissolves because the water molecules pull the molecules out of the lattice more rapidly than the molecules left in the lattice pull the dissolved molecules back. But when there is a good deal of solid in the water, the water molecules attract it instead of attracting fresh solid molecules from the crystal, so the attraction on the un-dissolved solid gets weaker and weaker; and when the solution has a certain proportion of solid in it, the crystal pulls the molecules in from the liquid as fast as the water pulls them out of the crystal and so no more dissolves. We then say the solution is saturated. Suppose we heat this solution and solid. The solid molecules in the crystal vibrate more quickly and more widely; accordingly, they travel further from each other's attraction and are more easily pulled out by the water molecules; consequently, more solid dissolves. It is almost always true that more solid can be dissolved in a hot liquid than in a cold one. The exceptions are not one case in ten thousand and probably have some quite sensible explanation.

If we cool a saturated solution, the water cannot retain all the solid against the pull of the molecules in the crystal. The molecules go to the crystal lattice and the crystals grow. Suppose, however, there isn't a crystal there to pull, but just a saturated solution. Very often crystals appear on cooling it, probably because molecules of solid happen to meet, and form a tiny crystal which then grows. Sometimes, however, no crystals appear, and the cold liquid is then said to be supersaturated, by which we mean that it is a far stronger solution than we could have made by dissolving the solid in the cold water! A good experiment is to take some hypo and just wet it. Put it in a tumbler stand this in hot water, and stir it until all the solid has gone. Then pour it while hot into a clean warm tumbler, cover it with a sheet of paper and let it cool. Don't disturb it. If all goes well, no crystals appear. Now tie a piece of solid hypo to a piece of cotton. Dip it for a moment in water and then lower it into the cold 'supersaturated' solution of hypo. Instantly it will begin to grow, and long spiky crystals will grow out from it every way. Pull it out, and the liquid will stay liquid as before. This experiment is not very easy, but is worth doing, for it shows what is meant by a supersaturated solution and also gives the vividest example possible of the way a crystal grows.

People have written large books about solutions: but we have all Science to glance at, and must return to the peculiar ways in which liquids behave.

LIQUID SURFACES

One of the first and most obvious properties of a liquid is that it has a level and flat surface. This is not really quite true. A rather more accurate way of speaking is to say that a liquid's surface is so arranged that it is at right angles to the force pulling on the liquid. If the only force affecting the liquid is gravitation, which pulls toward the centre of the earth, the surface of the liquid will everywhere be at right angles to a line drawn from it to the centre of the earth: a little thought will show that the surface of a liquid will be a bit of a sphere of the same size as the earth. Well, that is flat enough for ordinary purposes. Consider a swimming bath which is 50 yards square. The centre of this is one six-hundredth of an inch higher than the edges—not a very great difference from complete flatness. The fact that the surface of a liquid is level has been used for a good many purposes. In

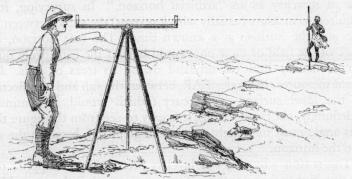

FIG. 31.—Illustrating the use of the water level—an instrument which is now obsolete.

engineering jobs, it is often required to make a road or a railway track or some other object flat and level. The oldest instrument of this kind (actually used by the Romans) was a "water-level." It was a long tube such as is illustrated in Fig. 31. If one plants a stick and looks along the two water surfaces and sees them in line with a mark on the stick at the same height as the instrument, then

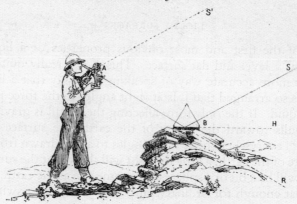

Fig. 32.—Use of mercury as an artificial horizon.

the bottom of the stick must be level with the place where the "water-level" is standing. As a second example may be taken the use of mercury as an "artificial horizon." In surveying, it is required to measure (usually with a sextant) the angle between the sun and the horizon at a known time. The true horizon, the edge of the field of view one would have if the earth were quite flat, is usually invisible on land owing to trees or hills. But if one measures the angle, S^1AR, between the sun and its reflection in the level surface of mercury (which would, if continued indefinitely, cut the horizon), it is easy to see from the figure that this angle must be exactly *twice* the angle, SBH, between the sun and the horizon.

The reason why water is level is pretty clear. Suppose one bit was higher than another. Then, underneath it there would be a bigger pressure than in the part of the liquid next door to it. The higher pressure liquid would push the lower pressure liquid away and would come down in doing so. This would only stop when no part of the liquid was higher than another, i.e., when it was level again! Another simpler way of looking at it is this. Suppose the liquid was not level. Then, however slight the slope was, the molecules would run down hill till they filled up the hollows. But water surfaces are not always level. Look at

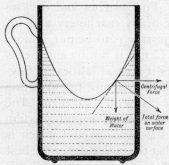

FIG. 33.—Form taken by tea rotating in a tea-cup. The curve is a paraboloid.

the edge of the water where it meets the side of your teacup: look at a drop of water on a greasy plate: look at the sea: look at tea climbing up a lump of sugar. Well, in all of these cases another force beside gravitation is influencing the water, which gets into the position where its surface would be at right angles to a force equal to all the forces on it. Stir your tea. Its surface goes into a shape like that in Fig. 33.

The "centrifugal" force (p. 165) pulls the tea sideways. Gravitation pulls it down and the two forces are equal to *one* force pulling at a certain angle between them. The liquid sets itself at right angles to this *one* force.

VISCOSITY

While liquids will always yield to a force which tries to change their shape, some liquids yield much more easily than others. Suppose we fill 7 tall jars with ether, petrol, water, paraffin-oil, olive oil and glycerine and "solid" pitch respectively, and drop a steel ball (say a bicycle bearing) into each. If it takes a second to reach the bottom of the jar of water, it will take only a third of a second to drop through the ether and a trifle longer to fall through the petrol. It will reach the bottom of the paraffin-oil in two and three-eighth seconds, of the olive oil in eighty seconds, of the glycerine in twelve and a half minutes, and of the pitch[1] in about 10,000 years.

We describe the difference by saying that ether and water are less *viscous* than glycerine and pitch. A very viscous liquid is what we call a "thick" liquid and a slightly viscous liquid is what we call a thin one. It is important to know the viscosity of an oil

[1] Pitch varies a great deal in viscosity.

which is to be used for lubricating. For watches and delicate machinery, a thin oil is wanted: for heavy machinery and for lubricating surfaces on which great pressure is to be put, a more viscous oil is needed. As a matter of fact, it is not by any means only the viscosity of an oil that makes it a good lubricant. Glycerine and castor oil are just about equally viscous, but glycerine is of very little use as a lubricant, while castor oil is excellent. The quality needed in a lubricant is the power of forming a film which sticks firmly to the metal of the bearings and which is not easily broken, and it would seem that the molecules of the best lubricants are attracted by metal surfaces in this way. All oils have long molecules and these perhaps get tangled together and are not easily forced apart by pressure.

One of the easiest ways to measure viscosity is to let the liquids (at a known temperature) flow out through a long fine tube: the longer it takes for, say, 10 cc. to flow out, the greater the viscosity. Hot liquids are much less viscous than cold. Six pints of boiling water will leak through a given hole in the same time as one pint of cold water. For this reason, a leaky car-radiator loses far more water when hot than when cold.

SURFACE TENSION

One of the most interesting things about a liquid is the way it behaves as if it was covered with a stretched elastic skin. There is

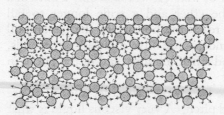

really such a skin on the surface of a liquid, but it is made of the liquid itself. Think of a molecule of water in the middle of a drop of water. There are molecules above it, below it, and on every side of it. Their attractions are all pulling on the molecule in different directions, and ac-

FIG. 34.—The molecules at the surface of a liquid are attracted inward and toward each other and therefore behave like an elastic skin.

cordingly the pulls all cancel out and the molecule goes where it likes. But, at the surface of the drop, the molecule is pulled by other molecules inside the liquid and at the surface and on each side of it, but by none outside the liquid. It follows, then, that the surface of the liquid is being pulled sideways and inward exactly like a piece of the stretched rubber of a toy balloon. The surface molecules cannot relieve the pull by going inwards because there must be some at the surface, nor by going sideways because, wherever they go on the surface, there will be just as many neighbours to pull them!

So we can think of every liquid as having a "surface tension" in consequence of which it behaves as if it was covered by a fine rubber membrane. It is not very difficult to show this is true. A steady hand will float a needle on water. The weight of the needle is not enough to force the surface molecules apart and let the needle through. Some insects make a living by surface tension: the whirligig beetles which rush merrily in circles on the surface of ponds can walk safely on the surface of the water without danger of putting a foot through. But a rather bigger insect is in great danger from water. Let it once put a foot through that treacherous skin and it will not get it out. It cannot break the invisible film of tugging molecules which clings to the wet leg. Its struggles break the film in other places and the dead insects floating on any pool tell the story. Some things are easily wetted by water (presumably because their molecules attract water molecules). Other things like oils and waxes are not. If water is scattered on a greasy surface, it does not wet it: the elastic film contracting makes the water drop's surface as small as possible, while the weight of the water pulls it as near the earth as possible. A compromise is reached by making a sort of bun-shaped drop. Mercury does not wet anything except metals, so when it falls it always forms drops. It has a very powerful surface tension, so these, if small and light, are almost perfect spheres. Plate III shows a microphotograph of mercury drops made by pressing a bigger drop with a finger tip. A hair is put beside the droplets to show their size.

For the same reason, small bubbles are spherical. No one ever saw a square bubble, but very few of us ever wonder why they are round. The outside of a bubble under water is a surface film: a soap bubble has two such films. These films try to contract and get as small as possible, and so they mould the gas within them into the shape which has the smallest surface for its size. Large bubbles under water are bun-shaped because the pressure of water on the bottom of them is greater than the pressure on the top.

Another striking way of showing this surface tension is to mix alcohol and water until a liquid is obtained which is just as heavy as the same bulk of olive oil. Olive oil will not float or sink in this. If olive oil is gently run into this liquid through a fine tube, it stays suspended in the liquid, neither floating nor sinking. The tension of its surface molecules, then, has no other force to disturb its action and the oil forms a great golden transparent and perfectly spherical drop. This experiment and many others were performed under the direction of J. A. F. Plateau in 1873. He never saw them, for he went blind more than thirty years before. The falling drop in Plate IV, is made of a mixture of aniline and benzene. It is just heavier than water and so falls, flattening itself slightly, but still forming a huge drop about an inch in diameter.

Liquids vary a great deal in surface tension and there are many ways of measuring this. We can measure the pull needed to bring a strip of metal out of the liquid: more easily we can measure the size of the drops the liquid forms when it falls from a jet. A liquid with high surface tension can hold a bigger drop together on the end of a tube than can a liquid with small surface tension. If the drops are weighed, the surface tension can be calculated. The easiest way of all is to see how far the liquid will run up a very narrow tube—but more about this later. The surface tensions of thousands of liquids have been measured. Water has a rather strongly pulling film—about three times as strong as alcohol— but the really exceptional case is mercury, the surface tension of which is seven times as great as that of water. This is why mercury so easily forms globules and also why it is almost impossible to get a bubble of mercury—the pull breaks the film.

Small amounts of foreign substances make a vast difference to the surface tension of a liquid. Everyone knows the "camphor boats" which are sold. A very light and small toy boat has a little bit of camphor fastened to the back. When it is put in water it swims sedately along and will go on for many hours. If you take a bit of camphor and scrape a few grains of it into some clean water, you will see the grains swim round and round till they have disappeared.

The reason for this is that the camphor dissolves more in one place (e.g., a corner) than in another. Now camphor lowers the surface tension of water, and so the part where the most camphor is dissolving is less pulled by the water than the rest. So, the camphor is pulled by the surface film away from the part where it is dissolving most quickly. A film of oil lowers the surface tension of water and therefore, in water with a film of grease on it, camphor will not move. If you rub your finger on your head (if you use hair-oil) and touch the water surface, the camphor

Negative end  Neutral end

- ● Carbon atom
- ○ Hydrogen atom
- ◎ Oxygen atom

FIG. 35.—The soap molecule (actually an ion).
(About 30,000,000 times magnified.)

stops. A film of a millionth of a centimetre thick will do this: it is probably a single layer of bulky oil-molecules.

These thin films are very interesting, and they are most easily studied by the help of soap films and soap bubbles.

A solution of soap gives very stable and durable bubbles—a "lather" is what we expect from a soap. The soap-molecule is a long snaky affair with a group at one end which has an electric charge, and therefore, a strong attraction for other molecules. A soap solution has a very low surface tension, and consequently the pull of the stretched film is not enough easily to break it. The film is a layer of water sandwiched between two layers of soap molecules. The soap molecule is like a snake, its head being an electrically charged group *which is attracted to water*, its tail being an "oil-like" group which is not. The attraction makes the film a strong one: it can be stretched because the water contains reserve soap molecules, ready to fill up any gaps.

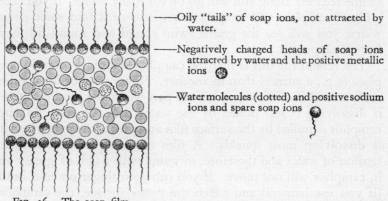

———Oily "tails" of soap ions, not attracted by water.

———Negatively charged heads of soap ions attracted by water and the positive metallic ions

———Water molecules (dotted) and positive sodium ions and spare soap ions

FIG. 36.—The soap film.

The best easily-compounded mixture for making soap films was invented by Professor C. V. Boys, who made a considerable study of these and wrote a book (*Soap Bubbles and the Forces which mould them*: S.P.C.K.) full of interesting experiments and pictures of them. He recommends a mixture of pure soap, water and glycerine. This can be bought ready made: however, by dissolving a three-quarter inch cube (about quarter oz.) of castile soap in half a pint of hot rain-water or distilled water, stirring in two ounces of glycerine and letting the mixture cool in a clean corked bottle, a very good substitute is obtained. Ordinary yellow soap may be used instead of Castile soap, but most toilet soaps are not so good. With a bottle of this and some wire frames we can find out some interesting things about soap films. The beautiful colours we will leave till we study light waves (p. 470). It is the shapes that will interest us now. First of all, we can show that a soap film pulls. Plate IV, A, shows a soap-film supporting a weight of 0.5 grams. As soon as the film breaks, the thread and weight drop. It is only the pull of the surface films that hold them up. In Plate IV, B, a heavy wire hangs by two threads. The soap film, stretched between them draws them together raising the wire.

Another good way of showing this is to make a film on a wire ring and drop a loop of fine silk (wetted with soap solution) upon it. Prick the film with a hot wire. It breaks; and the pull of the outer film makes the loop into a perfect circle (Plate IV, C, D). A sharply curved film presses more strongly on what is inside it than a less sharply curved one. Suppose we blow two soap-bubbles on the ends of a tube and then connect them by a tap. One is bound to be a little smaller and therefore more sharply curved. Its pressure will be higher than the other and so the air will flow from it to the other. This makes the little bubble smaller and its pressure therefore still higher, and the small bubble consequently blows up the big one. Another curious thing is that you cannot get a bubble shaped like a sausage. If a cylindrical soap-film is more than about three times as long as it is broad, one end swells and the other shrinks and it bursts.

FIG. 37.—A thin rubber bag, filled with water, taking the form of a drop.

It is only the surface film on a liquid which causes it to form drops. In a drop, we have the weight of the liquid pulling down and the tension of the film pulling up.

Fig. 37 shows how a thin rubber bag full of water takes the same shape as a drop. Watch a drop gathering and falling. It begins like Plate IV (a), it then gets longer (b), develops a waist (c) and drops. The actual dropping is too quick for the eye to follow, but an instantaneous photograph shows that a tiny droplet (d) forms between the main drop and the liquid left behind. This droplet is the remains of the "waist." The drops in Plate IV are of a mixture of aniline and benzene. This being only just heavy enough to sink in water forms large drops which fall very slowly.

Everyone has noticed how a drop of water

falling into water seems to shoot up again. It is very noticeable in a heavy thunderstorm and gives the impression that the rain drops are bouncing off the road. This is quite one of the most peculiar of simple happenings. It cannot be exactly explained but is almost entirely an effect of surface tension. In Plate V is illustrated high speed cinema films of drops of water falling into water, showing every stage of the process.

Try dropping drops of milk into tea which has just been poured out and you will get a blurred impression like all the photos on top of each other: but you will be able to see that the photographs of Plate V are real. Another very pretty phenomenon can easily be seen if you gently turn the tap off until the thin smooth stream of water begins to break up and give a quivery beaded effect. You can see here that something odd is happening too quickly for the eye to appreciate. What has really happened is that the tension of the surface film squeezes the stream into waists and finally into a stream of big and little drops.

A curious result of surface tension is that a liquid tends to move

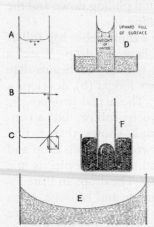

along a tube made of some material which it wets. If we dip a number of glass tubes in water, the water rises in them for a certain distance and finally stops with its surface set in a curve which we call a "meniscus." The narrower the tube is, the higher the liquid rises and the sharper is the curve. The simplest explanation of this is not very simple! Think of a water molecule (Fig. 38 A) in the surface and away from the wall of the tube. It is pulled sideways and downward by its neighbouring water-molecules. The pull *on* the surface is downward and as a liquid (p. 87)

FIG. 38.—Shape of a liquid surface in a narrow tube.

PLATE III

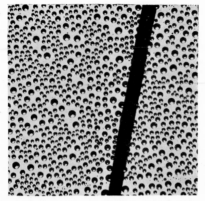

Microphotograph of droplets of mercury ($\times$ 50). Note that they are exactly spherical. The black strip is a human hair to indicate the size of the droplets. (From a photograph by Mr. F. Welch.)

Steel containing 1.5°/₀ carbon heated to 1,000° C. and quenched in iced water, showing crystals of compounds of iron and carbon ($\times$ 1,000). (By courtesy of Messrs. Charles Griffin & Company, Ltd., from Roberts-Austen's *Introduction to the Study of Metallurgy.*)

PLATE IV

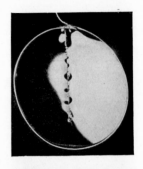

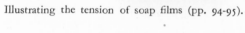
Illustrating the tension of soap films (pp. 94-95).

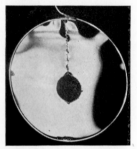

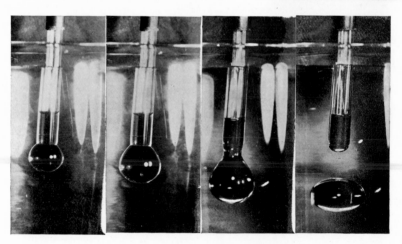

Four stages in the falling of a drop.

always keeps its surface at right angles to the pull on it, the
surface stays flat. Now think of a surface molecule near the
glass walls. It is pulled to the left by water molecules,
to the right by glass molecules and downward by water
molecules (Fig. 38 B). Now glass molecules attract water
molecules more strongly than these attract each other, so the
water molecule is pulled to the right harder than it is pulled to the
left; so the total pull made up of right, left and down is a *sideways*
pull (Fig. 38 C). The liquid sets itself at right angles to this.
Hence the curve. It is easy to see that the nearer the molecule is
to the glass, the more it will be attracted and the steeper the curve
will be. Fig. 38 (E) shows the exact shape of the surface of the
water in a tube of one-twelfth inch bore.

The consequence of this is that the water hangs on to the glass,
and the curved elastic surface, in trying to straighten itself, pulls
upward (Fig. 38 D). Something must balance the pull and the
only thing that can do it is the weight of the water. So the water
goes up the tube till its weight pulling down balances the curved
film pulling up. The narrower the tube, the sharper the curve
and the bigger the upward pull as is illustrated in Fig. 38 (G).

Fig. 38 (F) shows what happens when a narrow glass tube is
pushed into mercury which it does not wet. Remembering that
mercury molecules attract each other *more* than they attract glass
molecules, it may amuse you to figure out why it gives a convex
curve and goes down the tube.

A great many things follow from this. Any porous material
like lump-sugar, blocks of salt, chalk, sand, earth, cloth, etc., may
be thought of as a mass of interlacing tubes, and water or any
other liquid that wets them will rise through them to a certain
limited height, depending on the size of the crevices (the smaller
the higher) and the attraction of the liquid for the solid.

Water does not rise at all in a heap of stones, but if a heap of
sand stands in a puddle, it becomes wet several inches up. Hang
up a strip of blotting paper with one end in ink. The ink rises up
it, and if the strip is long enough you will see that it stops rising
after a time. This height varies both with the porous material

4

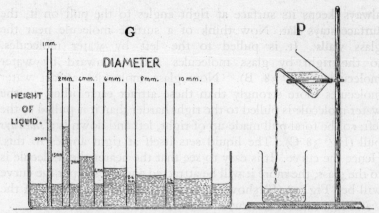

FIG. 39.—Capillary attraction. The diameters of the tubes are marked at the top: the height to which water rises is shown on the left of each. P shows how water traverses a skein of cotton as if it was a bundle of tubes.

(try a piece of sewing cotton instead of the blotting paper) and also with the liquid.

Not so very many years ago, paraffin oil had not been invented and our Victorian ancestors burned in their lamps colza oil, made from the seed of rape, a sort of wild cabbage. Vegetable oils have poor "capillarity"—as we call this power of rising in a tube—and so when the oil had sunk a little in the reservoir, it would no longer ascend the wick and the flame began to sink too for lack of oil. So lamps were made with very flat wide reservoirs so that the use of a little oil should not lower the level much (an elaborate clockwork arrangement was sometimes used to raise the level). Paraffin, a mineral oil, has much higher capillarity and rises up quite a tall wick without difficulty and the modern lamp has no need for a flat reservoir. The sauce-boat shape of the Roman lamp was necessary too, because of the poor capillarity of the olive oil they burnt. So many things depend on capillarity that there is only space to list a few of the most familiar. The wick of a candle, a bath towel, the rising of damp in a wall (a layer of non-porous pitch—a "damp-course"—stops it), moisture rising to the surface from water beneath the soil, the

absorption of sweat by clothes, are just a few of the everyday
things which depend on capillarity.

Why can't we use this capillarity to do some work? Suppose
a tube was constructed as in Fig. 40. Would not the water rise
up it, drop out of the end and, falling back, drive a little
wheel, so giving a perpetual motion? No,
alas, for as soon as the water surface
reaches the free end of the tube it ceases to
be hollow, and once a drop begins to form
there is no longer a pull up the tube, for the
bulging elastic "skin" of the drop gives
a push down. The liquid simply settles
itself so that its surface curve just pulls the
liquid hard enough to keep it where it
is. The same objection applies to any
way of pumping liquids by surface tension.

FIG. 40.—Attempt to get
unlimited work for no-
thing by a perpetual
motion.

HOW FLUIDS FLOW

Liquids and gases are distinguished from solids by the fact
that they flow. They can be pumped through pipes, and you have
only got to look at a hole in the road in London to realise how a
modern town is strung on a network of pipes, main-water,
sewage, high pressure water (for hydraulic machinery), ordinary
gas, high pressure gas for street lighting; while in America
steam is often laid on as well. You might think there was nothing
very much to know about flow through a pipe; you pump it in
one end and it comes out of the other! But pumping takes power
and power costs money, so it is at least necessary to see that all
your power goes to moving the water. If water is pumped slowly
through a pipe, it moves in an orderly way, every part going
straight down the pipe. The water moves quickest down the
middle because friction with the sides slows it up. If the water is
speeded up beyond a certain point, the flow suddenly becomes
turbulent, the pipe becomes full of eddies and a great deal of

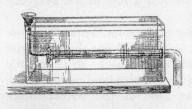

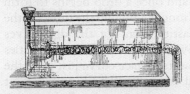

FIG. 41.—Showing stream-line flow (above) and turbulent flow (below).

energy is wasted in simply stirring up the water. This can be seen in water flowing along a wide glass tube if a little coloured water is introduced. (Fig. 41). The water goes in a straight stream until the speed of the water reaches a certain value, when it suddenly starts to twist and turn and eddy.

A great deal is heard of streamlining nowadays. A streamline is defined as a line drawn so that it everywhere points in the direction in which a liquid or a gas is flowing. Now one of the most important things you can do with a liquid or a gas is to move things through them. Engineers are spending time and business men mints of money in pushing ships through the water, and aeroplanes and motor cars through air.

Now, the only thing a ship is doing is thrusting itself through water and air, so any study is valuable which can enable us to find out the shape of the ships which need the least force to push them through water. The resistance of the water is of three kinds. The first is skin friction. The water adheres to the side of the ship and molecule is always being torn from molecule as it goes. Eighty per cent. of the coal the ship burns is spent on pulling water molecules away from their neighbours. Of course, this has been greatly studied. If any one could find some paint for a ship which would slip through water with half the friction of those at present known, he would make a stupendous fortune and win the America Cup. But as far as we can tell, any smooth surface is as good as another. In tropical waters, weeds grow quickly on ships' bottoms, and a growth of weed three inches long more than doubles the work of pushing the ship along. So

the bottoms of ships are coated with a greasy anti-fouling paint
to which weeds cannot stick. Beyond doing this and making the
ship as smooth and free from projections as possible not much
can be done. But there are two more things that may hinder a
ship. It may make eddies and it may make waves; both a useless
stirring of the sea.

If we consider the sea as flowing past the ship instead of the
ship going through the sea, there is absolutely no difference.

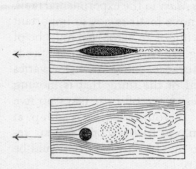

Suppose the ship was doing 30
knots. Imagine the sea, "ship
and all," put in a huge tank on a
giant railway truck and moved at
30 knots, the other way. The
ship would now be still, and the
sea moving, but no one could tell
the difference, if they couldn't see
the tank! So, we can study the
eddies a ship makes by letting
water stream past a model of it.
Now, it is found that the shape
which causes hardly any eddies
at all is the shape of a blunt-

FIG. 42.—The fish-shaped object hardly
causes any eddies as it moves, while
the ball disturbs the water extensively.

nosed fish (trust Nature to spot it!) (Fig. 42). If ships were
made with a blunt nose and tapered tail, they would waste no
energy in stirring the sea into whirlpools. But such a shape
would hardly be satisfactory, because the blunt bow would
make waves and be knocked about by them. So, for the last
century, a form tapered at each end has been used. A liner may
cost nearly £5,000,000, and its success depends greatly on its
speed. It is therefore important to be sure of the right shape
for it. This is done by trying out models. Exact models of
variously shaped hulls are carved from wax on a wooden
foundation: sixteen of these, each about 17 feet long, were tried
before the form of the great liner *Queen Mary* was settled. These
models are floated in a long tank 400 × 20 ft., and towed at a
speed which "corresponds" to what will be expected of the liner.

This speed is worked out thus: if the model is a certain *fraction*, say, a hundredth of the length of the liner, then the corresponding speed is the square-root of that fraction—in this case a tenth—of the real speed. The towing force required is measured by a dynamometer—a sort of spring balance—on the towing line, and the models are altered again and again till the shape with the lowest resistance is found. Waves can be created in the tank, and the behaviour of the liner in rough water can be predicted. Plate V shows a model of the *Queen Mary* in the experimental tank.

Streamlining for things which move in air is not so important unless they move very fast. The wing of an aeroplane must be of streamline shape: so must a racing car designed to go at speeds much above 100 m.p.h. The resistance of air or water varies roughly as the square of the speed of the thing that is moving through it. So, suppose the air-resistance of a car takes up five of its horse-powers at 100 m.p.h. It would then need 20 h.p. at 200 m.p.h., and 80 h.p. at 400 m.p.h. to overcome the air re-sistance. On the other hand, at 50 m.p.h. only $1\frac{1}{4}$ h.p. would be needed and at 10 m.p.h. only $\frac{1}{20}$ h.p.

It follows that racers must use streamline, but although at any speed it gives some slight advantage, ordinary motorists need not worry much about it.

A peculiar form of "streamline motion" is a whirlpool, eddy or vortex, all of them names for the same thing.

We have already seen that if a liquid is stirred round and round and so set spinning like a wheel, it forms itself into a cup-shaped hollow (Fig. 33), the surface setting itself so that the surface of the liquid is everywhere at right angles to the pull of the centrifugal force and the pull of gravity combined.

"Storms in a teacup" are well enough known to us, but in the sea quite big whirlpools may form. The usual reason for a whirlpool being formed is the existence of two parallel currents flowing opposite ways. Imagine two boards pushed opposite ways with two or three round rulers pressed between them. The rulers of course rotate. It is just the same with the slack water between two opposing currents. The most famous whirlpool is the Mäelström described with terrifying vividness and enormous exaggeration by Edgar Allen Poe in his story of that name.

A vortex seen in every house is a "free vortex." If you let the water run out of the bath, it almost always takes a circular, or rather spiral course, as it finds its way to the plug-hole, probably because it always moves sideways as well as towards the hole.

The shape is quite easy to understand. The "sideways" speed of the water remains the same, but as it nears the hole, its circular path gets smaller and so is traversed quicker: thus the speed of rotation gets greater. The centrifugal force is therefore greatest at the centre because the water is going round most quickly there: the gravitational pull is much smaller than this, and so the combined force of the two acts almost horizontally and at the bottom of the whirlpool the liquid will be nearly upright. At the outer part, the liquid moves but slowly, so that the pull on the surface is mainly downward and very little sideways. In Chapter XXXI, where storms are discussed, it is shown that a cyclone is a vortex of air, and it is explained why these blow anticlockwise round their centres in the northern hemisphere, and clockwise in the southern hemisphere. The same appears to be true of natural free vortices in water. Plate VI shows free vortices in lakes of the southern and northern hemispheres!

The difference between a forced vortex and a free vortex is that in the first (the stirred cup of tea) the centrifugal force is greatest at the outside: in the second, owing to the spiral motion quickening as the path of the water gets shorter, it is greatest at the centre.

Another kind of vortex is commonly found in tubes where water is running turbulently. The central core of rapidly running water pushes on the slacker water at the side. The stationary sides hold it back. Thus we get ring-vortices. A very clear idea of these is got by imagining a rubber ring which fits the inside of a glass tube and a rod which fits the inside of the ring. Thrust the rod down the tube and the ring will move like a ring-vortex, turning itself inside out as it goes.

Smoke-rings are ring vortices, as it is easy to see for oneself with the familiar apparatus of a boot-box and smouldering brown paper (Fig. 57).

HOW LIQUIDS EXPAND

Liquids expand when they are heated and expand a good deal more than solids. Since a liquid has no real length, we usually talk about the increase in volume or bulk which occurs when it is warmed. If we heat a cubic foot of alcohol from 0° C., the temperature of melting ice, to its boiling point, 78° C., it will increase in bulk by 150 cubic inches, while a cubic foot of steel heated from 0° C. to 78° C. increases only by 5 cubic inches. The reason for the expansion of a liquid is the increased motion of the myriad molecules of which it is composed, which naturally makes them spread apart: this is opposed by the attraction of the molecules for each other. In a solid, this attraction is fairly large: the attraction is the thing which keeps it solid. In a liquid the attraction is much less: though the molecules of liquids with rather unsymmetrical molecules like water attract each other quite perceptibly. These do not expand very much—water (near 20° C.) on the average, increases by about $\frac{1}{5000}$ of its bulk for each degree. The molecules of other liquids (e.g. chloroform) attract each other very feebly. There is consequently less force to resist the motion of the molecules and they expand a great deal more—chloroform on the average expands $\frac{1}{800}$ of its bulk for each degree it is heated.

One of the chief applications of the expansion of a liquid is in measuring temperatures.

We have talked a good deal about temperature without explaining what it is. Everyone knows that a thing which is hotter than another is said to be at a higher temperature: but when we measure temperature by numbers of degrees we need something more. The Centigrade system arbitrarily calls the temperature of melting ice 0° C., and that of boiling water 100° C. Then since mercury becomes larger by $\frac{1}{50}$ of its bulk when heated from the temperature of melting ice to that of boiling water—an interval of 100° C.—we say that 1 degree is the change of temperature which makes mercury expand or contract by $\frac{1}{5000}$ (actually 0.000182) of its bulk. If we use chloroform instead of mercury we call a degree the change of temperature which makes chloroform alter by $\frac{1}{800}$ of its bulk. A difficulty comes in here, because different liquids do not exactly keep step in their expansion. Two thermometers filled with mercury and chloroform respectively and both correctly marked at 0° C., and 50° C., would not show exactly the same temperature at 25° C. So if we are to agree exactly about the temperatures we measure, we must specify the stuff we are going to put in the thermometer. Mercury is the one ordinarily used, but hydrogen gas is sometimes preferred for very exact work. Finally, temperature is really the *energy* of the moving molecules, so it is possible indirectly to measure this energy and not depend on any arbitrarily chosen liquid to measure our temperatures.

In practice then the instrument chiefly used for temperature measurement is the mercury thermometer. Thermometers can be filled with other liquids (e.g., alcohol), but mercury is the best for most purposes. A thread of mercury is easy to see: it does not freeze except in Arctic conditions: it does not boil till near the melting point of lead and, above all, it expands very steadily. Alcohol is harder to see (though you can dye it) and it boils at 78° C.—a good way below the temperature of boiling water. It has, however, the advantage of expanding six times as much as the same volume of mercury and of being very hard to freeze.

A thermometer is simply a bulb with a fine uniform tube attached. The bulb is filled with liquid: the tube contains no air, the pressure of which would burst the bulb when the liquid rose too high. The tube is marked off in degrees.

The thermometers ordinarily used have small bulbs so that they hold very little liquid and are heated quickly: they have very fine tubes so that a very small increase of bulk takes the liquid a long way up them. Figs. 43–45 show several different kinds of thermometer. The one in Fig. 43 is a mercury-in-glass thermometer used for chemical work. It is long, narrow, and has no bulges so that it can be pushed through a hole in a cork. The one in Fig. 44 is a clinical thermometer for taking patient's tem-

FIG. 43.—Chemical Thermometer.
(By courtesy of Messrs. Allen & Hanbury, as are also Figs. 44, 45.)

perature: it has a tiny bulb so that it may reach the temperature of the patient in half a minute, a tube so fine that if you break it, you can hardly see the hole: a scale which goes from 95° F. to 110° F., which is about as cold or hot as a living human being can be. Finally, the tube has a kink in it. The great force of the expanding mercury pushes it past the kink but, though mercury cannot be squeezed smaller, it can easily be pulled in two and when the thermometer cools, the thread breaks at the kink.

FIG. 44.—Clinical Thermometer.

The mercury above the kink stays where it was, and the nurse can read off the temperature when she wishes. When she has read it, she shakes the mercury down past the kink into the bulb. Without this gadget, the nurse would have to read the thermometer while it was in the patient's mouth, a difficult job if he had a full moustache and beard.

A gardener wants to know in the morning whether there has been a frost in the night while he was asleep, and he also likes to know the highest temperature reached in the day. He commonly uses an ingenious apparatus called a maximum and minimum thermometer—shown in Fig. 45. It is an alcohol thermometer. The bulb is at F : the reservoir G is just a place for spare alcohol to go to. The alcohol pushes a mercury thread up

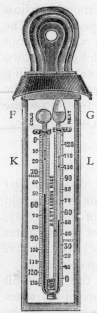

FIG. 45.—Maximum
and Minimum
Thermometer.

and down, and on each side of it is a little iron dumb-bell (K, L) with a feeble spring on it which stops it from slipping down the stem. When the temperature rises, the alcohol expands and the mercury (which does not wet iron) pushes L up the tube but leaves K behind. When the temperature falls, the mercury goes the other way and pushes K up the tube and leaves L behind. So, the bottom of L shows the highest temperature and the bottom of K the lowest. They are pulled down again by a magnet which attracts iron just as well through glass as through air.

The ordinary liquid-in-glass thermometer is used more than any other kind. It is cheap and accurate. But it has two great faults. It is no use below −100° C., which matters only to scientific men, not much use above 360° C., and no use above 500° C., which matters a very great deal to engineers. A second disadvantage is that it is rather easily broken. The other ways of measuring temperature are, first, bimetallic strip thermometers like the one described on page 63. These are now made accurate and cheap enough for most jobs but not accurate enough for scientific work. A mercury thermometer specially made will show a change of a thousandth of a degree centigrade—your own sense of temperature could notice a difference of about one degree under the most favourable conditions. A thermometer filled with hydrogen gas can be used at very low temperatures, for hydrogen does not liquefy above −252° C., but it is a complicated affair. Secondly, temperatures up to a red-heat can be measured by finding out how much electricity impelled by a fixed voltage will pass through a wire heated to that temperature. This is accurate but not very well suited for the use of other people than scientific men. Finally, very high temperatures can be judged by matching the light, say from a furnace mouth, against an electric light filament heated to known temperatures. The higher we get in the scale, the more doubtful we get about temperatures. The "melting point' of sodium sulphate is known within a thousandth of a degree (32.383 to 32.384) the boiling point of sulphur within $\frac{1}{25}$ of a degree (444.54 to 444.50): the melting point of gold within 0.6 degree (1062.2 to 1061.6) and the melting point of tungsten within 60 degrees (3340 to 3400°).

CONVECTION CURRENTS

When a liquid expands it gets bulkier but does not get heavier. So, a hot liquid is lighter, bulk for bulk, than a cold one. A cubic foot of ordinary cold water out of the tap, say, at 60° F., weighs nearly 62½ lbs., but a cubic foot of boiling water weighs only 59¾ lbs. Anything lighter (less dense) than a liquid floats on it; so it follows that hot water will float on cold water.

A simple experiment will show a lot about this. Half fill a tin with cold water. Hold a spoon on the surface of the water and gently pour hot water from a kettle into the spoon till the tin is full. Carefully remove the spoon. The hot water floats on the cold, and the tin remains boiling hot at the top and quite cool at the bottom for a long time. You may have dived into a swimming bath which has remained *undisturbed* in a hot sun for an hour or two. Underneath it is quite cold but a layer of warm water floats on the top. Perhaps the most interesting thing is to watch the water rising off a hot object. It is easier to see this in a glass vessel, but most households do not have any glass vessel that can be heated. If you rub a little blotting-paper in a saucer of water, you get a sort of "soup" of paper fibres. Put a saucepan of water over a small flame which heats it in one place only, and drop in a little of your paper fibre. You will see the fibres rising up with the hot water and going down with the cooler water, keeping up a regular circulation as long as heat is supplied. Another way of seeing the same thing is to float a bit of ice on a glass of lemonade. The heavy cold water from the melting ice can easily be seen sinking through the warmer lemonade.

Now this circulation of water (or convection, as we call it) is used for a great many purposes. In the first place it would be a terrible job to heat water at all without it. The water would get hot at the bottom of the pot or boiler where the fire was. The heat would not get away, for water conducts heat very

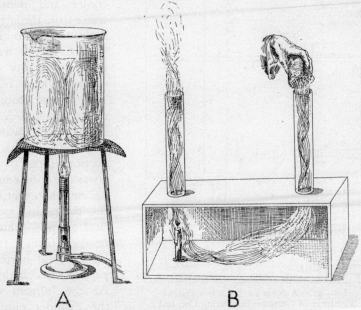

A   B

FIG. 46.—Convection currents. (A) in a liquid, (B) in a gas, their course being indicated by the smoke of smouldering paper.

poorly, and the liquid would boil at the bottom, but stay cold at the top till the steam bubbles stirred it up. Still worse would it be for heating large quantities of water for baths. We could have no hot water system, for how would the hot water be persuaded to circulate through it and back again? As it is, the household hot water system is quite an elegant piece of apparatus —to the scientific eye. The actual boiler only holds a few gallons of water; it has an exit pipe at the top and an entrance pipe at the bottom. These connect to the top and bottom of the cylinder in which the hot water is stored. The hot water from the boiler rises into the cylinder and the cooler and denser water from the latter flows back into the boiler. In this way a large quantity of water is kept hot. This flows round the circuit A A A A because the water in the left-hand vertical pipe must always be cooler and heavier than that in the right-hand vertical pipe which issues from the highest and hottest part of the cylinder. At the bottom of the cylinder enters

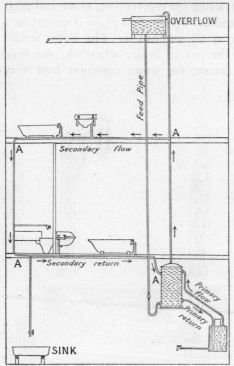

FIG. 47.—A domestic hot water system.
(Courtesy of Gresham Publishing Co., Ltd.)

a pipe from the cold water supply: this replaces the water drawn off and gives the necessary pressure to drive the hot water to any tap lower than the cold-cistern. When the fire is burning, the water in the cylinder gets hotter until either it boils or the speed at which heat is leaking away from the system to the air is the same as the speed at which heat is being supplied by the fire. It is not good to let the water boil, as, if the water is "hard," i.e., contains certain "lime" salts (calcium bicarbonate), a crust deposits in the pipes and some day blocks one or both of them.

Then, if the matter is allowed to get so far, the water cannot circulate: it gets very hot in the boiler and turns into steam, the pressure of which would burst the boiler and probably kill someone, were it not that the boiler has a safety valve at the top. How does the safety valve work? Very simply. Fig. 48 shows a simple safety valve. A few weights press a cap down on to a fairly sharp-edged hole which it fits well. If the ordinary main water pressure is 25 lbs. per square inch, and the size of the hole is $\frac{1}{20}$ square inch (about $\frac{1}{4}$ inch bore) and the weights weigh $2\frac{1}{2}$ lbs., clearly the water will not be able to push the cap up and so there will be no leakage. But suppose the exits are blocked and steam forms in the boiler. The pressure gets much larger, forces up the cap, and the steam and water come spurting out.

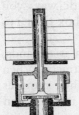

Fig. 48.—Simple dead - weight safety valve. (Courtesy of Gresham Publishing Co.)

Luckily, this does not often happen, for people notice that their hot water system is working badly and send for the plumber long before the pipes get blocked.

A central heating system works in just the same sort of way, but there is no hot cistern; the top exit pipe from the boiler leads through to the top room which requires to be heated, and then leads down through several radiators (which are simply pipes folded up to give a big surface) and so back to the bottom entrance pipe.

The column of water on the exit pipe side of the highest point is hotter than the column of water on the entrance pipe side. It is therefore lighter, and the cold and heavier side presses down more heavily than the hotter and lighter, and so flows down and pushes the hot water up. As long as the fire is alight this process goes on and keeps a steady stream of water through the radiators. A car is cooled by just the same arrangement. Here, the cool water in the radiator and the hot water in the cylinder-block cause a circulation just like a hot water system. It does not circulate very quickly, however, so most cars push the water round with a pump.

Water expands in a peculiar way which has a very important

effect on the under-water life of weeds and fish, as well as on our climate. Water contracts as it cools, like any other liquid, because its molecules slow down and do not force each other so far apart by their blows. But while water at its boiling point is simply a crowd of single water molecules, these begin to link into loose pairs as the water cools down, and into triplets as it cools further. Now, single water molecules pack much closer to each other than double ones and double ones pack better than treble ones: so that as the water molecules cool and link up like this, they begin to want more space and the liquid must expand. If you think of pouring tennis balls into a box in a random fashion (not packing them in any systematic way) you can see that 300 single balls would need a smaller box than 150 pairs stitched together, or 100 threes.

Down to 39° F., the water contracts more than it expands, between 39° and 32° F., it expands more than it contracts. When it freezes it all goes into triple molecules, and thus requires so much more room that ten cubic inches of water make eleven cubic inches of ice. This is why pipes burst when they are allowed to freeze. The water begins to freeze and somewhere freezes solid and blocks the pipe. This traps some unfrozen water and gives it no room to expand: when it freezes an enormous pressure is exerted and the pipe splits. The possible remedies are several. First of all you may leave the taps dripping: this keeps a steady supply of warmer water welling up from the main. The water companies simply hate this plan, and another objection is that the water usually freezes in the outside waste spouts. These get blocked and the water overflows in the night. If you have lead pipes, you can tap them into an oval. If the water freezes, it only pushes the oval into a circle. This plan is not much good because it is only useful once: the next time it freezes, the circular pipe bursts. Finally, the real remedy is to wrap the pipes in felt to make them cool slowly, keep a fire in the hall all night and leave the trap door into the attic roof open so that the warm air may rise and prevent the cold water cistern and its pipes from freezing.

Suppose a pond in winter has a temperature of 45° F. (water freezes at 32° F.), when a cold spell begins. The cold air cools the top layer of water and makes it denser than the water below which has not been cooled. So the cold layer sinks and a fresh warm layer comes to the surface to be cooled again. This goes on until all the water gets cooled to 39° F. Thereafter, the water expands as the air cools it, and the top layer of cold water is lighter than the less cold water below. So this layer stays at the top and does not sink. It rapidly gets colder and freezes. Now heat passes only very slowly through *still* water. Consequently, the water at the bottom of the pond only cools down very slowly, and it requires a long spell of severe frost to make the ice six inches thick, let alone to freeze it solid.

Now suppose the water—like almost every other liquid—had contracted as it cooled all the way till it froze. The top layer of pond water would have gone on cooling and sinking and being replaced by the warmer lower layer until the whole pond was at freezing point. It would then freeze, and ice crystals would shoot out through the whole depth of freezing water. The water would freeze to a sort of sludge of ice crystals and finally freeze to a solid block. Well, it may take several weeks for a "snow-man" to melt, and it is easy to see that a pond once frozen solid would thaw only on the surface throughout the whole winter. Ordinary fish and plants would not live—though, no doubt, creatures capable of spending a winter in ice would have been evolved. As it is, carp will survive freezing into a block of ice and melting out again after some weeks!

EVAPORATION

Even more important than the expansion of liquids by heat is the effect of heat in making them evaporate and boil. Everyone knows that a saucer full of petrol dries up in a few hours: a saucer of water in a few days and a saucer, say, of olive-oil so slowly that in any reasonable time the effect is not noticed.

Evaporation is quite a simple thing. Of the jostling molecules in a liquid, some are going slowly and some going quickly. A molecule which has had a push behind will go quicker than one which has had a push in front.

Now, at the surface of the liquid, the attraction of the other molecules (p. 90) is pulling back any molecules which hop out. If these are going slowly, the pull is too much and they fall back; if they are going fast, they may get out of range of the pull and float off in the air.

So, evaporation is the loss of the *speediest* molecules of the liquid. Now a speedy molecule is a hot molecule, so when a liquid evaporates it loses its hottest molecules and keeps its colder ones: consequently, it gets colder—a fact used in all refrigerators. Again, the hotter you make a liquid, the speedier are its molecules and—since the pull of the surface molecules stays the same—the more molecules will be fast enough to get away. So, the hotter a liquid is, the quicker it will evaporate.

Evaporation is not quite so simple as this, because molecules are continually coming back into the liquid as well as leaving it. Look at a corked bottle of beer. Does the liquid evaporate? Not unless the cork leaks. Molecules of water are always darting out of the liquid into the air above it: but molecules of water from the space above the liquid are continually taking headers into it. A liquid in a closed space evaporates until so much vapour—i.e., so many molecules of it in the form of gas—have accumulated in the space, that in every minute as many molecules come back into the liquid as leave it. A liquid in the open evaporates quickly because the molecules are carried off by air currents, and cannot dive back again. Winds help drying for this reason. We talk of the liquid "evaporating" when the molecules leave it and we talk of the vapour "condensing" when the molecules go back again.

What has just been said applies to all liquids, but some liquids evaporate much more easily than others. At a given temperature all molecules have the same average energy—they give an equal punch. This shows clearly that the very light ones like hydrogen must move far faster than the heavy ones like those of mercury. The chance of any molecule getting permanently out of a liquid depends first on its speed, secondly on the strength of the pull that keeps it back. So we shall expect first to find that liquids with light molecules will evaporate very easily, and, indeed, this is true. Liquid hydrogen evaporates rapidly, boils in fact at the very low temperature of $-252.8°$ C. Acetylene, the molecule of which is thirteen times as heavy as a hydrogen molecule, boils at $-82.4°$ C. Benzene (with 39 times as heavy a molecule) evaporates quite quickly: it boils at $81°$ C. Turpentine, with a molecule 68 times as heavy, evaporates very slowly: it boils at $156°$ C. This is a very rough rule indeed. The worst exceptions are water having a molecule only 9 times as heavy as a hydrogen molecule and boiling at $100°$ C., and liquid metals like melted aluminium which boils at $1800°$ C., although its molecule is only $13\frac{1}{2}$ times as heavy as a hydrogen molecule. The other thing which makes a liquid evaporate easily is a *feeble* pull from its fellows in the liquid. Compare the gases methane (the explosive gas in mines), ammonia and water.

The weights of their molecules are not far off the same (16, 17 and 18 units respectively), and if speed were all that mattered in evaporation, they should all evaporate about equally fast.

Methane has a beautifully symmetrical molecule: it boils at $-164°$ C. near the temperature of liquid air. Ammonia is not so symmetrical: it has one pair of odd negative electric charges at one side and these make the negative side of one molecule attract the positive side of the next. This attraction holds up the molecules a bit, and it does not boil until $-33.5°$ C. Finally, water has four negative charges all on one side of the molecule and so water molecules attract each other strongly, and water

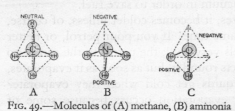

Fig. 49.—Molecules of (A) methane, (B) ammonia (C) water.

evaporates slowly and only boils at 100° C.

Evaporation is used first for getting rid of a liquid we do not want: secondly, for purifying liquids (p. 555): thirdly, for cooling purposes: and fourthly, in the steam engine for getting power—a use we will also leave till a later part of the book.

The simplest use of evaporation is for the drying of clothes or other wet material. The things which speed this up are, as everybody knows, warmth which speeds up the molecules, winds which carry them off and prevent them jumping back, dry air which has few water molecules to jump back. In factories where materials like rubber have to be dried, the things are often heated in a vacuum. In air, the escaping water molecules hit the air molecules and bounce back off them. In a vacuum this cannot happen. The vapour is pumped out of the vacuum so that it cannot get back to the rubber or what not. The chemist has a clever piece of apparatus called a vacuum desiccator. He puts anything he wants to dry in an airtight glass case in the bottom of which is some sulphuric acid and he then pumps the air out. The water evaporates in the usual way from the thing he is drying, and every water molecule that comes off finds its way in a few seconds to the sulphuric acid. Now sulphuric acid itself does not evaporate, and its molecules instantly hitch on to any water molecule they meet and will not let it go. So hardly any of the water molecules gets a chance to go back to the stuff from which they came.

On the large scale, many solids are manufactured from solutions; salt from sea-water or strong "brine" pumped up from salt-mines; sugar from cane-juice or beet-juice (to name at once two very big industries). These solutions of salt and sugar are usually evaporated in a vacuum in order to save fuel.

When a liquid evaporates, it becomes colder unless, of course, it is being heated at the same time. If you pour petrol, or better ether on your hand, it feels very cold: the petrol in the can is no colder than the other objects round it, but as soon as it evaporates, it gets cold. Why do liquids get cold when they evaporate? You will remember that evaporation occurs because some of the *fastest* molecules manage to get out of range of the others.

The temperature of anything is the average energy of the molecules, and the energy of a molecule depends on its weight and the square of its speed, so that if the fastest and hottest ones are getting away by evaporation, the slowest and coldest are being left behind. Evaporation then makes a liquid colder because it takes the hot molecules and leaves the cold ones. But what happens when the fast molecules have all gone? This never occurs, because collisions between the slower molecules speed up some and slow down others, so there is always some supply of fast molecules, but as the liquid gets colder, this supply becomes scantier and evaporation slows up and nearly stops.

Think for a moment what happens when water is boiled. The fastest, hottest molecules are going off as steam and so tending to cool the water down below boiling point. The water only keeps boiling if a flame beneath it is speeding the water up—in fact, if heat is being put in. When we boil a kettle, we are heating water and not making it any hotter, for the water just stays at boiling point. The heat we put in all goes to speed up the molecules and make them nimble enough to dart away from their fellows which are attracting them. This heat we call *latent heat*, and actually it takes six times as much to turn a pint of boiling water into steam as it takes to heat a pint of cold water to boiling.

The use of evaporation to produce cold is one of the very few ways in which we can cool a thing without having ice or some cold substance to cool it with. Damp clothes are chilly because the water in evaporating cools the clothes and so also the body. In some mines, the air is very damp, and in these, although a miner's clothes may be soaked with sweat, he does not feel chilly. The air is full of moisture and evaporation does not occur. Evaporation is the body's chief means of keeping its temperature down. Heat is always being produced by the "combustion" of food material in the body: heat is always leaking away into the air. The quantity of heat produced may be quite small, as when you are resting, or very large when you are running. The body must either keep its internal temperature within a very few degrees of 98.4° F. or die. It has two chief tricks. If it is cooling too fast, it closes the little blood-vessels in the skin and keeps the blood away from the surface; the skin goes pale and, since the blood is no longer warming the skin where the sensation of heat and cold resides, one feels cold: if this is not enough, it shivers, contracting the muscles, doing work and so rapidly burning more fuel. If, on the other hand, the body is producing more heat than it is losing and so begins to heat up, it sends the blood to the skin to meet as much cool air as possible and the skin flushes: next, if that does not suffice, it sweats freely, that is to say, exudes moisture which quickly evaporates and so cools the body. In a very hot moist climate, e.g., that of the Congo or Amazon basin, sweat does not evaporate easily and violent exertion may produce more heat than the body can get rid of, and the serious malady of heat-stroke results.

The earthenware cases sold as butter coolers and milk bottle coolers work in just the same way. They are soaked in water, and

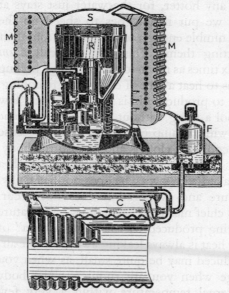

as long as they remain wet and in a draught, they keep quite cool. But stand them in a small closed cupboard and they are almost useless, for the air becomes moist and evaporation stops.

The most elaborate apparatus of this kind is that employed in refrigerators. In all the best known makes, a gas or vapour is turned into a liquid in one part of the machinery. This uses up heat or power. The liquid is then evaporated where the cooling is

FIG. 50.—The B.T.H. refrigerator. (By permission of the British Thomson-Houston, Co., Ltd.)

required. As an example of several excellent refrigerators, the B.T.H., made by the International Refrigerator Company may be taken. The principle is to evaporate a liquid into vapour to get the cooling, then by compressing the vapour to get the liquid back. The liquid used is sulphur dioxide, which boils below freezing point at 14° F. In Fig. 50 R is an electric motor which works a pump. This draws the gas sulphur dioxide from the cooler C of the refrigerator and compresses it into the space S round the motor. The compressing makes it warm (p. 138), and so it is passed into the coils M where it cools to room temperature. But *compressed* sulphur dioxide gas liquefies at room temperature, though the ordinary gas does not. Consequently, liquid sulphur dioxide forms in the coils and at intervals lifts the float of the level-regulator F and runs through into the cooling chamber C. Here, the pressure is low because of the action of the pump, and the sulphur dioxide evaporates and gets very cold; the gas returns to the pump and goes through the whole process again. The machine is taking heat from the inside of the refrigerator and giving it out again from the cooling coils at the top.

A minor use of evaporation is the way of roughly telling the height of a mountain. Now, the higher up you are, the less air there is above you, and so the less is the pressure of the air. The pressure of the air at various heights is shown in the table set out below.

Now, it is quite easy to find out the temperatures at which water

HEIGHT OF MOUNTAIN		BAROMETER		BOILING POINT OF WATER	
Metres	Feet	Millimetres of Mercury	Inches of Mercury	° C.	° F.
0	0	760	30.0	100	212
1000	3,280	674	26.5	96.7	206.1
2000	6,562	596	23.5	93.3	200.0
3000	9,842	526	20.7	90.0	194.0
4000	13,123	462	18.0	86.7	188.0
5000	16,404	405	16.0	83.3	181.9

boils at these pressures: the figures are given in the 5th and 6th columns of the table. To measure the height of the mountain, you put in your pocket a thermometer and at the top, make a fire and boil the instrument in some water. Notice the temperature and look up the corresponding pressure in the table, and also note the time. When you get down, find out what the air pressure (shown by the barometer) was, on that day and at that time, at the bottom of the mountain. If it was below or above thirty inches, add or take off enough to bring it to 30.000 inches, and then do the same to the pressures shown in the table. Then read off the height.

Take an example. A thermometer boiled at the top of Ben Nevis read 203.85° F. The barometer at Fort William (sea level) showed 29.70 inches at that moment. From the table, water boiling at 203.85° F. indicates a pressure of 25.1 inches. Add on 0.3 inches, making the pressure 25.4. This shows a height of 4,400 feet. Most people prefer a pocket barometer which shows the pressure more accurately: but if one's barometer is broken and one's thermometer survives, the method is sometimes useful. Before pocket barometers were employed, the thermometer method was a favourite one.

When a liquid evaporates, it produces a great deal of vapour. One cubic inch of water produces 1,700 cu. in. of steam at 100° C. This is because the molecules in a gas are so far apart. Suppose we do not give the cubic inch of water 1,700 cubic inches of space, but only 10 cubic inches! We heat it up: it does not boil at 100° C., but it does boil at 345° C. and turns into 10 cubic inches of steam at the enormous pressure of 2,300 lbs. per square inch. The vessel would have to be very strong, otherwise it would burst like a rather ferocious bomb. Suppose, however, we shut up the water in a very strong vessel only a little bigger than would hold it. Any ordinary vessel would burst or stretch, but if it was strong enough, the water would do a queer thing. As it heaped up, it would not boil but the pressure would rise and rise and finally at the huge pressure of 217.7 atmospheres (and at a temperature hotter than melting lead) the surface of the water would grow vague and wavy and it would just disappear into steam without boiling. Not many years ago, it was regarded as impossible to handle steam at these vast pressures, but recently, a remarkable steam boiler has been developed which actually generates steam at this "critical" pressure of 217.7 atmospheres (p. 262). This change of a liquid into a gas without boiling is rather difficult to study with water: but with ether it takes places at 193.8° C. and 35.5 atm., and can easily be studied in a stout-walled glass tube.

The huge pressures that water can develop if heated in a confined space are the cause of boiler explosions, happily rare, but terribly dangerous because of the clouds of scalding steam which are produced.

The most terrible explosions on earth are those of volcanoes; sometimes a whole mountain is shattered to fragments and every living creature near destroyed. It has been thought that these explosions are caused by molten lava meeting subterranean water and producing vast amounts of steam confined at huge pressures beneath the earth: but a commoner cause seems to be the accumulation of the steam and other gases, pent up under vast pressure in the glowing rocks of the earth's core. The pressure sometimes becomes huge enough to move mountains and "the hills are carried into the midst of the sea."

CHAPTER VI

GASES

WHAT GASES ARE

THE behaviour of a gas is easily enough understood if we
remember what it is. A gas is a very scattered assembly of
molecules moving as fast as bullets but not getting very far
before they collide with each other. Each molecule has a good
big free space round it: in fact, a molecule of a gas has about a
thousand times as much elbow-room as a molecule of a liquid
or a solid. Well, anyone can see that if this is a true picture of a
gas, it must be very light, because it is made up of a good deal of
emptiness and very few molecules. Picture a swarm of midges in
which each midge was about two inches from the next and you
will have a fair notion of the amount of elbow-room in a gas.
It follows from this that a gas will flow very easily, for the molecules will not get in each other's way, nor will they greatly
attract or repel each other. For the latter reason, it should be easy
to compress a gas: a solid or liquid is almost incompressible
because the repulsions of the electrical charges of which its
atoms are made up are far stronger than any forces we can apply.
In the case of a gas, the molecules are much too far from each
other to repel each other. Compressing a gas is like forcing a
struggling mob of people into a small room; reasonable strength
will do it. Of course, the idea of a gas as a swarm of busy molecules is not much more than a hundred years old. Gases are
so unlike any other kind of matter that many centuries elapsed
before people made up their minds that they were matter at all.
Air was so strange a material, light, invisible to the eye, yet so

powerful in motion as wind, that one of the Greek philosophers identified it with the soul and God. The word "gas" itself, invented by van Helmont in the sixteenth century is often thought to be connected with "geist" or spirit, a derivation which displays the same train of ideas.

One of the reasons why people before the eighteenth century knew hardly anything about gases was that they are difficult to handle. You can put a solid in a basket or a basin, you can pour a liquid into a jug, but a gas has to be handled in a special way. Suppose you have a bottle full of it. As soon as you uncork it, the gas molecules begin to spread into the air and the air molecules into the gas. The difficulty of handling a gas in air is just the same as you would find if you tried to pour yourself out a glass of milk under water at the bottom of a swimming bath.

The chief trick we use depends on the fact that most gases do not mix with or dissolve in water. Suppose we are making some hydrogen by putting zinc in hydrochloric acid—spirits of salts— we can fix a tube into the cork of the bottle containing the zinc and acid and lead the tube under water, Fig. 51 A.

The bubbles must all be hydrogen, for no air can get in. Now, we take a jar and duck it under water. This gets all the air out of it. We turn it up, mouth downward. The water does not run out—if it did it would leave a vacuum and the pressure of the air would force the water in again, in no time!

Now we put the jar over the tube: the hydrogen bubbles up into it. When the jar is full, we stopper it, usually by sliding a greasy glass plate over it. Fig. 51 shows how a gas can be collected and also how we can force a gas from one vessel to another. Some gases, like ammonia, dissolve very easily in water, and in that case we use mercury instead of water. Mercury is very expensive and very heavy, so we don't use it if we can help it.

Another way of getting a gas into a vessel is to pump the air out and then let the gas go in through a tap. This avoids using mercury or water.

On the industrial scale, there are three favourite ways of storing gases. First, they are stored in gasometers over water, or under a sliding piston or diaphragm; Fig. 52 shows a gasometer of the modern waterless type. The weight of the sliding partition is balanced by the pressure of the gas. Fig. 138 shows storage over water. In this case the weight of the iron holder is balanced by the upward pressure of the gas. Since the holder is very large and not extremely heavy, quite a small pressure per square inch will keep it up.

Secondly, gases are stored in cylinders under pressures as high as 1,800 lbs. per square inch. This squeezes a lot of gas into a little space as explained on p. 134. Fig. 53b shows a picture of such a cylinder.

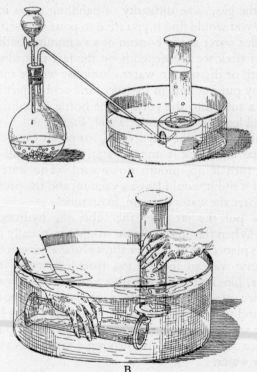

FIG. 51.—(A) Collecting hydrogen over water; (B) transferring a gas from one jar to another.

Thirdly, some gases can be made into liquids by compressing them, and these are sold in strong glass syphons or iron cylinders. When the valve at the top of the syphon (Fig. 53a) is opened, the liquid evaporates and the gas rushes out. One gas, acetylene, explodes when it is strongly compressed, so it is dissolved under moderate pressure in a liquid called acetone, just as carbon dioxide is dissolved under pressure in water to make soda-water. When the cylinder of acetylene dissolved in acetone is opened, the acetylene comes bubbling out like the carbon dioxide from soda-water. To prevent the acetone from being spilt, it is soaked up in porous material.

The selling of gas is now a big industry, and at least eighteen different kinds can be bought.

The great chemical works usually make their gases and use

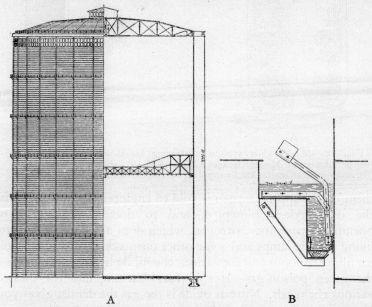

A   B

FIG. 52.—(A) A modern waterless gasholder. The gas is confined under a huge sliding diaphragm or piston which is kept airtight by sealing it with tar (courtesy of Waterless Gasholder Co., Ltd.). (B) The sealing system.

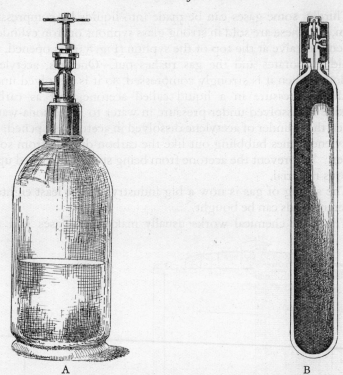

FIG. 53.—(A) A glass syphon containing liquid sulphur dioxide (by permission of Messrs. Boake Roberts & Co.). (B) A gas cylinder in section (from matter kindly supplied by The Chesterfield Tube Co., Ltd.).

them on the spot. Oxygen is sold to engineers for welding with the oxyacetylene blowpipe, and to doctors for sustaining pneumonia patients. Nitrogen, which does not burn, is sold for filling electric lamps and some other purposes. Hydrogen is sold for filling balloons and for various chemical purposes. Chlorine— the green poison-gas—is sold for bleaching and for making various chemicals. Nitrous oxide is the gas the dentist gives you. His two little cylinders contain nitrous oxide and oxygen. The nitrous oxide puts you under and the oxygen keeps you from suffocating. Carbon dioxide is sold in cylinders for making fizzy drinks and soda water, which are simply still drinks or water into which this gas has been forced under pressure. Ethylene and ethyl chloride are used as anæsthetics. Acetylene is used for lighting. Liquefied ammonia (not the solution in water you buy at the chemist's) is used for refrigerators, and so is liquefied sulphur dioxide. Argon—obtained from air—is sold for filling electric light bulbs, and neon, a gas of which the air contains only one part in 55,000, is extracted from it and is used to fill those brilliant neon-tubes which make the modern street so gay at night. So there are at least thirteen familiar gases you can walk into a shop and buy, packed in cylinders or "syphons."

One more gas is familiar enough to us all, the coal-gas, which Mr. Therm supplies to our houses. This is a mixture of half-a-dozen gases. It is mostly hydrogen and methane—the gas which causes explosions in coal mines—but it also contains the poisonous carbon monoxide and small amounts of several other gases. The way in which this gas is made and distributed is described on pp. 248—253.

THE BEHAVIOUR OF GASES

Only very slowly did the idea gain ground that air was a material substance like water or stone, and the chief thing that contributed to the progress of the idea was the discovery of the air-pump and the vacuum. It is easy to see how air behaves only when we have a space without air to compare with it. Most people know that air—and other gases—have weight, though they would be hard put to it to prove the fact to a hardy sceptic. If you fill a toy balloon with air and weigh it and then deflate it and weigh it again, not the faintest difference is noted. This seems odd at first, but the reason is simple. Look at Fig. 54 (a). On top of the scale pan is the balloon envelope and a column of air (including that in the balloon) reaching for miles up into the sky. The weight of air does not push the pan down, because the air is pressing on the pan equally upwards, downwards and sideways too. Now look at Fig. 54 (b). The balloon is still on the pan: so is the column of air. The weight is just the same—the only

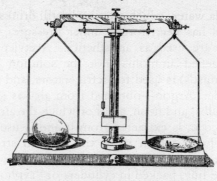

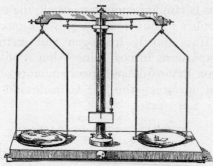

FIG. 54.—A toy balloon, if weighed in air, appears to have the
same weight whether empty or full (provided that the air in
the balloon is not under any pressure).

difference is that some of the air is inside the balloon instead of
outside it.

If we want to weigh air, we must weigh a vessel first *empty* of
air, then full of it. This is easy enough. We pump the air out
of a strong glass bulb and weigh it: then open the tap and let
it fill and weigh it again. If we do this, we find that a litre of
air—under the conditions which prevail in an ordinary living
room—weighs about a gram. To put it in a more concrete
way, the air in a sitting-room 15 × 12 × 8 ft. weighs about
as much as a small woman. Very roughly speaking, air weighs
about a thousandth of the amount the same bulk of water would
weigh.

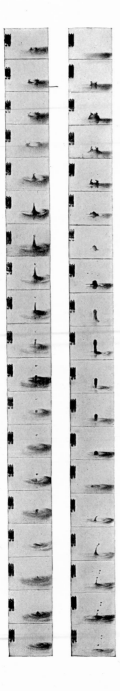

PLATE V

High-speed films of drops falling into water from different heights. *Left:* from 16 ins. height. *Right:* from 3 ft.
(By courtesy of the Royal Institution of Great Britain and Professor Allan Ferguson.)

Model of the liner *Queen Mary* under test in the experimental tank. (By courtesy of Pacific and Atlantic Photos, Ltd.)

Four liquids which do not mix (*v.*p.81).
(From a photograph by Mr. H. Pocock.)

PLATE VI

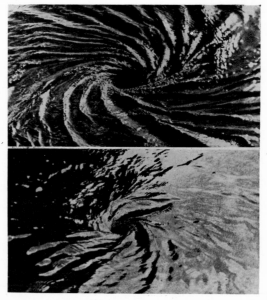

Free vortices. The upper is in the Southern Hemisphere (Arapuni Dam, N.Z.), the lower in the Northern Hemisphere (Loch Treig). (By courtesy of Messrs. Glenfield and Kennedy, and *The Mechanical World*.)

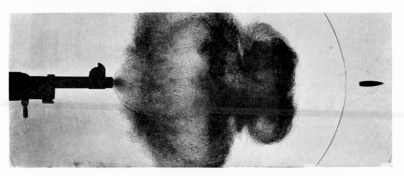

A bullet leaving a revolver. Note the spherical compression wave of expanding burnt gases, and the conical wave set up by the bullet. (By courtesy of Messrs. Philip Quayle, Ohio.)

AIR PRESSURE

FIG. 55.—A man carrying a weight equal to that of the air which always presses on his head and shoulders.

The tremendous quantity of air which wraps the earth like a garment—and incidentally keeps it warm like a garment too—has altogether a tremendous weight. As I sit here, the column of air pressing on my head and shoulders is a far greater weight than I could lift. Fig. 55 shows a man carrying eight half-sacks (140 lbs. each) of flour. This is just the weight of air which presses on each of our heads and shoulders as we go about our work. We are perfectly unaware of it, for an equal or very slightly larger pressure acting upward upon our feet and legs. bears us up. Our bodies (being made of solids and liquids) are almost incompressible and, as long as the pressure bears equally on every part, are quite indifferent to it. We need not boast of our power of supporting pressure; for fish, strange phosphorescent creatures with ferocious jaws, live a mile deep—perhaps deeper—in the sea. Here, the pressure on the back of a fish the size of a cod is about 120 tons, the weight of a large railway engine. As far as we can tell, they feel it not at all.

We live, then, at the bottom of a deep sea of ever moving gas, whirling and eddying from place to place. The air is hardly ever still even at ground level. The currents in it we call winds. They are caused chiefly by the difference of temperature between different parts of the world. Weather, as we shall see in Chapter XXXI, depends chiefly on winds and air-pressure, and it is therefore very important to have a way of measuring the pressure of the air. It was not until 1643 that any instrument was devised to do it. The principle is very simple. Let the air press on *one* side of something, but not on the other: see how hard the air pushes the thing. The simplest instrument for doing this is the mercury barometer. In a bent tube is some mercury. Above

5

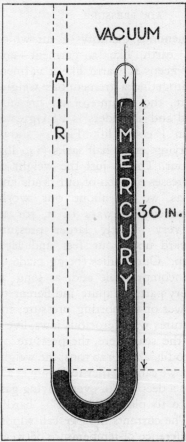

VACUUM

AIR

MERCURY

30 IN.

Fig. 56.—A column of air as high as the sky balances a column of mercury about thirty inches high. The height of this column depends on the amount of air which happens to be above the barometer at the moment in question.

the mercury on one side is *no* air (a vacuum), on the other side is the open air. The air outside pushes the mercury down: the vacuum inside, being nothing, can neither push nor pull, and accordingly, the mercury settles itself so that the weight of the air is just balanced by the weight of mercury. If the air pressure gets higher, it pushes the mercury up; if lower, it lets the mercury fall, in each case till the weight of mercury balances the weight of air. Why do we use mercury? First, it is so heavy that a short column of it, about thirty inches long, balances the whole column of the air up to the sky; secondly, it does not evaporate. Glycerine barometers are sometimes used, but they have to be about 25 feet high, which is not at all convenient!

A mercury barometer is quite simple in principle, but in practice takes a good deal of skill to make. The chief difficulty is in filling the tube, which must not contain any air or moisture. These stick to find their way into the vacuum of the mercury which therefore the sides of the tube and so press on the wrong side registers too low a pressure.

Space does not allow me to tell how these troubles are got over. Suffice it to say that the bent tube is most scrupulously cleaned, completely filled with mercury and then set upright. The mercury falls to the height where it balances the air pressure and leaves a vacuum on top.

The ordinary barometer is the aneroid. It is simply a springy steel box with no air inside. The air squashes it in and the spring pulls it out, and the box settles in a position where the air pressure is just balanced by the spring. If the air pressure increases, the box is squashed in a little more: if the pressure decreases, the spring pulls the box out a little more.

The motion is rather small, so a system of levers and cogwheels magnifies it so that it moves a clock hand. The advantage of the aneroid is that it is small—some are no bigger than a watch—and also that there is no mercury to spill. These two facts make it portable. Against an aneroid is the fact that springs often get weaker as time goes on, and as it is the spring that balances the air pressure, the readings will alter. For accurate scientific work, a mercury barometer—with many refinements—is always used.

THE FLOW OF GASES

The flow of gases is almost exactly like the flow of liquids. Since gases are light, and their molecules are so far apart that they attract each other but slightly, gases are very easily set moving, and it is quite difficult to keep them still. All that was said about the streamlining in liquids is true for gases.

Gases form eddies. The ordinary cyclone or "depression" which we read of in the "Weather Report" is a large but fairly feeble eddy of air: a tornado is an intense and rapid vortex of air. These we shall talk of again in connection with weather. Gases, however, give us the best chance of studying a ring-vortex, the ordinary smoke-ring. Some accomplished people can blow smoke-rings. Most of us are content to make them with the help of a boot box with a round hole the size and shape of a penny in one end. The best smoke is made by putting in the box two little saucers, one containing concentrated hydrochloric acid, the other the strongest ammonia, the vapours of which mix and give a dense white smoke of particles of sal-ammoniac. If, however, these potent chemicals are thought objectionable, smouldering brown paper can be put in a saucer in the box or the lid can be lifted at intervals and tobacco smoke blown into it. In any event, when the lid of the box is tapped, a beautiful smoke ring issues from the hole. Look at a smoke-ring carefully; you will see that it is always turning itself inside out, like a rubber ring rolled down a broom stick. This motion gives us a clue as to why you get a smoke-ring by tapping the box.

The tap shoots a column of smoke out of the hole. The

FIG. 57.—Smoke-rings (From Sherwood Taylor's *The Young Chemist*, by permission of Messrs. Nelson.)

inside goes out unhindered, but the edge of the box delays the outside. This sets the gas between the middle and edge spinning, and it "rolls" forward through the air just as a ball rolls along the table. The friction of the air slows it up, and after a time the spinning becomes slow and air currents blow the ring away.

COMPRESSED AND LIQUEFIED GASES

Nearly all the machines or inventions that employ air use it for its compressibility. Pneumatic tyres, air-guns, pneumatic drills, chisels and riveters all make use of the fact that pressure makes air contract and that when the pressure is released, it expands once more. Air behaves like a perfect spring.

Air-cushions and air-mattresses are comfortable because they spread the pressure of the body evenly over it. If you sit on a small hard chair, the hundred pounds odd of your body is supported by the two bony projections from your pelvis ("ischial tuberosities") in your buttocks and these squeeze a layer of muscle and skin between themselves and the chair. If one is thin, the pressure on this muscle may be 20 or 30 lbs. per square inch. If one is fat, a thick layer of liquid fat may keep the bones away from the chair and distribute the pressure over perhaps a hundred square inches. This makes the pressure perhaps only one pound per square inch—which is much more comfortable. Now lie on an air mattress. The pressure on it is a hundred pounds, but it is spread over about six square feet (about a thousand square inches) so that the pressure on each square inch of the body is only one tenth of a pound.

Air and all other gases are very compressible and if the pressures are not too enormous they are all equally compressible. It may seem odd that gases as different as oxygen, hydrogen, chlorine, and steam are all equally compressible, but the reason is not difficult to understand.

It follows first from the fact that all molecules have the same average energy at any given temperature; in other words, any molecule at, say, 10° C., whether of oxygen or hydrogen or chlorine, on the average hits just as hard as any other. The light swift molecules of hydrogen on an average hit just as hard as the slow heavy ones of chlorine. Secondly, it follows from the interesting fact that the same volume of any gas contains the same number of molecules. In actual fact, a gallon of oxygen, hydrogen or any other gas at 0° C. contains 1.23×10^{23} (123,000,000,000,000,000,000,000) molecules.

Very well, then, every gas contains (under the same conditions) just as many molecules as any other and every kind of molecule on the average hits just as hard as every other kind, and it is the blows of these molecules that are the pressure of a gas. If I sit on an air-cushion, why does it support me? The gas has no more substance in it than a swarm of gnats, but the myriads of molecules are beating against whatever restrains them with the speed of rifle bullets and it is the rain of tiny blows on the inside of the air cushion that supports me.

Now suppose you put enough pressure on a gas to halve its volume—to make a pint of it into half a pint. That half-pint has as many molecules in it as the pint had. There are twice as many molecules in the gas, so it hits twice as many blows on a given area as it did when it was a pint. Accordingly, it is thrusting on its container twice as hard and it has twice the pressure.

The rule then is, double the pressure and you will halve the volume—or in scientific language, "The volume of a gas at a given temperature is inversely as the pressure upon it." This is called "Boyle's Law," after the famous Robert Boyle, who discovered it in 1662. Fig. 58 expresses very simply what happens if pressure is put upon any gas.

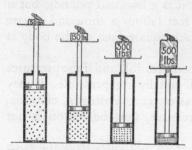

FIG. 58.—Showing how a gas is influenced by pressure in accordance with Boyle's Law.

But you may say—"If it is true that each time you double the load you halve the volume, it follows that a big enough load would make the gas disappear almost to nothing; where, in that case, would the molecules go?" The answer is that Boyle's Law is only true at pressures which are not too high.

The molecules are crowded by the pressure towards each other, and when they get very near to each other they get within the range of each other's attraction. If the gas is one like carbon dioxide or sulphur dioxide, the crowded molecules may pull on each other so strongly that they hang together and the gas becomes a liquid. It is thus possible to turn many gases into liquids simply by compressing them. Ammonia, carbon dioxide, sulphur dioxide, chlorine and some other gases can easily be turned into liquids in this way. Any gas in fact can be turned into a liquid by compressing it—as long as it is not too hot.

The jostling of the molecules, which we call heat, *prevents* the molecules clinging together and making a liquid; the attraction of the molecules pulls them together and *causes* them to make a liquid.

If there is a strong attraction, as with ammonia or carbon dioxide, pressure will liquefy the gas even if fairly warm; but gases like oxygen or hydrogen can only be liquefied by pressure if their molecules are calmed down by a great deal of cooling. So, if we try to see what happens if we compress a gas to the greatest extent possible, we find that it starts by halving its volume each time we double the pressure. Then we begin to find it more than halves its volume when we double the pressure on account of the molecules attracting each other. Then either the gas collapses into a liquid or, if it is too hot to do this, increase of pressure drives the molecules still nearer and makes the volume smaller. Now the molecules get so close that they repel each other, and as their outer rings of electrons get nearer the repulsion between them gets huge and the gas becomes more and more difficult to compress and finally is incompressible as a liquid or a solid. The liquefying of gases is an important industry. A gas takes up several hundred times as much room as it does in the form of a liquid and so if we want to send it by train, or ship it, it is best to send it as a liquid. Chlorine gas—the green poison-gas—is used for many quite beneficent purposes such as bleaching, making dyes, medicines, etc. A ton of chlorine as gas would have a volume of 422 cubic yards. It would take about forty railway trucks to hold it.

If chlorine is compressed, it collapses to a greenish liquid, which is run into closed steel boilers mounted on railway wheels. A ton of chlorine as liquid occupies only one cubic yard. The chlorine under the pressure of some seven atmospheres (105 lbs. per 1 square inch) in the boiler remains liquid permanently. If the boiler were to be smashed up in a railway accident the effects would not be quite as disastrous as might be expected, for the evaporation of the liquid would cool it intensely and the gas would be but slowly evolved.

Gases like oxygen and hydrogen will remain liquid only at

very low temperatures (—150° to —250° C.) and so it is almost as difficult to keep them liquid at ordinary temperatures as it would be to keep water liquid if the world were red-hot! Accordingly, we transport oxygen and hydrogen compressed in cylinders to 120 times the pressure of the air. If the cylinder holds 1 cubic foot, we can accordingly pack 120 cubic feet of gas into it. Higher pressures would be too dangerous.

Air, oxygen and such other gases as cannot be liquefied by simply compressing them at ordinary temperatures are now easily liquefied on the large scale by what is called "regenerative cooling."

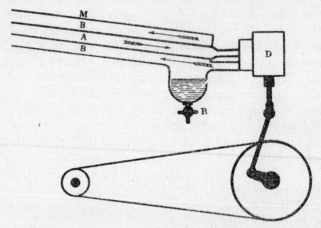

FIG. 59.—Liquefaction of air, very diagrammatically illustrated. Compressed air at room temperature enters at A and expands in the engine D, so doing work at the expense of the energy of its molecules. The issuing cold air passes out through the tubes B, so cooling the incoming air before it reaches the engine. When the incoming air is so cold that it liquefies on expansion the liquid air collects at R. (Courtesy of Messrs. Dunod & Cie., from Claude's *Air Liquide, Oxygène, Azote, Gaz Rares*.)

To liquefy air, we want a temperature of — 185° C., compared to which the North Pole is a hot-house. Now cooling is just the slowing up of molecules: to liquefy air we want to slow up its molecules. How shall we do this? Well, if you want to slow up a stream of water you can make it push a water-wheel round; if you want to slow a horse, let it pull a cart; if you want to slow a molecule, let it do some *work* and so part with some of its energy. The method finally adopted is this. First compress your air and let it cool down to room temperature. Then make your cold compressed air push the piston of an air engine round. The piston is speeded up only by slowing the molecules down; in other words by cooling them. The air which comes out of the engine is at about − 50° C. But this is not nearly cold enough; and this is where the clever trick comes in—we use this cold air to cool the compressed air before it reaches the engine. Our next lot of air reaches the cylinder at, say, − 40° C., and by pushing the piston slows down its own molecules and comes out at, say, − 90° C. This very cold air cools the incoming air still more, so that ever colder air goes on coming into the cylinder and air much colder still leaves it, until quite soon − 180° C. is reached and the air liquefies. Liquid air boils at about − 185° C., and therefore boiling liquid air is a very good means for making things extremely cold.

Plate VII shows some of the interesting properties of liquid air. In Plate VII, A, B, some mercury has been poured into a circular groove and frozen to a solid ring by pouring liquid air on it. The ring when dipped in water freezes on to itself a layer of ice and at the same time melts to liquid mercury which can be seen flowing away. Any moist substance freezes to a stony hardness: grapes and flowers (Plate VII, C, D) which have been frozen in liquid air can be broken with a hammer as if they were made of glass. Indiarubber cooled in this way is as brittle as sealing-wax (Plate VII, E). Despite its intense cold liquid air can safely be poured over an unprotected hand (Plate VII, F): the warm hand makes the liquid air evaporate to gas and make a nonconducting cushion between itself and the palm. Air contains nitrogen and oxygen: since the nitrogen evaporates more quickly than the oxygen, the liquid after standing consists mainly of liquid oxygen. Oxygen is the gas which combines with substances when they burn. In Plate VII, G, a cigarette has been soaked in liquid oxygen at – 185° C. In spite of this more than Arctic cold it blazes so furiously when lighted that it is consumed in a few seconds.

A final curious effect of liquid air is to make many dark-coloured substances paler. Sulphur (Plate VII, H) becomes snow-white when cooled in liquid air: when it is allowed to warm up it becomes yellow once more.

Just as we can cool a gas by making it do work, so we can heat it by doing work upon it. Suppose, instead of letting the gas push the piston, we apply power to the piston and make it push the gas. This speeds up its molecules and makes it hot. It follows, then, that if we compress a gas it becomes hotter. The best example of this is seen in a bicycle pump, which becomes very warm when a tyre is inflated. You might think this was due to the friction of the piston, but if you try working the pump without a tyre, you will find it does not heat up noticeably. Another very different example is the Föhn wind. If the wind blows from the top of a high mountain where pressure is low to the bottom where pressure is high, the air in the wind becomes compressed and gets much warmer. A warm wind of this kind is often experienced in Switzerland and is called a Föhn. The same thing is often found in Canada, where the wind blows from the top of the Rockies to the plain below; two feet of snow have sometimes been melted in a single day by it.

The expansion of a compressed gas is used in driving steam-engines, petrol-engines, hot-air engines, etc., but these may be left till pages 261–275. The air-gun and explosives will give us sufficient examples for the present. An air-gun is an arrangement by which air is pumped into a receiver and then used to force a lead slug out of the barrel of a gun. Its efficiency is only limited by the pressure of the air it contains.

The ordinary rifle also works by compressed gas and makes this gas in the cartridge. A cartridge is a box of some fairly soft metal containing at the base a cap filled with some explosive which goes off very easily when struck. The body of the cartridge contains some comparatively slowly burning explosive like cordite which is mainly guncotton, a substance made by soaking cotton in a mixture of nitric and sulphuric acids. Now, a molecule of guncotton is a string of units each of which contains six atoms of carbon, seven atoms of hydrogen, three atoms of nitrogen and nine atoms of oxygen, all stuck together in an insecure fashion. The chemistry of explosives is considered again on pp. 635–637. Let a flame once touch it or let it receive a really hard blow and the unit breaks up into some ten molecules of various gases, carbon monoxide, steam, nitrogen, etc.

Now you can put a gram of cordite in a cubic centimetre space. But the gram of mixed gases it turns into would at atmospheric pressure and temperature occupy about a thousand cubic centimetres of space. But the heat of the cordite flame is near two thousand degrees centigrade, so that the gas would be greatly expanded and would occupy several thousand cubic centimetres! The result of several thousand cubic centimetres of gas, being produced in a cartridge which holds only one cubic centimetre, is an enormous pressure. In a modern rifle, the maximum pressure on the base of the bullet is not far from a weight of two tons, and consequently the expanding gas drives it out of the barrel and, bursting forth behind it, makes a wave of compressed gas which, when it presses on the drums of our ears, we hear as a report. Plate VI shows a triumph of photography, a picture of a bullet leaving a revolver. The photo was taken by the light of an electric spark. The bullet and the compression wave are very clearly seen.

Gases expand very largely when they are heated. We saw that a cubic foot of steel expanded by 5 cubic inches when heated from 0° C. to 78° C., while a cubic foot of alcohol expanded 150 cubic inches over the same range. A cubic foot of air when heated from 0° C. to 78° C. expands by no less than 493 cubic inches. An interesting thing is that all gases expand to exactly the same extent when heated under the same conditions, which is by no means true for liquids or solids. When a liquid or solid is heated and expands there are two forces at work. The molecules are speeded up and so tend to swing in bigger orbits or to get further from each other. This effect is the same for all solids or liquids. But the attraction of the molecules opposes this effect; consequently substances whose molecules attract each other strongly will expand little and *vice versa*. But the molecules of gases are too far from each other to attract each other appreciably, so the effect of heating them is simply to increase the speed and energy of the molecules and make them bounce off each other harder and so fly farther apart. As the same rise of temperature *means* the same increase of energy, all gases expand equally.

The expansion of gases is very large, but it is not very useful for measuring temperatures because they expand and contract not only when the temperature alters but also when the air pressure alters. The expansion of a gas is sometimes used to measure rather high or very low temperatures and also for very accurate work. An air thermometer is rather a difficult affair to handle, and it is used only in the laboratory.

The expansion of a gas is easy enough to see. Hold a toy balloon (filled with air, *not* hydrogen) near the fire and you will see it swell up and grow tighter and larger. Put an empty bottle in hot water, take it out and cork it; let it get cold, pull out the cork, and you will hear the air hissing past the cork as you remove it.

A gas expands very much when it is heated and air consequently gets lighter (less dense) when heated. The most obvious example of this is the obsolete hot air balloon, the first machine which took an adventurous man into the air. If a balloon is to float in the air, it must weigh *just the same as* the air whose place it is taking. If the envelope of the balloon, the car and its occupants weigh 400 lbs., then the air or gas in the balloon must be 400 lbs. lighter than the same bulk of outside air.

Now, suppose we warm some air from 20° C. to 100° C. It expands to $\frac{373}{293}$ of its volume, or in other words 293 lbs. of the hot air take up the same room as 373 lbs. of outside air. So that 293 lbs. of hot air and 80 lbs. of envelope, man, etc., will together just float in air at 20° C.

So 5×293 lbs. of hot air would lift 5×80 (or 400) lbs. of balloon and occupants. Now 1465 lbs. of hot air is a lot. A pound of hot air occupies about twenty-five cubic feet, so the balloon, to lift 400 lbs., would have to hold about 37,000 cubic feet, which means that if the balloon was round it would be about 40 feet in diameter, not an impossible demand. The first hot-air balloon was lifted by a fire of chopped straw burnt beneath the opening of the balloon. The obvious danger was fire; consequently hydrogen, much lighter than any hot air, has been used in balloons for the last hundred years and more. The inflammability of hydrogen is a serious danger in airships propelled by internal combustion engines: consequently, in the U.S.A. where the light and non-inflammable gas helium can be cheaply made from natural gas (p. 228), airships are filled with it. In Europe the cost is prohibitive.

Hot air balloons are still seen at firework shows, and a well-known paper toy sold in crackers ascends nobly to the ceiling by the same means.

The lightness of hot air has many far more important uses. It makes the smoke go up the chimney, the "fug" in a hot room go to the ceiling, and carries smoke away from our towns. The pilot of an aeroplane or glider flying from a cool grass meadow over a baking hot piece of ploughland feels a current of warm air carry him up with it, and the pilot of a glider uses these currents to gain height. Cold air, of course, also tends to sink. You would expect that a garden at the bottom of a valley would feel less frost than one on a hill, but actually the cold air flows down to it, and it has the worst frosts of all.

PART II

POWER

CHAPTER VII

SPEED

RELATIVE SPEED

THE first and most obvious thing about all the elaborate machinery by which our civilised world is run is that it moves. In a sense, we can think of nearly all machines as being arrangements for turning one sort of motion into another sort.

A trip-hammer turns the round-and-round motion of a pulley into the up-and-down motion of a hammer; a typewriter turns the pressure on a key into a sharp accurate rap with the type-face followed by a shift of the carriage; a pump converts the rotatory motion of a wheel into the motion of water along a pipe.

If we are to understand machinery, then, we must know something about motion.

There are four chief things we can say about a moving thing. First, how fast is it moving? Second, is it speeding up, slowing down or remaining at a steady speed? Third, in what direction is it moving? Fourth, how much matter is moving?

First of all, let us think about speed, and let us take a car as the object moving—for you cannot think of motion without something which moves.

How fast is the car moving? You look at the speedometer and say "35 miles per hour," by which you mean, that if the car went on at its present speed in a straight line for an hour, it would be 35 miles distant from its present position. This seems all right until someone says "The earth is spinning so fast that a stationary car on its surface is moving at about 700 miles an hour: your car is going due west, so really it is travelling at 700 − 35, that is, 665 miles an hour *backwards*."

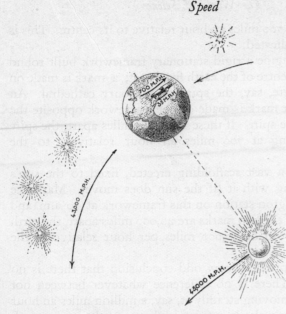

FIG. 60.—Relative velocity.

You find it hard to deny this until someone says, "But the earth is travelling once a year round the sun, in an orbit ninety-three million miles in radius. It is therefore going at the rate of 43,000 miles an hour and, as the time is midday, this speed is carrying the car forward at the rate of 43,000 — 665 or 42,335 miles an hour."

"No," says the third hearer, "for the whole solar system is drifting through space towards the star Vega at 45,000 m.p.h., and consequently the car's speed is 87,335 m.p.h."

"But," says the fourth, "are you sure that the stars, by the shift of which we judge the sun's drift, are really still? They may all be moving away from us at 10,000 miles an hour. If this is so, we must be going 10,000 miles per hour quicker than we think."

The moral of all this is, that there is no possibility of saying at what speed a thing is moving. All you can say is how much *faster* it is going than *something else*.

The car is moving at 35 miles an hour relative to the earth's surface. By this, we mean, that if we drive a peg in the earth at the beginning of the hour and let the car move at the same pace for an hour, then drive another peg, they will be 35 miles, measured along the earth's surface, apart. The surface of the earth is moving at 700 miles an hour relative to its centre. This is a little more complicated.

Suppose we imagine a rigid stationary framework built round the earth and the centre of the earth fixed to it; a mark is made on framework opposite, say, the spire of Salisbury cathedral. An hour later, another mark is made on the framework opposite the new position of the spire. If these were 700 miles apart, the spire would be travelling at 700 miles an hour relatively to the centre.

Again imagine a vast scaffolding erected, fixed to the sun's centre, and moving with it (if the sun does move). Mark the position of Paddington station on this framework at 10 a.m. and again at 11 a.m. If the two marks are 40,000 miles apart, the earth is moving at a speed of 40,000 miles per hour relative to the sun.

All this leads up to the very odd conclusion that there is no *absolute* motion. There is no difference whatever between not moving at all and moving steadily at, say, a million miles an hour as long as everything else is moving with you at the same speed. If the earth is dashing through space at twelve miles a second, it makes no difference to anything on the earth as long as it meets nothing from outside the earth!

Still more, suppose the earth and something else, say a meteor, were *alone* in space and getting nearer to each other at 20 miles a second. Is there any means whatever by which we can tell if the earth were still and the meteor, which is going to hit it, were going at 20 miles a second; or whether the earth were going at 20 miles a second and the meteor were still? The crash would be just the same, and there would be no way of telling which were moving: for this and other reasons, Science has come to the opinion that there is no such thing as speed, pure and simple, but only *relative* speed. Most speeds in everyday life are measured relatively to the surface of the earth, and it is mostly in astronomical matters that the question of relative motion arises.

MEASURING SPEED

We measure speed as a rule in miles or kilometres per hour. Engineers often measure it in feet per second, and men of science usually in centimetres per second.

Many different arrangements are used for measuring speeds. In most of them, we time something over a distance and so have to measure a time and a distance.

Perhaps the simplest case of speed measurement is the timing of the winner of a race. The judge tests his watch to see if it is accurate. He starts it as he sees or hears the gun and stops it as the runner crosses the line. In this way, the time is measured to $\frac{1}{5}$ of a second. The distance is measured with a tape measure or better with a surveyor's chain which does not stretch. If the runner goes 100 yards in 10 seconds, he would go (if he could run for an hour at the same pace) $\dfrac{100 \times 3600}{10}$ yards $= 20\frac{5}{11}$ miles in an hour. But we have not really measured the runner's speed at any moment: we have only measured the speed at which he would have moved if he had run from start to finish at the same pace. This is true of almost all speed measurements: they all measure the average speed of something over some given distance.

The simple method of timing which depends on a man's eye and a stopwatch is now not considered good enough even for timing important athletic events, let alone very high-speed events like the world's land or air speed records. In 1935, Sir Malcolm Campbell broke the world's land-speed record with an average speed of 301.129 m.p.h. over a measured mile. This speed was the average of two runs in opposite directions, as is required for such a record. An error was made by which his time for one run was given as 12.18 seconds instead of 12.08. The former figure gave 298.013 m.p.h. for this run, the latter gave 295.566. Thus a difference of only $\frac{1}{10}$ second made a difference of 2.447 m.p.h. in the result. No one can judge time by a stopwatch closer than to $\frac{1}{5}$ second; consequently, a stopwatch is useless for high-speed work.

Athletic events and others where the speed is not too great for high speed photography can be timed by taking on the same film a high speed cinema film of the runners and an accurate chronometer! When the film is developed it is quite easy to see the time when the winner crossed the finishing line. Plate VIII shows such a record of a racing aeroplane.

The electric current moves so nearly instantaneously that it gives us the best way of timing anything, such as a car, which moves extremely fast. If we can make the moving car switch on a current at the beginning of the measured mile and do the same at the end, we can make these currents register themselves.

In one form of this apparatus (Fig. 61), a ribbon of paper is drawn steadily along by a clockwork motor: two pens rest on it and draw two straight lines. The near pen is drawn aside exactly every half second by an electromagnet which receives an impulse of electric current through a switch which is opened and shut by an accurate clock. So, as the paper is drawn underneath it, the near pen draws a line with a series of kinks, each of which was made just half a second after the last. The other pen is pulled sideways by a spring, but just held from moving by a strong permanent magnet. This magnet has insulated wire coiled round it in such a way that when the current flows through the wire, it is oppositely magnetised and so ceases to be a magnet for the moment. The coils are joined to wires which go through 2 or 3 dry cells (not shown)

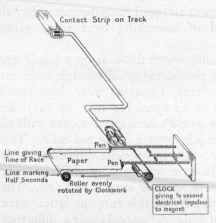

Contact Strip on Track

Line giving
Time of Race
Pen
Paper
Pen
Line marking
Half Seconds
Roller evenly
rotated by Clockwork
CLOCK
giving ½ second
electrical impulses
to magnet

FIG. 61:—Diagram illustrating the principles
of the electrical timing of a race.

to "contact strips" lying on the track at the beginning and end of the measured mile.

These strips are long closed rubber tubes with two brass strips attached to their inside surfaces and, therefore, kept apart by the air-pressure. When the car runs over the first, the brass strips touch and the current flows instantly through them and the battery to the magnet coils. The coils demagnetise the magnet for a moment and it can no longer hold the pen which flies off and makes a mark across the moving strip. Other magnets then at once pull the pen back to where it was before. When the car crosses the second strip, the same thing happens again and another mark is made on the strip. By counting the half-second kinks between the two marks, the time is known to the nearest half second. If the timing marks come between two half-second kinks, we can measure the distance from the mark to the

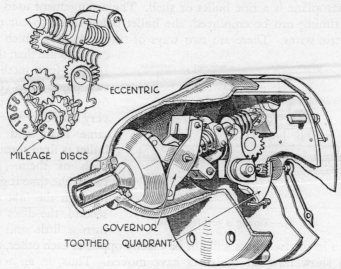

ECCENTRIC

MILEAGE DISCS

GOVERNOR
TOOTHED QUADRANT

FIG. 62.—A speedometer. The governor turns with the shaft connected directly or indirectly to the wheels. The weights on it fly outward and draw backwards the lever, which carries the toothed quadrant, which in its turn operates the hand on the dial. The mileage counter (inset) gives a good example of the use of worm gearing (p. 186) to reduce speed. (Courtesy of *Motor Cycling*.)

kink to one hundredth of an inch. The "kinks" are two inches apart, so it is possible to measure the time to $\frac{1}{400}$th of a second.

The ordinary speedometer has a shaft, connected by some form of gearing to the transmission or to the wheels of a car, and it measures the speed at which this shaft is turning.

In the instrument shown in Fig. 62 the four weights hinged to the turning shaft fly outward against the pressure of a spring as the result of the "centrifugal force." These weights by so doing operate the gearing moving the hand on the dial.

In other patterns of speedometer the turning shaft operates a little dynamo and generates electricity. The greater the speed, the higher is the voltage. This is measured by a voltmeter the dial of which is marked in miles per hour instead of volts.

The only man-made object which goes faster than a racing car or aeroplane is a rifle bullet or shell. The arrangement used for car timing can be employed, the bullet being made to cut two electric wires. There are two ways of timing bullets which are easier to use than this. In the first method, two paper discs (Fig. 63) are spun round very rapidly on the same shaft and the bullet is fired through both of them. Between the time it goes through the first and second, the discs will turn a little and the

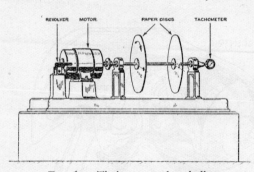

FIG. 63.—Timing a revolver bullet.

holes in the two discs will not be exactly opposite each other, and will show how far the discs have moved. Thus, in an actual example, the discs spun at the rate of 55 turns a second. The distance between them was a foot and the position of the holes showed that the discs had made $\frac{1}{24}$ turn while the bullet travelled between them. One turn takes $\frac{1}{55}$ of a second, so $\frac{1}{24}$ of a turn takes $\frac{1}{24} \times \frac{1}{55}$ of a second, so in $\dfrac{1}{24 \times 55}$ seconds the bullet goes a foot and in a second it goes 24×55 feet $= 1320$ feet; 1,320 feet per second is 900 miles per hour. This is slow; for some bullets travel at speeds of 3,000 feet per second, or even more.

All the methods we have described measure the average speed of something over a distance: there are one or two ways of measuring the speed of a thing at a particular moment. The first is simple. Let it collide with something and see how hard it hits! This would not be of much use for a racing car, but it does very well for a bullet! If the bullet is fired so that it beds itself in the wooden face of a heavy pendulum slung in the particular way shown in Fig. 64, the faster the bullet is travelling, the further the pendulum will be swung backward. The distance it swings can be measured by letting it push a brass rod (R) back over a scale. Suppose the pendulum weighs 120 lbs., and the bullet $\frac{1}{16}$ lb., and the pendulum took $\frac{3}{4}$ second to swing from right to left and it was pushed back three inches by the blow of the bullet then not very difficult mathematics show the speed of the bullet to be

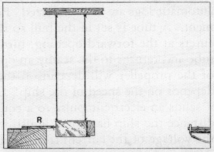

FIG. 64.—Measuring a bullet's speed by a ballistic pendulum.

$$\frac{120}{\frac{1}{16}} \times \frac{22 \times 3}{7 \times 12 \times \frac{3}{4}} = 2,011 \text{ feet per second.}$$

One of the most important speeds to measure—and one of the most difficult—is the speed of a ship. It is quite easy to time a ship, but it is not at all easy to tell how far it has gone. In cloudy weather there may be no chance of seeing the stars or sun, from which the position of the ship can be calculated. Accordingly—unless wireless signals can be employed—the captain must judge where he is by plotting out on the chart, first his direction (from the compass readings), then the distance, which he gets from the time he has travelled and the speed. The speed is measured by throwing the "log" overboard.

The oldest method is to throw overboard the log-ship, which is a piece of wood weighted with lead to keep it upright in the sea. It is assumed that will remain still relative to the water.

To the log-ship is attached a thin line which leads to the ship. The line is then allowed to run out from a reel and enough line is first run out to leave the log-ship clear of the ship's wake. The line has a knot on it every 47 ft. 3 inches, and the number of knots that pass through the officer's hand in 28 seconds (measured by an hour glass) is counted. Now 47 ft. 3 in. in 28 seconds is 1 nautical mile (6,080 feet) an hour, so that, if say, 6 knots run out in 28 seconds, the ship is going 6 nautical miles an hour— ("six knots").

The log-ship is nowadays only used on small boats and various automatic logs are now preferred. Forbes' log is a better arrangement. A tube is set in the hull so that, as the ship moves, water enters at the forward opening, turns a little propeller inside the tube and returns to the sea by an opening further aft. The speed of the propeller will depend on the flow of water which again depends on the speed of the ship. Each time the propeller turns it sends an electric impulse to a counting dial, so registering the distance the ship has gone: it also works a little electric dynamo, the voltage of the current from which depends on the number of revolutions it makes: this current operates a voltmeter, the needle of which shows the speed of the ship in knots.

By these methods the speed of the ship *relative to the sea* is got. But the sea is always moving over the earth, and so the ship which the captain has found to be travelling, say, at 12 knots faster than the sea, may be in a contrary current of 4 knots, and so be travelling at 8 knots only relatively to the sea bottom.

In shallow water, a ground-log which sticks to the bottom can be used, but in deep water, the currents must be looked out on the chart and due allowance made. The fact that currents vary with wind and tide makes "dead-reckoning"—as this way of

finding a ship's position is called—a rather uncertain one and
many good ships have been lost through trusting it too well.

Is there any limit to speed? Relative speed is the only speed
we know anything about. The slowest speed possible is obviously rest: but the quickest speed? At one time it was thought
that there was no reason why two objects should not be moving
towards or away from each other with any speed however
enormous. Einstein, however, showed that no speed relative to
the observer could be greater than that of light: 186,300 miles per
second. The arguments for this are such as a book of this kind
cannot give, but it seems quite certain that *if we measure time and
distance by light signals* as we do in astronomy—and on earth as a
rule—the velocity of light is the maximum one which can be
observed.

There is real experimental evidence for this. If we measure the
speed and mass of an electron travelling at enormous speeds of,
say, 20,000 to 180,000 miles a second, we find that the faster it
goes, the more massive (heavier) it becomes, and from the
figures we can work out that if it went at the speed of light, its
mass would become infinite. Clearly, its mass cannot be more
than infinite, so it cannot go more than 186,300 miles a second.
Now, all matter is made, partly at least, of electrons: so nothing
can go faster than light.

It should not be difficult to see that it is not possible to distinguish uniform motion from rest. St. Paul's is at rest, relative to
the earth's surface but in rapid motion relative to the sun: It is,
therefore, both at rest and in uniform motion and there is no
reason to prefer the view from the earth to the view from the sun.
It is easy to see that a thing "at rest" remains so until some *force*
acts on it and puts it in motion. But a thing at rest relatively to
one body may be in rapid uniform motion relatively to another!
It must then be clear that a body in uniform motion remains
moving uniformly until some force is exercised either to speed it
up or slow it down. This is always a little difficult to picture,
because, on earth, everything that moves has a force tending to
stop it—the force of friction. As a thing moves, it touches other

things and sets their molecules moving too, and in this way it parts with some of its motion to the molecules around it. It consequently slows down and the surrounding molecules speed up or in other words become hot. But, suppose, there was no force to impede the thing and no molecule to collide with it, why should it ever stop?

FORCE

We have already said that a thing remains at rest or moves uniformly until a force speeds it up or slows it down. This gives us a chance to define what a Force is.

A Force acting on a body is defined as that which tends to increase or diminish its speed in any particular direction. We can most easily see what is meant by a force if we think about the force which the pull of the earth exerts on, say, a pound weight. If you release a pound weight—drop it—it always goes in the same direction—that is to say, towards the centre of the earth. This gives us the first point, that a force is *directed*.

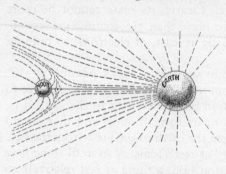

The direction in which a body is pulled, by a particular force, is called a line of force. Thus (neglecting the attraction of the sun and moon) bodies fall straight towards the centre of the earth. We can picture then the earth as surrounded by lines of force radiating out from its centre. (Fig. 65). But

FIG. 65.—Lines of gravitational force between the earth and moon. (The effect of the sun's gravitation is here neglected.)

suppose the attraction of the moon comes in also. This is very feeble at the earth's surface (only about $\frac{1}{29000}$ of the earth's attraction): in the same way the earth's attraction is rather feeble at the moon's surface—

about a hundredth of the moon's attraction. Even this means that a man on the moon (if there were one) who could jump eight foot four in height—an easy task on the moon—when the earth was overhead, could only jump eight foot two when it was underfoot. On earth, high jumpers don't bother about choosing a time when the moon is overhead, for it would only give them about an extra two-hundred-and-fiftieth of an inch

But both the earth and the moon would pull quite strongly on a body between them, and Fig. 65 shows the "lines of force" around them. Of course these lines are not really there, but just show which way a heavy object like a brick would travel if released at any point. The real "gravitational field" is more complicated because the attractions of the sun and the other planets have to be taken into account.

The next point about a force is that it causes the body it acts on to accelerate—that is to go faster and faster—or decelerate —go slower and slower. Consider again what happens if you drop a pound-weight. The weight moves more and more rapidly as time goes on. If it is dropped (in a vacuum, the air exerts a force on the weight and complicates things), it is falling at the speed of 32 feet per second at the end of the first second, 64 feet per second at the end of the next second, 96 feet per second at the end of the next second. At the end of each second, it is moving 32 feet per second faster than at the end of the second before. We express this by saying that it has an acceleration of 32 feet per second per second. On the moon, which is lighter and attracts things more feebly, it would be moving at 5 feet per second at the end of the first second, at 10 feet per second at the end of the next second, 15 feet per second at the end of the third. The acceleration would be 5 feet per second per second. Pretty clearly, the stronger the force, the more rapidly it will speed a given thing up or slow it down, and we measure forces in this way. The usual unit of force is, in England, a pound-weight— the force which would make a thing weighing a pound speed up at the same rate as if it were falling in a vacuum (32 feet per second per second): the scientific unit is a *dyne*, the force which would make a gram of anything go, at the end of each second, 1 centimetre per second faster than it went at the end of the second before.

HOW THINGS FALL

The study of the way things fall gives us a good idea of how a force acts.

Suppose we drop our pound weight over a precipice (imagining the air away). At the end of the first second, it will be going at the rate of 32 feet per second and it will steadily speed up; there is no obvious reason why it should not go on falling faster and faster as long as the pull of the earth remains the same. In actual fact, this never happens: the air makes the weight speed up less quickly, and the quicker it goes, the more does the air's effect on it increase. Roughly, if the weight doubles its speed, the air quadruples its resistance: if the weight goes a hundred times as fast, the air resists it a hundred hundred—ten thousand times as much. The result is, that every falling body finally reaches a state when the air slows it down just as much as the pull of the earth speeds it up. You can see this very easily with a toy balloon which has only a small weight but has a big area and therefore a large air-resistance. If you release it, it falls more and more quickly for a few inches; then drops at a steady pace.

The same is true of very small rain drops. They have often fallen a mile but are not going any faster than the eye can follow. The calculation of this "terminal velocity" is rather complicated, because so many things have to be allowed for; but for a perfectly smooth ball the following rule holds pretty closely.

Multiply the radius of the ball (half the diameter in centimetres) by itself: multiply the answer by the density of the ball (the number of times it is heavier than the same bulk of water) and multiply the answer by 1,220,000. The answer is the greatest speed (in centimetres a second) the ball can reach, if it falls through ordinary air. First let us consider a tiny droplet of water such as makes up a country mist. It may be $\frac{1}{50}$th of a millimetre in diameter, that is, $\frac{1}{1000}$ cm. in radius. Its density is one. So the utmost speed it will reach is

$$\frac{1}{1000} \times \frac{1}{1000} \times 1,220,000 = 1.22 \text{ cm. a second.}$$

Thus, a droplet like this takes about two seconds to drop an inch. In actual fact, movements of the air are always stirring up the mist and the droplets hardly settle out at all.

Next, take a raindrop about two millimetres ($\frac{1}{12}$ of an inch) in diameter. Its radius is a tenth of a centimetre, and consequently its terminal velocity is $\frac{1}{10} \times \frac{1}{10} \times 1,220,000 = 12,200$ cm. per second. This is about 274 miles an hour. As a matter of fact, a raindrop never reaches this speed because the air pushes it out of shape and it is never a perfectly round ball. A sphere falls faster than an object of any other shape.

Finally, consider an iron ball about the size of a tennis ball: (diameter 6 cm., density 7). It would reach a speed of $3 \times 3 \times 7 \times 1,220,000$ cm. per second—about four hundred and fifty miles a second. Actually, this could not be reached because the force of gravity of the earth gets weaker as we get farther from the earth, and to get up this speed the ball would have to fall for twenty million miles with the earth pulling all the way as hard as it does at its surface.

But these rough calculations and all experiments on falling bodies combine to show that everything falling through air, or water, in fact any gas or liquid, can reach a certain speed in falling and cannot exceed it. This has a great importance to animals. An animal is a bad shape for quick falling, and its fur or feathers or hairs give it a big air resistance. A caterpillar can fall from the highest tree and will never fall fast enough to hurt itself when it lands. Even a mouse will get only a severe bump which will not be enough to kill it. A cat can fall a long way and get only a severe shaking. Even a large dog can jump from a window 20 feet high and not break a bone. A man, on the other hand, is likely to damage himself by a ten-foot fall.

A daring parachutist has jumped from an aeroplane five miles up, and only pulled the cord releasing the parachute when a mile from the ground. He found that he reached a velocity of about 140 miles an hour, but actually slowed up to 110 miles an hour when he got to the denser air a mile and a half above the earth. This shows that a man who throws himself from an aeroplane falls no harder than a man who jumps out of a racing car and accounts for the fact that men sometimes survive the most surprising falls.

In a vacuum, which obviously offers no resistance to a fall, all objects, light or heavy, fall at the same speed and the caterpillar would hit the ground with as severe a bump—in proportion to its weight—as the elephant.

In water, on the other hand, the resistance to motion is far greater than in air and no creature can sink (by its own weight) fast enough to damage itself on the bottom.

We have thought about what happens when things fall: of more practical interest is what happens when they are thrown or otherwise projected into space. Leaving aside the resistance of the air, if a thing is thrown straight upwards, its upward speed gets *less* at the end of each successive second by 32 feet a second. Thus, if a rifle bullet was fired at 3,200 feet per second straight upward, after a hundred seconds its speed would be nil, and it would start to fall. It can be calculated that it would reach a height of about 30 miles! Actually, the air resistance is very large indeed, and such a bullet would probably not go more than ten or fifteen miles up. However, we do not often want to hurl things straight into the air, but we do very often want to hurl them at something.

Take the case of man on a flat plain, a thousand yards from a target he is trying to hit with a rifle. The moment the bullet leaves the rifle it will start to fall and it will fall all the time it is travelling to the target. We will leave out the air resistance for the moment and suppose that the bullet does not slow down on the way. The bullet we may consider to move at 3,000 feet per second, so it will take one second to reach the target. But in a second a bullet falls sixteen feet, so if the rifle is pointed at the bullseye, the bullet will hit the ground. To keep it at the right height, we must fire the bullet a little upwards so that it will rise for the first half of the journey and then drop just enough to reach the level of the target at the end of the second. It clearly ought to be at the highest point half-way along its course.

A bullet (or anything else in a vacuum) falls four feet in half a second, so the rifle must be pointed so that the bullet starts *forward* at 3,000 feet a second and *upward* at the right pace to carry it up just four feet before it starts to fall. This pace can be worked out to be sixteen feet a second. If the barrel is 3 feet long, the bullet is in it for $\frac{1}{1000}$th second. If it is to go up at the rate of sixteen feet a second, it must go up $\frac{1}{1000}$th of 16 ft. in $\frac{1}{1000}$th second, or nearly one fifth of an inch while it traverses the 3 feet of barrel. So the end of the barrel must be $\frac{1}{5}$ of an inch higher than the breech and this would be assured by making the

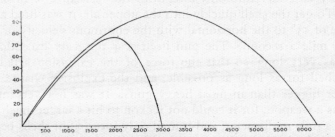

Fig. 66.—The paths of a bullet fired at 1300 feet per second and at an angle of $3\frac{1}{2}°$ to the horizontal in a vacuum (upper curve) and in air (lower curve). The heights are drawn on a larger scale than the ranges in order to exaggerate the height of the curves and so make their shapes clearer.

backsight (as adjusted for 1,000 yards range) $\frac{1}{5}''$ higher than the foresight. The bullet does not go straight to the target, but moves in a curve all the time it is going forward: at first it goes quickly up, then more slowly till at the top it neither rises nor falls but goes straight on. Then it begins to fall and the curve starts to drop more and more quickly. This kind of curve is called a *parabola*. You can see it very well when a cricket ball is hit into the air or when a firehose is played on a building. Actually, the path of a bullet or cricket ball is not a true parabola, because instead of going evenly forward at the same pace, it slows up owing to the friction of the air. The end of the curve is therefore steeper than the beginning, as Figure 66 shows.

A small heavy slowly moving object like a steel bicycle ball is least affected by air resistance: a large light object like a toy balloon or a very swift object like a bullet is most affected.

The most remarkable success in avoiding the air resistance which slows down projectiles was attained by "Big Bertha," the gun which shelled Paris from 76 miles away. It succeeded in hurling a shell, weighing 264 lbs., this enormous distance by shooting it into the upper air. The shell at the top of its course was twenty-four miles above the ground and for 55 out of the 76 miles it travelled through the upper air which had a tenth of the density and therefore only a tenth of the resistance of ordinary air. To get the shell quickly into the upper air, it was fired at an angle of 55° to the horizontal with the enormous velocity of just on a mile a second. The gun itself was not very exceptional: it was very long, so that the force of the explosion acted on the shell for as long as possible, and the explosive charge was rather bigger than in most heavy guns. It was not very much use as a weapon, for it could not reckon to hit a target much less than a mile in diameter, and it fired only forty-eight shells before it needed reboring.

GRAVITATION

We have talked a good deal about the pull of the earth or *gravitation* without much attempt to explain it. It is, indeed, very difficult to explain. Everything attracts everything else, and "the force of attraction between two masses varies inversely as the square of the distance." This is a neat way of saying that if the force of attraction between two masses is one unit when they are 25 feet apart, it will be $\frac{25}{1} \times \frac{25}{1}$ units (625 units) when they are one foot apart and $\frac{25}{100} \times \frac{25}{100}$ units ($\frac{1}{16}$ unit) when they are 100

feet apart. This is Newton's
Law of Gravitation, and is the
foundation of astronomy.
Einstein's work has slightly
modified it by saying the "distance" must be measured along
"world-lines," which may be
slightly curved when near very
heavy objects like the sun. But

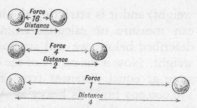

Fig. 67.—Illustrating the distance-
square principle.

no one has explained Gravitation yet, and it seems in many ways
quite unlike the other attractive forces that we know (electrical
and magnetic). Gravitation is a very feeble force, and is most
difficult to measure unless one of the attracting masses is a vast
body like the earth. It is rather important, however, to know how
much two objects attract each other because in that way we can
weigh the Earth.

Suppose a lead ball A weighs a ton (a million grams), and its
centre is a metre from the centre of another ball B, which is
about as big as a large shot and weighs a gram. Now the ball B is
attracting the earth[1] with a pull equal to its own weight (1 gm.

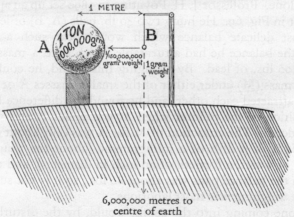

Fig. 68.—Illustrating a method by which the earth can be
weighed.

[1]The ball, of course, attracts the earth just as much as the earth attracts the ball.

weight) and it is attracting the lead ball A with a pull which we can measure or calculate from the results of the experiment described below; we will suppose it is $\frac{1}{150000000}$ of a gram's weight. Now if the centre of the earth and the centre of the ball A were at equal distances from the ball B, the earth would be 150,000,000 times as heavy as A (for it is attracted 150,000,000 times as much). But the earth's centre is about 6,000,000 metres from B so its force is $\frac{1}{6000000} \times \frac{1}{6000000}$ of what it would be were its centre only a metre from B. Since in these circumstances the earth would appear to be 150,000,000 times as heavy as a ton weight, it is really 150,000,000 $\times$ 6,000,000 $\times$ 6,000,000 times as heavy and its weight is 5.4 $\times$ 10^{21} tons. The actual value is 6 $\times$ 10^{21} tons.)

No experiment to determine the force of gravitation can be a simple one, because the attraction of two bodies of a size that can be handled and at a reasonable distance from each other is only a thousand-millionth of their weights. Consequently, the balance which will measure this attraction must be far more accurate than even a good chemical balance. All sorts of minute errors have to be allowed for. However, we can at least see the kind of way it can be done. Professor J. H. Poynting in 1890 set up an apparatus like that in Fig. 69. He hung two 40 lb. balls (A, B) of lead from the most delicate balance which would bear such a weight. Under the balance he had a turntable which bore a mass (M) of about 300 lbs. of lead. By swinging this round, he could bring the big mass (M) under either of the smaller masses A or B. The masses attracted each other, and he found the difference between the position of the pointer when M was under A and when M was under B. The attraction of M for A was only about equal to the weight of a fifth of a milligramme (about the weight of a droplet of water, a fortieth of an inch in diameter), and the total load on the balance pans was about 80 lbs., so it is not surprising that the weighing was most laborious.

Anyone coming into the room, would, by the disturbance of the air and the vibration of their tread, cause a far bigger motion of the balance than the attraction of the masses could. Accordingly,

PLATE VII

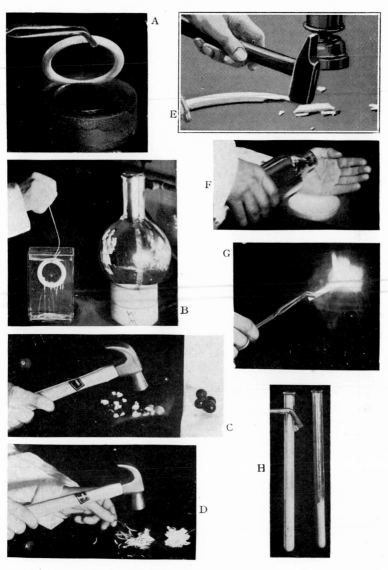

Experiments with liquid air. (See pp. 137, 138,)
(E. by courtesy of Messrs. Dunod et Cie, Paris.)

PLATE VIII

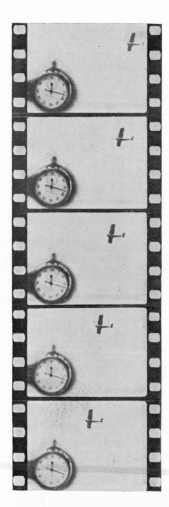

Timing an aeroplane by photographing
it and a stop-watch at the same time.
(By courtesy of the Askania Werke
A.G., Bambergwerk, Berlin.)

(*Above*) The gyroscope does not
fall because it resists the tendency
of gravity to alter the angle of its
axis. The downward force makes
it precess anti-clockwise. (*Below*.)
A gyroscope balancing on a taut
wire. (By courtesy of Messrs.
Griffin & Tatlock, Ltd.)

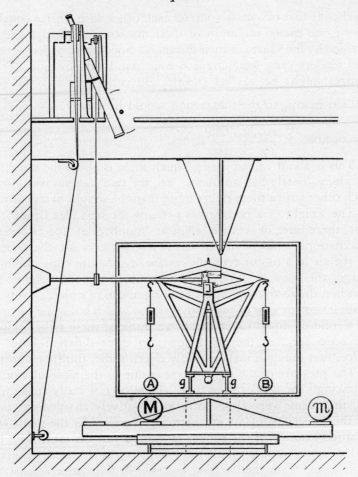

Fig. 69.—Poynting's apparatus (modified from the author's drawing.
Phil. Trans. 1891).

the balance was set up in a bricked-up cellar, and observed
through a telescope. The motion of the pointer was magnified by
a mirror reflecting a spot of light on to a scale. The turntable
was worked by a pulley.

Many such experiments have been done and the conclusion

6

reached is that two masses attract each other with a force equal to about one fifteen-millionth of their masses multiplied together, divided by the square of their distances. Suppose two locomotives and tenders each weighing 200 tons stand side by side. Their centres might be 12 feet (nearly 400 cm.) apart. A ton is a million grams, so their attraction would be nearly $\dfrac{1}{15,000,000} \times$

$$200,000,000 \times \frac{200,000,000}{400 \times 400} \text{ dynes.}$$

This is about 17,000 dynes, which force is about the weight of 18 grams, nearly half an ounce. So, the two locomotives attract each other with a force rather more than the weight of a penny.

The weight of a body gives perhaps the best idea of a force, but there are of course a great number of forces beside gravitational ones. Familiar examples of forces are the *pressure* of the air in a motor tyre, the *tension* of the wire rope pulling a barge, the *magnetic attraction* and repulsion of one magnet for another, the *electrostatic attraction* or repulsion of a piece of rubbed sealing wax for a bit of paper, the *cohesion* which holds the particles of a solid or liquid together. If we think of these rather closely we soon see that they boil down to three different kinds of force, first gravitational, secondly electrostatic, thirdly magnetic.

The pressure of the air in a tyre is due to the molecules of air "striking" the walls of the tube. They do not really strike it at all: they come very close until the negatively charged exteriors of the molecules of air are *electrically* repelled by the negatively charged exterior of the rubber molecules. In the same way, the pull of a wire rope is simply the pulling of the electrically-charged iron atoms from their settled position in the lattice against the attraction of these atoms. If you object that it is not the wire rope that pulls the barge but the horse or tractor, the force they exert is still electrical. We do not know much about muscular contraction, but it is pretty clearly a shifting of large electrically charged molecules. The tractor works by the *pressure* of gas in its cylinder, and we have seen that this is electrical too.

Magnetic forces are closely related to electrical ones. The

latter are the forces between stationary electrical charges: the former are due to the alteration in electrical forces which occur when electrical charges move (p. 309 *ff*).

Think now of something which moves steadily—a train going at 60 miles an hour. Here, the forces all balance. The steam pressure in the cylinders provides a force pushing the train forward. The friction of the rails, the friction of the air, the friction of the internal machinery, the air pressure on the front of the train (bigger than that on the back) all add up to make a force pushing the train back just as hard as the steam pressure pushes it on. Consequently, there is no total force on it, and it gets neither faster nor slower. Suppose we slip a carriage. The friction is now less because fewer wheels are turning, and there is less air resistance, etc., so the steam pressure now pushes the train forward more strongly than the reduced friction holds it back. The forces now do not balance and there is an excess of force pushing the train on. Consequently, it goes faster: but as it moves faster, so the friction becomes rapidly greater. The friction increases as the square of the velocity (if you go three times as fast, you get nine times the friction); so very soon the force of friction gets big enough exactly to balance the driving force and the train settles down again to a steady but higher speed of, say, 65 miles an hour. If a thing is still or moving *steadily*, you can be sure there are at least two forces on it, balancing each other. If a thing is accelerating or decelerating, it is because the forces on it do not balance.

Just as it requires force to stop a thing moving, so it also requires force to change the direction in which it is moving. It is well known that if an effort is made to turn a car sharply when it is moving at high speed, the back of the car tends to continue to move in the same direction as before. The adhesion of the tyres to the road opposes this, but if the speed of the car is great enough, tyres will not hold it, and the back will continue

FIG. 70.—The tendency of the hind part of the car to continue to travel in the same direction causes a skid.

in a straight line while the front turns, and a skid will result.

A more important fact follows from the need to apply a force to change the direction of a force. When a wheel rotates, each piece of it is having its direction of movement changed the whole time. Consequently, each bit of the rim tends to go on in a straight line and so fly off the wheel. The wheel holds together only because some force acting *towards* the centre of the wheel holds the rim in position. In the case of a fly-wheel, this force is the tension of the steel. This inward force is needed to keep changing the direction of motion of the rim as it rotates. We often, though not with the approval of physicists, regard the tendency of the rotating body to leave the circle as equivalent to a force which just balances the inward pull needed to keep the body in its orbit. This outward pull of the rotating body is called centrifugal force. If the body does not fly to bits, it is because this centrifugal force is just balanced by the tension of its material. The notion of centrifugal force will be used throughout this book, because those of us who are not physicists will find it easy to understand.

CENTRIFUGAL FORCE

The force is not very hard to calculate. If any particle is swung round in a circle, it pulls away from the centre with a force equal to nearly one and a quarter times its weight in pounds multiplied by the radius of the circle in feet multiplied by the square of the number of revolutions per second. So, a seven pound weight swung round on the end of a three foot string twice a second, pulls on the string with a force of $1\frac{1}{4} \times 7 \times 3 \times 2^2 = 104$ lbs. weight.

It is not difficult to see from this formula that the rim of a big flywheel run at high speed must be pulling outward with tremendous force. The only way it can get outward is by flying to bits: the strength of the metal of the rim prevents this as a rule, but occasionally a wheel is run too fast and bursts. A cast-iron flywheel with a solid rim will burst if the rim runs at more than about 18,000 feet a minute.

Well, cast-iron flywheels are sometimes 30 feet in diameter, so that 18,000 feet per minute rim-speed is only about 200 revolutions a minute, or rather more than three a second. When a flywheel does burst, tremendous damage is done. Every bit of the metal shoots off with its speed of three hundred feet a second, about as fast as an old-fashioned cannon ball: consequently a bursting flywheel does as much damage as an exploding bomb. The chief cause of the accident is increase of speed. The flywheel of an engine may run at a safe pace while the engine drives a heavy machine: then the driving-belt breaks and all the power of the engine goes to speed up its flywheel and disaster follows. The remedy is to have a flywheel of fairly small size, so that the engine at its greatest pace cannot drive it at the danger speed. Circular saws have also been known to burst and inflict terrible wounds. It is the usual practice to calculate the least strength of a

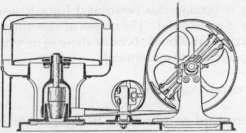

FIG. 71a.—Section, "Weston" Pivot underdriven hydro-extractor. (Watson, Laidlaw & Co., engineers.)The clothes are placed in the inner vessel (which is perforated) and rotated 1000-1500 times a minute. (Courtesy of the Gresham Publishing Co.)

wheel necessary for the highest possible speed and then to make the wheel ten times as strong as this. The highest speeds ever used in engineering work are in certain turbines, which rotate up to 10,000 r.p.m., and these are not much in favour.

So far, we have considered centrifugal force as a danger, but it is made useful in a great number of machines. The simplest perhaps is the centrifugal dryer. Suppose you have a great quantity of wet clothes. You can dry them by hanging them in a current of air: this, however, wants a good deal of room and a good deal of time. If you hang up a wet stocking, a certain amount of water is drawn out by gravity and drips off the toes. Now, centrifugal force can be made much stronger than gravity. So the laundry puts its clothes in a perforated metal basket, usually 30 inches in diameter and 14 inches deep and spins this round 1,200 times a minute. The clothes are held by the basket: the water is not, and flies out sideways. The force on the water is about 750 times its weight, so it is no wonder that after ten minutes of this spinning, the clothes, though not dry enough to wear, are dry enough to iron. Chemicals like soda crystals are also dried in this way.

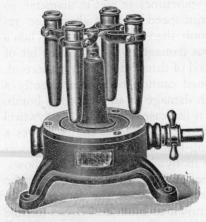

FIG. 71b.—A laboratory centrifuge driven by a water-turbine. (Courtesy of Messrs. Griffin & Tatlock.)

You will remember that a fine particle of, say, mud sinks

very slowly because its tiny weight is opposed by the buffets of the darting molecules in the liquid round it. Now since centrifugal force can be made so much stronger than gravity, a muddy liquid which would take days to settle will clear in a minute or so if whirled round a thousand times a minute. If a little tube of pond water (containing thousands of microscopic creatures) is spun in a centrifuge, as the machine illustrated in Figure 71b is called, the force drives them all to the bottom of the tube. The microscopist can then examine the few drops of liquid at the bottom and be confident of finding there all the living creatures which were in the water.

If really enormous speeds are reached, it is possible not only to make "large" particles like micro-
scopic animals
sink, but even to
cause some of
the biggest mole-
cules like those
of egg-white or
the red pigment
of blood to settle
out. Naturally,
the bigger the
molecule the
easier it is to
drive it to the
bottom of the
liquid, and by
centrifuging solu-
tions of various
compounds, we
can find out
the size of the
molecules.

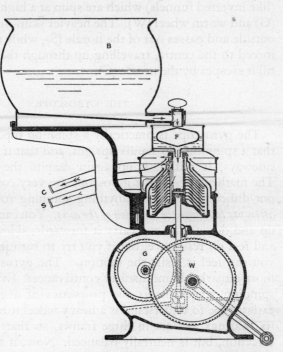

This is useful

Fig. 72.—The cream-separator. (From material kindly supplied by the Dairy Supply Co., Ltd.)

because it is precisely the largest molecules which cannot be measured in any other way. Svedberg's ultra-centrifuge rotates at such tremendous speeds that a particle in the liquid contained in its tube is forced outward with a hundred thousand times the force of gravity.

The cream separator is simply a centrifuge. Cream consists of the fat globules in the milk (Plate I). These are a little lighter than the whey in which they float, but since they are very small, they rise to the surface only slowly. In the cream separator, the milk flows from a bowl B into a float chamber which is prevented from overfilling by a float F which rises and blocks the entrance. The milk then goes to the underneath of a nest of metal cones (like inverted funnels) which are spun at a high speed by the gears (G) and worm wheel (W). The heavier skim-milk is thrown to the outside and passes out of the nozzle (S), while the lighter cream is forced to the centre, travelling up through the holes in the cones till it escapes by the nozzle (C).

THE GYROSCOPE

The gyroscope is practically a spinning top. Everyone knows that a spinning top stands upright, and that if you push it gently sideways, it will bob up again despite the force of gravity. The mathematics of the gyroscope are very complicated, but it is not difficult to see that anything spinning round an axis *resists attempts to change the direction of the axis*. You can move a gyroscope up and down: you can carry it forwards, sideways or backwards and feel no resistance, but if you try to turn it through an angle, you can feel it resist the motion. The gyroscope is one of the most remarkable mechanical contrivances. Every heavy rapidly-spinning wheel shows the properties of a gyroscope, but the easiest type to understand is a heavy wheel turning very easily on its bearings and set in three frames, so that it can turn in any direction, but is neutrally balanced. Now, if this heavy wheel is set spinning—the faster the better—it will be found that its axis tends to remain pointing in the same direction. Each point on

the wheel continues to move in
the same direction as far as the
rotation lets it and, if the axis were
to be shifted, every point would
have to change its direction of
motion. Now, the earth is turning
all the time: a stick stuck in the
ground at the equator points at six
a.m. in a direction at right angles
to the direction it had at midnight.
But the gyroscope keeps its axis
steady, though the earth moves;
so if the gyroscope is kept running
for six hours, its axis will have
apparently shifted from vertical to
horizontal. But it is the earth that

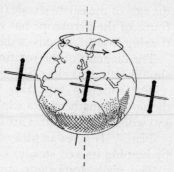

Fig. 73.—Showing how a gyroscope keeps its axis pointing in the same direction
and so appears to turn a
somersault as the earth
rotates.

has moved while the gyroscope stays still. An ingenious gyroscopic clock has been made to work in this way, and although
it is not possible to make it reliable because of friction at the
pivots, it shows most clearly that the earth does really rotate.
The instrument is just a gyroscope with its *axis* at right angles to

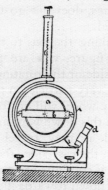
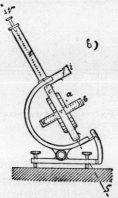

Fig. 74.—Two patterns of gyroscopic clock. The rotating portion (a) and the rings
(b) and (c) and the pointer (i) attached to them remain still while the frame and
scale (f) turn with the earth. (Courtesy of Messrs. Spon, Ltd., from Schilovsky's
The Gyroscope.)

the axis of the earth: a scale (i) and pointer (f) show how much the frame of the gyroscope has shifted, while the ring (c) attached to the ring (b) and the axis of the gyroscope has stayed still!

The diagram of the rotating earth and the stationary gyroscope should make this clear (Fig. 73).

The spinning top stays upright because it is a gyroscope, though the mathematics explaining why it rises from the ground and wobbles and waltzes are extremely complicated.

Plate VIII gives an idea of some of the things a gyroscope does by keeping its axis steady.

The really important applications of the gyroscope are the gyro-compass and the ship's stabiliser.

A very interesting property of the gyroscope, on which is based its use in the gyro-compass and ship's stabiliser, is its *precession*. The principle of this is that, if in spite of its resistance an attempt is made to push the axis of a gyroscope out of the straight, it does not tilt the way it is pushed but does so *at right angles to the direction of the push and at right angles to the axis*. If you push it west it goes north or south according to the way it is turning.

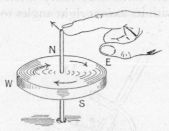

FIG. 75.—Precession in a gyroscope. When pushed to the west, it tips to the north.

It is not too difficult to understand why a gyroscope, unlike other things, does not go the way it is pushed.

By pushing the axis to the west as in the figure, you are pushing the west side of the rotating wheel down. Every particle on the west side of the wheel will be forced to go down: this downward motion is continued as they travel to the north: on the east side, the rim is tipped upward and this upward motion is continued to the south. The result is that the gyroscope tilts down towards the north and away from the south.

This tilting at right angles to a push is called precession. The Sperry ship-stabiliser described below is a gadget which gives a big gyroscope attached to a ship a push at the right moment to make it tilt the whole ship the opposite way to the rolling of the waves. The preventing of the rolling of ships is obviously a most valuable thing. A perfectly steady liner would attract all the people who were afraid of sea sickness! It is easy to see that if a huge gyroscope is stowed away in the hold with its axis either horizontal and across the ship or vertical, it will resist the attempts of the ship to roll sideways and so turn the axis of the gyroscope.

This has been tried and proved very successful in stopping rolling. It is not adopted, however, as much as might be expected, first, because the ship-owner is unwilling to sacrifice the space needed to stow it, and secondly on account of the expense of fitting it. The largest liners are so steady that it is generally felt that there is no need to stabilise them. The Sperry stabiliser has, at the bottom of the ship, a very large gyroscope with a vertical axis. A little gyroscope with a horizontal axis is also provided. Now, when the ship starts to roll to the right, it tips the small gyroscope and this "precesses" (tilts forwards) and so operates a switch which starts an electric motor going in one direction

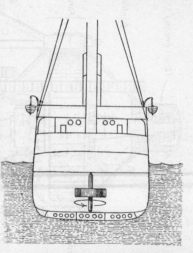

FIG. 76.—A large gyroscope in the hull of a ship would tend to prevent rolling and pitching. This simple arrangement has, however, many disadvantages: Fig. 77 illustrates a system in practical use.

or the other, according to which way the ship has rolled. The electric motor is geared to the casing of the big gyroscope and forcibly tips the whole thing backward. This has the effect of making the big gyroscope heel violently over to the left and so force the ship in the opposite direction to that in which it was driven by the waves. When the wave

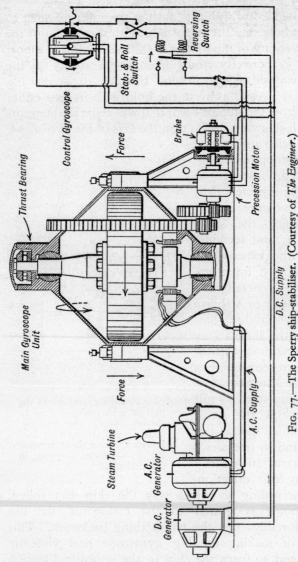

Fig. 77.—The Sperry ship-stabiliser. (Courtesy of *The Engineer*.)

Main Gyroscope Unit

Thrust Bearing

Control Gyroscope

Force

Brake

Precession Motor

Stab: & Roll Switch

Reversing Switch

D.C. Supply

A.C. Supply

Force

Steam Turbine

A.C. Generator

D.C. Generator

begins to recede, the little control gyroscope, being no longer forced sideways by the ship, is pulled back into position again by springs. This switches off the m o t o r and switches on a brake w h i c h stops the "precession" of the big gyroscope. As soon as the ship begins to roll the other way, the little control gyroscope feels it, closes the other switch, sets the motor going the other way and so forces the big gyroscope to go to the right, so stopping or at least decreasing the roll.

It is easy to see from Fig. 73 that the gyroscope, if its axis is pointed to a particular star (say the North Star) will remain pointing to it however the earth moves or the gyroscope moves. Suppose we start up a gyroscope with its axis pointing to the North Star. Then, wherever we take it on the earth it will point to the North Star and so will operate as a kind of compass.

A simple gyro-compass of this type would not be practically useful, for the mounting cannot be made perfectly true, and consequently minute forces act on the rotor and make it precess. Thus the best gyroscope that can be made shifts its axis by some 5 degrees a day.

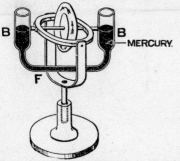

Moreover, near the poles its axis would be almost vertical. The Sperry gyro-compass is an arrangement by which an electrically driven gyroscope carrying a compass card automatically keeps itself horizontal as well as north-seeking and by making use of the effect of gravitation, forces the gyroscope to return to the north-south meridian even if it has been compelled to deviate slightly from it.

Fig. 78.—The essential parts of the gyro-compass.

It is essentially an electrically driven gyroscope to the axis of which are attached two vessels of mercury B, B, communicating by a fine tube F (Fig. 78). Suppose such an instrument is put down anywhere in the world with its axis and mercury tubes pointing in any given direction, say east and west. (Fig. 79 *a*.) As the earth rotates the axis of the gyroscope remains fixed in space and so relatively to the earth tips upward on the east side and downward on the west, as shown in Fig. 79 *b*. The mercury flows to the lower side which becomes heavier and so exerts a force (f) on the axis, tipping it downward on the west side. This, of course, makes it precess *southward* on the west side and this process continues (Fig. 79 *c*, *d*) until the axis and mercury tubes are in the north and south meridian. (Fig. 79 *e*.) This is what we require. It is easy to see that once this has happened any dis-

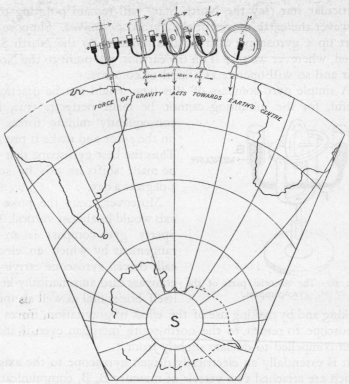

FORCE OF GRAVITY ACTS TOWARDS EARTH'S CENTRE

S

FIG. 79.—How gravitation and the earth's rotation make the gyro-compass
seek the N.S. meridian. (From material kindly supplied by the Sperry
Gyroscope Co., Ltd.)

placement of the axis from this meridian will make the gyro-
compass go through stages *a, b, c, d, e,* once more, and that
consequently the axis (and compass card attached thereto) will
oscillate about the north-south meridian, actually shifting back
and forth through about one degree every hour and a half.

The advantages of the gyro-compass will be best understood
when the disadvantages of the magnetic compass have been
discussed (p. 312 *ff*). The gyro-compass is a standard fitting for
the ships of the British Navy and for most large liners.

CHAPTER VIII

Simple Machines

WORK

THERE are a great many devices by means of which a force acting in one direction may be made to act in another direction and by which weak forces acting over a long distance may be converted into strong ones acting over a short distance and *vice versa*. These devices are levers, pulleys, screws, wedges, gears and so on, and they are all included under the title of "simple machines."

When a force acts on a thing without moving it (as for example, the earth pulls at the roof of a house without shifting it) no work is done. *Work* in the scientific sense is done *when a body, acted on by a force, moves*.

If a pound weight is lifted from the floor to the table, a distance of, say, three feet, then we have moved something for three feet against a force equal to a pound's weight. Clearly, the bigger the force the more is the work and the bigger the distance it moves, the more is the work. So, allowing ourselves a little mathematics,

$$W = d \times f$$

where W is the amount of work and d is the distance through which a force f moves.

Now this has been leading up to our simple machines—levers, pulleys, screws, jacks, and so on. The great thing to grasp about all machines is that you never get any more work out of them than you put into them. In all these machines you move one part with a certain force for a certain distance and the result is that another part moves with a different force for a different distance.

175

Think, for example, of a vice. You turn the handle with a force of say 10 lbs. weight for a whole turn. Your hand exerting a force of 10 lbs. weight has moved through, say, a foot. The jaws of the vice move as a result, let us say, $\frac{1}{8}$ of an inch. If there was no friction, you would get as much work out of the vice as you put in. The work you put in was 10 lbs. weight × 1 foot.

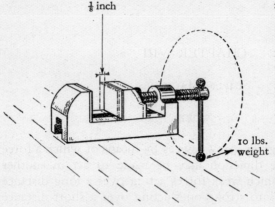

$\frac{1}{8}$ inch

10 lbs. weight

FIG. 80.—The vice: a simple machine.

The work you get out is the same, but as the jaws only move $\frac{1}{8}$ inch ($\frac{1}{96}$ foot) you can say that the work done by the jaws is ($\frac{1}{96}$ foot) × (the force they exert). So it follows that

$$(\tfrac{1}{96} \text{ foot}) \times (\text{the force of the jaws}) = 10 \text{ lbs. wt.} \times 1 \text{ foot}$$
$$\text{and the force of the jaws} = \frac{10 \text{ lbs. wt.} \times 1 \text{ foot}}{\tfrac{1}{96} \text{ foot}}$$
$$= 960 \text{ lbs. weight.}$$

So a vice gives a way of turning a force of 10 lbs. weight into a force of 960 lbs. weight, nearly half a ton! Actually, some of the work put in is used up in overcoming the friction of the screw, and so the final force is not as much as 960 lbs. weight.

The general rule for a machine is:—multiply the force you put in at one end by the distance it moves and divide by the distance through which the "other end" moves. The answer is the force the machine exerts. Something will have to be knocked off the answer to allow for friction.

LEVERS

The most ancient and famous machine is the Lever. We do not know who invented it: almost any savage who uses a stick as a tool must use it sometimes as a lever. The simplest lever is a plain bar or stick. One part, the fulcrum, rests against something to hold it still. Another part rests against the thing which is to be moved and a third part is pulled or pushed.

Fig. 81 shows the principle. A ten-foot crowbar is being used to lever up a log, a force of about half a ton being required to accomplish this. In each picture the lever rests on a stump—the fulcrum. In the lower picture it is easy to see that the log will move one-ninth of the distance through which the handle moves. The work done at each end is the same, so nine *times* the man's force is exerted through *one-ninth* of the distance.

In the upper picture the fulcrum is at the end of the lever, and you will see that the log moves one tenth of the distance through which the man lifts the handle, and is moved by ten times as great a force as the man puts into the handle.

Clearly, there is no reason why any weight, however huge, should not be lifted by a strong enough and long enough lever.

Suppose a man wants to lift a thousand-ton rock with a crowbar. The theory is very simple. Suppose a man can press on the end of a ten-foot lever with a force of a twentieth of a ton. Suppose he presses his

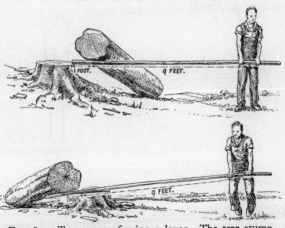

Fig. 81.—Two ways of using a lever. The tree stump is the fulcrum.

end of the lever down a foot. Then the work he does
is $\frac{1}{20}$th ton × 1 foot or $\frac{1}{20}$ foot-ton. The thousand-ton
rock exerts a force of 1,000 tons weight, so to move it a foot
would need 1,000 foot-tons. Consequently, our $\frac{1}{20}$ foot-ton would
only move it $\frac{1}{20000}$ foot or about $\frac{1}{1600}$th of an inch. The rock,
if it was to move this little distance would have to be only $\frac{1}{160}$th
of an inch from the fulcrum!

Now, in practice, there is very little use in lifting a rock $\frac{1}{1600}$th
of an inch: you cannot see it has moved, so even if you could do
it, it would be useless. Of course by having a lever 16,000 feet
(3 miles) long, and pressing it down 1,600 feet you could raise the
rock an inch: but then no one could handle such a lever which, if
strong enough, would weigh thousands of tons. Again, the
fulcrum takes the whole of the weight of the lever and its load,
and it would not be easy to get a
fulcrum which would not give under
a thousand ton pressure at a single
point! So a single lever is in practice
limited to increasing a force from
ten to perhaps fifty times.

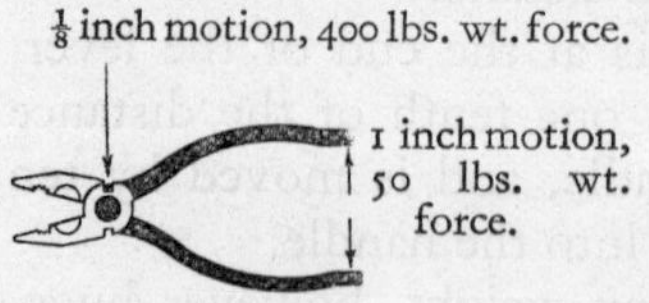

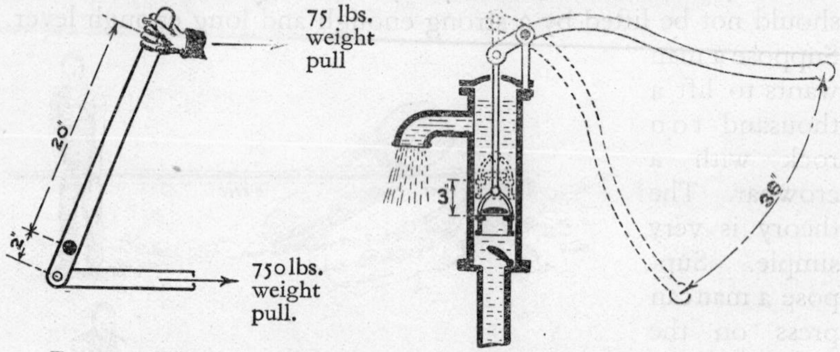

FIG. 82.—Wire cutters, brake-lever and common pump, in all of which
a lever increases the force exerted at the expense of the distance
through which it travels.

Levers are used in many pieces of machinery, some complicated, some simple. Weighing machines, wire-cutters, brakes,
pumps depend on the principle and almost all automatic

machinery depends on the use of levers.

Fig. 82 shows several kinds of simple machines depending on levers.

Another well-known type of lever is the lever jack commonly used in garages. Fig. 83 shows it in use. The long handle may be three feet long, and the short part only 6 inches. Consequently,

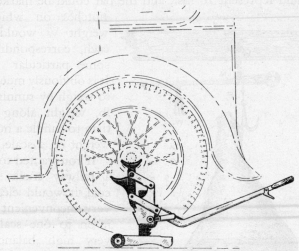

FIG. 83.—A car jack. The downward force applied to the handle, say 100 lbs. weight acting through 6 inches, gives an upward force, applied to the hub, of 600 lbs. over a distance of one inch.

it will lift with a force six times that with which the mechanic presses down the handle. A ratchet is provided so that the car once raised remains where it is put.

The opposite effect, that of converting a large force into a smaller one, is not so often needed; it is chiefly required in weighing machines. The simplest weighing-machine of this kind is the steelyard. Plate IX shows a very beautiful Roman one, some 2,000 years old, and Fig. 84 shows a modern one in use. The weight C is made so that when there is no load on the hook and the weight W is at the o mark (N) the two halves of the steelyard balance and hang level. Now suppose there is 100 lbs. of meat on the hook and the bearing of the hook is an inch from F. The "leverage" of this side is 100 lbs. × 1 inch. If the weight W is 10 lbs., then if it is moved 10 inches away from F its "leverage" will be 10 lbs. × 10 inches and the instrument will balance again. So it is easy to see that every inch the weight is moved along the bar would represent 10 lbs., and the bar could be marked with

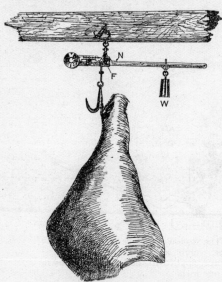

FIG. 84.—A butcher's steelyard.

notches on which the weight W would hang, each corresponding to some particular weight. It is obviously much easier to weigh by running a 10 lb. weight along a bar, than to handle a hundredweight on a scale.

If you wanted to weigh a railway truck full of coal, it would clearly be very inconvenient to run it on to one scale of a very high balance and put about 250 hundredweights on the other side. So, we use a lever or system of levers so arranged that a quite small weight at one end lifts a very large weight at the other end. Fig. 85 gives an idea of the principle of a weighbridge. The platform (shown as transparent) is supported on two big levers (L), linked together in the centre (J), and having their fulcrums (F) supported by the masonry of the pit over which the platform stands. Since the four places (S) where the platform rests on the levers are only about a twentieth of the way from the fulcrum, a weight of five tons on the platform gives a downward push of only about five cwt. on the link. The link at J pushes another lever (O), and

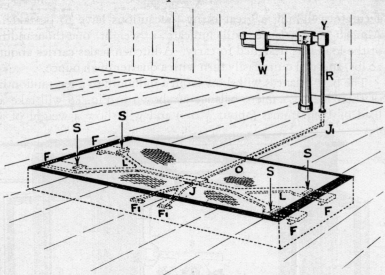

FIG. 85.—The principle of the weigh-bridge.

in the same way the five cwt. pull near the fulcrum is reduced to a pull of 25 lbs. or so at the other end. This other end (J¹) pulls on a rod (R) which is linked to the short end of a steelyard (Y), and so a weight (W) of a pound or two, slid up and down its beam, is enough to balance the whole five tons! These machines are very accurate. The best of them will show the difference if one good-sized lump of coal is taken out of a full railway truck!

The lever is sometimes used to increase speed. A typewriter key is an example. The key is moved down about ½ of an inch. The type face moves 4 inches in the same time. Consequently, it goes 8 times as fast and hits the ribbon a smart and rapid blow.

The ordinary weighing machine or balance is a sort of lever with two equal arms. All balances have a beam which turns on a knife-edge to make friction as small as possible, and two scalepans which hang also from knife-edges. Most balances have a pointer to show when they are swinging evenly. Everyone knows how to weigh on a balance, but when it comes to very accurate weighing a great many precautions have to be taken. Almost any balance will indicate a weight one-thousandth of the load it is designed to carry. A kitchen scales carries about 20 lbs. and will quite easily turn with a quarter of an ounce.

The best balances will show from a millionth to a ten-millionth of their load. A micro-balance as shown in Fig. 86 will take a load of 10 grammes (about $\frac{1}{3}$ oz.) and will show a weight of a

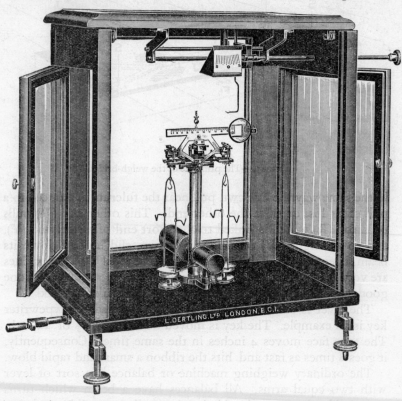

FIG. 86.—An extremely sensitive balance, as used for microchemical work. The weighing is performed by moving a minute loop of wire along the beam (as in the steelyard) by means of the milled head on the right. A magnified image of the pointer and a scale are projected on a small screen, and the distance the pointer is deflected from the vertical defines the weight to within a millionth of a gram. (Courtesy of Messrs. Oertling Ltd.)

thousandth of a milligramme (about the weight of a scrap of human hair, only as long as it is thick—$\frac{1}{250}$ inch). A bullion balance will weigh a man (50 kilogrammes) and easily show a difference of a tenth of a gramme, just about the weight of a drop of water. These accurate balances are simply ordinary scales accurately made. Their beams are made like girders so as to be stiff and light. Their knife-edges are made of the hard stone agate ground to a perfect V-shape and they turn on flat pieces of agate, set on the scale pans and beam supports. The weights are gold-plated so that they shall not tarnish and get heavier. A weight of a tenth of a milligramme would be far too tiny to handle so, after the weights have been got right to the nearest milligramme, a little wire loop is moved up and down the beam until the pointer swings just as many divisions to the right of the zero-mark as it does to the left.

If a balance is to show less than a ten-millionth of its load—say a hundred-millionth—great precautions are needed. The little air-currents in the case upset it, and so the air must be pumped out before the final weighing. The heat of one's face makes the beam expand unequally, so the pointer is observed through a telescope!

Weighing is, perhaps, the most exact kind of measurement we can make. Any ordinary laboratory has a balance which will measure a difference of one ten-thousandth of a gram in a load of a hundred grams. It is very much more difficult to measure a difference of a ten-thousandth of an inch in a length of a hundred inches and still more to measure a difference of a ten-thousandth of an hour ($\frac{1}{3}$ of a second) in a hundred hours.

PULLEYS

You have certainly watched weights being raised by pulleys, cranes and windlasses. Pulleys can be fitted together so that by pulling long lengths of rope through them, the pulleys are only raised a short distance. Fig. 87 shows two compound pulleys as these arrangements are called. The first of these has

ten ropes. If the end is pulled down ten feet, these ten ropes will be *altogether* 10 feet shorter, so each will be one foot shorter, and the pulley will rise a foot. Then, if the rope is pulled ten feet with a 50 lb. pull, the pulley (which moves, only one foot) will have a 500 lb. pull (50 × 10 = 500 × 1). This would be exactly true if no work were used up in moving the pulleys and bending the ropes. Actually, a good deal is wasted in this way.

Garages and engineering shops make much use of differential pulleys. They will lift an enormous weight and have the advantage that when the chain which goes over the pulleys is released the weight does not drop. The principle of the pulley is that an endless chain runs over three pulleys. The two top

FIG. 87.— Compound pulley.

ones, A and B, are made in a single piece and are of slightly different sizes, say, 20 inches and 19 inches circumference. Suppose by pulling on the chain the top pulleys are made to go round once: 20 inches of chain has been pulled off the big pulley and only 19 inches have been pulled on to the little pulley. So there is an inch less chain in the loop between them. Each of the two sides of this loop will be ½ an inch shorter, so by pulling in 20 inches of chain the lower pulley C rises half an inch. So, if no friction were present, the weight lifted would be 20 ÷ ½, forty times the pull on the chain. Actually, about half the force is wasted in this way, so that the force is increased only about twenty times. Still, this is enough to allow a man to lift a ton and if the top

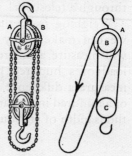

FIG. 88.—Differential pulley

pulleys are made more nearly the same size, still more advantage is gained.

SCREWS AND CRANKS

The screw is the ideal way of turning a little force into a big one, or a rapid motion into a slow one. It is clear that any screw moves forward by the width of one "thread" when the screw is given one turn.

A vice (Fig. 80) is the simplest example of the use of a screw to obtain pressure, and by putting a long enough handle on a vice, any force can be obtained. In actual practice, if a long handle is fitted to a vice and much force is used to screw it up, it simply breaks the iron base. Screw jacks are very commonly fitted to cars. To lift the back axle of a good sized car, a force of about half a ton weight is needed. The simplest sort of screw jack used by engineers has a strong screw which passes through a heavy base turned to fit it. The screw is turned by a rod fitting into a hole in the top of it. The platform at the top rotates, so that it does not move with the screw threads, which may be 4 to the inch. Then one turn of the handle raises the platform $\frac{1}{4}$ inch. To do this, the handle is turned through a complete circle: if the bar is 18 inches long, this will be about 57 inches: consequently, the force you put on the handle travels 57 inches while the car rises $\frac{1}{4}$ of an inch. Consequently, to lift

half a ton, a force of only $\dfrac{1}{2 \times 57 \times 4}$ tons or 5 lbs. weight would

be needed if there were no friction. The friction is fairly considerable, however, and two or three times the force calculated has to be used. The car-jack usually has an arrangement of cog-wheels by which it can be operated without getting under the machine. The principle is just the same.

The flypress is used for many jobs, such as stamping out bits of metal, bending them to shape between dies and so on.

FIG. 89.—The simplest type of screw-jack.

It is a screw with a heavy lever with a big iron ball on it. The ball is sent flying round: when the die touches the metal, it is suddenly stopped in a fraction of a second.

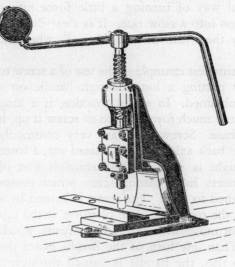

A force is measured by multiplying the weight acted on by the acceleration or deceleration produced by it. Suppose the iron ball weighs 20 lbs. and is spun at 5 feet a second and stopped in one inch by the die biting on the metal. This means that it is decelerated at the rate of 150 ft. per second. The force needed to do this is about 45 lbs. weight. The screw

FIG. 90.—The flypress.

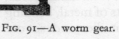

FIG. 91—A worm gear.

moves down, say, one inch for each turn (60 inches) that the ball makes, so the force is magnified 60 times and the dies squeeze the metal with a pressure of 45 × 60, or 2,700 lbs. (about one and an eighth tons). Again, here some of this force will be wasted on friction.

Finally, the "worm-drive" is a very useful way of increasing power and decreasing speed. It is a screw which fits into slanting cogs on a gear-wheel (Fig. 91). Clearly, each turn of the screw advances the wheel by a distance equal to the pitch of the thread. If the wheel is 90″ in circumference and the threads of the screw are 2″ apart, it will go 45 times slower and exert 45 times the turning force of the driving shaft.

An electric motor runs best when going fast, turning at 500— 4,000 revolutions per minute. If it drives a worm-gear, it is easy to get great power and a speed of only a few dozen turns a minute. Fig. 91 shows a worm-drive of this kind. Fig. 62, illustrating the speedometer, shows another. The worm gear is rarely used to increase speed. It can only be used in this way if the threads are very far apart. An example is shown in Fig. 72.

Several other less important devices can be used to magnify power. The wedge is a well-known one—not much used in machinery because it wastes a great deal of work in friction. Suppose a wedge is one inch thick at a distance of six inches from its point: then it separates two objects by one inch for every six inches it is driven in; so that (friction excluded) it would give six times as much outward force as we put downward force upon it. Actually, most of this is used up in friction, and indeed, if the friction between the wedge and the thing it opens were not so great, it would be forced out again.

The machines we have dealt with have mostly been arrangements by which a straight pull or push is turned into a stronger (or weaker) straight pull or push. Actually, most modern machinery is driven by power supplied as *rotation*, i.e., by revolving shafts, pulleys or belts. Accordingly, very many devices have been made by means of which rotation can be made slow or quick, powerful or weak.

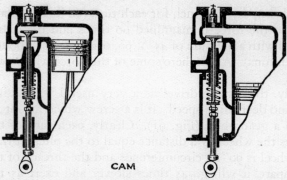

CAM

FIG. 92.—A cam turning the rotary movement of a shaft into the up and down motion of a valve.

First, let us look at ways in which circular motion (as of a wheel) can be turned into reciprocating or back and forth motion. The cam and eccentric are the simplest of these. A very good example is the arrangement which opens and shuts the valves of a car. The cam revolves with the shaft and lifts and drops the tappet rod as it turns. An eccentric is a similar device. It is just a solid wheel with its axle *not* at the centre. This wheel fits smoothly in a ring and Fig. 93 shows how it moves the ring, and anything attached to it up and down.

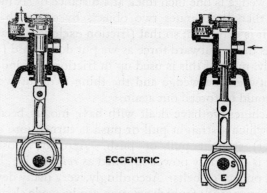

ECCENTRIC

FIG. 93.—An eccentric E turning the rotary movement of the shaft S into the reciprocating movement of a piston.

The cam and eccentric give rather a small motion and waste a good deal of work as friction, and the standard engineering way of changing a reciprocating motion into a circular one and vice-versa is the connecting rod and crank. The essential parts

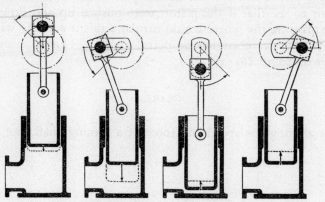

Fig. 94.—The rotating movement of a shaft is here converted into the up and down motion of a piston.

are shown in Fig. 94 where a rotating shaft is driving the piston of a pump. The principle will be clear enough. It should be noticed, however, that the piston is moving rapidly in the middle of the strokes (II and IV,) and is stationary at the top and bottom (I and III). Consequently, the driving engine feels a jerky resistance, and if it is strong enough to pull the piston past the positions II and IV, it will be wasting power at I and III. It is usual, then, to connect several pumps to the same shaft as in Fig. 95. In this case, one pump is always in the middle of its stroke so that the wheel pulls steadily all the while. The same principle is applied in the internal combustion engine (p. 269).

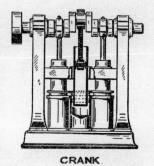

CRANK

Fig. 95.—Three pumps (the middle one in section) driven from a single crankshaft.

If only one pump is to be driven, a heavy flywheel is usually fitted. At the top and bottom of the stroke when the engine has no pulling to do it does useful work in speeding up the flywheel a little, and the flywheel in its turn helps the engine to push the piston through the middle part of the stroke. It is not difficult to see that if the piston were pushed up and down by steam pressure the wheel would turn and this is actually what is done in the steam engine or petrol engine. This is discussed further on pages 261–275.

GEARS

For altering the speed and force of a turning shaft, the chief

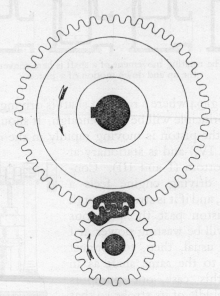

Fig. 96.—The small wheel has 20 teeth and the large one 50 teeth. The bigger one will have $\frac{2}{5}$ of the speed and $\frac{5}{2}$ of the power of the small one.

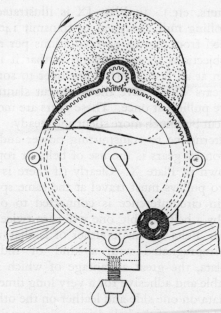

FIG. 97.—Increase of speed by gearing
in a grinding wheel.

means used are gearwheels. If two cogwheels are in mesh as in Fig. 96 and one has, say, 20 teeth and the other 50 teeth, then the bigger one will run at $\frac{2}{5}$ of the speed and will exert $\frac{5}{2}$, i.e., $2\frac{1}{2}$ times the power. Almost every machine uses gearwheels. A grinding-wheel (Fig. 97) gives a good example. If you turn the handle once the wheel turns 6 times. It only turns with $\frac{1}{6}$ of the power, as you can see if you hold the wheel when it is still with one hand and press the handle with the other. You need much more force to turn the handle than to stop the wheel turning.

Gearing down to get increased power or decreased speed is used in pumps; in motor cars, which we will talk of later; in liners driven by turbines; in rolling mills where ingots of iron are rolled into rails, and on a far smaller scale in gas-meters and all such counting machinery (mile-recorders for cars, revolution counters, etc.). In Plate IX is illustrated the helical gearing of a rolling mill, designed to transmit 140 h.p. and to reduce the speed from 720 to 34 revolutions per minute. One of the chief objections to cog-gearing is that it is intolerably noisy when run at all fast. This is got over to some extent by using helical gears which have the teeth cut slantingly so that several teeth are pulling at once. These gears are more expensive and difficult to cut but much more silent and steady.

The chief alternative to transmitting power and altering the speed of rotation by gears is the use of belts or ropes. The use of belts is shown in Plate X. Clearly (if there is no slip) the rims of the two pulleys must travel at the same speed. So, if a pulley 5 feet in circumference is connected to one 2 feet in circumference by a belt, the big one will turn twice for the little one's five times. Belts are made either of leather or of strong cotton duck, impregnated with a kind of indiarubber-like gum called balata, the great advantage of which is that it remains soft, pliable and adhesive for a very long time. Sometimes the belt has balata on one side and leather on the other.

The great advantage of the belt drive is that any fitter can in an hour or two arrange a belt by which one machine can drive another, whereas gearing would have to be specially built. Moreover, a belt can easily be inclined at almost any angle, and a mere crossing of the belt serves to reverse the drive.

Belts are most useful for the smaller engineering jobs. The maximum power which a belt will transmit is limited. Thus, a very good 6-ply belt, a foot wide, running at 3,000 feet a minute, will transmit 114 h.p. It will be seen that a belt drive to transmit, say, 20,000 h.p. would be very unwieldy.

Where very large quantities of power have to be transmitted, a rope drive is often used. The engine which produces the power drives a drum cut into grooves. In each of these runs a rope passing over a similar drum elsewhere in the building.

The advantage of a rope drive over a belt drive is that the rope obtains a much better grip of the pulley, whilst a rope drive is much less costly than a chain drive, and is not so

PLATE IX

A Roman steelyard. Note the two fulcra. If it is suspended by the lower one, the same movable weight will balance a heavier load. (By courtesy of the British Museum.)

Double helical gearing designed to transmit 140 h.p. and reduce speed from 720 r.p.m. to 34 r.p.m. (By courtesy of Messrs. Crofts [Engineers], Ltd., Bradford.)

PLATE X

A miner cutting coal in a cramped position.
(By courtesy of Messrs. Fox Photos, Ltd.,
London.)

Oil-wells.
(By courtesy of the Oil Well
Supply Company.)

The use of belts for transmitting power.
(By courtesy of The Dunlop Rubber Company.)

A Pelton wheel. Note the
form of the buckets.
(By courtesy of the English
Electric Company, Stafford.)

FIG. 98.—Rope-drive in a large cotton mill. (After photograph supplied by Messrs. Thomas Hart, Ltd.)

limited in length; for if the pulleys are large enough a rope drive may be as long as 80 or 90 feet between shaft centres, or on the other hand the pulleys may be almost touching each other. Speeds may be from a few hundred feet per minute to 5,000 feet per minute.

The pulleys have to be large, as small pulleys quickly break up ropes; for pulleys of say 2 feet diameter, 1 inch diameter ropes are suitable, and so on up to 6 feet diameter, which is the minimum for 2 inch diameter ropes.

Ropes are generally made from cotton (hemp is not very suitable for power transmission) and are designed to have a low rate of stretch and to be pliable.

The main drives in a large cotton mill are shown in Fig. 98. The engine is 1,750 h.p., and the rope speed about 4,800 feet per minute; the ropes used are cotton driving ropes made by Messrs. Thomas Hart, Ltd., of Blackburn.

VARIABLE GEARS

There are several purposes for which it is required to vary the speed of the machine driven without varying the speed of the engine. A motor-car engine gives very poor power when running slowly; on the other hand it cannot push a car up a steep hill

7

quickly, so it is desirable on hills to be able to make the driving
wheels go at a slower speed with greater power. Consequently,
all cars have some arrangement by which different gear-wheels
can be enmeshed at "low gear" and "high gear." Figs. 99 and 100
shows a rather simple car gear-box in the positions of first speed,
second speed, third speed and top gear.

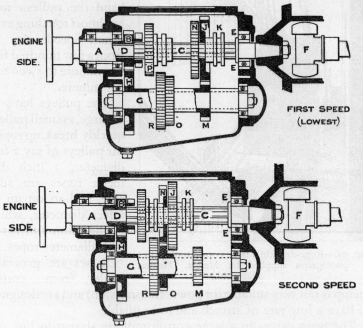

FIG. 99.—Simple four-speed gears. First and second speeds.

The engine turns the mainshaft A with gear-wheel B upon it.
Inside this gear-wheel, but not attached to it, is a shaft C which
drives the car. This has "feathers" cut on it (see top wheel in
Fig. 101, which shows the shaft C in section) so that the various
gear-wheels N, J, P, etc., can be slid along it by the gear lever
which pulls on the notches K, etc. First, then, realise that the
engine *always* turns the wheel B, and this always meshes with
the wheel H and so turns the layshaft G. But since the shaft C

only fits into a bearing in the shaft A, it does not turn round
unless it is in some other way connected to shaft A. When the car
is in "neutral," gear wheel B is going round. It is turning the
layshaft G, but in the neutral position none of the gear wheels
R, O, M is in mesh with the gear wheels P, N or J, and accordingly nothing happens.

Now, we are going to get into first speed (Fig. 99, top). The
lever pulls the wheel J till it meshes with the gear-wheel M.
Now gear-wheel B has, say, 20 teeth and gear-wheel H 40, so
one turn of B means ½ a turn of H. Gear-wheel M meshes with
gear-wheel J. J has twice as many teeth as M, so one ½ turn of M
means ¼ turn of J. Thus, one turn of the engine gives only a
quarter turn of the shaft. The ratio is then 1 : 4 (this will be
further reduced about five times in the back axle). Now we change
from first to second. The lever is pulled back to neutral. This
unmeshes the wheels J and M and puts the box back as before.
Next we push the lever into third speed notch. This action forces

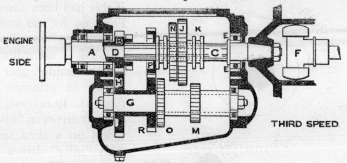

FIG. 99a.—Simple four-speed gears. Third speed.

wheel N to mesh with wheel O. B (20 teeth) drives H (40 teeth)
which goes at the same speed as O (25 teeth), which drives N (28
teeth): the reduction is consequently 1:2.36. Now, we go into
third. Pull the lever back to neutral, so unmeshing N and O.
Now push the level into the second notch. This puts wheel P in
mesh with wheel R. Since R has 28 teeth and P 21 teeth, it is easy
to see that the reduction is now only 1:1.5.

Finally, we go into top gear. P and R are unmeshed by pulling

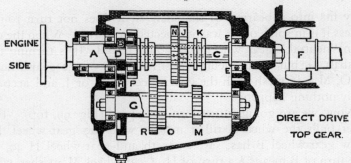

ENGINE SIDE

DIRECT DRIVE
TOP GEAR.

Fig. 100.—Simple four-speed gears. Top speed.

the lever to neutral (Fig. 1), and then the lever is pulled to the top position. This forces projections on the gear-wheel B to enter holes cut in the gear-wheel P so that B and P go round as one wheel. But as P is on the shaft C this shaft will go round with it and the engine and tailshaft revolve at the same pace!

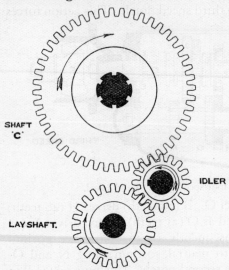

SHAFT 'C'

IDLER

LAYSHAFT.

REVERSE GEAR.

Fig. 101.—Principle of reverse gear. (Remember that the layshaft turns the opposite way to the engine.)

What about reverse? If this had been shown, Figs. 99 to 100 would have been too complicated: accordingly, the reversing gear is shown in principle in Fig. 101. In reverse, the layshaft drives an "idler" wheel on a *third* shaft. This "idler" drives the shaft C. The sizes of these wheels are so proportioned that reverse shall be a very low gear, the reduction being about 1:5. It is important to remember that the differential gear (p. 354) in the back axle makes the driving wheels turn some 5 times slower than the tail-shaft, so our true reduction of speed would be roughly 1:20, 1:12, 1:7½, 1:5 and 1:25 in first, second, third, top, and reverse gears respectively.

Gear boxes are the worst things about cars. They make them noisy and the most difficult thing in driving is to get the engine and car going at the right relative speeds so as to be able to change gear noiselessly. The self-changing gears usually have the sun-and-planet-wheel gearing where all the gear-wheels are in mesh all the time. The gear depends on which wheel is being driven, and which is driving. Space forbids a full explanation: but it is clear that if the gears are always in mesh it is impossible to make the hideous crashing noises which are heard when the novice tries to enmesh two gear-wheels moving at very different speeds.

No one has yet found a satisfactory substitute for the car gear box. The gears of a car may be noisy and difficult to handle but they give very little trouble. Any complicated arrangement which took their place would probably be an extra source of un-reliability and expense—at least until experience had been gained by the manufacturer at the expense of the driver.

HYDRAULIC MACHINES

All the machines we have talked about are made entirely of solids. Other important engineering devices such as the hydraulic press depend on the behaviour of liquids.

The first thing (from the engineer's point of view) to realise about liquids and gases is that they transmit pressure evenly in all directions. If you press a solid, it transmits your pressure in one direction, but a liquid or gas does so in every direction equally. Each molecule jostles its neighbour freely and tries to escape in any and every direction from the pressure you apply. Fig. 102 shows the idea. The solid column transmits the pressure in only one direction; the liquid, in all directions.

In order to force a liquid to move from one place to another against a force—such as gravity—we use pumps, and all pumps except the centrifugal and axial flow types depend upon valves. A valve is an arrangement which lets liquid through

FIG. 102.—A solid transmits a force applied to it in one direction only: a liquid does so in every direction equally.

in one direction but not in the other. Figs. 103, 104 show two kinds of valves. Those in Fig. 103 are poppet valves, those in Fig. 104 are flap valves.

The simplest of pumps is the force pump, and Fig. 103 shows

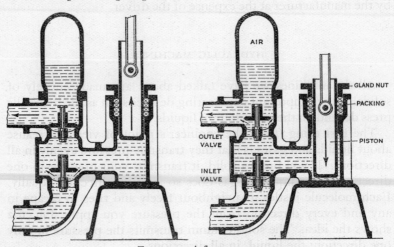

FIG. 103.—A force pump.

the kind of force pump that is used for most small pumping jobs. A force pump will raise water to a very great height: the only limits being the power that can be put on the piston and the difficulty of preventing pipes from leaking under a head of, say, a thousand feet of water. The pump has a cylinder with a piston which is made to fit perfectly by packing which is forced against it by a "gland nut." When the piston is drawn up, it does not leave an empty space—a vacuum—for the pressure of the air on the water outside makes it drive the inlet valve open and so fill the pump-barrel. When the piston is forced down, the piston presses on the water, which forces the inlet valve to shut and the outlet valve to open, and the water is forced out. As this pump would make the water flow in jerks, an air vessel is often included in the exit pipe. The water rushing out on the exit stroke compresses the air and enters the vessel: while the inlet stroke is going on, the air expands and forces the water out again. In this way there is a more continuous flow and no violent changes of pressure. The force pump is much the commonest type. It is used for almost all pumping except where large volumes of water or dirty water are concerned.

The force pump (and indeed any other pump) must not be more than 32 feet above the water it is to pump, because it depends on the pressure of the air to force the water into its cylinders. The pressure of the air is only enough to raise water 32 feet. This is an awkward thing where water has to be obtained from a deep well, or to be pumped from the bottom of a deep mineshaft. The pumps have to be at the bottom of the shaft or well, not more than 30 feet (and best not more than 20 feet) above the water. If the well or shaft is narrow, it may be difficult to get at them, so the cylinder is put at the bottom of the well, and a very long piston rod reaches to the surface where the driving machinery is arranged. A heavy counterweight is made to balance the heavy rod.

For jobs where water has to be raised only a few feet, the ordinary garden or lift pump is used. This, like the force pump, has an inlet valve at the bottom; but the other valve is in the piston (Fig. 82). It operates on exactly the same principle as the diaphragm pump (Fig. 104) which is a lift-pump with a leather disc instead of a piston. When the disc is raised (2) water enters: when it is forced down (1) the water opens the valve in the diaphragm and passes to the other side. On the third stroke (2) the water is lifted out by the exit pipe and new water enters from

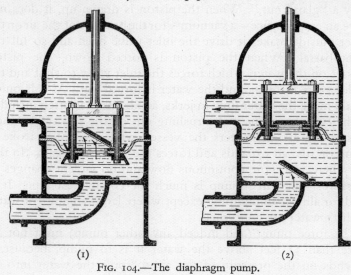

FIG. 104.—The diaphragm pump.

below. The diaphragm pump has the advantage that it can pump muddy or dirty water. Mud gets between the piston and cylinder of an ordinary pump and either jams it or very soon wears it out. The diaphragm pump has nothing that mud can damage. When it comes to pumping really dirty water which may have pebbles, leaves, paper and so on in it, no pump with valves is much use, because the solids prevent the valves from closing. The best pump in this case is the centrifugal pump or the axial flow pump, and one of these is almost always used where large volumes of liquid have to be handled.

The principle of the centrifugal pump is simply that of setting the water spinning at a high speed. The water therefore flies

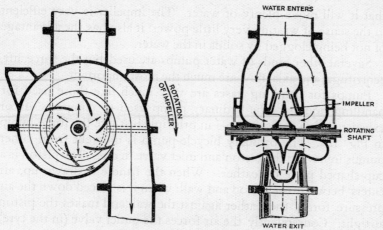

FIG. 105.—Centrifugal pump.

outward (just as it does when you twirl a mop), and the centrifugal force drives it out of the exit pipe. In the simplest pump, the water is admitted to the centre of a ring of vanes (the impeller) which turns at the rate of, say, 25 times a second. The water is set whirling by these, is driven outward and escapes by the discharge pipe. Sometimes a ring of fixed vanes is set round the impeller to guide the water towards the exit pipe: if these are not used a certain amount of energy is wasted by the water being flung against the sides of the pump.

The axial-flow pump is shown in Fig. 106. It is simply a ship's propeller set in a tube. The propeller drives the water up, and if one reflects that a propeller can push a liner, it is clear

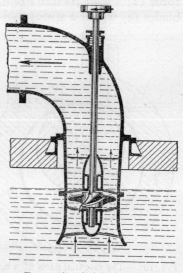

FIG. 106.—Axial-flow pump.

that it will move plenty of water. The impeller is very efficient in the sense of wasting very little power: it also has the advantage of not being clogged by solids in the water.

Several other kinds of water pumps are used, but the force, lift, centrifugal and axial flow are much the most important.

Pumps for handling gases are very much like those used for handling liquids. The ordinary pump used to compress air or exhaust air is a force-pump—in principle just like the force-pump in Fig. 103. The ordinary bicycle-pump is different from other pumps in having the piston and inlet valve in one. The piston is a cup-shaped piece of leather. When the handle is drawn up, air enters between the piston and wall: when it is forced down the air pressure forces the leather against the wall and makes the piston airtight. Consequently the air forces the outlet valve (in the tyre) open and the air enters the tube.

The air-pumps, used to get the air out of a vessel as completely as possible and leave a vacuum, are of two chief types. The first are oil-sealed rotary pumps. A casing (1) contains a shaft or rotor (2) which travels round and carries with it two movable blades (3) which a spring holds against the casing. It is easy to see that air must be entering from pipe (4) all the time and being pushed out into pipe (5). Air can never get back from pipe (5) to pipe (4) because the shaft touches the casing. The efficacy of the device depends first on a very accurate fit of the blades and rotor to the casing, and secondly on there being no possibility of air leaking in along the bearings of the shaft. To ensure this the casing is wholly immersed in oil.

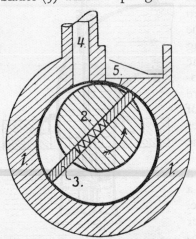

Fig. 107.—The essential parts of a rotary air pump. (Courtesy of Messrs. W. Edwards & Co.)

These pumps are used for

removing the air from thermos flasks, electric light bulbs, wireless valves, X-ray tubes, etc.

A single stage rotary oil-sealed air pump in good working order will remove all but three-millionths of the air from a vessel. No pump, however, can make a perfect vacuum. The best that has been done is to remove all but a ten thousand millionth of the air. But there are such a vast number of molecules in a small amount of air that a vessel the size of a wine bottle, when evacuated to this extent, would still contain ten million million molecules.

A pump which is still simpler and gives the most perfect vacuum of any is the mercury diffusion pump, which has no moving parts at all. A diagram is shown in Fig. 108. The actual apparatus is usually made of glass. Some mercury is boiled in S and the stream of mercury vapour, which at a low pressure has a very big volume, rushes out through past the baffle *e*. The mercury atoms hit the air molecules from the tube H which leads to the vessel to be exhausted and knock them on to the exit tube V. The mercury vapour is very easily condensed, so that as it passes over the part of the tube which is cooled by the water-jacket K, the mercury is all made to condense and to run back into the boiling tube.

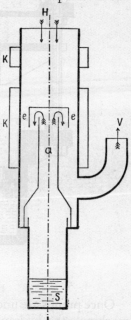

There are two ways of getting rid of the last traces of air from an evacuated vessel.

The first is used in wireless valves. A little of some substance such as magnesium, which can combine with air and forms a solid, is introduced into the valve and then heated. The magnesium turns all but a trace of the air into solid magnesium oxide and nitride.

Another method is to have a glass

FIG. 108.—Diffusion pump. (Courtesy of Messrs. W. Edwards & Co.)

tube containing a little hard charcoal (best made from coconut shell) attached to the vessel from which the air is to be removed. The tube is cooled with liquid air, whereupon the charcoal in some rather odd way attracts to itself almost all the gas left in the vessel. The tube is then softened by a flame and sealed off to remove the charcoal and the gas with it.

The chief obstacle to obtaining a perfect vacuum is the tendency of every solid surface to attract to itself a very thin layer of gas (about one molecule thick), which is held close to the surface atoms of the solid by their quite powerful attractions. These films remain attached to the vessel and may afterwards release some of the gas and diminish the vacuum.

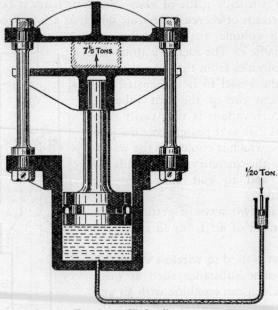

FIG. 109.—Hydraulic press.

Once pumps are understood, we can study that most interesting machine—the hydraulic press. It depends on the fact that any fluid has the same pressure throughout (barring minor factors such as depth, etc.). If you put a pressure of 1 lb. on a square inch of the liquid, the liquid will press on every bit of the vessel that contains it with an extra force of 1 lb. per square inch.

Let us take for example the sort of hydraulic press which is used to forge steel—to compress great steel ingots into the shapes we require. The principle is shown in Fig. 109. A little pump forces, say, a cubic foot of water into a big cylinder. Now if the cross section of the cylinder of the little pump is a square inch and there are 1728 cubic inches in a cubic foot, clearly it will have to move 1728 inches (i.e., make 1728 one-inch strokes) to put a cubic foot of water into the big cylinder. The big piston has a cross section of a square foot. So, to make room for a cubic foot of water, it moves up a foot. Now you will get (barring friction) as much work out as you put in, so if the little piston is pushed in with a force of a hundredweight ($\frac{1}{20}$ ton) and it moves 1728 inches (144 feet) the work done is $\frac{144}{20}$ foot-tons. This is the same work as is done when a force of $\frac{144}{20}$ tons weight, i.e. seven and a fifth tons' weight moves a foot.

But the big piston *does* move a foot and *does* do $\frac{144}{20}$ foot-tons work. So it exerts a force of *seven and a fifth tons*. This gives a splendid way of turning a little force into a big one. The chief points in making such a press is that there should be no leakage and not too much friction.

Both these troubles are overcome by fitting a U-shaped leather collar between the big piston and cylinder (Fig. 109): the greater the water pressure, the more firmly is the collar forced against the cylinder and the piston.

Fig. 110 shows the use of such a press in squeezing oil out of nuts such as "monkey-nuts." The nuts are contained in per-forated boxes B, B, which telescope into each other. Water is forced from the pump F into the casing L and drives the ram R upward, squeezing the nuts with a pressure of many tons. Strong steel pillars P hold the casing to the top: it must be remembered that the whole pressure put on the nuts is taken by these pillars.

The hydraulic jack used for lifting motor cars is on just the same principle. A tiny pump forces oil into a much wider cylinder and so drives the ram up carrying the car with it.

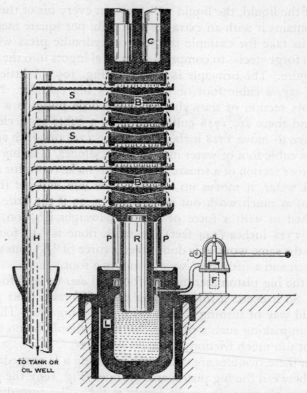

FIG. 110.—Use of hydraulic press to squeeze oil out of nuts.

Another rather important machine using liquids is the fluid flywheel fitted to several makes of car. The advantage of it is that the engine can turn slowly, "tick over," without moving the car, while, as soon as the engine speeds up, the car is driven too. The simplest way to think of it is as a paddle-wheel driving oil round and round, while immediately surrounding it is a turbine driven by the oil. The "turbine" part is driven only when the oil is circulating rapidly.

CHAPTER IX

POWER

ENERGY

WORK, we have seen, is measured by the distance over which a force is exerted. Energy is a capacity for doing work. There is, rightly, a great deal of talk about energy both in physics and in engineering and it is really necessary to understand what it means.

Suppose there is a candle on a table in front of you. You ask me, "How much energy has that candle?" and the question can only be answered if you tell me what you are going to do to it. If it weighs 2 ounces and falls three feet to the floor, it can do $\frac{3}{8}$ foot-lb. weight of work, but if it fell out of the window, it might do a great deal more. The candle is at rest, relative to the other things in the room, and so relatively to them has no "kinetic energy" of motion. But relative to, say, a loose meteorite floating about in space, it has a tremendous speed (the speed of the earth) and so could give a most violent blow to the meteorite or anything on it, if a collision could be staged: so, relative to the meteorite, it has enormous kinetic energy. It also has heat energy. It cannot do any work, however, with it, for it is no hotter than the other things in the room, and heat will not flow from it to them. On the other hand, if you dropped it into liquid air, the air would boil violently and the gaseous air produced could do work, say, by driving an engine. If the candle is lighted, it will produce a good deal of heat energy, though even here we do not know how much till we have settled whether it is going to burn with a smoking flame or a clear one. In fact, no one can say how much energy a *thing* has, but they can say as a rule how much energy a *process* has. Thus they can say that dropping a 2 oz. candle to the floor 3 feet lower produces 5,100,000,ergs (p. 210) of energy, that burning it in such a way that it changes to carbon dioxide and water only, produces 23,800,000,000,000 ergs and so on.

This fundamental energy appears in several different forms. In the first place, all energy is either potential energy or kinetic energy.

Potential energy is the capacity for doing work which a thing has on account of its *position*. Kinetic energy is the energy a thing has as a result of its *motion*.

The energy of the water in a tank at the top of a house is potential energy. The same water rushing from a tap below has less potential energy, for some of its potential energy has changed into energy of motion—kinetic energy.

Kinetic energy is energy of motion. A thing with kinetic energy can do work by setting other things moving faster and itself being slowed down. The energy of a gale or a jet of water or a rotating flywheel is kinetic.

Heat energy is really kinetic energy. A hot thing has rapidly moving atoms: by slowing these down (i.e. cooling) it can speed other slower (cooler) atoms up and so do work.

Electrical energy may be potential (as when two charged bodies at a distance attract or repel each other). It can also be kinetic. When a charge of electricity moves (as along a wire) it has energy in virtue of this motion. This is what we call magnetic energy.

Radiation—light, radiant heat, X-rays, radio and so forth— is also a form of energy, and it is, as we shall see in Chapter XV, a rapid alternation of electrical kinetic energy changing into electrical potential energy and back again billions of times per second.

Chemical energy is really electrical potential energy, for it is the energy that molecules can produce by rearranging their atoms, which are made up of electrical charges. If the explosive liquid, nitroglycerine, is struck with a hammer, the atoms in it share up their electrons in another way with the result that it changes into half a dozen different gases and at the same time produces enough energy to cause a violent and destructive explosion. A ton of coal and 12,400 cubic yards of air, if the coal is lighted, give out 34,000,000 B.Th.U. of heat energy. We say, then, that the coal and air before they are lighted have 34,000,000 B.Th.U. or, what is the same thing, 8,568,000,000 calories of chemical energy. It is in this sense that we speak of our food as providing so many calories of energy.

Finally, mass is energy. Matter can be destroyed (in radioactive charges and probably in the stars) and becomes one of the other forms of energy, e.g., radiation. So we can reasonably think of all energy as matter or all matter as energy. The theory of relativity and actual experiments indicate that every gram of matter is equivalent to 9×10^{20} ergs of energy.

Energy can never be destroyed. It can be turned into other kinds of energy—sometimes useless for practical purposes—but it is never destroyed or changed into nothing. This statement we call The Law of Conservation of Energy.

Suppose a brick is dropped from the ceiling on to the floor. Clearly the brick has less energy on the floor. It can do less work. Where has this energy gone? The answer is that the ordered motion of the molecules downward was changed by the impact into a disorderly motion in every direction. The brick and the floor it hits become a little *hotter*. The *potential* energy of the brick at ceiling level changed into *kinetic* energy of the falling brick, which on hitting the floor became *heat* energy of the brick and floor. If you wish to prove that kinetic energy can be changed to heat energy, hammer a nail on an anvil as violently and as quickly as you can. It will soon become too hot to touch. A blacksmith can hammer a horseshoe red-hot! Every machine turns a good deal of work into heat whether it is intended to or not. All the energy which is "wasted" in overcoming friction is turned into heat.

It is known exactly how much kinetic energy is needed to

produce a certain amount of heat. Thus the energy furnished by a ten-horse-power engine working for an hour will raise about 14 gallons of water from the freezing point to the boiling point. We can always turn this amount of kinetic energy into heat, but unfortunately we cannot turn this quantity of heat into the same amount of kinetic energy.

The turning of electrical energy into heat and radiant energy in a glow-lamp, the turning of chemical energy into heat energy in a candle, are familiar enough: in all these cases simple rules tell us what quantity of one kind of energy we get from a given amount of another.

Thus, all the following quantities of energy are the same and can be changed into each other.

1.000 *calories of heat energy* (a calorie[1] is the amount of heat that will make a cubic centimetre of water one degree (C.) hotter);

4.18 *joules of electrical energy* (a joule is the amount of energy of a current of one ampere at a potential difference of one volt flowing for one second);

41,800,000 *ergs of kinetic energy* (an erg is the amount of energy needed to make a gram weight move one centimetre per second faster than it moved in the second before);

4.65×10^{-14} *grams of mass*. Mass, we have seen, is equivalent to energy, and under certain conditions matter can be converted into such forms of energy as heat. This occurs, we believe, in the sun and stars.

Chemical energy is reckoned in calories, i.e., the quantity of heat it can be turned into.

For practical purposes we usually reckon energy as horse-power-hours. A horse-power-hour is (as you would expect) the amount of energy an engine of one horse-power produces when it works for an hour. Another important measure of energy is the Board of Trade Unit used for electricity. One horse-power-hour = .746 (nearly ¾) of a Board of Trade Unit. This is 1000

---

[1] A Calorie, with a capital letter, is 1,000 calories with a small letter.

A British Thermal Unit is the amount of heat which will make 1 lb. of water 1° F hotter. It is 252 calories.

watts, a watt being the energy furnished by a current of 1 ampere at a potential of 1 volt, flowing for 1 second.

Power is not the same thing as energy. Energy is the capacity for doing work, power is the rate of doing work. The usual unit of power is a horse-power, which was originally invented by James Watt as a way of defining how powerful his engines were. A horse-power is rather more than an average horse can do, at least for a long period of steady work. It is the amount of power needed to raise 33,000 pounds 1 foot in one minute; or 550 lbs. 1 foot in one second. It would take the same amount of energy to raise 550 lbs. through a foot in a second or in an hour; but it takes 3600 times as much power to raise it in the former time.

It is interesting to test one's own horse-power, and the easiest way (not suitable for anyone with a weak heart) is running upstairs. If you can run up a flight of stairs in 5 seconds and you weigh a hundred lbs., and the top of the stairs is 15 feet above the bottom, you are lifting 100 lbs. 15 feet in 5 seconds. This is equivalent to lifting 1500 lbs. 1 foot in 5 seconds or 18,000 lbs. 1 foot in 1 minute. A horse-power raises 33,000 lbs. a foot in a minute, so your horse-power would be $\dfrac{18,000}{33,000}$ or $\tfrac{6}{11}$ horse-power. The record for a man seems to be about

FIG. 111.—One horse power raises 550 lbs. through 1 foot in 1 second.

$2\tfrac{1}{4}$ h.p., but this can only be kept up for a very short time and about $\tfrac{1}{4}$ h.p. is a good average for such an exercise as long distance cycling or sculling.

The horse-power of an engine is measured in several different ways. The simplest of all is to couple it to a dynamo and so turn the work it does into electricity which is easily measured by volt-meters and ammeters. Suppose the engine makes the dynamo generate a current of 50 amperes at 100 volts. Then the dynamo is producing 50 × 100 watts and the horse-power is $\dfrac{5000}{746}$ = 6¾ nearly; for 746 watts is one horse-power.

A second method is to make the engine do work against a brake, the pull on which can be measured. Fig. 112 shows a modern form of the Kelvin brake. The engine which is being tested turns a drum round which a rope is wrapped. A spring balance shows the pull on the end of the rope and a weight holds the rope taut. Suppose the spring balance shows a pull of fifty pounds weight; the radius of the drum is 5 feet and the shaft turns 200 times a minute, and the weight weighs 450 lbs. Well, the friction of the rope on the drum and the pull of the balance, together hold up the 450 lbs. weight. The spring balance holds up 50 lbs. of it, so the engine is keeping 400 lbs. of weight from falling. It is doing this with the rim of the drum, which is 2 × 5 × ²²⁄₇ about 31.4 feet long. Consequently, the rim goes at 31.4 feet × 200 revs. = 6280 feet a minute. So it is really lifting a weight of 400 lbs. through 6280 feet, every minute, which is the same as lifting 2,512,000 lbs. through 1 foot every minute. One horse-power lifts 33,000 lbs. 1 foot in a minute, so our engine exerts $\dfrac{2,512,000}{33,000}$ or nearly 76 h.p. All the work our

Fig. 112—Testing the horse-power of an engine.

engine does is turned into heat: the heat produced would boil a hundred gallons of water every hour, so it is very necessary to run plenty of water through the drum to keep it cool!

SOURCES OF POWER

The modern world is run by machinery. All this machinery has to be driven by something—electricity, gas, wind, coal, petrol, etc. So the sources of power are really fundamental to modern civilisation.

How are our machines driven? Practically everything is driven by a steam engine, a gas engine, an oil engine, an electric motor, a water-wheel, or very rarely a windmill. Now these engines must get their energy from somewhere. The steam-engine and gas-engine and oil-engine are, in effect, burning either coal or oil: in fact, turning the *chemical energy* of these fuels and of air into *heat-energy* which is turned into the *kinetic energy* of revolving wheels. Electric motors are driven by electricity generated from dynamos, driven by steam engines or oil engines or water turbines. So electricity either comes from coal or oil or else from the energy of flowing water. Beyond a few things worked by hand or by animals and just one or two sun-boilers and tide-motors, these are the sources of all our power.

Wind and tide account only for very little of our power, so it is on COAL, OIL and WATER-POWER that our civilisation rests.

As far as we know, coal is being made, if at all, far more slowly than we are using it up: the same applies to oil. They will last our time, but it is not so certain that they will last another 500 years. Water-power will always last, for the sun brings the water back to the hills as fast as it runs off them, but it is not likely that even if every river in the world were driving its water-wheels and turbines, the resulting water-power would supply the present needs of the world. Tides and wind offer a vast supply of power, though rather a difficult one to use. The world's standby as far as power goes is still coal.

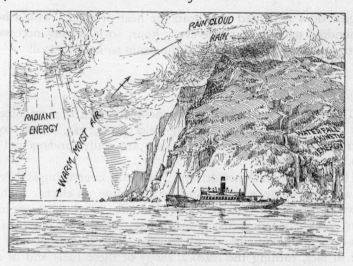

FIG. 113.—The energy of the sun's rays raises moist air to the hills: the moisture condenses as rain and as it runs down to the sea, the energy originally provided by the sun reappears as kinetic energy of moving water, e.g. the waterfall, which we can utilise in a turbine.

All power ultimately comes from the heat of the sun or the motions of the earth, moon and sun. Three hundred million years ago queer plants growing in ancient forests used the power of the sun's rays to turn the carbon dioxide gas in the air into starch and sugar and cellulose—just as modern plants are doing to-day. You can read more of it on pp. 614 *ff*. These forests became submerged in swamps and marshes, and became embedded in something rather like the peat of modern bogs. In time, the bogs became buried under mud, and ages of pressure and warmth deep under the earth changed the woody fibre, the leaves, the spores of these plants into the black, strong material we call coal. More than $\frac{9}{10}$ths of coal is carbon.

The power that turned the carbon dioxide of the air into carbon was the energy of the sun's rays: when we burn the coal it becomes carbon dioxide once more, and the sun's energy locked in the coal for three hundred million years is again manifest as light and heat. Oil, too, is believed to be the product of subterranean heat and pressure on some ancient microscopic creatures

Fig. 114—The energy of sunlight, utilised by ancient coal-forests and by the minute plants (later devoured by animals) in the ancient seas, is transformed *via* coal and petroleum to the heat and light-energy used in our homes.

which abounded in primæval seas. These got their substance from carbon dioxide and water, and the energy which built these substances into fats was the energy of the sun. When oil burns, it gives carbon dioxide and water, and your car is consequently driven by the burning sunshine which beat on the sea a hundred million years before there was a man.

Water-power is quite clearly sun-power. The sun evaporates the sea. The water-vapour drifts to cooler regions and falls as rain on the high hills. The water running down from these, gives up its energies to turbines—energy which the sun gave it by raising it on high (Fig. 113).

Wind-power too is chiefly sun-power, and the power of the earth's rotation: differences of temperature set winds blowing (p. 717). Tidal power does not come chiefly from the sun. The moon attracts the water of the sea and holds it back so that while the earth rotates, the tide remains heaped up at rest relative to the moon. This is just as if the tide were running round the earth the opposite way to its rotation. The tides, of course, washing along the sea bottom, slow up the earth. They also pull the moon back (for of course the tide attracts the moon just as much as the moon attracts the tide). So, the motion of the tides is always slowing down the moon and the earth. The earth has been thought to

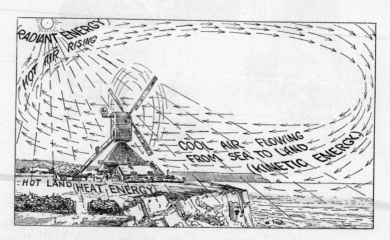

FIG. 115—How the radiant energy of the sun is transformed to kinetic energy of wind and thence to useful work.

take about $\frac{1}{30}$ second longer to rotate at the end of each century than it took at the end of the last, but the evidence for this is quite shaky. The energy of the tide is now wasted, but around the coasts of Great Britain alone some 12,000,000,000 horsepower are waiting for anyone who could spend the capital necessary to make them available.

At present, the world is squandering capital. The coal measures took millions of years to make: man has found them and like a spendthrift just come into a fortune, he is making his patrimony fly. England's supplies may last 500 years: the world's supplies perhaps 3,000 years, assuming the quantity of coal used does not greatly increase.

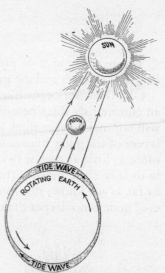

FIG. 116.—How the kinetic energy of the rotation of the earth and of the revolution of the moon are made available as the kinetic energy of the tides.

This time is only a moment in the history of the earth, standing in relation to the earth's life as a fraction of a second to a day; it will pass, and the world's coal and oil will be gone. Man will then have to use the heat of the sun and the power of the winds which the sun causes: these will last his time—for his species is likely to be extinct long before the sun cools appreciably; he may use the power of the tide, for it will be hundreds of millions of years before the earth slows down much: or he may use the huge store of heat in the interior of the earth at present beyond our reach. Finally, he may be able to unlock the stores of power in the atom. We need not think that our descendants will lack power: they will have it, but will get it in new and strange ways. But none of those who read this will see the year 2050, so it is the way that power is now obtained which affects us most.

COAL

The prime source of power is coal, from which almost all of England's power and the greatest part of the world's is derived.

Coal does not occur like chalk or granite, in great hills. Even an enormously thick peat-bog when dried and hardened into coal will not make a very thick layer and so coal is found in "seams"—layers of irregular thickness rarely as much as ten feet thick, and often as little as one or two feet. The rock above and below coal is usually shale or slate (hardened mud), and so coal seams are, as far as we know, not found at very great depths. The deepest coal mine is no deeper than a mile and a quarter.

FIG. 117.—Reconstruction of a coal forest as it flourished 300,000,000 years ago. (Courtesy of Messrs. Henry Holt & Co.; from Chamberlin and Salisbury's *Geology*, Vol. II.)

If there is good reason to hope that a coal seam underlies a piece of land, the first thing to do is to find out whether the coal exists, and if so, how deep it is, how thick the seams are, and whether it is of good quality. The best thing to do, is to sink a trial shaft several feet in diameter, but as this is very expensive, it is more usual to drill boreholes. A hollow drill, usually a diamond drill (Fig. 19), is used and the "cores" cut out by it are brought up and examined. The holes may be sunk a mile in depth, but in England we rarely go so deep. If the coal is of good quality, and in seams thick enough to work, the next step is to sink a shaft down to the coal. This will ultimately be the passage by which men, coal and air are brought up and down and through which the subterranean water, which almost always gives trouble, is pumped to the surface.

The method of sinking a shaft depends very greatly on the ground it has to penetrate. It is a well which may be as small as 4 feet by 6 feet, or as large—in some American collieries—as 13 feet × 52 feet. If it is to be sunk in hard rock, a number of holes are bored, five or six feet deep, and charged with dynamite: this is exploded, and when the fumes have cleared, the broken rock is hoisted out and fresh borings and blastings are made.

The shaft may be sunk as quickly as six feet a day, but a slower pace is usual. The shaft is commonly lined with timber or concrete, or sometimes cast-iron, such as you see in a tube-lift. An unlined shaft might fall in. Very soft or watery soils are very difficult to deal with, for they fall in as fast as they are dug out. Many different plans have been used for them. One of the most interesting is to sink small bore-holes in the ground and inject liquid concrete. This sets solid and the shaft is sunk through the concrete. Another still queerer way, used for wet soils, is to drive bore-holes round the edge of the place where the shaft is to be, and sink in these a ring of 6 inch pipes: inside these are lowered $1\frac{1}{2}$ inch pipes. Down the latter, strong salt solution, cooled below 0° C., is pumped and thus in a month or so a ring of ground is frozen solid. Inside this ring of hard ground the soft wet soil is quickly excavated and an iron lining is put in. Once this is done, the ground is allowed to thaw, but no water can then get into the shaft. Every coal mine in Great Britain is compelled by law to have two shafts.

These shafts once sunk, a tremendous system of galleries is cut in every direction. One pit may radiate over a square mile or more from the shaft. It is quite common for the single pithead you see at the surface to be the entrance to a town of dark galleries and roads, much larger than the mining village above it. A thousand acres is not large for the workings of a coal mine.

The coal is not taken from the ground close to the bottom of the shafts: if it were, there would be danger of the ground collapsing and blocking these. Two main "roads" usually lead to the shaft: one is used for hauling coal, the other is for the miners coming and going from their work.

There are several different ways of working a coal mine. You cannot just hew the coal out and take it away, for the coal is the only thing that holds up millions of tons of overlying rock! The "bord and pillar" way of working leaves pillars of coal to support the roof: the method is a little difficult to understand, so the more frequent "long-wall" way of working will be described.

Suppose the seam of coal is level and about 3 feet 6 inches thick. Clearly, the roadways cannot be cut only in the coal itself, so they must be cut in the coal and in the "roof" of rock above it. The stone which is taken out in doing this is used to make a strong wall on each side of these main roads and these are roofed with steel or timber to prevent them falling in. When the part of the mine where the coal is being worked is reached, a long gallery runs all the way along the edge of the untouched coal. In this gallery, the miners cut the coal, which is then taken to the main roads and so back to the shaft. When the coal is cut away, the road and the props are moved forward again. The space left by the coal taken away is filled up with the loose "goaf" or stone rubbish, which is taken out at the same time as the coal.

This gradually crushes down and the rock above collapses on to it. This does no harm, as the main roads are well supported. Fig. 118 gives some idea of long-wall working.

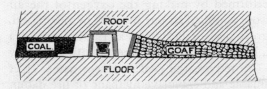

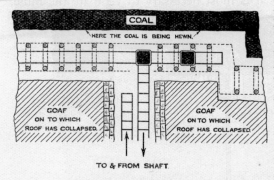

TO & FROM SHAFT

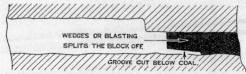

FIG. 118—The long-wall system of mining.

The miner's chief job is cutting the coal from the seam, and since coal is brittle and small coal or coal dust is not as valuable as big coal, he has to try not to break it up too much. For this reason, blasting is not greatly employed and when it is, a rather mild type of explosive is used. The miner who cuts the coal has one of the hardest jobs on earth. He often has to do it in a very constricted space, illuminated by a feeble lamp (Plate X).

The method is to cut a deep groove in the face of the coal, leaving an overhanging block. The block is split off either by blasting or by driving wedges, and loaded into a truck on rails and pushed or hauled to the main roadway whence it is hauled, usually mechanically, to the bottom of the shaft.

Machines for cutting the coal are often used, and where there is room to handle them are preferred to hand-labour. Actually, in only about a third of the British mines can they be used, either for lack of space or because the props needed to keep the roof up get in the way.

The coal when once cut may have two miles to travel, and the miner, once at the pit-bottom, may have as far to walk to his work.

A man working uses up a good deal of air—for our muscular

effort is ultimately performed by making the oxygen of the air combine with the glucose supplied to our muscles by our blood. He also produces a great deal of heat, and as the bottom of a mine is hot and moist, he finds it difficult to get rid of his heat by evaporation (p. 117). Moreover, the coal produces gases, chief of which is the inflammable and explosive methane or fire-damp. For all these reasons it is most necessary to ventilate the mine,

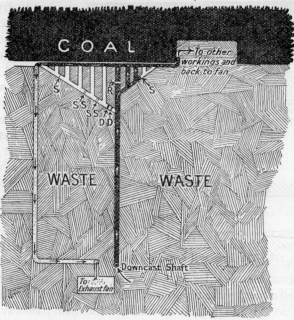

Fig. 119—How a coal mine is ventilated.

and to ensure that through every road and alley-way flows a supply of pure clean air. Roughly speaking, a hundred cubic feet of air per man per minute should be supplied.

In England, the used-up air is sucked out of the mine by means of huge fans as much as forty feet in diameter, as high as a three-storey house. These are run slowly, but smaller fans run quickly are often used. A big mine may need half a million cubic feet (a church-full) of air every minute. The air is thus sucked out through one shaft and so is compelled to enter by another.

Very great care has to be taken to guide it through every single working in the mine. The diagram (Fig. 119) gives some idea of the way this can be done. The difficulty lies in the fact that a mine is a complicated maze of workings; and the air therefore, if not prevented from doing so, would take a short cut from the intake to the exit and never go near the coal face. Every passage-way, therefore, which is not in the direct line through which the air is intended to go, must be closed by wooden doors (D); or fabric screens (S); where the passages fork, a regulator (R), which is a partition with a sliding shutter, regulates the amount of air which goes to each.

There are only a few mines where there is no inflammable gas evolved from the coal. In these few, the miner lights himself by a candle or an oil lamp, often stuck on his hat. But in the vast majority of mines, the coal gives out gases which will burn and explode if the air of the mine contains a sufficient proportion.

The gas is called Fire-Damp by the miners, and it can often be heard whistling out of cracks in the coal. A fair specimen of fire-damp might be three-quarters methane—which is the stuff of which about half of our ordinary illuminating gas is made. The chief difference between fire-damp and ordinary gas is that the former is not poisonous. Ordinary gas has carbon monoxide in it—fire-damp has not. Another dangerous explosive is fine coal dust. Almost any inflammable fine powder will explode if mixed with air. Thus, you are not allowed to take a light into a flour-mill for fear of explosion. A mixture of air, fire-damp and coal dust is very dangerously explosive, and in "fiery" mines explosions will occur in spite of the precautions taken. The best precaution is good ventilation which sweeps the gas away. Equally important but more difficult to enforce is the precaution of seeing that no flame or spark which might explode the gas can be made in the mine. Miners are searched to see that they do not bring matches into the mine and the mine is lighted by some arrangement which cannot set the gas alight. Electricity is used in mines which have little or no gas, but it introduces danger from stray sparks.

The miner himself may carry an electric lamp rather like an electric torch worked by an accumulator, or a safety lamp burning oil. The safety lamp does not give much of a light but it is really safe, and, above all, it warns the miner when the air contains much gas. The principle of the safety lamp is that a flame will not pass between two cold metal surfaces very near to each other, for these cool the burning gas down till it will no longer burn. Thus, a flame will not go through cold copper gauze nor will it go through a narrow chink between two pieces of brass.

Fig. 120 shows a safety lamp. The air enters at A, passing through two layers of copper gauze and then down between the thick outer glass chimney C and the thinner one D. It supplies the flame on the wick, and the burnt gases pass up the metal chimney and out through three copper gauzes. If there is a dangerous amount of gas about, it forms a pale mantle of flame round the bright oil-flame and the miner knows there is danger. If the flame sets alight to the air-gas mixture, this may burn *in* the lamp but the flame cannot pass outside and explode the air and gas in the workings. Why shouldn't the miner open the lamp? You might think he would not be fool enough, but there are always a few fools in every job, and a simple device prevents him from opening his lamp. An iron bolt which cannot be reached from outside is held by a spring so that it locks the brass base from being unscrewed. When the lamp is to be filled *outside* the mine, it is stood on a powerful magnet which pulls the iron bolt

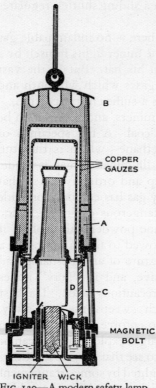

COPPER GAUZES

B

A

D C

MAGNETIC BOLT

IGNITER WICK

FIG. 120—A modern safety lamp (Courtesy of Messrs. John Davis, Ltd., Derby)

PLATE XI

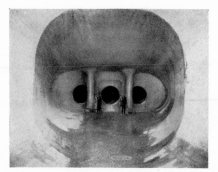

The lower end of the tunnel carrying water from Loch Treig and Loch Laggan
to the British Aluminium Company's works at Fort William.
(By courtesy of *The Engineer*.)

The turbines and dynamos of the British Aluminium Company's works at
Fort William.

PLATE XII

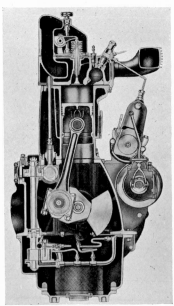

Section of cylinder of A.E.C. compression-ignition engine, as fitted to omnibuses, lorries, etc. (By courtesy of The Associated Equipment Company, Ltd., Southall, Middlesex.)

A 600-h.p. gas-engine driving a dynamo. (By courtesy of the National Gas and Oil Engine Company, Ltd., Ashton-under-Lyne.)

down and allows the lamp-man to unscrew the top. If the lamp goes out in the mine, it can be relit by a spark from the "igniter," an arrangement like a petrol lighter. All the same, accidents continue. Sometimes it is blasting, "shot-firing", that causes them. There is a list of "permitted explosives" which are supposed not to be able to set light to gas. These do not seem to be quite safe and it is considered that "shot-firing" is the chief cause of colliery explosions. The effect of an explosion is of course disastrous. It is not a shattering explosion like that of a shell—it is half-way between burning and explosion, the sort of thing that happens when the gas-fire goes off with a pop—but vastly magnified. The most disastrous effect is that the air is rendered useless for breathing. The burning uses up the oxygen, and the roads are left filled with deadly "after-damp" (nitrogen, carbon dioxide and carbon monoxide) which often cuts off the retreat of men in distant parts of the workings. The doors and so forth on which ventilation depends may be destroyed, so that the foul air cannot be removed. Worst of all, the explosion often causes the roofs to fall and cut off the retreat of the miners. But actually explosions, though appearing very terrible, kill far fewer miners than other accidents. In two recent years, explosions killed only 246 men out of 2,048 who were killed in mines. Roughly, one collier in every thousand is killed by some kind of accident each year, and about 180 in every thousand (more than one in six) are injured badly enough to keep them 3 days from work. The chief causes of injuries are accidents due to falls of roof and to collisions with trucks of coal in the narrow and congested roadway. Very little improvement has been made, and when we compare the dangers of coal mining with those of the farm labourer or mechanic we wonder whether these men are well enough paid at an average wage of 44s. a week (1935). For years the miners have said that the owners do not take enough precautions against accident: the owners say the same of the miners: doubtless there is justice on both sides.

The coal, while we have talked of accidents, has found its way to the pit shaft whence a winding engine hauls it to the surface. The winding engine is quite a problem in itself. It must stand

8

idle when nothing is being hauled, then heave up five or six tons of coal quickly to the surface. The best of these engines will haul five tons of coal vertically up a shaft a third of a mile deep at thirty miles an hour.

The boiler of the engine must always be ready to give a big supply of steam at a moment's notice. On the other hand, it is bad business to keep burning the whole time a fire of sufficient power to give this big supply. So an "accumulator" is used. A

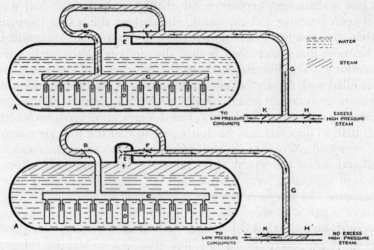

FIG. 121—Steam accumulator. In the upper figure such part of the boilers steam as is not required is being forced *into* hot water, further raising its temperature. In the lower figure the supply of high pressure steam is cut off, and by opening the valve F steam is being supplied *from* the superheated water in the accumulator.

reasonably small boiler gives a continuous supply of steam at, say, 150 lbs. square inch pressure, which is forced into another boiler of hot water. The steam condenses under the pressure and superheats the water, i.e., raises its temperature, to say, 180° C., much above the ordinary boiling point. When a big supply of steam is needed, the accumulator is connected to the engine and as the steam enters the cylinders of the engine, the pressure falls and the water boils supplying the large amount of steam required. The temperature of the water falls, of course, as it boils, but long before the water has become too cool to boil, the coal has been hauled to the top, and the boiler is charging up the accumulator again.

When the coal is at the top, it is by no means fit to be sold. The top and bottom of a coal seam are usually black shale, looking just like a bit of coal to the amateur eye. But shale does not burn, and worse, it splits in the fire with loud explosions which used to be common in coal fires when coal was not so well "cleaned."

Sometimes the shale is separated by throwing the coal on a travelling band from which a line of pickers take out the bits of shale. More often, machines are used. A coal cleaning machine is very ingenious. Try and think of a machine to separate irregular lumps of slate from irregular lumps of coal! The coal is screened (sieved) into bits all about the same size and these are washed in a stream of water. Now slate is twice as heavy as coal, and so it is possible to regulate the current of water so that it carries off the coal and leaves the heavy slate.

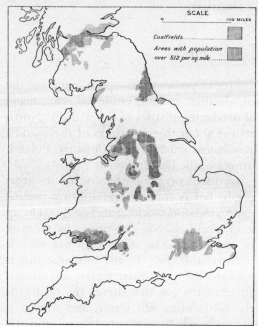

The coal is dried and goes to the trucks on the sidings and thence all over the world. Great Britain turns out about 250,000,000 tons of coal a year: the whole world turns out about 1,500,000,000 tons. This would be a conical hill of coal as high as Snowdon and four miles round the base.

Fig. 122—Showing the connection between coal and population.

The places in the world where coal is won are still the parts of the world where people congregate, and where goods are made and money changes hands.

Fig. 122 shows a map of England with the coal area of England shown in horizontal shading, while the vertical shading shows the areas in which the number of people per square mile exceeds 512. It tells its story!

The coal, once sold, is used in many ways. It may be burned in a steam engine, made into coal gas, burned to make electricity, used in smelting iron and so forth, or nowadays even made into petrol, or it may be burned in the grate or kitchen range. Roughly, the uses are one-fifth to the home, one-fifth to the iron and steel works, a tenth to the railways, an eighth to the gasworks and the rest, rather less than half, is used to drive the engines of thousands of factories and to make electricity.

OIL

The second greatest source of power is oil—petroleum and the various materials, petrol, paraffin, gas-oil, crude oil, etc., made from it. The greatest oil-producing district of the world is North America, which accounts for about three-quarters of the world's supply. The other quarter comes chiefly from Rumania, Poland, South Russia, Persia, Burma and the East Indies.

Petroleum does not, as many people think, occur in great subterranean lakes or pools, but is found soaked into a porous material such as sand or soft sandstone rock. Sand easily takes up one-third of its volume of liquid, as you can prove by pouring water into a tumbler of dry sand. The oil always has with it enormous volumes of inflammable gas. In the oilsands, this is highly compressed—up to 500 lbs. per square inch—and when a well is sunk, it is the force of the gas that drives the oil to the surface. Underneath the oil is often salt water, and over it is always some non-porous rock which prevents the oil and gas from escaping. Fig. 123 shows how gas, petroleum and water occur in an oilfield. The gas is usually highly compressed, and if the field is tapped near the top of the oil formation, a supply of this gas may be obtained. It is mainly methane— the fire-damp of coal mines—and is a most excellent fuel. In America it is collected and pumped to all the neighbouring towns as gas-supply. Fig. 123 gives only a general idea of an oilfield: very many other arrangements

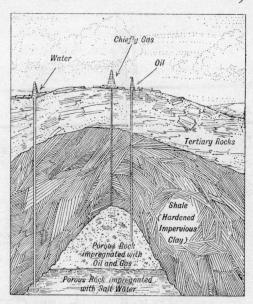

FIG. 123—Diagram of an oil-field.

of rocks are possible, but in most of them, the light oil finds its way to the top of some sort of dome-shaped mass of porous rock.

When a new oilfield is struck, the gas and oil may escape from the porous sands into the casing of the borehole with such violence that a vast jet of oil, gas and sand may run to waste for months. The spray of oil falls for miles round: the roar of escaping gas is unbearable. Very often the air is so full of gas that the bystanders are half anæsthetised by it.

Most oilwells are now drilled by the rotary method (Fig. 124). A tall framework called a derrick is erected. This, the most conspicuous thing about an oilwell, is needed so that the drill stem can be hauled out of the hole by ropes going over pulleys at the top of the derrick. At the bottom of the derrick, is a rotating table (T) which is driven, usually by a chain, from an oil-engine or steam-engine.

The table has a square hole in it and through this passes a

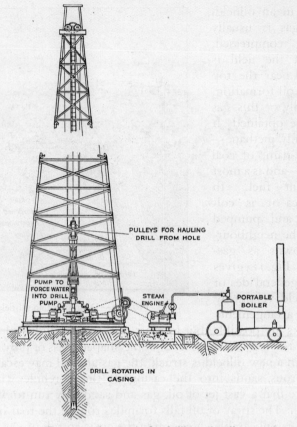

FIG. 124—Rotary rig for drilling oil-wells.

hollow stem, to which many lengths of pipe are attached. To the end of these a hollow drill is connected. As the table turns, the weight of the drill stem forces the drill to grind away the rock. Water or, better, thin mud which is heavier and supports the walls of the hole, is pumped down the stem, and washes the mud to which the rock is converted up to the surface. This goes on until the drill is blunted, when it has to be hauled to the surface and re-sharpened. As there may be three thousand feet of drill stem, and the derrick allows only 100 feet to be drawn up at once, this is very wasteful of time.

When the oil is nearly reached, a flow of gas is usually encountered, and the hole is then lined by lowering a casing of iron pipes into it. This prevents the boring from caving in. The drilling once done, it remains to extract the oil. If there is likely to be a great pressure of gas, a massive steel valve is fitted to the top of the casing and the final drilling is done through this.

Sometimes the huge pressure of gas blows away the casing head, derrick and all, and the oil runs to waste, but in most wells the gas drives the oil easily and smoothly to the surface. In order to use the pressure of the gas to the best advantage, a "casing-head" of some kind is fitted. Fig. 125 shows a "Packer-Jet." A pool of oil and gas collects round the bottom of the pipes. The compressed gas travels up the outer pipe and at the same time pushes

FIG. 125—Casing-head and Packer-jet of oil-well.   Valve of Packer-jet.
(Courtesy of the British Oil Well Engineering Co., Ltd.)

the oil up the inner one. The gas finally escapes by valves into the oil pipe and lifts a froth of gas and oil to the surface. This goes to the storage tanks. In some American oilfields, the casing-head gas is pumped to towns several hundred miles away, but in many oilfields it is wasted.

The well in time flows more and more feebly and finally deep-well pumps have to be used.

In 1927 twelve hundred and fifty million barrels of crude oil were produced. This quantity represents a continuous flow of oil at a rate rather less than the flow of the Thames through London in a dry summer. The yearly total would fill a lake six miles square and ten feet deep. The weight of the oil produced each year is some 200,000,000 tons: this is only about a seventh of the weight of the world's yearly supply of coal, which is therefore still the most important source of power and heat.

The petroleum as it comes from the earth may be yellow, red-brown or greenish—not unlike a heavy lubricating oil. It is almost entirely made up of the elements carbon and hydrogen. Carbon and hydrogen atoms may be hitched together to make many thousands of kinds of different molecules and several hundred of these varieties are to be found in any sample of crude oil.

Crude oil, is then a medley of different hydrocarbons. Page 233 shows some of the chief molecules in it. Now it is easy to see that since all molecules at the same temperature have the same energy—for the temperature of a thing is the energy of its molecules—the little light ones must be moving fast and the big ones slowly. So, if one heats petroleum—that is, speeds up its molecules—the first ones to be speeded up enough to fly away from the liquid in the form of vapour will be the lightest ones. In the same way, if we cool petroleum vapour, the heaviest molecules will be the first to change back to liquid and the lightest molecules will need the most cooling to make them cling together into the liquid form.

The modern way of refining petroleum is to pump it through tubes set in a furnace (Fig. 126), keeping the pressure so high that

CRUDE PETROLEUM

is separated by refining into

PETROL with such
molecules as

Hexane   Pentamethylene   Di-isopropyl
(black balls represent carbon atoms, white balls
hydrogen atoms)

PARAFFIN OIL with larger
molecules such as

Nonane   Decahydro-naphthalene

GAS OIL with still larger
molecules such as

Eicosane

LUBRICATING OIL with very complicated molecules consisting of carbon chains in rings and branches

PARAFFIN WAX with molecules like———↓

ASPHALT with huge molecules of unknown size and form.

FUEL OIL often separated into

it will not boil. It is then discharged into the base of a tower filled with shelves. The hot petroleum, as soon as the pressure on it is released, bursts into vapour. All the lighter molecules pass up the tower as vapour: the heaviest ones, however, refuse to boil and stay at the bottom: these constitute fuel oil. The vapour partly condenses to liquid oil as it goes up the tower; and as the vapour bubbles through the condensed oil on the shelves, it

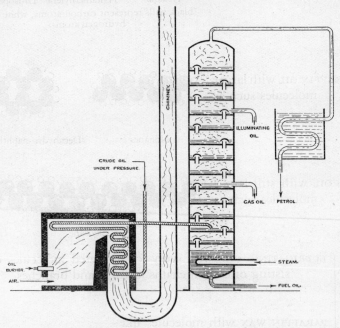

FIG. 126—Diagram of modern petroleum refining plant.
(From material supplied by Messrs. A. F. Craig & Co.)

leaves most of its own heavier molecules behind, and takes up the lightest ones from this oil. Steam, blown into the fuel oil at the base, helps to hasten the lighter molecules on their way.

The result is that heavy gas-oil finds its way to the lower shelves: less heavy paraffin-oil (illuminating oil) can be run off about half-way down, while petrol vapour leaves the top of the tower uncondensed. This petrol vapour is run through water-cooled tubes and so turns back to liquid petrol.

Paraffin and petrol are further refined by treating them with various substances which take from them the sulphur compounds which give the raw liquids a foul smell.

The fuel-oil left at the bottom of the rectifying tower is often made into lubricating oil, paraffin wax and asphalt.

The process of refining gives us:

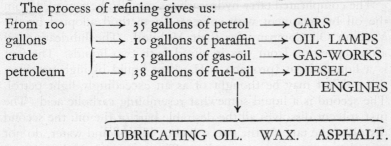

From 100 gallons crude petroleum

→ 35 gallons of petrol ——→ CARS
→ 10 gallons of paraffin ——→ OIL LAMPS
→ 15 gallons of gas-oil ——→ GAS-WORKS
→ 38 gallons of fuel-oil ——→ DIESEL-ENGINES

LUBRICATING OIL. WAX. ASPHALT.

Lubricating oils must have a high boiling point so that they will not evaporate or burn easily. On the other hand they should not contain any wax, which makes them go solid in cold weather. To make them, the heavy fuel oil is heated in a boiler and the vapour which comes over is condensed. The stuff which remains behind in the boiler is a kind of asphalt, used for road-making. The liquid which comes over is called wax-distillate. It is cooled, whereupon the wax separates out (just as fat separates from olive oil or sugar from honey in cold weather). The mixture of wax and oil is squeezed through cloth by presses. The wax remains behind and the oil passes on. The oil is again distilled and then filtered through fuller's earth, which takes out much of its dark colour and also stops particles of wax. Several processes have been applied to lubricating oils to help them to stand up to the very severe conditions of temperature which obtain in motor-car cylinders. Hydrogenation, applied to the well-known Essolube, is one. It is performed by treating the oil with hydrogen gas in presence of certain catalysts which make the oil and hydrogen combine. The effect is first to convert the many complicated hydrocarbons, which are most easily broken up by heat, into a few more resistant ones: secondly, to turn the sulphur and nitrogen and oxygen compounds in the oil (which are useless and deleterious) into sulphuretted hydrogen, ammonia and water which are easily removed. The advertisements have very fully informed the public of the effect of the process in improving the heat-resisting and other qualities of the oil.

The complicated tarry hydrocarbons can also be removed from the oil by treatment with solvents—a method adopted by the Vacuum Oil Company for their Mobiloil. The lubricating oil after separation from wax is mixed with two liquids. The first is a liquefied gas (propane, C_3H_6) kept liquid by high pressure: this solvent may be thought of as an exceedingly light petrol. The second is a liquid somewhat resembling carbolic acid. The first solvent dissolves all the desirable part of the oil: the second dissolves the tar. As the two solvents, like oil and water, do not mix, they separate out on standing. The top solution is lubricating oil in propane, the lower is tarry matter in the "tarry solvent." Both of these are distilled, so separating the solvents which are used once more. The resulting oil is very resistant to high temperatures and consequently deposits very little carbon in use; it also is more fluid at low temperatures, so ensuring easier starting. The figure below illustrates the method.

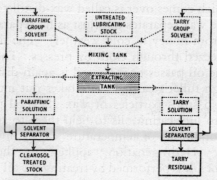

FIG. 127—Illustrating the Clearosol process for refining lubricating oil.
(Courtesy of the Vacuum Oil Co., Ltd.)

The "paraffin-wax" separated from lubricating oil is squeezed free of oil and as it is cheap, waterproof, white, odourless and tasteless, it finds uses in a great many different trades. It is used chiefly for making candles, but a good deal is turned into waterproof waxed paper for packing. Some is used in polishes and as an electrical insulator.

Oil and the petrol, etc., made from it are very convenient fuels indeed. A liquid is far easier to pack and store than a solid. Moreover, as we shall see, a liquid can be vaporised and burnt inside the cylinder of an engine—a much more efficient way of making power than burning coal under a boiler to make steam. The different oil products are used for different jobs.

Petrol is easily turned into vapour and is therefore the perfect fuel for internal combustion engines—cars, aeroplanes, etc. On the other hand, it is very easily set alight, which makes it unsuitable as a household fuel, and it is expensive, which makes it unsuitable for driving the engines of steamships, factories, etc.

Paraffin oil is not so suitable for internal combustion engines, as it is difficult to get it into vapour unless some special arrangement is fitted. Since you can dip a lighted match into it without setting it alight, it is safe enough for household use in oil-stoves, lamps, Primus stoves, etc.

Fuel-oil is difficult to vaporise and difficult to set alight. The only way to burn it is as a spray. The Diesel engines (p. 272 *ff.*) use a fine spray of oil instead of the petrol vapour of an ordinary petrol engine. They are greatly used in ships and very heavy lorries and stationary engines, but till recently have been too heavy for use in motor-cars and aeroplanes. Much fuel-oil is used by spraying it into the furnace chamber below the boiler of a steam engine. This is the chief way of using oil on board ship.

WATER POWER

The third great source of power is water. To use water-power efficiently a fairly rapid fall is needed. The Thames water, if we could make it do work all the way from the hills to the sea, would give more than 10,000 h.p., but in fact it is not easy to design efficient machinery to use the motion of gently flowing water. The ideal condition for using water-power is at a waterfall where the water can be made to fall steeply down great pipes to the turbine below. In only a few places in England is it possible to use water-power. The British Aluminium Co. at Lochaber has the biggest electrical undertaking in this country run by water-power, and a description of this will give a very fair idea of the way water-power is used.

But first of all we must look at the way in which moving water can be made to give up its energy to a water-wheel or turbine. There are two chief types of water turbine, namely the reaction turbine and the impulse turbine.

The reaction turbine depends on the fact that the force that a jet exerts on the water that spurts from it is the same as the force that the water exerts on the jet. The simplest form of reaction turbine is the ordinary lawn sprinkler (Fig. 128). If a pulley were

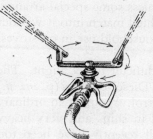

connected to the revolving head, the sprinkler could clearly be made to do work. The simplest kind of impulse turbine is the water-wheel, where a jet strikes vanes or buckets set on the edge of a wheel and so drives it round. Both kinds of turbine are greatly employed.

Fig. 128—A lawn sprinkler, the simplest reaction turbine.

The energy of the water is energy of motion: consequently, a 100% efficient turbine would leave the water which has passed through it standing still! This is of course impossible, but water turbines may extract 85% of the energy of the water.

The reaction turbine is designed so that its rotating part if held still would change the direction of the water stream. The stream resists this change by driving the rotor. Fig. 129 shows a large reaction turbine driving an electric motor. The water enters the vanes of the stator and thus is made to flow spirally inwards. It then flows inwards and downwards between the turbine blades of the rotor and so forces them to rotate in the direction of the arrow. This kind of turbine is very effective where heads of water from 10 to 300 feet are available. Very high pressure water up to 1,000 feet or more is better dealt with by the Pelton wheel.

The Pelton wheel is used where the quantity of water is small and its pressure is great. It is very efficient and its efficiency depends on the shape of the buckets on its rim (Plate X). If the jet of water merely struck a flat stationary plate, it

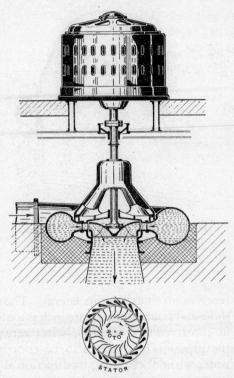

FIG. 129—A reaction turbine driving an electric motor. Below is shown a horizontal section of the vanes in the outer fixed part (stator) and the inner moving part (rotor).

would fly out sideways with much energy, all of which would be wasted (Fig. 130 *b*). The Pelton bucket, however, is so designed that if held still it would catch the jet of water and return it in the *direction in which it came* at about the same speed (Fig. 130, *a*, *b*). But when the wheel is running, the rim is going nearly as fast as the jet of water, so the water leaving the bucket is travelling *forward* with the bucket at just about the same speed as it is deflected *backward* by the bucket. Consequently the water actually has almost no velocity at all! It drops dead from the wheel, which

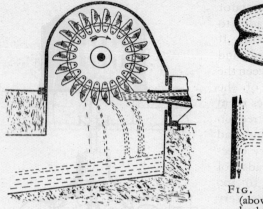

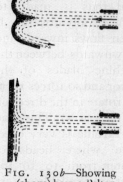

FIG. 130a—The essential part of a Pelton wheel.

FIG. 130b—Showing (above) how a Pelton bucket returns the water in the direction it came from, while a flat plate (below) deflects it only through a right-angle.

receives up to 85% of its energy. The control of water at up to a thousand pounds per square inch is a tricky business. Valves must be contrived to shut off the water very slowly for fear of bursting the pipes. They must also be contrived to throttle down the water without changing its direction at all, for the Pelton jet must hit its bucket square in the middle. The usual valve is a "spear" valve in which a spear-shaped piece of metal can be screwed forward to block the jet to the required extent.

The ordinary water-mill is partly of the impulse type and partly operated by the weight of the water.

The designing of a suitable turbine is, however, the smallest part of the building of a plant to operate by water-power. The greatest part of the task is usually the bringing of the water to the works. The maps show how the British Aluminium Company have arranged their undertaking. The area (Fig. 131, sectional; Fig. 132, plan) is a *basin;* water always flowing down into it from the hills has formed two lakes, Loch Laggan and Loch Treig. Loch Treig, the lower and

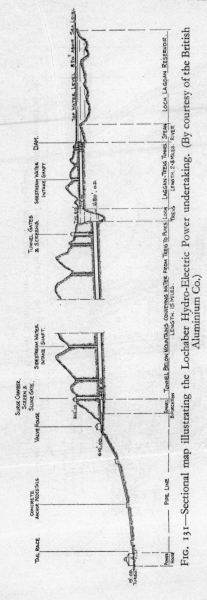

FIG. 131—Sectional map illustrating the Lochaber Hydro-Electric Power undertaking. (By courtesy of the British Aluminium Co.)

nearer, is 819 feet above sea level. Some fifteen miles away lies Fort William with a harbour and a railway to bring raw materials and take away the finished products. Between the two, however, lie the hills, the obstacle of which was conquered by driving two tunnels, four and fifteen miles long respectively, to lead the water to the power-house and turbines. The tunnels are designed to lead the water by a gentle fall till it is some 600 feet above the works. Thence, a pipe-line carries the water to the turbines. Fig. 131 shows the way the tunnels lead the water from the two lochs. In order to use as much as possible of the water in Loch Treig, the tunnel had to enter the *bottom* of the loch: this, of course, presented great difficulties.

No such tunnels had ever been bored in Great Britain. Only one in the world is longer.

The ground was carefully surveyed and the tunnel was started by sinking shafts or tunnels in the mountain sides in ten different places. By carefully working out the direction

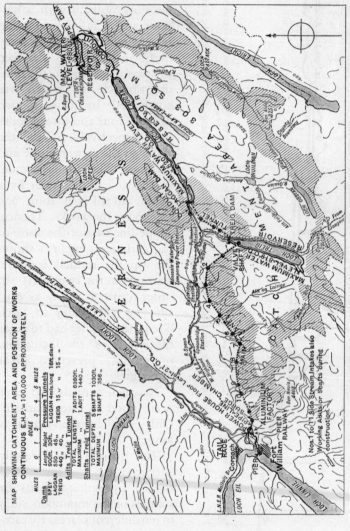

Fig. 132.—Map of the Catchment area of the Lochaber Hydro-Electric Power undertaking.
(Courtesy of the British Aluminium Co. and of *The Engineer*.)

of boring the ten different tunnels all met accurately. The rocks were mostly very hard, granite, porphyry and schist[1] being encountered. Needless to say, the engineers did not carry the top end of the tunnel into Loch Treig itself! They completed the tunnel everywhere else, lined it with cement and finally bored to within about 20 feet of the lake. They then honeycombed the rock with borings in which *two tons* of explosive (gelignite) were placed. Everything was cleared out of the tunnel; and it was filled up with water so that the water of the loch should not rush in and carry the rock with it into the tunnel. The explosives were ignited by electricity and the rock was blown away, leaving the tunnel open into Loch Treig.

Previously, of course, the Fort William end of the tunnel had been completed. At this end the tunnel has a shaft 30 feet wide and 240 feet deep sunk down to meet it: this shaft, the "surge-chamber," allows room for the water to accumulate if the power plant is suddenly shut off. A sluice gate to cut off the water can also be worked from here. The tunnel next connects up to three pipe-lines made of steel pipe, six feet in diameter. Two of these lead through the valve house where the water flow can be regulated, and thence down a steep slope to the turbines, which are huge Pelton wheels. These are coupled direct to the electric motors, which provide the current for manufacturing the aluminium—a process further described on pp. 690, 691. Plate XI shows the power-house. Contrast its light and airiness with the furnaces of a steam-plant.

The world's greatest single source of water-power is Niagara Falls. Here there plunges over a precipice some 200,000 cubic feet of water every second. If all this water were led through turbines, about 4,000,000 h.p. could be generated. Actually, about a quarter of the water is used and 950,000 h.p. generated. There is a treaty between Canada and the U.S.A. limiting the quantity of water each may take. Niagara Falls is near to great centres of population and rich sources of minerals, so that it

[1] A hard crystalline rock resulting as a rule from the effect of great subterranean heat on shale or slate.

gives power where there are works to use it, people to run the works and customers to buy the goods. Other great falls such as the Victoria Falls in Rhodesia, which could probably generate nearly a million h.p., are far from centres of population. Possibly, if the black races develop, this great fountain of free power may cause an industrial area to spring up round it: the climate, perhaps, makes it impossible for white men to build up great industries there. The same applies to the Kaieteur Falls of British Guiana and to many others.

Actually it seems that about 30,000,000 h.p. are generated from water-power, while, if all the chief sources of water-power (excluding tides) were used, some 240,000,000 h.p. could be made.

The British Empire—excepting Canada, which generates more than 5,000,000 h.p.—has not greatly developed its huge resources.

WIND AND TIDE POWER

Coal, oil and water supply almost the whole of the world's power. A few odd fuels like wood are here and there used for power, but these could never be really important. The three neglected sources of power are wind, tides, and the internal heat of the earth. The difficulty about using wind-power is that it takes a large, bulky and expensive wind-wheel to develop quite a small horse-power; that when the wind is feeble a huge and light wind-wheel is required to obtain any power, and when the wind is strong it is very apt to blow a large light wind-wheel away. Moreover, the power is not available all the time, and no one knows whether or not there will be a wind, say, a fort-night to-day at nine in the morning. So any system of wind-power must be able to store a supply of energy when the wind is strong, to be used up on days when it is calm. Now it is not easy to store a great deal of energy. The most efficient way is to turn it into electricity and store this in accumulators, but accumulators are so expensive that this is not a paying proposition. Various other plans have been proposed: it has been suggested that the wind-wheels might pump water up to a high reservoir from which a continuous supply of water would flow to a turbine. Some such plan might be used, but it seems at present very unlikely that wind-power will compete with coal and oil. At present windmills are occasionally used for pumping water and more rarely for generating electricity.

The use of the tides seems more promising. Every day the sea rises and falls some 15 feet twice a day. In some places this is much exceeded. In one square mile of sea alone the tide power, if it could all be utilised, would give 15,000 h.p. all day long. The difficulty is to use the power. An experimental tide-plant was recently tried out at Avonmouth where the tides are very high. The principle is to allow the tide to run in and out of a large dammed-off dock through a turbine. The turbines, which will work with a low pressure of water, such as the tides give,

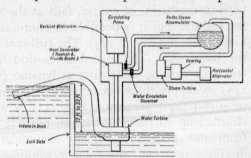

FIG. 133.—The power-unit of the Shishkoff Hydro-thermal power-plant. (Courtesy of *The Engineer*.)

are not very efficient and the difficulty really is to build the necessary locks, dams, etc., for an amount of money which can be repaid by the power that can be obtained from the turbines. There is little doubt that if coal and oil were to run short we should soon invent ways of using tide-power very efficiently indeed, and probably in the end get the power even more cheaply than coal and oil-power. At present, however, no one will spend the money required to develop our tide resources. The experimental plant tried out at Avonmouth Docks employed the Shishkoff Hydro-thermal system, which, although the plant is not now in use, operated successfully for some time. It

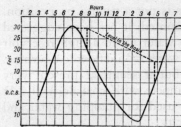

FIG. 134.—Curve showing level of sea at different times. Dotted line shows level in the dock-basin. (Courtesy of *The Engineer*.)

embodies several interesting principles, notably the remarkable idea of turning work into heat and storing this. Fig. 134 shows the way the tide rises and falls in the river. Take the period from high-water (7 a.m.) to the next high-water (7.30 p.m.). The sea fills the basin and at high-water the gates are shut, and by 8.45 a.m. the tide has dropped so that the water in the river is 10 feet below that in the basin. This is a sufficient head to work the turbine. The level in the basin, of course, falls as the water goes out through the turbine, but it is possible to continue to run it till a quarter to five (8 hours out of 12½). The turbines then have to stop while the basin fills. The ingenious notion is employed of driving from the turbine shaft, first a dynamo (vertical alternator, Fig. 133) to supply the current needed, secondly a sort of propeller or stirrer (heat generator, Fig. 133) in which water is violently churned up so that the friction heats it to boiling. The steam from this goes to a steam accumulator—already described in connection with the colliery winding engine—and so makes a store of superheated water under great pressure. During the 4 hours out of the 12½ when the turbine has not water enough

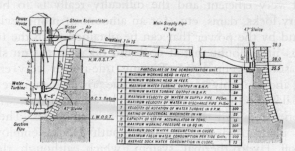

FIG. 135.—Section of Shishkoff experimental plant.
(Courtesy of *The Engineer*.)

to work it, the charged steam accumulator works a turbine which drives a dynamo and generates the electricity. In this way the tide-plant can give a permanent and continuous supply of power. The trouble, however, is still the great cost of the basin which stores the water.

There remains the internal heat of the earth. It is found that a deep mine gets about a degree Fahrenheit hotter for every hundred feet we descend, so that at a depth of 25,000 feet the temperature would be well above that at which water would boil. So it would seem just possible to let water flow down a pipe to the bottom of a bore-hole of that depth and use the steam from it to drive an engine. The difficulties are at present enormous. No one has ever made a hole deeper than 7,348 ft. (about a mile and a half), and very deep holes are tremendously expensive.

In volcanic regions, however, the heat is much nearer the surface and it has been found possible to get power from the jets of steam which issue from the ground in certain districts in Italy, where the rocks are believed to be molten only a mile underground. Similar plant could be erected in most volcanic districts, but unfortunately eruptions and earthquakes make these very unsuitable for factories and power-houses!

DISTRIBUTION OF COAL-POWER

Coal has the great disadvantage of being a solid, and a solid is the least convenient form of material to distribute. Compare the ease of occasionally turning a gas-tap with the difficulty of stoking a fire. This is not the only disadvantage of burning solid coal. An equal disadvantage is that a coal fire or furnace cannot be kept steady. The coal is stoked at intervals and the fire becomes alternately hotter and cooler. A gas fire or oil fire will stay steady for days together.

A very successful attempt to overcome these difficulties has been made by the expedient of grinding the coal to an extremely fine powder and blowing it through pipes to the place where it is needed. The first and obvious advantage is the ease in handling

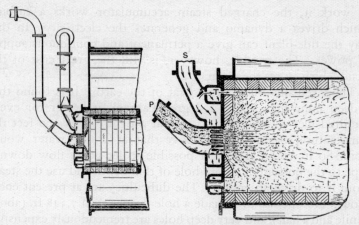

FIG. 136.—Coal powdered in a mill such as that of Fig. 392a is blown through the pipe P into the furnace chamber. Further air from the pipe (S) assists the combustion. (From material kindly supplied by the British Rema Mfg. Co., Ltd.)

it; the second that small coal and slack can be used; a third that the same blast of air can carry the coal dust into the furnace, burn the coal and sweep away the ash.

The powdered coal dust is burnt almost like a gas in a special burner. Fig. 136 shows an installation for heating a Lancashire boiler by powdered coal. The coal-dust and air (P) pass through the face of the burner, from slots in which further air (S) issues. A small supply of air (T) round the edge of the setting prevents damage to the firebrick lining.

It is obvious, however, that pulverised coal is useful only for large furnaces and that it would be quite unmanageable for domestic heating.

COAL GAS

Coal can be turned into gas in various ways, the simplest of which is to heat it. Watch a lump of coal when put on the fire: it gives out a smoke which later catches alight and burns with a bright flame. This smoke is very impure coal-gas. After

a time no more flame comes from the coal and it simply burns
with a bright red glow. If a bit of this glowing coal is quenched
in water, you will see that it is coke.

Now, if anything is to burn, it must have air, and so to get the
coal-gas without burning it the coal is heated in wide tubes
called retorts (Fig. 138), into which air cannot enter. In Fig. 138
is shown a plan of a modern gas works. The coal is first broken,
then raised by a mechanical elevator to bins, from which it runs
down to the retorts. These are long firebrick shafts heated by the
flame from a furnace. The waste heat of the latter is used to
raise steam in a boiler. As the coal passes down the retorts it is
slowly raised to a bright red heat and gives out all its gas in an
impure state, mixed with steam, tar-vapour, etc. The coal, when
it reaches the bottom of the retort, has become coke: this is
cooled, broken up, sorted into sizes and sold.

Why should coal contain "gas"? Coal contains about 90% of
carbon and 4 per cent of hydrogen by weight. To this is to be
added some nitrogen, some sulphur and some ash.

These elements are not merely *mixed* in the coal but their

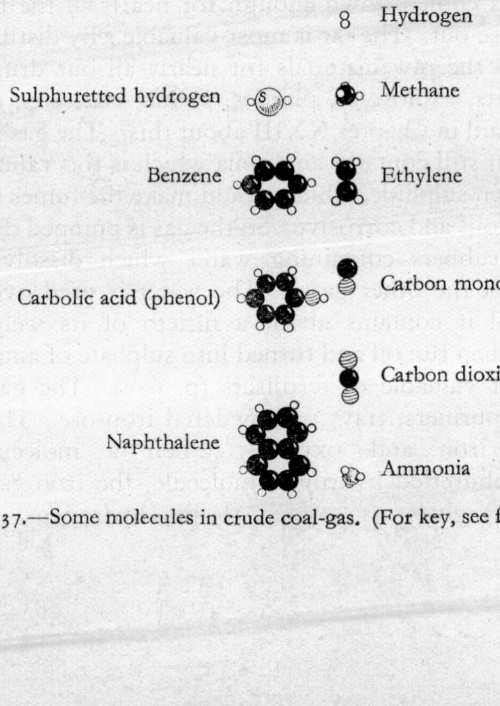

FIG. 137.—Some molecules in crude coal-gas. (For key, see footnote, p. 567.)

atoms are combined in rather complicated meshworks about which we do not yet know a great deal. When the coal is made red hot, its atoms are speeded up tremendously: in the retort the complicated meshworks of atoms are broken to small pieces. Some of these pieces, chiefly networks of carbon atoms, remain as coke; but the smaller pieces or molecules fly off as gas. Among these (Fig. 137) are the simple molecules of hydrogen, methane, ethylene, carbon monoxide, carbon dioxide, ammonia, sulphuretted hydrogen, and the more complicated molecules of benzene, carbolic acid and naphthalene, and a hundred or so other substances.

Roughly speaking, half the gas is hydrogen, a third is methane and a tenth is carbon monoxide; of the rest 1% may be ammonia, 2% hydrogen sulphide, and 4% other substances. If we let some of the gas escape as it comes out of the retort, it looks quite unlike coal gas. It appears to the eye just like the thick smoke which rises when a shovelful of small coal is thrown on a hot fire. The smokiness is due to droplets of water and tar. As soon as the gas cools, most of the tar and steam condense, and by passing the gas through water-cooled iron tubes (Fig. 138, condensers), it is cooled down enough for nearly all the tar and water to condense out. The tar is most valuable. By distilling it, motor-spirit and the raw materials for nearly all our drugs and dyes, disinfectants, explosives, plastics, scents, etc., etc., can be made. More is said in Chapter XXIII about this. The gas is now fairly clear, but it still contains ammonia which is too valuable to lose and hydrogen sulphide, which would make the fumes from a gas flame poisonous and corrosive. So the gas is pumped through washers and scrubbers containing water which dissolves the ammonia but not the other gases. The water is used over and over again until it contains about a fiftieth of its weight of ammonia. It is then run off and turned into sulphate of ammonia, one of the most valuable of fertilisers (p. 649). The gas next passes through purifiers, trays of powdered iron-ore. This is a compound of iron and oxygen. When a molecule of this meets a sulphuretted hydrogen molecule, the iron captures the sulphur and gives its oxygen to the hydrogen.

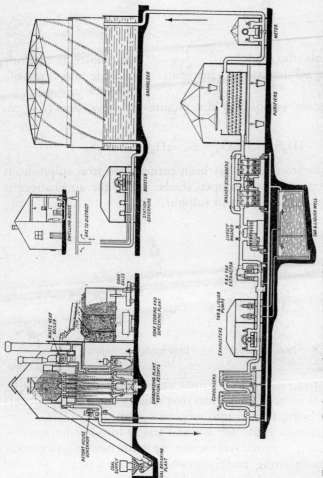

FIG. 138.—Coal gas made in the VERTICAL RETORTS passes to the CONDENSERS where tar, benzol, water is removed. It is then washed with water in the WASHERS and SCRUBBERS to remove ammonia and passed over iron oxide in the PURIFIER to remove sulphuretted hydrogen. It is then measured and stored in the GASHOLDER whence it is driven at a fixed pressure to the district supplied. (Courtesy of Messrs. Eyre and Spottiswoode, Ltd., from Meade's *New Modern Gasworks Practice*.)

One molecule iron oxide[1] and three of sulphuretted hydrogen change to One molecule of iron sulphide and three of water.

The chemist symbolises the picture we have drawn as an equation

$$3H_2S + Fe_2O_3 = 3H_2O + Fe_2S_3$$

When all the iron oxide has been turned into iron sulphide, it is thrown out in heaps in open sheds. Here, the air changes it back to iron oxide again and sulphur.

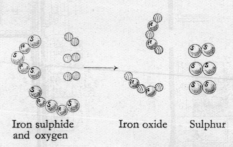

Iron sulphide   Iron oxide Sulphur
and oxygen

Thus, the iron oxide can be used again and again and finally, when there is more sulphur than iron oxide in it, it ends a profitable life by being turned into sulphuric acid!

The gas is now ready for use and passes into the huge gasometers where it is stored over water, or in the newest gasometers under a huge "piston," and thence it is driven at a steady pressure to the town.

Very large gas-works purify their gas more elaborately. It

[1]Oxygen atoms are represented with line shading: iron atoms are marked Fe: sulphur atoms S: the very small spheres are hydrogen atoms.

pays to do this, because all the impurities taken out are useful for some other purpose.

Our ton of coal has now been split up into four chief products:

> 230 lbs. of gas.[1]
> 112 lbs. of tar.
> 20–40 lbs. of ammonia as ammonium sulphate.
> 1550 lbs. of coke.

The gas is used for domestic purposes, heating, cooking and lighting chiefly. It is rather expensive for large-scale heating or driving machinery, but for domestic work and for small heating jobs about factories it is invaluable.

The tar, when distilled, gives us benzol for motor-spirit, disinfectants, naphthalene and anthracene (invaluable for making dyes) and finally leaves behind pitch, which, when melted, is sprayed on our tar-mac roads.

By making coal-gas at as low a temperature as possible, less gas and more tar is obtained. It has been found possible to turn this tar into valuable motor spirit by hydrogenating it. The tar is mixed with some molybdenum sulphide, which helps on the reaction but is not used up, and hydrogen gas is pumped into it.

The product is a very good yield of motor spirit. This process, if developed, can make Great Britain independent of the overseas oil-wells from which her petrol is now taken.

PRODUCER GAS

In making ordinary coal gas, the coal is split up into gas, liquid by-products and coke. It is a common practice to turn the coke into gas also. This can be done by making it combine with the oxygen of the air or with steam.

The "producer" is a simple arrangement for turning coke into gas. It depends on the fact that coke—which is carbon—burns in the oxygen of the air and gives the gas carbon dioxide.

[1] These figures vary according to the quality of the coal.

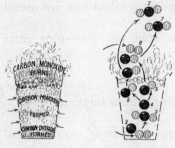

FIG. 139.—How carbon monoxide is formed in a coke fire. Oxygen molecules (1) enter and combine with carbon atoms (2) making carbon dioxide (3), which with more carbon (4) makes carbon monoxide (5, 5), which meeting with more oxygen (6) burns to carbon dioxide (7).

This gas will not burn, but when it passes through red-hot coke it changes to carbon monoxide, a gas which will burn!

To turn coke into gas, all that is needed is to let air pass up through a thick layer of red-hot coke. You can see this happening in a night-watchman's brazier or a red glowing coal fire. The air passes in at the bottom, and at the top, burn pale-blue flickering flames of carbon monoxide.

The "producer" is simply a large stove. Air (oxygen and nitrogen) enters at the bottom and carbon monoxide and nitrogen leave at the top. This mixture, of course, cannot burn—as it does in the bucket of coke—because there is no air above the coke in the producer. Producers are often used to fire furnaces. The gas-works in Figure 138 is fired by a producer. Air enters below, passes through the layer of glowing coke and leaves it as producer gas—carbon monoxide and nitrogen. This meets a supply of air in the upper part of the

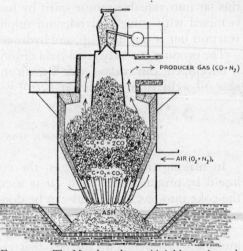

MOND PRODUCER

PRODUCER GAS (CO + N$_2$)

$CO_2 + C = 2CO$

$C + O_2 = CO_2$

AIR (O$_2$ + N$_2$),

ASH

FIG. 140.—The Mond producer. Air is blown through a mass of glowing coke. The issuing gas is a mixture of inflammable carbon monoxide and inert nitrogen. Note the arrangements for adding fuel and withdrawing ash without admitting air.

furnace and burns, so heating the retorts.

Producers are often used to drive large gas-engines and a lorry has been marketed which carries a little producer on the running-board. This is fed with charcoal and the producer gas is burned in the engine! The arrangement is of course bulky compared with the petrol engine; but it is very useful to be able to run a lorry on charcoal in savage countries where petrol cannot be obtained.

WATER GAS

Another way of turning coke into gas is to make it white-hot and blow steam over it. Each steam molecule combines with a carbon atom and makes a molecule each of carbon monoxide and hydrogen, both inflammable gases. If we represent a carbon atom by a black ball, an oxygen atom by a grey ball and a hydrogen atom by a small white ball we can express what happens as:

FIG. 141.—Carbon and water $\longrightarrow$ carbon monoxide and hydrogen.

Unfortunately, the coke cools down in a few minutes and has to be heated up again by an air-blast.

The water-gas from the steam and coke has excellent heating-power. Unfortunately it is odourless and very poisonous, so that if it is supplied to houses escapes may occur and poison the unfortunate inmates, who are not warned by the smell. Attempts to scent the gas have not proved successful and in England, at least, it is chiefly used for mixing with coal-gas, which has a powerful smell of its own.

HOW WE MAKE HEAT

The energy in coal, oil or gas is chemical energy. When they burn—that is to say, combine with oxygen—this energy appears as heat. For many purposes, it is as heat we want the energy, but for many others we want it as work.

First of all, let us think about heating. There is no difficulty about getting a full measure of heat from coal, oil or gas: you have merely to set them alight and supply them with plenty of air. The problem is rather to get the heat where it is wanted and at the right temperature.

First of all, suppose we are heating an ordinary room. We can do it by a coal fire, a coke stove, hot-water pipes, a gas fire, an electric fire (and one or two less important ways).

Everyone likes the coal fire best, though everything is to be said against it. Though it is not very expensive, it is very wasteful of heat. Only about one-fifth of the heat of a bright coal fire enters the room and the rest goes up the chimney. A dull fire is far less efficient even than this. All the valuable ammonia, motor-spirit and other by-products of the coal are wasted. A horrid smoke ascends to the sky and befouls our lungs and makes London fogs. Coal, too, is dirty and bulky to store and heavy to carry. But unquestionably we like the coal fire best. It looks beautiful—a thing that matters a great deal in one's house. It sends its heat into the room as radiation, which means that the body is warmed where the heat rays fall on it, while the transparent air stays fairly cool. But there is little doubt that if the coal fire were forbidden and factories which (quite unnecessarily) emit clouds of black smoke were heavily fined, in a few years we should be rejoicing in the change. London would have the clean bright sunshine of the country. Its buildings would be white where now they are black; its stonework would no longer corrode away.

No factory could afford to burn coal in the uneconomical way that an open grate does. The engineer realises that when he buys a ton of coal, he is buying, say, 34,000,000 British Thermal Units of heat, enough to heat a hundred tons of water from 60° F. to boiling point, and that heat he means to have as far as it is possible. He does not intend to let valuable combustible gases and carbon go up the chimney as smoke, and so he supplies enough air to burn the coal completely to carbon dioxide and steam. Even the waste gases—nitrogen, carbon dioxide and steam—which have to escape up the chimney, have every available calorie of heat extracted from them.

Let us look for a moment at the boilers of the modern steam turbine such as runs an electrical generating station. In the first place the biggest possible area of boiler is exposed to the flame, so that by the time the gases leave the boiler they have given as much heat as possible to the water. This is accomplished by the

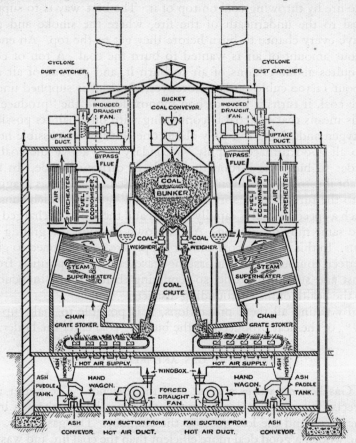

FIG. 142.—A modern boiler installation.

9

use of a water-tube boiler in which almost all the water is in comparatively narrow tubes which present a huge surface the hot gases.

The gases then pass through a feed-water heater (fuel economizer) where they give up still more heat and so warm up the water that is going to be supplied to the boilers. Finally they flow over tubes through which the air supply to the grates is passing, so giving up more heat still.

In order to burn the coal effectively, it is not advisable to stoke the fire by throwing coal on top of it. The best way is to supply coal to the underneath of the fire, where the smoke and gas have every chance to burn before they get to the top. An enormous amount of air is wanted to burn the coal. A ton of coal requires about 11 tons of air to burn it, and 11 tons of air are about 12,500 cubic yards. Moreover, if the air is supplied under the coal, it turns it into carbon monoxide as in the "producer"; this means that the coal is combining with only half its possible oxygen and giving out only about one-third of its possible heat. So all good furnaces supply "secondary air" above the coal in order to burn the carbon monoxide to carbon dioxide. In the plant illustrated, an automatic stoker is used. The coal is dragged into the furnace on a sort of "chain-mail" grating which runs at such a speed that all is rapidly burned and the ash is discharged by the same moving grating. Air is blown through the grating by fans. In this way the coal and air supply are proportioned to give perfect combustion. The issuing gases are often purified from dust and sulphur dioxide, so rendering them entirely innocuous to the health of the surrounding district.

By taking all these precautions, it is possible to make up to 80 % of the heat produced by the burning coal enter the boiler.

HEATING BY GAS AND ELECTRICITY

Gas heating varies a great deal in efficiency. The hotter the fireclay in a gas fire can be made, the more heat is thrown into the room and the less goes up the chimney. The gas fire is, on the whole, a good deal more efficient than the coal fire and wastes less than half its heat up the chimney.

The most efficient way of using gas is in a flueless heater. This sends all its heat into the room, but of course has the disadvantage of using up the air and causing no ventilation.

The electric fire requires no chimney, for it produces no fumes and needs no air, and so all the heat it gives is used to warm the room. But the electricity was made from coal and the best generating plant can only turn about 27% of the heat of the coal it burns into electricity. Some of this is lost in distributing it, so that the electric fire is really giving you only part of the heat of a coal fire at the generating station.

CENTRAL HEATING

Hot water or steam gives the most efficient way of warming rooms. All the warmth goes into the air of the rooms and an efficient type of boiler uses some half of the heat of the coke it burns in heating the hot water, and all this heat goes to heat the room. The disadvantage of the system is that it does not ventilate—coal or gas fires carry a stream of air through the room to the chimney—and it does not radiate much. It is much pleasanter to have the skin warmed by radiant heat and surrounded by cool moving air than to have it warmed by still hot air. None the less, the cheapness and convenience and safety of hot-water heating make almost every big building use it. The cost of the different methods of heating a room work out roughly as follows. Taking coal and coke at £2 a ton, anthracite at 90s. a ton, gas at 8½d. a therm, and electricity at 1d. a unit, the costs are estimated.[1]

Central heating	12
Coke stove	12
Open coal fire	21
Anthracite stove	22
Flueless gas-heater	31
Gas fire	50
Electricity	100

[1] Adapted from *House Heating*, by Margaret Fishenden: Witherby, 1925.

HEAT AND WORK

A problem which has only been solved in the last 150 years is a method of turning heat into work. The answers to it are the steam engine and the internal combustion engine. From these two almost all our power is drawn and on them our whole civilisation rests. Suppose, by some miracle, our steam engines, our gas engines and oil engines were all destroyed. At once electricity would fail, for it is nearly all made by driving dynamos with steam (or rarely oil) engines. Gas could perhaps be made for a few days for our heating, but only in the smallest works could the coal, etc., be handled by men and horses. Meanwhile, the trams have stopped, the ships have stopped, the cars have stopped. The towns in a few days are short of food: a few days more and the town population is freezing and starving. Ten years later the population would be back at the six million or so who lived in England in the eighteenth century, farming and carrying on the ancient crafts by hand. Civilisation does not depend on the engine, for in the seventeenth century Europe was civilised; but the keeping of forty-five million people in reasonable comfort in this little island is only made possible thereby. Let us, then, look at the steam engine as the prime reason for modern industrial civilisation and look on its chief inventor, James Watt, as the man who, in the whole of history, has had the greatest influence on the world.

By burning coal (or oil) we get heat. By this we mean that coal and air molecules moving quietly at the ordinary temperature combine, so forming molecules of carbon dioxide at some 1500° C. These molecules are moving several times as fast as those of carbon dioxide at ordinary temperatures and so have far more energy.

Coal and air combine or "burn," and *hot gas*, a medley of violently moving molecules, is obtained. We want to turn that violent haphazard jostling of molecules into an orderly circular motion of a wheel!

The steam engine's answer to the problem is this. Make the molecules of the hot gas jostle against and so speed up the molecules of a boiler and let these again speed up the molecules of water in the boiler. If the water-molecules are speeded up enough, their attraction will no longer hold them together and they will fly off as the gas, steam. Make a *movable partition* (a piston) against which the steam molecules can knock. When they have pushed it one way, bring the steam to the other side of the partition and let the molecules push it back again.

Connect to the partition some device for turning back-and-forth motion into circular motion and the job is done.

If you do not like that solution of the problem, let the steam molecules jostle against one side of a set of vanes stuck in a wheel and not against the other. In this way, they will push the wheel round. This is the principle of the turbine.

Now it took a great many years to learn to make an engine which would work efficiently—that is to say, which would turn a reasonable proportion of the motion of the steam molecules into motion of the piston. It can be proved theoretically that a steam engine can turn only a certain proportion of the heat given to it into power and the very best steam engine yet made cannot turn a quarter of the coal's heat into work. It seems very prodigal to let three-quarters of our good heat go to waste; but if you do not like it, your only remedy is to use an oil-engine which wastes only three-fifths of its heat. And as oil, in England, is more expensive than coal, you may be worse off than ever.

THE STEAM ENGINE

The steam engine first of all requires a boiler in which the steam is generated. An elaborate boiler is shown in Fig. 142. For smaller installations a Lancashire boiler (Fig. 143) is a favourite type, though many other designs are in use. The Lancashire boiler has its fire in a cylindrical space surrounded by the water. The fuel burns on the grate and the flame and hot gas travel down the centre and then underneath the boiler and away through the flue to the chimney stack which provides the draught. This arrangement gives plenty of time for the fire-gases to hand over their heat to the water. The water in the boiler boils at a temperature which depends on the pressure. If the boiler delivers steam at 60 lbs. pressure, the boiling point will be 145° C. The boiler has safety-valves which open when the pressure goes above some fixed value. They are in principle like the valve described on page 111. The tendency is to build boilers to operate at ever higher pressures: one has been used which actually turns water straight into the same volume of steam without any boiling (p. 121) at 374° C. and 3158 lbs. per square inch. Higher pressures, we shall see, mean greater efficiency.

Look at it this way. You put energy into the steam engine as heat. The higher the pressure of the steam, the hotter it is: consequently, the higher the pressure, the more energy goes into the engine per pound of steam. Now the steam comes out of the engine as a puff of steam at, say, 100° C. (as in a locomotive) or as water, if the engine has a condenser. Now, when the steam comes out of the engine, it carries with it heat which has not been turned into work: again, when it condenses, it gives up heat to the condenser water and this heat cannot be turned into work.

Suppose, then, that a certain amount of steam when it leaves the engine takes with it 1000 calories of heat. Now, if we put this steam into the engine with energy equal to 1500 calories, we shall get 500 calories back as work and waste 1000. But if we put the steam into the engine with 2000 calories of energy in it, we shall get 1000 back as work and waste 1000. So, in the first case we should waste two-thirds of our fire's energy; in the second case only one-half. So clearly the *greater* the energy of the steam when it enters the engine and the *less* its energy when it comes out, the more efficient our engine will be. Any heat that escapes from the engine as heat will lower its efficiency. So the tendency of steam-engine makers is first to use high

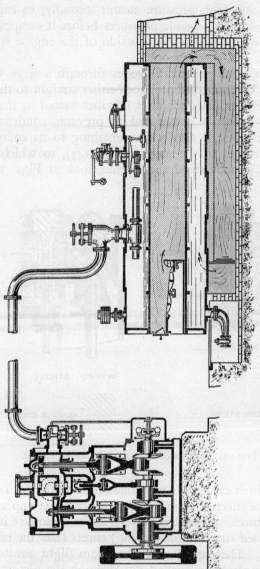

Fig. 143.—Lancashire boiler and reciprocating steam engine.

temperature and high pressure steam: secondly, to expand the
steam to the lowest possible pressures before it escapes or condenses; thirdly, to protect the outside of the engine from cold
air.

The steam, once generated, passes through a large valve by
which it can be controlled and goes either straight to the engine
or the superheater, which is a set of tubes heated by the furnace
gases. This makes it hotter and so prevents condensation to
water in the pipes; it also adds something to its energy. The
steam now comes to the engine (Fig. 143), to which a valve
admits it. To understand the engine, look at Figs. 144, 145.

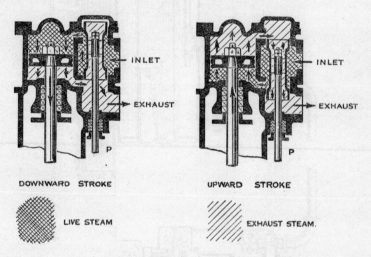

DOWNWARD STROKE

LIVE STEAM

UPWARD STROKE

EXHAUST STEAM.

FIG. 144.—Course of steam in reciprocating engine.

The shaft which carries the wheel has an eccentric (p. 188) on it,
which has the effect of moving the piston-valve (P) up and down
as the shaft turns. When this valve is at the bottom of its stroke,
the compressed steam (dark shading) enters *below* the piston and
forces it up. The expanded waste steam (light shading) from
the previous stroke is pushed out through the piston valve to

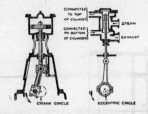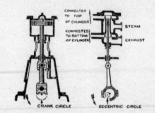

FIG. 145.—Illustrating the way in which the position of the valve is controlled by the position of the piston. The right band figure shows the position one quarter revolution or half-stroke later than the left-hand figure.

the exhaust pipe. When the piston reaches the top, the piston valve is moved up by the eccentric. Live steam now enters above the piston and forces it down while the expanded steam from the last stroke escapes.

Now it would be wasteful to let steam escape which has not fully or fairly fully expanded; and it would appear that we are doing this; actually, however, the piston valve cuts off the supply of compressed steam to the cylinders when the piston has moved only a quarter or less of the way up or down the cylinder and the compressed steam already in the cylinder drives it the rest of the way by expanding. The steam is even then not fully expanded, accordingly it may enter (as in the engine shown in Fig. 143) a second and much larger low pressure cylinder, where it expands still more; in large marine engines it commonly goes to a third one. If the final cylinder was open to the air, the steam could only expand till its pressure was the same as that of the air, 15 lbs. per square inch; but, in efficient engines, the steam exhausts into a condenser which is a space containing no air and kept cold by water cooling. The steam here condenses back to water. The pressure in this condenser is very small indeed, perhaps only ½ lb., and the steam can expand as much as the size of the cylinders will allow it to.

We can see, then, how the steam gives an up and down movement to the piston rods. This is changed to a circular motion by the arrangement best seen in Fig. 145, and already discussed

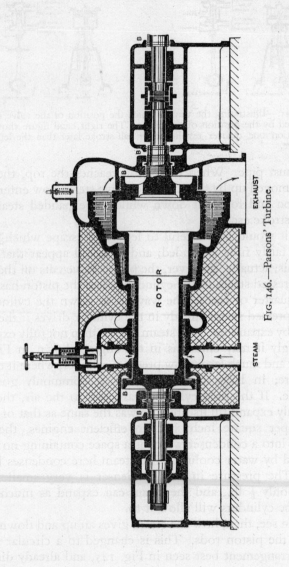

FIG. 146.—Parsons' Turbine.

on page 189. The shaft always carries a heavy flywheel, for the piston is not exerting any turning force on the shaft at the extreme top and bottom of the stroke (Fig. 94), and the kinetic energy stored in the heavy flywheel carries it past these points. The "governor" deserves a note. A steam engine is normally required to turn at a steady speed whether loaded or not. Suppose you are driving a circular saw with it. The tendency would be, as soon as the log was sawn through, for the engine, having no resistance to oppose it, to speed up (compare page 163). The governor has two balls held by springs and these rotate with the shaft. As the shaft speeds up, centrifugal force throws them outward. This has the effect of closing the valve admitting steam to the cylinders, thus slowing the shaft. If the shaft slows down, the opposite effect occurs. A governor of a similar type is used to regulate the speed of gramophone motors; one of these is shown in Fig. 416.

The turbine is very efficient for large units and high speeds. What we worked out about efficiency is true for it also. The steam must enter it at very high temperatures and pressures and expand to the lowest temperatures and pressures if the heat supplied to the boiler is to do the greatest possible amount of work.

A steam turbine (Fig. 146) has a long rotating portion (rotor) which is set with small blades set diagonally to the direction of rotation rather like the blades of a propeller, only far more numerous. This rotor turns in a casing (stator) also set with blades more or less at right angles to those on the rotor. Fig. 147 shows the blades as they would be seen if the casing were transparent. The steam enters at the narrow end of the turbine. The first set of blades on the casing turn it so that the steam hits the moving blades and thrusts them on: as the steam leaves them it gives them a sort of backward kick like the recoil of a gun when fired. This has the chief effect in moving the rotor. The next set of fixed blades catch the steam and again direct it on to the next set of moving blades. This continues all the way as the steam progresses (to the right) along the space between the

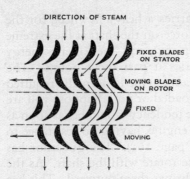

DIRECTION OF STEAM

FIXED BLADES ON STATOR

MOVING BLADES ON ROTOR

FIXED

MOVING

FIG. 147.—Arrangement of blades in Parsons' Turbine.

casing and rotor. The steam is encouraged to expand by making the rotor wider as the steam goes further. Finally, the steam emerges and passes to the condenser (not shown in figure). One of the most difficult problems in designing the turbines is to prevent steam from leaking along the shaft. Packing such as used in the pumps on p. 201 or the cylinder of Fig. 144, would not do, for turbines move so fast that tremendous friction would develop. The principle finally adopted is to raise the surface of the ends of the rotor shaft and of the casing into sharp ridges which fit into each other (BB). Steam does leak across these, but the path for it is so long and crooked that very little gets away. The steam pressure obviously thrusts the whole rotor to the right, so the bearings have to take a large thrust. The large wide bearings (on the right) are particularly well able to resist this force.

The reciprocating (cylinder-and-piston) engine and the turbine each has its place. The first is suitable for small units and works well both at low and at fairly high speeds and is exceedingly reliable and robust. It is used in most small ship's engines, in locomotives and in innumerable factories. The turbine is more efficient. The finest modern plants will turn just over thirty per cent. of the heat energy of the fuel into power, while the best reciprocating engine gives but little over twenty per cent. It is ideal for driving high-speed mechanisms such as electric motors: it is particularly valuable in large units such as are needed in generating plant. In recent years it has gained much ground because gearing has been developed that can slow its rotation down to any extent required. The efficiency of the turbine in turning heat into work is surpassed by that of internal combustion engines; but since in most countries coal is a much cheaper fuel than oil or gas, the steam turbine holds its own.

The simplest internal combustion engine to discuss is the petrol engine, because almost every reader has access to one; Fig. 148 shows the essential portion of it—the cylinder, piston, valves, ignition and crankshaft. The principle of every internal combustion engine is that a charge of air and something that will

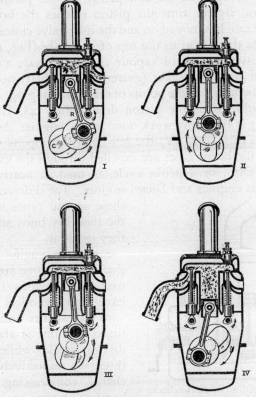

FIG. 148.—The Otto cycle in a petrol engine.

burn is set burning in the cylinder. The heat generated expands the air and burnt gases and these thrust down the piston. The internal combustion engine is very efficient because the energy of the burning gas at the beginning of the stroke is so much higher than that of the exhaust gases. Moreover, all the energy is generated in the cylinder and there are no such losses as occur in the steam engine when the heat has to be transferred from furnace to boiler. In Fig. 148 (I) the piston is being dragged down by the crankshaft (C) pulling on the connecting rod (R). The cam (p. 188) has lifted the inlet valve (I) and the cylinder fills with the "charge" of air and petrol vapour produced in the carburettor. By the time the piston reaches the bottom of its stroke, the cam has moved on and the inlet valve closes. The shaft now carries the piston to the top of its stroke (Fig. 148, II) and so compresses the petrol vapour and air to, say, a sixth of its bulk. The contact-breaker (geared to the shaft) now causes a spark to pass between the points of the sparking-plug. The charge explodes and drives the piston down (Fig. 148, III)—on this stroke only is there any work done by the engine. As the piston rises again (Fig. 148, IV) the left-hand cam opens the exhaust valve and the burnt gases are expelled through the exhaust pipe. This, the Otto, or 4-stroke cycle, is used in nearly all petrol engines, gas engines and Diesel engines. The difference between these several types is chiefly in the fuel they burn and the way they ignite it.

Since the engine drives the shaft only on one stroke out of four, the obvious thing is to have four cylinders (Fig. 149) with the sparks and valves so timed that one is always at the driving stroke while the other three are respectively taking in charge, compressing it and exhausting burnt gases. Hardly

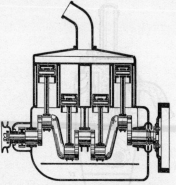

FIG. 149.—Section of four-cylinder internal combustion engine.

any have fewer than four cylinders—six or eight give a still smoother drive.

The part described is the essential part of the petrol engine. To it must be added, first, gearing from the crankshaft to the small shafts which turn the cams and to the mechanism which makes the contact which delivers the current to the sparking plug; secondly, an efficient oiling system, for the internal combustion engine becomes very hot and so easily burns up and destroys its oil; thirdly, a cooling system by which water circulates round the walls of the cylinders; fourthly, some arrangement

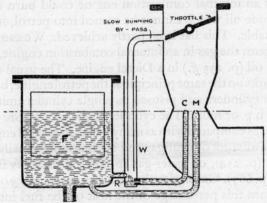

FIG. 150.—A simple type of carburettor. (Courtesy of Messrs. Chapman & Hall and Mr. A. W. Judge; from the latter's *Carburettors and Carburation*.)

for regulating the proportion of air and combustible gas in the charge. The last process is performed by the carburettor. There are many varieties. Fig. 150 illustrates a simple pattern.

The petrol from the tank enters the float-chamber F in which, by means of a needle-valve opened and shut by a float, a constant level of petrol is kept. There are two jets, a main jet M at such a level that petrol just does not overflow from it, and a compensating jet C fed by a fine orifice R which will only supply fuel at a constant and slow rate. The suction of the engine lowers the pressure in the carburetter and consequently petrol is drawn from both jets and evaporates in the in-rushing air. At low speeds both jets give their full supply and a rich mixture results: at high speeds the more vigorous suction draws a greater supply from M but cannot draw any greater supply from C, and so the proportion of petrol to air is diminished. The slow-running by-pass provides a rich mixture when the engine suction is too feeble to withdraw a sufficient supply from jets C and M.

The petrol engine is very efficient: it will turn some 25% of the energy of its petrol into work. But petrol is expensive fuel. Only about one-third of crude oil or 27% of coal can be turned into petrol. If an internal combustion engine could burn coal or the part of crude oil which cannot be turned into petrol, it would be most valuable. This has been partly achieved. We can gasify our coal and burn the gas in an internal combustion engine, or we can burn fuel oil (p. 233 *ff.*) in a Diesel engine. The usual type of gas engine works on the same principle as the petrol engine, but employs very large cylinders and pistons, as single cylinder units generate up to 200 h.p. or more. The cylinders may have a bore and stroke of four feet as compared with as many inches in a petrol engine. They may burn a mixture of coal-gas and air, but more usually burn producer gas (p. 254), or water-gas (p. 255), or the gas from blast-furnaces (p. 687). Gas engines have shown an efficiency of 29–30%, i.e. they turn this percentage of the heat of the fuel into power.

The engine which has made and is making the greatest advances is the Diesel. The Diesel engine has the vast advantage of burning heavy oil and thereby using the part of crude oil which the petrol engine cannot employ: its efficiency is very great and it requires no unreliable electrical apparatus for ignition. Fig. 151 shows the essential part of a Diesel engine. The engine generally resembles the petrol engine, but there is no carburettor. In place of the sparking plug is a jet through which a pump can force a fine spray of oil. In Fig. 151 (1) the piston is descending and the inlet valve has been opened by a cam mechanism. *Pure air only* is drawn into the cylinder. In Fig. 151 (2) the inlet valve closes: the piston now rises and compresses the air far more highly than the fuel is compressed in the petrol engine: thus, it may be compressed 25 times

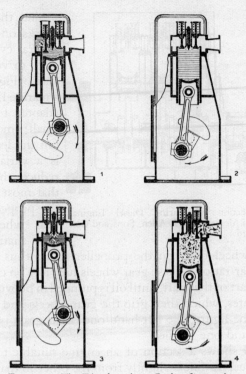

FIG. 151.—The Diesel engine. Cycle of operation.

instead of 5 times. This makes the air very hot. When the piston is at the top of its stroke (Fig. 151, 3) a fine spray of oil is injected into the cylinder from a small pump worked by the engine. This instantly burns in the hot compressed air and forces the piston down. This is the working stroke. The piston now rises, the exhaust valve is opened and the hot gases are driven out (4). The reason why the Diesel engine has not displaced the petrol engine is its weight. The very high pressures require very strong and heavy parts. None the less, it is now being rapidly developed. Many of the London buses are run by Diesel engines and even aeroplane engines of this type have been built; whether they will be extensively employed for the private car seems less certain.

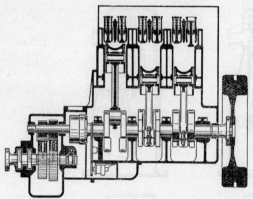

FIG. 152.—Section of marine Diesel Engine. (Courtesy of Messrs. W. H. Allen, Sons and Co., Ltd., Bedford.)

Since the Diesel only works on one stroke, several cylinders usually drive a single shaft. Fig. 152 shows a marine Diesel engine adapted for driving a small motor-coaster. On the left hand side is a variable gear to reduce the speed to that most suitable for the propeller. Two gear wheels on the main-shaft mesh with two gear wheel cogs on the propeller shaft; thus giving two different gear-ratios. These gear wheels turn idly on central plates which are part of the shaft, until oil is pumped in between either set of these plates, which then grip the gear wheels and take up the drive. In the figure, the left-hand one (high gear) is driven and the right-hand one is idle.

Plate XII shows a section of an engine suitable for driving a lorry or a bus. It differs slightly from the other in that the charge is compressed into a bulb where it is fired. The section only allows one valve (the exhaust) to be seen; note the cam and push-rod on the left. These engines are made in units of 130 h.p. and are suitable for bus or lorry work.

The Diesel engine is perhaps the middle-powered engine of the future. It may not surpass the steam turbine for very large installations nor the petrol engine for the low-powered units—but for units designed to provide 100–1000 or more h.p. it seems to have advantages over every other form.

The other really important source of power is the electric motor. There is no practicable large-scale method of making electricity except by the dynamo, and the dynamo must be turned by engines driven by water, oil, coal or their products. But electricity gives the supreme method of distributing power, so that about the most important use of the steam turbine or water turbine is to make electricity by which the whole power supply of a town can be sent along a wire thinner than your little finger.

It is essential then to understand something about electricity and to take a long digression while we discover something about what it is and how it behaves.

CHAPTER X

ELECTRIC CURRENTS

WHAT IS ELECTRICITY?

THE statement is often made that nobody knows what electricity is. Well, no one knows what anything is! Of matter, we know that it is made of atoms, which are collections of minute particles—electrons, protons and neutrons—bound in certain patterns. As we have already stated, the atom has a small central nucleus containing the heavier positive protons and neutrons[1]: its outer portion consists of electrons. Matter, then, consists of electrons, protons and neutrons *bound into atoms.* Electricity, we know, consists of electrons—and sometimes protons—*free to move.* What an electron or proton is, we do not know. After all, the only way we can explain what a thing *is,* is to say: "It is made of so-and-so, has such-and-such a shape and is moving in a particular way." The questioner can always ask what "so-and-so" is, and will finally get back to a question that cannot be answered. Science does not aim at an ultimate and complete explanation of anything, but knows it must be content to explain everything in terms of one or a very few entities such as "energy," "space," "time," etc. We know a few things about electrons: we can tell roughly what size they are, what they weigh, how strongly they attract each other, but we cannot tell what an electron is made of.

The likeliest view is that an electron is a portion of energy: we cannot really picture this, but anything we *can* picture about the electron seems to be untrue. Think of it then, for the present,

[1]See pages 528 *ff.*

as a tiny particle of energy, as much smaller than an atom as a grain of salt is smaller than a house.

The electricity which moves along wires and snaps through air as sparks is simply a crowd of these electrons. These electrons, we say, have a negative *charge*: simply a short way of saying they have the power of repelling each other and of attracting another kind of particle (the proton), which is said to have a positive charge. The words negative and positive are quite misleading and when we apply them to electricity it is as well to forget all other ideas we attach to these words in common life. The positive particles—except in most exceptional circumstances —remain a part of an atom of matter in the central nuclei of the atoms. As it is very difficult to remove all the (negative) electrons from any atom (except that of hydrogen), it is very difficult to get positive particles—protons—by themselves.

The negative charge of an electron is equal to the positive charge of a proton and an atom of matter has just as many negative electrons as positive protons: consequently an atom, taken as a whole, has no charge at all. If an atom picks up and holds some more electrons it becomes negatively charged: if it has a few of its electrons knocked off, it becomes positively charged, for it has then fewer negative electrons than positive ones. These charged atoms are called *ions*, a term we shall have to use fairly often. Fig. 153 shows how an atom of copper could be ionised in this way.

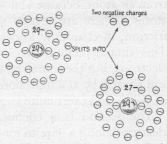

A piece of metal or anything that conducts electricity has in it some electrons which are only loosely bound to atoms or not bound to them at all. If the piece of metal is negatively charged, it has more electrons than its own atoms pro-

FIG. 153.—A copper atom (left) is electrically neutral, having 29 positive charges and 29 negative charges. It can be broken up in various ways into two electrons, each with a single negative charge, and a copper ion (right). This is positively charged for it has 29 positive charges and only 27 negative charges.

vide. If it is positively charged, it has fewer electrons than this.

Electricity then, as ordinarily met with, is a crowd of electrons, minute particles capable of movement and repelling each other vigorously. From this notion it is easy to see what is meant by the quantity of electricity and the potential of electricity. The quantity of electricity is simply the number of free electrons—this is what we measure in "coulombs" or in ampere-hours. The potential of electricity (which we measure in volts) is its tendency to flow. The electrons repel each other; the nearer they are to each other the more powerfully they repel each other and the more force they will exert in their effort to get away. So the quantity of electricity is the number of electrons; the potential of electricity measures the tendency of the electrons to get away from each other.

THE MAKING OF ELECTRICITY

If we want to get electricity—electrons—we have to get it from an atom, because almost all the electrons in the world are in atoms. There are several ways of doing this. The first is by friction, mechanically knocking a few electrons off by rubbing. This simple method gives very little electricity, i.e., very few electrons, but these may be very crowded into a very small space and so may be at a high potential (thousands or tens of thousands of volts), and exert quite large forces.

The second is a chemical way: persuading atoms to send electrons along a wire to ions which need them more badly. This is the method of an electric battery. It is convenient but expensive. It yields electricity at a low potential (1–3 volts).

The third method is to set the free electrons in a metal wire moving *to* one end and *away from* the other by attracting them with a magnet. This is what is done in the dynamo.

Dynamos may be designed to give electrons at almost any potential, but 50–5,000 volts is usual.

FRICTIONAL ELECTRICITY

The frictional method of making electricity was the first to be discovered. It is no longer important, but it is very simple to handle experimentally, and so gives the beginner an easy way of finding out a few things about electricity. Take a stick of sealing-wax (or a vulcanite pen), a bit of fine thread—best silk —and a little bit of dry cork the size of a pea. Stick the cork to the thread, best by a tiny dot of sealing-wax, and hang the thread to something (the edge of a lamp shade or a shelf will do). Now rub the sealing-wax with a woollen material like a coat sleeve, bring it near the hanging piece of cork, but don't touch it. The cork is *attracted by the wax*. Now, the reason of this is that

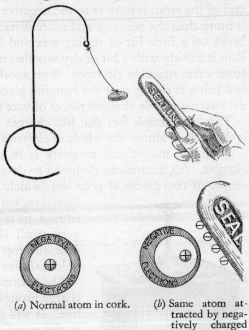

(*a*) Normal atom in cork.   (*b*) Same atom attracted by negatively charged wax.

Why the sealing-wax attracts the cork.

FIG. 154—Electrical attraction.

the rubbing knocked off a few of the outer electrons of the atoms of the wool and the wax, and, on account of some peculiarity of these which we don't know much about, the loose electrons stuck to the wax rather than the wool. The sealing-wax, then, was left with a few extra negative electrons. These clustered on the outside of the wax.

When the wax came near the cork these electrons attracted the positive nuclei of the carbon, hydrogen and oxygen atoms in the cork, and repelled the negative electrons so that the atoms in the cork instead of being like Fig. 154 *a* became like Fig. 154 *b*. The result was that the end of the cork nearest the wax became slightly positive and the other end slightly negative. The positive end of the atom is nearest to the negative wax and so is pulled to it more than the negative and more distant end is repelled. Now break off a little bit of sealing-wax and hang it up by a thread. Rub it briskly with a bit of dry woollen material: this will give it some extra negative electrons. Rub another stick of sealing-wax and bring it slowly near the hanging piece. It will be found that the two negatively charged pieces of wax repel each other.

This very simple fact that like charges repel and unlike attract is the basis of almost the whole of electrical science.

A simple use of this property is in detecting small electric charges. An instrument designed to do this is called an electroscope. If two pieces of gold leaf (which is extremely thin and, therefore, extremely light) are hung from a metal rod in a glass case, a very small electric charge brought near the top of the rod makes the gold leaf diverge.

The reason is simple. Suppose the charge brought near the top is positive. It will pull the loose electrons in the metal to the top of the rod. The gold leaves at the bottom will be left with fewer negative charges than positive ones, and so they will both have a positive charge and repel each other. A gold leaf electroscope is not very easy to make because the gold leaf is very tender and sticks to everything it touches.

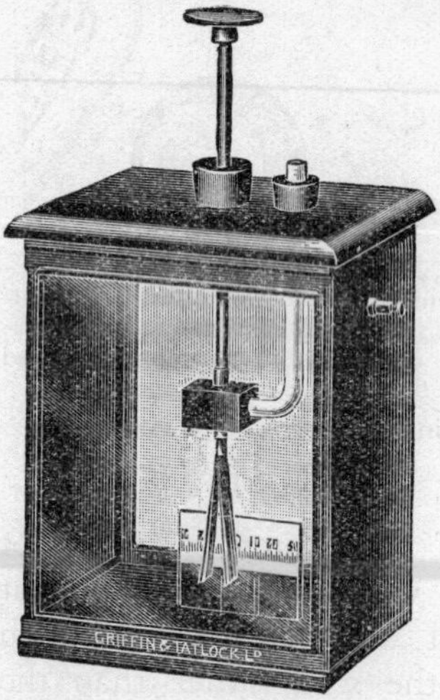

Fig. 155.—Gold-leaf electroscope (Courtesy of Messrs. Griffin and Tatlock).

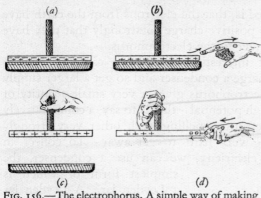

(a)   (b)

(c)   (d)

FIG. 156.—The electrophorus. A simple way of making electricity at a high potential.

A simple gadget which gives electricity at a high potential, and which anyone can make is an electrophorus (Fig. 156). It gives enough electricity for a slight spark and if it is used to charge a condenser quite respectable quantities can be obtained. Get a tin lid, best about six inches in diameter and melt some resin (sulphur or shellac does very well) and pour it in and let it set. Scrape the top flat with a knife or chisel, cut a disc of tin about half an inch smaller in diameter and stick on it a handle which won't conduct electricity—a wax candle makes a good one. Rub the resin vigorously—best with a catskin or a warm dry flannel. This gives it a negative charge. Now put the tin cover on it (a). This repels the loose electrons in the cover to the top of the tin, leaves the bottom free of loose electrons, and therefore the bottom, having more positive protons than negative electrons, is positively charged. If you took the cover off now, you would get no electricity, for, once out of the reach of the attraction of the resin, the electrons would just go back where they were before.

But now suppose you touch the top of the tin plate with your finger (b). The electrons in the metal, still repelled by the electrons of the resin, go chasing through your body down into the earth. Now remove your finger. The top plate has now fewer electrons than at the beginning, for some have gone into your finger. Lift it off by the non-conducting handle (c). It has a strong positive charge and you can do some amusing experiments with it. First, you can see it spark. It will give a quite perceptible spark with a faint prick and a tiny crackle when you hold your knuckle close to it. What has happened is, that the electrons from the earth have been attracted by the positive charge so strongly that they have jumped from your finger to the electrophorus.

One of the most interesting things you can do with the electrophorus is to charge a condenser and so get a larger supply of electricity. The electrophorus gives a very small quantity of electricity at a very high potential—that is to say, a comparatively small number of electrons, repelling each other very strongly and, therefore, trying very hard to get away. To collect an adequate charge of electricity, we can use a condenser, the simplest form of which is a Leyden jar. A Leyden jar is a glass vessel like a jam-jar coated internally and externally to $\frac{2}{3}$ of its depth with tin foil. There is some metal connection to the inside tin foil. The outer foil is connected to the earth so that any charge on it will leak away. To charge the jar, the inner coating is connected to the source of electricity, which must be at a high potential: frictional electricity or that from an induction coil is suitable—a battery is useless. Electrons flow in and give the inner coating a negative charge. They repel some of the negative electrons in the outer foil to the outside of it. (Fig. 157, *a*). These are repelled down the wire to the earth, where there is always plenty of room for electrons.

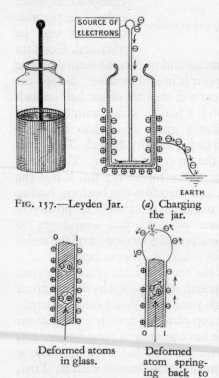

FIG. 157.—Leyden Jar.   (*a*) Charging the jar.

Deformed atoms in glass.

Deformed atom springing back to normal.

b) Wall of Charged Jar   (*c*) Discharging the Jar.

At the same time, the atoms both of the outer foil and the glass between are deformed (Fig. 157 *b*), their positive nuclei being pulled towards the inner coating and their negative outsides being pushed away from the inner coating. This goes on until the force pulling the deformed atoms back into shape just balances the repulsion of the negative electrons and attraction of the positive protons.

The final result is a crowd of negative electrons on the inside of the jar and a crowd of spare positive charges (atoms from which some electrons have been driven off to the earth) on the outside. The glass in between has every atom strained out of shape like a bent spring, storing up in this way a great deal of energy. Now bring a wire from the outer coating near to the inner one! The negative electrons are attracted by the positive. They leap the gap as a spark, and in doing so, heat the air and rattle its atoms till their electrons jump to bigger orbits (pp. 434–436) and so give out light. The atoms in the glass, springing back to their normal shape, repel the electrons out of the inner foil and so help the vigorous discharge. A Leyden jar is a simple condenser: the condensers used in magnetos, wireless sets, etc., all have conducting plates, corresponding to the inner and outer coating of the jar, and a non-conducting material, air or wax, between them, corresponding to the jar itself. If you have a Leyden jar, you can charge it with the electrophorus by repeatedly charging the cover and letting it touch the knob of the jar.

The Leyden jar illustrates what the electrophorus will not— the electric shock. The electric shock is still not entirely understood. If you let a small Leyden jar—a big one might be dangerous —discharge itself through your body, you feel a sharp twitch or contraction of the muscles through which the electricity passes. If an electric current passes through the eye, a flash is seen: if through the tongue, a peculiar taste is noticed. It would be dangerous, however, to employ the Leyden jar for these sensitive organs. Electricity has the effect of stimulating nerves of the body to transmit their messages. The motor nerves, when stimulated, make the muscles contract, the sensory nerves give a sensation of pricking, tingling or pain, the nerves of taste produce a taste sensation, the nerves of the eye give a sensation of light. The reason why electricity stimulates nerves is not clearly understood, but some light is thrown on it by our discussion of the action of nerves on p. 887. It seems that the electric charges displace the charged atoms in the "palisade-layer" of the nerve fibre and so set an impulse going.

The fact that electricity stimulates nerves is at once useful and dangerous. The muscles of paralysed limbs, which the patient cannot move by will, can often be stimulated by electricity to contract. This exercises the muscles and in many cases brings back function to the nerves which supply them.

A great deal of rubbish is talked about medical electricity. Some of the belts containing electric batteries which are said to perform marvels by strengthening and increasing "nervous energy" would probably be quite as effective without the battery —as long as the patient believed it to be present.

The electric shock is real enough. That peculiar creature, the electric eel, and a dozen or so other fish found this out a few million years ago, and evolved a most remarkable electrical generating set which gives a shock which will kill a small animal and stun a large one. No one can explain how their curious electric organs work: they are modified muscles and all muscles probably work electrically. A violent electric shock will kill a man: the most familiar example is death by lightning stroke. Huge potentials as from a lightning flash or a power line may burn and disrupt the body, but it is not clear why smaller potentials can kill, often leaving no trace. Electricity clearly affects the nerves, without which very few of the functions of the body can continue. Victims usually die at once or recover entirely. Sometimes artificial respiration is useful, and it should be always tried.

The ordinary house-supply currents at 200—230 volts rarely cause fatal accidents because the resistance of the body to the passage of electricity is great, and so very little passes through it. If, however, the body is well "earthed" these voltages may kill. The most dangerous case is when a man sitting in a bath touches a defective switch. The water and pipes make a perfect connection to earth, and death almost always occurs. Never fix electrical apparatus within reach of the bath!

Before leaving the subject of frictional electricity, we may remark that though it has not many uses, it most definitely has its dangers. Petrol is a non-conductor and so is silk. When a silk frock is cleaned by rubbing it in petrol, enough electricity may be generated to give a spark and cause a fatal fire—another reason to use the non-inflammable solvents, like carbon tetrachloride, for cleaning. Even violent stirring of some of these non-conducting liquids may liberate enough electricity for a spark to be formed.

DISCHARGES AND SPARKS

The way in which electricity passes through gases is extremely interesting, and by studying it Crookes in 1879 was led to the most important physical discovery of the last century—that of the electron itself.

Ordinary air can hardly be said to conduct electricity at all: almost, if not quite, all the electricity that passes through it is carried by ions, atoms of gas which have lost a negative electron and are ready to pick it up again. There are always a very few of these in the air, and as we shall see, strong electrical potentials have the power of making more. Let us see first how these ions can carry a charge away. Suppose we have a nega-

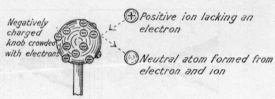

Negatively charged knob crowded with electrons

⊕ Positive ion lacking an electron

◎ Neutral atom formed from electron and ion

FIG. 158.—How a charge leaks away.

tively charged knob (say, connected to a Leyden jar). This is crowded with electrons all repelling each other. Any positive ions in the gas will be attracted to the negative pole and take an electron from it and so change back to an ordinary atom. Thus, the charge will slowly diminish. The number of ions in air is very small, and so a charge leaks away only slowly *unless* it is high enough to make ions for itself. Suppose now we have a direct current dynamo pumping electrons into a wire connected to one of its terminals (the negative one) and out of the wire connected to its other terminal, and suppose the force it applies to the electrons is what we call a few hundred volts. Let us connect to the negative wire a point, and to the positive wire a plate. If we increase the voltage by running the dynamo faster and faster, we find that at first no current passes, then a small current accompanied by a peculiar light effect which we call a brush discharge (Plate XIV), and finally, when the voltage is high enough, the current leaps the gap as a spark.

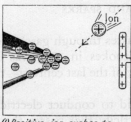

(1) *Positive ion rushes to negative point*

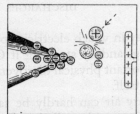

(2) *It hits an atom of gas and breaks it into another positive ion and a pair of electrons*

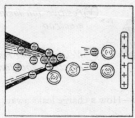

(3) *The ions already formed take electrons from the negative point and become atoms. The electrons repelled away from the point hit a pair of gas atoms*

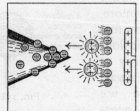

(4) *and break these into ions and electrons The disturbance of the atoms by the collision makes them glow*

FIG. 159.—A brush discharge.

There are always a few positive ions in the air—atoms from which an electron or two have been detached. These are drawn to the negative point with a high velocity (Fig. 159) (1) and break up other atoms as they near it (2). These atoms break into one or two electrons and a positive remainder. The positive remainders travel to the point and take from it electrons, so becoming atoms once more (3). The electrons, detached from the atoms in the collision are repelled from the point with high velocities (3) and finally reach a speed at which they can break up more molecules (4) into electrons and positive remainders. These glow, for reasons which will appear later (p.433 *ff.*) and travel to the negative point; the liberated electrons are thus attracted to the positive plate and return to the dynamo. The current passes slowly with the accompaniment of a bright spark-like light at the point— where the atoms are being broken into ions and electrons (Fig. 159) (2), then a dark space where the electrons and ions are being speeded up by the attraction or repulsion of the charge on the point, then a blue luminous area where the electrons, having reached a high speed, break up fresh atoms to electrons and positive ions (4), giving out light in the process. Beyond this again is a dark space through which the electrons journey to the plate. These areas are visible in the vacuum discharges (Plate XIII).

An electric charge always concentrates itself at a sharp point, so it is from a point that a brush discharge is likely to take place. Plate XIV shows an electric spark at a potential of a million volts. Every roughness on the ball gives out a "brush discharge"; the very high potential makes the electrons travel far and so gives a large "brush" of light, caused by the electrons in the atoms, disturbed by the flying electrons, jumping back to their ordinary positions.

These "brush discharges" are a real difficulty with high tension electricity. If one wants to transfer enough electricity to do a certain amount of work from one place to another, one can move a lot of electrons at a low potential, or a few at a high potential: just as you can do the same work by a gentle blow with a big hammer or a powerful blow with a little one. The large quantities of low-potential electrons need a big cable if they are to pass freely and easily: the few high-potential ones need only a small cable: consequently, it is economical to send electricity at high potential. At very high potentials, trouble begins with brush discharges: everything must be rounded and smooth to avoid them. For very high voltages, near a million, tubes are used rather than wires, because the wires themselves are sharply curved enough to cause a brush discharge. Moreover, alternating current flows only on the outside "skin" of the wire and tubes are therefore more economical.

The lightning conductor is pointed so that the electric charge of the cloud may more easily flow to it. That rare and eerie phenomenon, St. Elmo's fire, is a brush discharge from a cloud on to the mast of a ship. It is seen as a pale streamer of light topping the mast, and was naturally regarded with awe and horror— particularly as it occurred only in stormy weather.

When the voltage is high enough, or the distance between the positive and negative poles small enough, a spark or arc may pass. The spark and the arc both proceed by turning the atoms of a gas into charged ions, the flow of which carries the current.

A brush discharge occurs easily only from a point: if we have two charged plates or large knobs (particularly if close together) a spark appears. Suppose we have two metal knobs, say half an inch apart and connected to some source of electricity—say, a dynamo. We increase the speed of the dynamo steadily and thus increase the voltage, i.e., the overcrowding of electrons on the negative knob and the depletion of electrons from the positive one. Almost nothing happens till a certain voltage is reached, when there is a flash, a crackling noise, and electricity passes. The greater the distance the knobs are apart, the higher the voltage required. Roughly speaking, a charge of 2,500 volts will jump half a millimetre and thirty thousand volts will jump a centimetre. The 132,000 volts carried by the main grid lines, would jump a gap of over two inches. Plate XIV shows the discharge at a potential of a million volts.

The spark is a single discharge of electricity and lasts a very

PLATE XIII

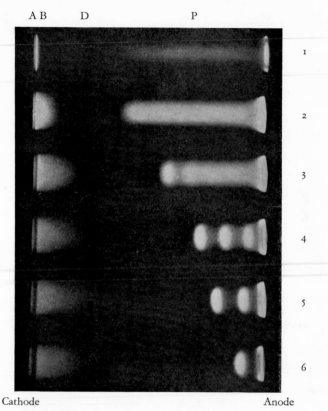

Cathode   Anode

Electrical discharges in an evacuated tube. Pressures are between 1 mm. and 0.1 mm. of mercury and decrease from the top picture downward. A—narrow negative dark space. B—faint negative glow. D—dark space. P—positive column. (By courtesy of Messrs. The Williams and Wilkins Company, Baltimore, U.S.A., from Darrow's *Electrical Phenomena in Gases*.)

PLATE XIV

Arc-welding. Note screen to protect welder's eyes. (By courtesy of the English Electric Co., Ltd., Stafford.)

A huge electric spark: potential 1,000,000 volts. Note brush discharges from sphere.
(By courtesy of Metropolitan Vickers, Ltd.)

A lightning flash. (By courtesy of J. F. Yocum, Esq., California, and the Meteorological Office, London.)

short time indeed. A photograph of a flying bullet taken by the light of an electric spark (Plate VI) appears absolutely sharp, showing that the spark lasts only about a millionth of a second.

The spark discharge seems to start like a brush discharge by a few positive ions from the air travelling to the negatively charged pole: these probably help to attract from the metal a few of the electrons of the current. These, once expelled from the metal, are repelled by their fellows and attracted by the positive pole, and move with such vigour that they each break up not one but many air atoms, giving many more electrons. These are violently accelerated by the attraction and repulsion of the poles and break up more atoms still. The whole effect then is a violent breaking up of atoms and shooting of negative electrons to the positive pole. The positive charge is thus made smaller, and the electrons are no longer pulled by it enough to make them break up the air atoms. So the spark stops. And all this happens in a millionth of a second? Yes, an electron moves so rapidly that a thousand electrons *in succession* could make the journey across the spark gap during the millionth of a second it lasts. The positive ions, the remainders of the air atoms from which the electrons were taken, are slow movers and are practically left standing during the flash.

The very large spark shown in Plate XIV pales before the tremendous sparks produced by moving air and water in a thunderstorm.

The tremendous sparks of lightning witness the huge potentials reached in the clouds; though in fact, the *quantity* of electricity—the number of electrons—in a lightning flash is a good deal less than is supplied by a small flash-battery in half a minute.

The earth has a negative charge—it contains some free electrons. The air conducts electricity very feebly. Actually, it is rather a puzzle why this conduction, though feeble, does not quickly carry off the whole charge from the earth; and for this and other reasons it is believed that the earth is generating electricity in its interior. It is not this rather small amount of electricity conducted from the earth to the air that causes thunderstorms. We know very little about the way electricity is generated in a storm cloud, but it is generally believed that the electricity results from a combination of a rapid upward wind with falling rain. G. C. Simpson's theory is based on the fact that a drop of water falling

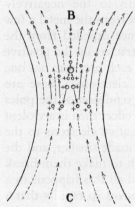

through an upward wind breaks up into smaller drops: the water becomes positively charged and the surrounding air negatively charged. This much is proved by experiments. He goes on to suppose that in a thunderstorm an upward wind first converges and then diverges, as in Fig. 160, so that at the centre there is a more rapid wind than at B or C. The drops fall from the high cold region B. They grow as they fall because they are cold and water vapour condenses on them, but as they grow, they break and break in the rising current until near the centre they become small enough to be carried up again by the wind. They carry up the positive charge they have gained from the breaking. They then grow again and start to fall and break up once more, every break increasing their positive charge. Finally, the positive charge becomes so great that the cloud's attraction for negative electrons is such that these burst from another part of the cloud or from the earth as a flash of lightning, and restore the negative electrons the positive water drops have lost. In their course they ionise the atoms of air and so produce more electrons and the flash proceeds just as does an electric spark. It travels along a route which is probably determined by the attraction of the cloud and the tracts of air which are most easily ionised. As Plate XIV shows, the track of lightning is usually very crooked.

FIG. 160.—Illustrating a possible way in which the charge on a thunder cloud may be built up.

A lightning flash may often have a voltage of 200,000,000. A voltage of 2,000,000 has been obtained on earth. Plate XIV shows a photo of a million-volt arc. The amount of electricity in a lightning flash is often only 20 coulombs, the amount of electricity burnt by a 60-watt lamp on a 210 volt circuit in a minute.

The effects of lightning are rather an anti-climax to its formidable appearance. A lightning flash will of course kill a man—but several have survived: it will split and scorch buildings and trees in a curious manner, and it sometimes melts the surface of rocks to a glassy film.

Lightning conductors are fitted to most buildings. They are simply a metal point connected by a stout copper band to the earth. If the air is highly electrified, a brush discharge carries away much of the electricity through the point safely to the earth. If the building is struck by lightning, the copper band may carry a small discharge to earth and so save the building.

ARCS AND ARC-WELDING

The arc is formed when a fairly large current at quite a low potential (*c.* 50 volts) passes between two poles of some material which can vaporise. If two carbon poles attached to the lighting circuit are touched and separated (a resistance should be inserted to prevent the fuses blowing), a spark first passes and produces ionised carbon vapour. The current flowing through this heats it just as it heats any conductor, and the heat vaporises more carbon. The light of the white-hot vapour ionises the vapour itself so that the gap of an arc is always filled with white-hot ionised carbon vapour. The arc is at once exceedingly hot and exceedingly brilliant. The arc lamp is discussed with other sources of light (p. 449). An arc can be struck between metal poles and, unless they are very well cooled, they are soon melted. The iron arc is greatly used as a means

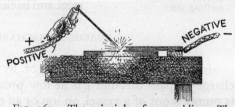

FIG. 161.—The principle of arc welding. The arc is struck between an iron rod held in the hand and the seam to be welded. The metal is melted and on solidifying gives an extremely strong joint. (See also Plate XIV.)

of welding iron and steel. Suppose two pieces of iron are to be joined: they are clamped together and connected to the negative pole of a dynamo designed to give very big currents of 200 amps or more with a low voltage of 25–50, which, by the way, does not give any appreciable shock. The positive cable from the dynamo goes to an electrode consisting of a thin iron bar. The operator has his eyes and face protected by a mask with a deep-blue glass window and his hands are protected by gloves, for the iron arc gives out showers of sparks and a blinding light full of ultra-violet rays which are most injurious to the sight. He touches the work with his electrode and then moves it $\frac{1}{16}$ inch or $\frac{1}{8}$ inch away. An arc forms and the metal of the work and the electrode fuse together to a pool of molten metal, securely uniting the two pieces of iron.

Arc-welding is very easy to apply, and it is even replacing riveting: the iron frames of new buildings are now often silently welded into a single structure instead of being weakened by rivet holes and then noisily hammered together with rivets.

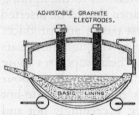

FIG. 162.—An arc furnace for melting steel.

The arc furnace gives enormous temperatures, but also has the advantage that no current of air or other gas need be introduced. Air is bad for molten metals, usually tending to make their castings brittle. Fig. 162 shows a diagram of an arc furnace for making steel. The arc jumps from the graphite pole to the steel and back to the other graphite pole.

VACUUM DISCHARGES

Most interesting effects are got by causing an electric discharge to pass through gas at low pressure. If most of the gas is pumped out of a vessel, an ion or an electron will be able to go much further without being stopped by collision with atoms, and finally, if the pressure is made low enough, an electron may go ten or twenty centimetres unhindered.

If the air is gradually pumped out of a tube furnished with two plate-electrodes kept at a potential difference of several thousand volts, a luminous discharge appears when the pressure nears $\frac{1}{1000}$th of an atmosphere (Plate XIII).

Just the same sort of thing is happening as in the brush discharge, but since there is less air, and collisions are now much fewer, the whole phenomenon is more spread out. At B, positive ions are being dragged to the metal and are ionising the atoms of gas to more negative electrons and positive ions. These positive ions take up the electrons from the plate. The ionisation makes the gas glow B. The electrons repelled by the plate speed up; they finally reach a pace when they can split up atoms into positive ions and electrons, causing a band of glowing gas. This is the positive column (P)—a long stretch of ionised glowing gas. The positive ions travel back, the negative ions go on and supply the deficiency at the positive plate. The positive column is best seen in Plate XIII (2): it is this band of glowing gas which gives the light in the Neon tube.

This is only a general notion of what is found when electrical discharges traverse a moderately exhausted tube. By slightly altering conditions, peculiar bands of light, etc., may be produced.

Gases, too, glow with very different lights. The Neon tubes enormously used for advertising signs are examples of discharge tubes, and are discussed in Chapter XV.

Suppose we continue to exhaust our discharge tube (Plate XIII, 3—6). The luminous clouds shrink back from the centre of the tube, and the dark space (D) increases until, when the pressure in the tube is only a millionth of an atmosphere, the luminous appearances in the gas have entirely ceased, though electricity is still being conducted. The walls of the tube glow with a greenish light. Invisible "rays" are passing through the tube, and these rays are a hail of electrons travelling from negative pole to positive with huge speed.

THE ELECTRON

We have *assumed* the electron to exist up to now: here we can *prove* it to be a material particle of electricity: we can measure its speed, mass and charge. The illustrations of the two experiments shown in Fig. 163 explain how we know some of these facts. In the first place, these "rays" must proceed in straight lines, because they will cast a shadow. If they barged their way from atom to atom as an ion does, they would find their way round an obstruction just as a moving crowd surges round a pillar box. They behave, instead, like bullets fired from a machine-gun: an obstruction provides "cover" from them.

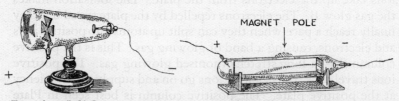

FIG. 163.—(left) Streams of electrons casting a sharp shadow. (right) Streams of electrons deflected by magnet pole. They are made visible by their effect on a fluorescent screen (p. 515).

That the rays consist of or carry charges of electricity is also clear, because if we intercept them on a metal plate, it becomes charged. Additional proof is given by the fact that they are repelled by a negative charge and deflected by a magnet just in the same direction as is an electric current (Fig. 163). That the cathode rays are material particles is shown by their having a measurable weight, as explained below.

These experiments show that the rays move in straight lines and that they carry negative electric charges. They might be ions —atoms carrying electric charges—had not their weight been measured and been found to be far less than that of any atom.

To weigh these particles is more difficult. Obviously, no sort of balance is any good, and the only method that can be used, is to see how much they are turned aside by a given electric field.

Clearly, a cannon ball going at 1,000 miles an hour is harder to turn aside than a pea going at the same pace. The task of deducing their weight from the deflection was not easy, for both their speed and the size of their charge influence the amount they are deflected, but the conclusion reached was that the particles in the cathode rays each weighed only $\frac{1}{1840}$ of the weight of a hydrogen atom. Their charge was nearly 4.75×10^{-10} electrostatic units, and their velocity depended on the voltage but was not far off ten million centimetres (sixty miles) a second.

No matter what the material of the tube and plates were, nor what was the gas with which the discharge tube had been originally filled, the particles obtained were of exactly the same weight and had the same electric charge. The conclusion was that these particles were electricity and that they formed a part of all matter, because, after all, electricity can be obtained from every element by various means (such as making it part of a battery, rubbing it in a friction machine, etc.). It was a longish step to show that matter of all kinds was made up of nothing but these electrons and positive charges.

BATTERIES

Electric batteries afford a very compact and portable way of getting electricity at a low potential. They are not of any use for public electricity supply, because they all depend for their energy on turning a *metal* into a compound and metals, even iron, are comparatively expensive. The generating station depends on turning the much cheaper *coal* into carbon dioxide, and making the heat energy so obtained into mechanical energy, and turning this into electrical energy. Very roughly speaking, a flash-lamp battery burns zinc while a generating station burns coal.

The essentials of an electric battery are two different metals (carbon may replace one of them) in a solution which can react chemically with one of them—that is to say, make its atoms join up with others and make a molecule. When these two metals are joined by a wire, a current of electricity flows along it.

The metals are chosen so that one is very easily affected by acids—zinc is suitable—and the other is not.

While hundreds of batteries can be devised, there is only one that is at all often used nowadays: this is the Leclanché cell. All dry batteries and the ordinary bell batteries are varieties of this.

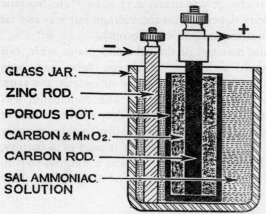

GLASS JAR.

ZINC ROD.

POROUS POT.

CARBON & Mn O₂.

CARBON ROD.

SAL AMMONIAC. SOLUTION

FIG. 164a.—The jar type of Leclanché cell, much used for bells.

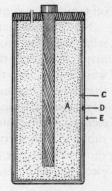

FIG. 164b.—The Leclanché dry cell. The central rod B is the carbon rod: A is carbon and manganese dioxide sewn up in a bag C corresponding to the porous pot. Next comes card-board D and the zinc case E which is both container and electrode. The whole is soaked in ammonium chloride solution and sealed with pitch.

The simplest Leclanché cell is as depicted in Fig. 164a. There is a zinc rod, a solution of ammonium chloride (sal ammoniac) and a pot, made of porous earthenware which lets liquid and electricity pass, containing a carbon rod packed round with manganese dioxide.

Now, the zinc is made up of zinc atoms: each has a nucleus, three complete groups of electrons and a pair of outer electrons which are rather easily lost.

The ammonium chloride solution consists of water in which are floating ammonium ions and chloride ions. Ammonium ions are nitrogen atoms with four hydrogen atoms round them. These contain eighteen protons and seventeen electrons, and so

have a positive charge. The
chloride ions are chlorine
atoms with one extra electron,
and so have a negative charge.

When the zinc and the carbon are connected by a wire,
the fun begins. The zinc atoms
discard their two outer electrons and go off into the solution as positive zinc ions.
They cannot do this in the
ordinary way because, if they
did, the discarded electrons
would pile up a big negative
electric charge on the zinc,
pull the positive ions back,
and turn them into zinc atoms
again. But in the battery, the
electrons do not stay to make an electric charge on the
zinc. They go off down the wire, enter the carbon, and
start attracting the *positive* ammonium ions. Each time one of
these touches the carbon, an electron hitches up to it and turns it
into a molecule of ordinary ammonia and an atom of hydrogen.
The ammonia remains dissolved in the water of the solution.
The hydrogen sticks to the carbon, and after a few minutes
covers it up, and if the battery is working fast, it slows it down.
This is where the manganese dioxide comes in. It has a lot of
oxygen to spare, and this oxygen combines with the obstructive
hydrogen and turns it into harmless water.

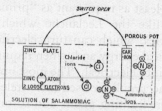

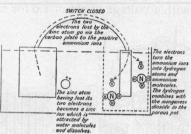

FIG. 165.—The chemistry of the
Leclanché cell.

The Leclanché cell then takes electrons out of zinc atoms:
these go round a wire through lamps, bells or whatever you will
to the carbon pole where they turn ammonium ions into ammonia and hydrogen—which is finally turned to water. Dry
batteries work in exactly the same way. Instead of having a free
liquid which can slop about they have their ammonium chloride
solution soaked up in some porous material (Fig. 164*b*).

At least as important as "primary" cells, which is the name for cells like the Leclanché which makes electricity, are storage batteries, which can turn electricity, passed through them, into chemical energy and, when required, will turn the chemical energy back into electrical. The most important battery of this kind is the lead accumulator used for wireless work, batteries for cars, small electric lighting plants and so on. It gives a very steady current with a voltage of about 2.0 for each pair of plates.

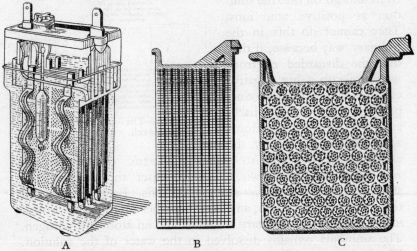

FIG. 166—(A) Accumulator (B) negative plate (C) positive plate. (From material kindly supplied by The Chloride Electrical Storage Co.)

The explanation of the accumulator is a little hard for those who know no chemistry; but it is perhaps worth giving an account of its working which is not too difficult, though possibly not complete.

The accumulator has two lead plates which may be of several patterns. In the cell illustrated (Exide) the plates are both of a hard alloy of lead with a little antimony. The hard lead is unaffected by the acid and serves only a support. The negative plate is in the form of a grid into the interstices of which is forced a paste of pure spongy lead. The positive plate is perforated with holes into which are forced "rosettes" of pure corrugated lead which expose a large surface. These plates stand in a mixture of sulphuric acid and water. When the cell is fully charged (Fig. 167) the positive plate becomes coated with a brown compound of lead and oxygen called lead peroxide, while the other plate is pure lead. The solution contains negative sulphate ions, each a sulphur atom joined to four oxygen atoms, and positive hydroxonium ions, each a single positive proton linked to a water molecule. If the plates are connected by a wire (Fig. 167) the lead atoms give up two electrons and turn into lead ions. These do not go off into the solution, but combine with a sulphate ion from the solution and settle down on the plate as white lead sulphate. This takes the heavy sulphate ions acid out of the solution and is the reason why the acid, during discharge, becomes lighter, *i.e.* of less specific gravity. As explained below, during charge, the sulphate ions return to the water: thus a

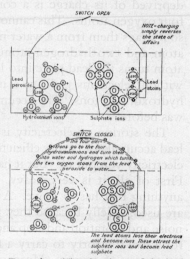

FIG. 167.—The chemistry of the lead accumulator. Above the charged cell is shown: below, the process of discharging.

hydrometer shows an increase of specific gravity during charge.

The electrons go off round the wire, and attract the positive hydroxonium ions to the plate. Here, there is a general re-arrangement. The electrons and the positive hydroxonium ions make water and hydrogen. The hydrogen takes the oxygen from the lead peroxide and leaves behind pure lead.

This goes on until the accumulator has run down, at which point all the lead peroxide has changed to lead. So the discharged accumulator has plates coated with pure lead and lead sulphate respectively. Now you connect it to the electric supply to charge it up. The electrons of the current go to the lead ions in the lead sulphate plate and turn them back to lead. The sulphate ions float off into the solution. These and other sulphate ions, being negative, are attracted to the plate of pure lead and give up their electrons to it. These electrons are forced back by the charging dynamo to the other plate. The sulphate ion deprived of its charge is a combination of a sulphur atom and four oxygen atoms. This cannot exist without two extra electrons, so it drags them from a water molecule, turning it into an oxygen atom and two hydrogen atoms without electrons. The oxygen atom turns the lead plate into lead peroxide: the hydrogen atoms without electrons pick up a molecule of water each and make hydroxonium ions. The accumulator is now charged again as it was before!

The storing of electricity is a great field for inventors. The lead accumulator is very efficient—you can get back almost all the electricity you put in—but it has several thoroughly bad features. First of all, it is very heavy. This makes it nearly useless for anything that has to move. A few electric vans run by batteries are used, chiefly because they pay a low tax, are very free from noise and vibration and stop and start very easily: but it is wasteful for a five-ton lorry to carry a ton and a half of accumulators as its source of power. Moreover, storage batteries are slow to charge, for the electricity can only be put in at a certain rate. Lastly, they are rather short-lived. A couple of years is a good life for the starter battery of a car.

A great many batteries have been devised to overcome these defects, but none appears to have done so at all completely. Some of the alkaline cells are lighter than the lead cells but are still heavy.

If a really light and strong quick-charging storage battery could be devised it would revolutionise transport. The cars or vans fitted with it would ordinarily be left charging overnight: garages would have arrangements to charge it up in five minutes or so. An electric motor driven by a battery is comparatively light: it gives tremendous acceleration and very little trouble.

The danger of fire from petrol would be eliminated, and the noise and exhaust fumes of our streets would be halved. No gears would be needed on an electric car, for some motors pull even better at lower speeds than at high. If any of my readers wants a hundred million pounds, let him invent and patent a light, strong storage battery which can be charged in a few minutes. There is nothing theoretically impossible about it: but no one has yet found the way to do it.

ELECTROPLATING

Certain kinds of molecules, those of acids like sulphuric acid or hydrochloric acid, alkalis like caustic soda, or salts like common salt or copper sulphate consist of a positively charged part and a negatively charged part which are bound together by electrical attraction. A common salt crystal (p. 47) is just an orderly assembly of positive sodium ions (sodium atoms with one electron missing) and negative chloride ions (chlorine atoms with an extra electron). When salt is dissolved in water, these float about separately, so that a solution of salt is just a crowd of separate sodium ions and chloride ions.

Just in the same way, a solution of copper sulphate is a solution of countless copper ions and sulphate ions. The copper ions are copper atoms with two electrons missing (Fig. 153), the sulphate ions are each a sulphur atom bound firmly to four oxygen atoms—these five atoms having two extra electrons shared between them.

Now, suppose we want to plate a spoon with copper. We make a solution of copper sulphate: we connect a copper plate to the positive terminal of a single dry cell and the well-cleaned spoon to the negative plate

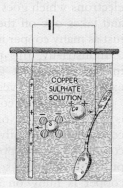

FIG. 168.—The principle of copper plating. The spheres vertically shaded represent oxygen atoms, that marked S a sulphur atom, that marked Cu a copper ion. The spheres are about thirty million times natural size, a drop contains millions of millions of them.

and let them hang there for half an hour or longer. A beautiful pink coating of copper soon spreads over the spoon. If we leave it long enough, the copper plate will be entirely eaten away and deposited on the spoon.

Fig. 168 shows what has happened. The electrons crowd into the spoon and charge it negatively: accordingly, it attracts the copper ions. These barge their way through the water molecules and reach the spoon. From it they each take a pair of electrons and become copper atoms, firmly attached to the spoon. Meanwhile, the sulphate ions are repelled by the spoon and attracted by the plate. When they reach it, they hand over their two extra electrons to it and these go round to the battery again. But, the sulphate group left—a combination of a sulphur atom and four oxygen atoms—immediately takes two more electrons from a copper atom in the copper plate and makes a copper ion, itself becoming a sulphate ion once more. So, each pair of electrons which goes round, deposits a copper atom on the spoon and takes one off the plate. The solution remains the same, for just as many copper ions enter it as leave it.

Industrially, this process of electroplating is very important indeed, because it gives a way of putting a thin layer of an expensive metal over a cheap one.

The process of copper-plating which has just been described is used chiefly in order to prepare other metals to receive a coating of nickel, silver or gold. Another use for it is for refining copper. When copper is made by smelting, it has various impurities including some silver and gold. An ingot of impure copper is hung on a bar connected to the positive pole of a dynamo, and a thin plate of pure copper is suspended from a metal bar electrically connected to the negative pole. Both hang in a solution of copper sulphate. The impure copper dissolves, and because copper is easier to electrolyse than most metals, it deposits on the pure copper plate while other metals, like iron, which may have been in the ingot remain in the solution. Any gold or silver sinks to the bottom as a mud which is recovered and refined.

But to return to the chief use of electro-plating—the coating of metals with another metal.

Nickel is plated in much the same way as copper. The positive plate is an ingot of nickel, the solution is nickel sulphate with some ammonium sulphate, and the negative pole is made up of the things which are to be plated. The coating is not very brilliant, so it is polished afterwards. Zinc and cadmium are sometimes plated on iron to prevent it from rusting. The most important plating, however, is with silver, gold and chromium.

Silver and gold plating are done from a solution of the very poisonous potassium cyanide. A silver plate is the positive pole, a solution containing silver nitrate and potassium cyanide is the liquid, and the forks or what not, the negative pole. Fig. 169 shows the very simple way a silver article can be gold-plated. Needless to say, great care must be taken in handling the exceedingly dangerous potassium cyanide.

Chromium plating is a comparative novelty. Chromium is extremely hard —harder than steel. It takes a brilliant polish, does not tarnish, and has a fine blue-white lustre. It is clearly an excellent metal with which to coat anything. Unfortunately, it proved a very difficult metal to deposit. The difficulties have been overcome now, and chromium plate is seen everywhere.

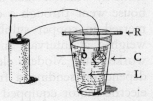

FIG. 169.—Gold-plating a silver match-box. The liquid (L) is potassium cyanide solution; the anode is a gold ring, the cathode (C) the well-cleaned silver matchbox. Both are suspended from an insulating rod (R), e.g., a pencil. The potassium cyanide solution dissolves the gold and the current redeposits it on the silver.

In order to get a firm solid coating of any metal which will not flake off, two rules must be followed. First, the voltage must be low and the current must not exceed a certain number of amps. per square inch plated. Secondly, the things to be plated must be very clean. A touch of a greasy finger is often enough to prevent the metal from sticking.

This process of electrolysis gives a way of measuring the

amount of current which passes. Every atom of copper deposited from copper sulphate means that two electrons have passed: an atom of copper weighs nearly 1.05×10^{-22} grammes, so that every gram of copper deposited means that 20,000,000,000,000,000,000,000 electrons have passed. We do not measure quantities of electricity by the number of electrons, but by coulombs, each of which is about 6,000,000,000,000,000,000 electrons. A coulomb is actually the amount of electricity which passes in a current of 1 ampere flowing for one second. It is found, then, that every gram of copper deposited in an electrolytic cell means that 3,085 coulombs have passed. This was used in one of the first kinds of electric meter. An arrangement was made by which a small known fraction of the current going to a house went through a cell made up of two copper plates immersed in copper sulphate solution. The negative plate was weighed at intervals and the amount of electricity used was worked out. Modern electric meters are of a different type, and depend on sending a fraction of the current through a small electric motor equipped with an arrangement for counting the number of times it turns.

CONDUCTION OF ELECTRICITY

Electrons, when they travel along a wire, probably thread their way between the atoms of the metal. However they travel, it is certain that the bigger the wire the more readily they can get through it. A wire of a square inch cross section lets a hundred times as much electricity through in a given time as a wire of $\frac{1}{100}$th square inch cross section, if the same voltage is applied to the two ends. Materials too, differ enormously in the power of letting electricity through. Silver tops the list as the best conductor, the other metals let through from 94% to 2% of the amount of current carried by a silver wire of the same size and length.

All other things are much worse conductors. Solutions of

acids, alkalis and salts conduct fairly well, and are electrolysed at the same time. Absolutely pure water only just conducts electricity, and such substances as glass, sulphur, wax, resin, diamond, etc., practically do not conduct at all.

Naturally, we need some way of measuring how well or badly a given wire conducts and we settle on a quantity called its resistance to express the amount it diminishes a current that passes through it. We say that a wire has a resistance of an *ohm*, if, when its ends have a potential difference of a volt applied to them, a current of an ampere flows. A very convenient rule (Ohm's Law) tells us that the resistance of a wire is the voltage applied to the ends of it divided by the current that goes through it. Take a 60–watt, 220–volt lamp as an example. A watt is the rate of working when the current of 1 ampere flows at a potential drop of 1 volt. So, a 60–watt lamp working at 220 volts is passing $\frac{60}{220}$th ampere. The resistance is the voltage (220) divided by the current $\frac{60}{220}$ amp. and this is equal to about 807 ohms.

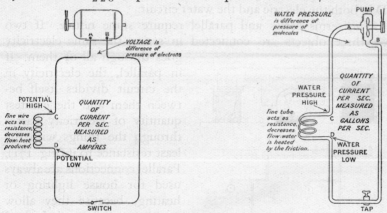

Fig. 170.—The resemblance between the flow of electricity and of water.

An electric current passing along a wire has been compared to a flow of water through pipes and, as long as you consider only its flow, this is a good comparison. Its magnetic and inductive effects used in transformers, motors, etc., have no real parallel in a water stream.

In Fig. 170 we have the resemblance set out more fully. A dynamo drives electrons round a circuit as a pump drives water. The difference of pressure (potential energy) of electrons at pole A and pole B is the voltage drop or "potential difference" or "electro-motive force" driving the electrons round. The difference of pressure of water at A and B represents the same thing for a water circuit. The quantity of electricity is measured in coulombs, so the flow per second past every point is measured as coulombs per second. A coulomb-per-second is called an ampere. The flow of water would probably be measured in gallons per second. Obviously, the *same* quantity of water passes every point in the circuit during any given second—if it did not, water would be accumulating somewhere. The same is true of electricity: the amperage of a single circuit must be the same throughout. The pressure (voltage) of course drops steadily from A to B. It will drop most where the resistance is greatest. Thus, the biggest drop of pressure will take place between C and D in both the electric and the water circuit.

The terms series and parallel require some notice. If two or three objects are connected in series, the same electricity goes through all of them. If in parallel, the electricity in the circuit divides itself between them and the greatest quantity of electricity passes through the things with the least resistance to it (Fig. 171). Parallel connections are always used for house lighting or heating, because they allow one lamp to be switched off without affecting the others.

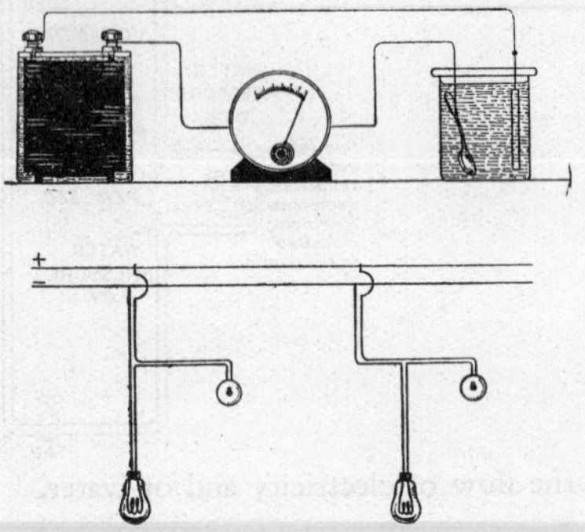

FIG. 171.—Circuits in parallel and series. In the upper illustration the accumulator, ammeter and plating cell are in series. In the lower illustration the two lamp-circuits are in parallel.

The lamps are in parallel and, therefore, can be lighted independently: but the lamps and switches are in series.

Suppose the two lamps shown in Fig. 171 are of 60-watt and 30-watt size. The 60-watt lamp has *half* the resistance of the 30-watt one. The pressure of the mains is the same for each, so twice as much electricity flows through the 60-watt lamp.

What happens to the energy lost when an electric current flows through a wire without apparently doing any useful work? The answer is that the "resistance" is the slowing down of the stream of electrons by collision with the atoms of the metal of the wire. These are speeded up and consequently become hot: the energy of the electricity is thus turned into heat and sometimes light.

There is quite a simple rule which tells how much heat will be obtained when electricity flows through a lamp, wire, etc. It is that the heat is C^2rt joules. Multiply the current (C) in amperes by itself, multiply this by the resistance (r) of the wire or lamp and this by the time (t) in seconds and you get the amount of heat in "joules." Divide this by 4.18 and you get the heat in calories— one calorie is the amount of heat that makes a gram of water one degree Centigrade hotter.

Let us calculate the heat given by the 60-watt lamp in an hour. Actually, only about 1.5% of its energy appears as light, so we can neglect this. The current is $\frac{3}{11}$ amp., the resistance is 807 ohms, the time 3,600 seconds. Accordingly, the heat is $\frac{3}{11} \times \frac{3}{11} \times 807 \times 3,600$ joules = about 285,000 calories. This would heat about six pints of cold water to boiling.

Electric lighting we will leave until we come to talk about light. But electric heating has many merits, and this is a good place to discuss it. In the first place, electric heating needs no air and gives no fumes to be carried off by chimneys. Consequently we can put an electric heater inside a boiler where every bit of its heat will go into the water: an electric fire can stand in the middle of a room and none of its heat need go up a chimney. So the heat it gives is very economically used. The trouble is that it is expensive. A ton of coal gives at least thirty million British thermal units of heat; a therm of gas gives 100,000 British thermal units; a unit of electricity gives 3,416 British thermal units.

Accordingly, if we have £2 to lay out in heat, we may buy:

A ton of coal at £2 and get 30,000,000 British thermal units.

56½ therms of gas at 8½d. a therm and get 5,650,000 British thermal units.

480 units of electricity at 1d. a unit and get about 1,500,000 British thermal units.

Now, a coal fire at best only sends 25% of its heat into a room, so that of its 30,000,000 British thermal units only 7,500,000 are any good; if the gas is burned in a gas fire, 50% are used, so the heat used comes to 3,000,000. The electric fire sends all its heat into the room so that you will get the whole 1,500,000. It appears from this that electric heating is about twice as expensive as gas heating, and gas heating twice as expensive as coal heating, but it must be remembered that we have assumed a rather high price for coal and a low price for electricity. Actually, a great deal of the cheapness of coal heating is nullified because a coal fire cannot be turned out when a room is unoccupied.

An electric heater is simply a long wire wound on a support which does not conduct electricity and which will stand a high temperature. Fireclay or mica are ordinarily used. It does not matter whether the wire is straight or coiled: it gives just the same amount of *heat* but by coiling it we save space, and also make it cool less quickly and therefore reach a higher *temperature*. The advantage of this is that the wire becomes red-hot and gives out radiant heat as well as warming the air.

The wire is usually made of an alloy of nickel and chromium. Other metals (except the very expensive platinum) would oxidise, get thin, and burn out in a short time.

Electric heaters for water are just the same in principle. The heating coil is usually in a metal case.

The length of wire must be such as to let the right amount of current through. If it is too long, the current will be too small and the heat will be less: if too short, the current will be so large that the wire gets too hot and burns out.

The heating effect of the current is used in the fuse-boxes fitted in every house. Suppose there were no fuses and two

electric wires were allowed to touch, as by accident they sometimes do. There would be very little resistance to the current, so
a huge current would pass and very great heat would be
generated in the wires, probably setting the house alight. To
avoid this, it is arranged that the current flows through a thin
piece of wire, usually fine tinned copper or often an alloy of tin
and lead. If a greater current than the house supply requires
flows through this, it gets hot before the other wires—because its
resistance is higher—and so is melted and breaks the current. It
is very dangerous to mend fuses with thick wire (or, indeed, any
but proper fuse wire) because if a short-circuit occurs the wires
may burn out elsewhere than at the fuse.

A common type of ammeter for measuring current depends on
the heating effect. A wire is stretched and a light spring holds it
taut. When a current passes the wire becomes hot and expands.
The spring pulls it down and so moves the pointer. It is not an
extremely accurate instrument, but it is foolproof and stands
knocking about.

MAGNETISM

Magnetism is closely connected with electricity, and a great
many important applications of electricity depend on it. The
most important of all, the dynamo and electric motor, depend on
magnetic forces—so also do the telegraph, telephone and many
other devices.

The permanent magnet has been known since very early
times.

A particular iron ore called lodestone or magnetite was
discovered to have two very peculiar properties: it would attract
pieces of iron to itself and, when hung by a thread, it would
always set itself with one particular part to the north and another
to the south.

Magnets of lodestone are now rarely met with, for stronger
and less bulky magnets can be made of steel. How is a magnet

made from a plain piece of steel? Two ways are known. First, it
can be stroked with another magnet always in the same direction
(Fig. 172), secondly, it can be wrapped with a coil of wire through
which a big current is passed (Fig. 178, Plate XVI).

Steel is the only thing which can be made into a permanent
magnet: pure iron becomes a magnet when treated as above but
loses its magnetism as soon as the magnet is removed or the
current is cut off. A few other metals are attracted by a magnet;
nickel and cobalt fairly well, and a couple of dozen metals
(mostly rare ones) very slightly indeed. Most common metals
are, on the contrary, very feebly repelled by a magnet. A very odd
exception to the rule are the Heusler alloys which are quite
strongly magnetic though entirely made of non-magnetic metals!
A typical specimen might contain 61% copper, 24% manganese
and 15% of aluminium.

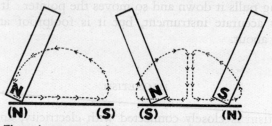

**The pole produced where you leave off stroking
is opposite to the stroking pole.**

FIG. 172.—How a piece of steel is made into a magnet by
stroking it with one or more magnets.

Suppose we have in our hand a magnet: a bar magnet is
perhaps best, but a horseshoe magnet will do very well. What do
we notice about it? The first and most obvious thing is that it
attracts iron and steel. But it is very soon noticeable that it does
not attract them equally all over. The middle of the magnet
has practically no attracting force: this is strongest at the two
ends—called the poles. Are the poles the same? They attract iron
equally strongly, and as long as you only try the effect of them on
ordinary iron, you won't find any difference.

But now mark one end of your magnet with an inkspot or a bit of stamp paper and take a long needle. Stroke it a couple of dozen times with the marked pole of the magnet, always going from eye to point. This will turn it into a magnet. Stick it into a slice of cork and float it on a saucer of water. Put your magnet at the other end of the room, so as not to disturb it. Your needle will now set itself north and south: it is a compass in fact. Suppose the end of it which points to the north is the end with the eye. Call that the north-seeking pole and the other the south-seeking pole. Now bring your magnet slowly near it. The marked pole will attract the point and repel the eye. The unmarked pole will attract the eye and repel the point. We say, then, that a magnet has two opposite poles, one of which points to the north when the magnet is free to move: the other points to the south. Two north-seeking or two south-seeking poles repel each other: a north-seeking and a south-seeking pole attract each other. Every magnet has two poles of this kind. Suppose you try and get a magnet with one pole by breaking it in half. Well, your two new magnets will grow a fresh pole at the broken ends! When we have seen what magnetism is, the reason will be clear.

Magnetism is not at all easy to explain. Every atom of iron is supposed to be a tiny magnet which can swing about freely. Consequently, if we bring another magnet near it, all the north poles are made to point the same way. This makes the whole piece of iron into a magnet. If steel is used, the iron atoms in it are prevented, presumably by the carbon atoms in the interstices, from moving easily, but once dragged round they stay round, and so a piece of steel, once made a magnet, stays a magnet.

This explanation is very well in its way, but it does not explain why an atom of iron should be a tiny magnet. If nothing except atoms gave magnetic forces this would be difficult to explain, but as we shall see later on, an electric current flowing in a circle acts exactly like a magnet. A loop of wire as in Fig. 177 has a north and a south pole like a magnet, and if free to move sets itself north and south like a compass needle. If the direction of the current is reversed, the poles change places. Now an electric current flowing in a circle is a crowd of electrons moving in a circle. Atoms are made up of electrons, believed to be revolving in circles: so every atom ought to be a magnet. But every atom is not: and the reason is, that most atoms have as many electrons racing round them clock-wise as anti-clockwise, and their magnetic forces cancel. Iron and a few other elements have unsymmetrical atoms, in which the electrons are not all paired so as to cancel their magnetic forces. Consequently an atom of iron behaves like a tiny ring of wire carrying a current. In an ordinary piece of iron the rings lie higgledy-piggledy (Fig. 173), and as many atoms are exerting their forces in one direction as in another. Consequently, a piece of iron is not a magnet. But bring a magnet near it, and all the ring-currents themselves set in the same direction: all pull the same way and together exert quite a big force, The iron has become a magnet.

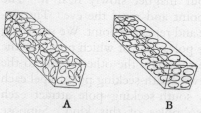

A   B

Fig. 173.—An unmagnetised bar of iron or steel (A) is thought to consist of atoms, each a tiny electric circuit, lying with their circuits at random in any plane: their effects therefore cancel out. The fully magnetised bar (B) has all these circuits in a plane at right angles to its length—consequently their effects reinforce each other.

The really unsolved problem is why the iron atom is in this way so different from, say, the feebly magnetic nickel atom and so like it in other ways.

The mariner's compass is a fairly ancient instrument. At one time it was believed that the Chinese knew of the compass as long ago as 2500 B.C., but there does not seem to be any reliable record of its use before about A.D. 1300.

In Europe, the use of it in the form of a floating needle is first mentioned between A.D. 1100 and 1200, and the pivoted compass was known before A.D. 1300.

The principle of the compass is simple enough. It is a magnet suspended so as to turn freely. The whole earth is a magnet with its north pole in the Arctic and its south pole at the Antarctic. and the earth's poles attract or repel the compass-needle's poles. The Magnetic Poles are not at the true north and south poles, which are the axes on which the earth turns. The consequence of this is that the compass does not point to the true north. It points about 13° west of north in London.

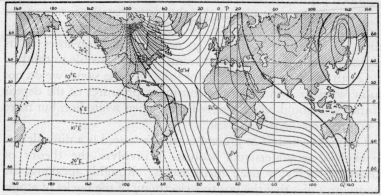

FIG. 174.—On this map all places where the compass has the same deviation lie on the same line. On the darker lines lie the places where the compass points to the true north.

In Cuba it points about 4° east of north and at Cape Town about 25° west of north. It follows then that if a ship is to be steered by a compass, the captain must have a map showing in what direction the compass points in that part of the world. Worse still, the magnetic poles of the earth are always steadily shifting. In 1660 the compass pointed due north in London: in 1800 it pointed 24° west of north: somewhere about A.D. 2000, it is likely to point due north again.

An ordinary compass points along the earth's surface roughly to the magnetic pole. If we suspend a magnetic needle so that it can swing up and down, it points more or less *through* the earth to the magnetic pole.

It is not easy to understand why the earth should behave as a magnet. The obvious theory is to suppose that its interior is

made of iron, and its high density rather supports this. The rocks
at the earth's surface are on the average about two and a half
times as heavy as water. But the earth itself is more than five times
as heavy as a globe of water of the same size. Clearly, then, the
interior of the earth must be very dense. Ordinary iron has a
density of 7.84. Meteorites, too, which are thought to be bits of
exploded planets or stars, are usually mainly iron.

The serious thing against this theory is that the inside of the
earth is presumably very hot. Molten lava comes out of it, and
mines become hotter as they go deeper. But iron loses all its
magnetism at a red heat, and it seems then impossible to think of
the earth as a magnetized lump of iron. All the same, we do not
know whether iron under the enormous pressures of the depths
of the earth could be magnetized even when white hot, but there
is no great reason to believe it.

The view which is at present chiefly favoured is a difficult one
to explain or understand because it involves the theory of
Relativity and very deep mathematics. Roughly speaking, the
theory provides that the positive electricity of the nuclei of atoms
is being annihilated in the earth's interior, forming energy
(which is one source of the earth's interior heat) and the negative
electrons left behind slowly find their way outward to the crust
and then pass upward through the air and away from the earth.
This passage of electricity outward is well known, and we have
always been puzzled to know where the electricity came from.
Now the earth is spinning, and a spinning electric charge gives a
magnetic field.

When the quantities are worked out mathematically, it seems
that if the earth was losing $\frac{1}{20}$th of its mass in ten million
million million years, this would give enough electricity to
account for its magnetism. Actually, the earth is probably only
two or three thousand million years old, so this loss would not be a
very great one.

Now, the sun is presumably made of much the same stuff as
the earth: it is hot like the earth, far hotter, and it is rotating
like the earth. It gives out torrents of electricity—streams of

electrons come from it as far as the earth. Consequently, the sun should be a magnet too.

Now, we can't go to the sun and try a compass on it, but we have a way of studying its magnetism. When light is produced by a glowing atom, it is the shifting orbits of the electrons in the atom that fix the wavelength (p. 433*ff.*) of the light. If the glowing atom is placed in a magnetic field, these orbits are slightly altered, and where light of one wavelength was produced before, light of two or three slightly different wavelengths is produced instead. Now, the spectrograph (pp. 462*ff.*) gives us a way of measuring the wavelength of the sun's light and by comparing the light that, say, glowing sodium gives in the sun and on the earth, we find that there is a huge magnetic field on the sun. At the sun's poles it is over 100 times the highest pull of the earth's magnetism, and in the vast swirling storms of the sun-spots it may rise to forty times this value.

Let us return to the earth once more. The compass is a useful guide in spite of the irregularities that have to be allowed for. More ships are still steered by the magnetic compass than by the gyro-compass (p. 172), although the latter has none of the former's defects.

The earliest compasses were just a magnetised needle stuck in a little piece of wood and floated on water. The next step was to balance a magnetised needle on a pivot and many pocket compasses are still of this type. The chief disadvantage of these compasses is the long time the needle swings before it settles. This is got over by filling the compass with alcohol and water which slows down its wagglings.

The ship's compass, instead of having a needle which points to markings on a ring, has several needles attached to a card marked with the points of the compass (Fig. 175.) The whole card turns on a sapphire balanced on a needle. These compasses are also often filled with a mixture of alcohol and water to steady the card. The compass of a ship always stands in one place—on the binnacle or pedestal. The rolling and pitching of the ship would make it almost impossible for the card to turn freely, so the

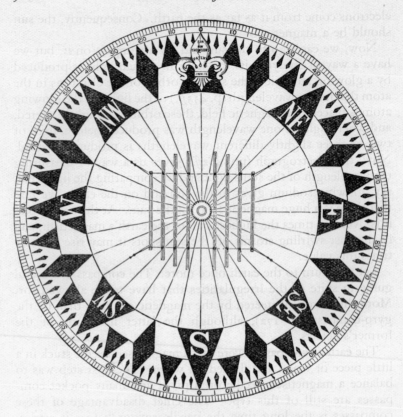

FIG. 175—The moving card of a ship's compass with attached magnetic needles. (Courtesy of Messrs. George Philip & Son, Ltd., and Capt. Lecky, from the latter's *Wrinkles in Practical Navigation*, who also kindly furnished Fig. 175a.)

compass is swung in gimbals (pivoted rings such as are used to support the gyroscope of Plate VIII); these keep it always level. To minimise the effect of the oscillations a bowl containing a viscous liquid such as castor-oil is attached to the base of the compass; its sluggish movements lag behind the oscillations of the compass and gimbals and so slow them up.

A compass needle is a magnet and is therefore attracted by iron. As a modern ship is full of iron and steel it is very necessary to get rid of their attraction. The only way to do this is to put pieces of iron and small magnets near the compass in such positions that they pull the needle exactly as strongly as, and in exactly the opposite direction to the iron and steel in the ship. To do this, the ship is pointed N, S, E and W, and the iron masses and magnets in the pedestal are adjusted until the compass shows the correct reading in every direction.

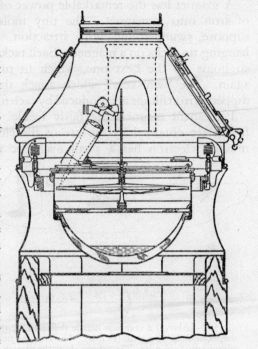

FIG. 175a.—Section of compass supported on binnacle.

The ordinary magnet has two poles. Both of these will attract anything near it, so that the force of the magnet will anywhere be a combination of the forces from the two poles. The direction of the force can be depicted by a line and it is easy in a very pretty way to make the magnet draw the pattern of its own lines of force.

Get a magnet and put a stiff sheet of paper over it and dust on to it some iron filings. Any garage will have plenty on the bench round the vice: if they are greasy rinse them with petrol. Now tap the paper. The magnet turns each filing into a tiny magnet and the force makes it set in the direction of its pull. Plate XVI shows patterns obtained with a horseshoe magnet.

A magnet has the remarkable power of turning another piece of iron into a magnet. The tiny molecule-magnets are, we suppose, swung round by its attraction. This is well shown by hanging tin tacks on a magnet. Each tack becomes a magnet and so holds up the next one, which in turn becomes a magnet again. The "whiskers" which attach themselves to a magnet dipped in iron filings are produced by each filing attracting the next.

Permanent magnets are fairly feeble. The largest magnetic forces are obtained by the use of the electric current. Now, a moving electron has a small magnetic field. Consequently, a current of electricity flowing along a wire exerts a small magnetic force. You can show this by floating a magnetised needle in a saucer of water so that it lies just below a wire (Fig. 176). On touching the ends of the wire with a flash battery, the needle

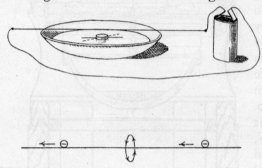

FIG. 176.—(Above) a compass needle deflected by the magnetic field of a wire (Below). The circular field surrounding the wire. The arrows show the direction in which a north magnetic pole would be attracted.

flicks sideways. The lines of force of the field—that is to say, the lines showing the direction in which it would pull a north-seeking magnetic pole, go round and round the wire. If you look along the wire, so that the electrons are going away from you, the direction of the field is in a circle, anti-clockwise round the wire. That a circular current behaves like a magnet may be seen by constructing a floating battery and loop as illustrated in Fig. 177. The loop sets itself with its axis in a N—S meridian as illustrated. The plates might be zinc and copper and the liquid dilute sulphuric acid.

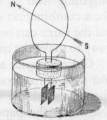

FIG. 177.—A circular current acting as a magnet.

The force round a wire carrying a reasonable current is not great, but by coiling the wire in a spiral a considerable force can be concentrated in the small space within the spiral, for the magnetic field of each turn of wire acts in the same direction. Fig. 176 shows such a coil encircling a rod of iron. In actual practice a great number of closely coiled turns are employed, for the strength of the field you get depends on the current you pass and the number (and diameter[1]) of the turns of the spiral. The more the current, and the more turns there are, the greater is the field. Unfortunately, the more wire you have the greater is the resistance of the wire to the current and the less current can be made to pass. To get the very biggest magnetic fields, huge currents of 5,000 or more amperes are used. However, these very powerful magnetic fields are used only in scientific experiments.

The magnetic force produced by an electric current is used for a great number of practical purposes.

A spiral coil of wire with a current flowing round it is called a solenoid. It gives a fairly uniform magnetic field with a north pole at one end and a south pole at the other.

If a rod of iron is placed in the middle of a solenoid, the magnetic force makes all the magnetic atoms of the iron face the same way (Fig. 178). Consequently the iron is converted into a powerful magnet. If soft iron is used, the iron ceases to be a magnet as soon as the current is cut off. This arrangement of a piece of iron encircled by a coil of wire is called an electromagnet.

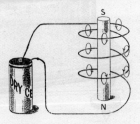

Fig. 178.—The magnetic field of the wire carrying the current is a circle clockwise round it. Consequently all the lines of force within the spiral point the same way and sum up to a considerable magnetic force.

Big electromagnets are greatly used for handling masses of scrap-iron, etc. Plate XVI shows one of the favourite patterns.

When the current is sent through the

[1] The diameter does not matter in a long spiral. In a short one, the greater the diameter the less the magnetic field.

coil of wire the lines of force pass through the iron and it becomes a powerful magnet. When it is switched off again the iron ceases to be a magnet. The photograph shows a mass of scrap iron suspended by an electromagnet. Fragments and scrap of this kind are obviously difficult to move quickly: the electromagnet affords a very easy way of picking up and dropping it.

To turn from big magnets to little ones, we find in the solenoid one of the most sensitive ways of detecting (and measuring) a small electric current. Most sensitive ammeters and voltmeters consist of a coil of wire within which is suspended a magnetic needle like a compass needle. When the current flows the coil creates a magnetic field which deflects the needle.

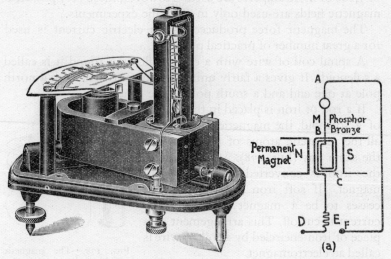

Fig. 179.—A movable coil galvanometer (1). The instrument with cover removed (by permission of Messrs. Griffin and Tatlock.) (2) Diagram of wiring.

The most sensitive type has a movable coil instead of a movable magnet as shown in Fig. 179. The current goes through a little coil of wire hanging by a conductive springy thread of phosphor bronze. The coil carries a little mirror. A spot of light is reflected by this on to a scale. On either side of the coil are the

PLATE XV

Turbo-alternator to generate 25,000 kilowatts.
(By courtesy of the English Electric Co., Ltd., Stafford.)

The armature of a dynamo designed to generate 37,500 kilowatts.
(By courtesy of the English Electric Co., Ltd., Stafford.)

PLATE XVI

Electromagnet lifting a heavy load of steel scrap. (*Below*) Section of same showing coils (*b*). (Demag Photo: from the manufacturers, Duisburg, Germany.)

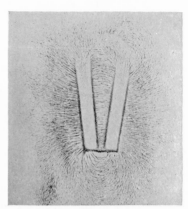

The lines of force of a horse-shoe magnet.
(From a photograph by Mr. H. Pocock.)

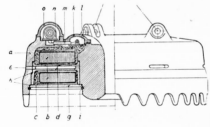

The record-breaking Union Pacific oil-driven train.
(By courtesy of *The Oil Engine*.)

poles of a powerful magnet. Suppose a current flows. The suspended coil becomes a magnet and the big magnet pulls it round till the spring of the suspension wire balances the pull. The coil carries the mirror with it, and the light-spot shifts along the scale. An instrument of this kind will detect a current of as little as 10^{-10} amperes.

An electromagnet is the easiest way to make an electric current do some simple act at a considerable distance. The telegraph gives the best example of this. It requires a battery, usually of fair voltage as the resistance of the long wire is considerable, a tapping key to cut off and switch on the current and an inker at

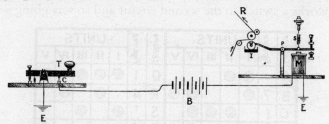

FIG. 180.—Simple telegraph. T, tapping key; C, contact; B, battery; M, electro-magnet; S, spring supporting inker; P, pivot; I, ink; W, inking wheel; R, moving paper tape; E, E, earth.

the far end (Fig. 180) to record the message. When the key is pressed down, the current flows through the battery and the key to the coil of wire round the iron core (M). This becomes a magnet and pulls the inking wheel on to the strip of paper which is all the time unrolling itself. When the key is released, the wheel springs down. It is unnecessary to use a double wire. The earth is used as one wire: it is a vast reservoir of electrons and the battery may be regarded as drawing them from the earth at the receiving end and discharging them into the earth at the sending end.

The morse code used for telegraphic purposes has only two signals, a long one or dash and a short one or dot. The letters of the alphabet, numbers and figures are all represented by combinations of these. Instead of (or as well as) an inker, the telegraph usually has a buzzer (p. 325) which sounds when the key is pressed down. This makes it easy for anyone who has learnt to do so to interpret the signals by ear.

The telegraph is being steadily superseded by the telephone, which is just as simple to instal and is much easier to use. It does not, however, write down its messages!

Where the telegraph line is long the resistance of the wire diminishes the current and the signals become faint. To remedy this relays are commonly used: These are another application of the electromagnet. Suppose the line extends 500 miles: this is divided into several circuits, each with its own battery. The signal-current in the first circuit operates an electro-magnet. This works a switch in the second circuit and so sets going a new

Letters	Figures	UNITS					Letters	Figures	UNITS				
		I	II	III	IV	V			I	II	III	IV	V
A	:	●	●				Q	1	●	●	●		●
B	?	●			●	●	R	4		●		●	
C	(		●	●	●		S	'	●		●		
D	2	●			●		T	5					●
E	3	●					U	7	●	●	●		
F	1/	●		●	●		V	)		●	●	●	●
G	3/		●		●	●	W	2	●	●			●
H	5/			●		●	X	£	●		●	●	●
I	8		●	●			Y	6	●		●		●
J	7/	●	●		●		Z	.	●				●
K	9/	●	●	●	●		/	/		●			
L			●			●	✳	✳	●	●	●	●	●
M	'			●	●	●	−	=				●	
N	−			●	●		+			●			●
O	9				●	●	Letter Space				●		
P	0		●	●		●	Figure Space		●	●		●	●

FIG. 181.—The teleprinter code. A circle represents a pulse of current in one direction; a blank square a pulse in the other direction. (Courtesy of the G.P.O.)

signal-current as strong as may be wished. The second circuit has also a relay which sets the third going and so on till the destination is reached.

The modern telegraphic apparatus is the teleprinter. This is a complicated mechanism which can hardly be understood without seeing it. It has at the sending end a keyboard like a typewriter: at the receiving end is a printing apparatus. Briefly, the depressing of the key corresponding to any letter causes five successive pulses of positive or negative current, differently arranged for each letter, to be sent out. These at the receiving end operate what is almost a combination lock. Each signal "unlocks" one of the 31 latches corresponding to one of the 31 letters or stops: this latch stops a rotating wheel of type at the right point for the required letter to be printed on a paper tape. These machines send about 65 words a minute with very little strain to the operator and none to the receiver.

Submarine cables are a more difficult problem. You cannot put relays at the bottom of the sea, and so a current has to travel say, 4,000 miles without any reinforcement. All sorts of problems

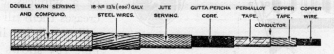

DOUBLE YARN SERVING · 18·N° 13½ (·090″) GALV. · JUTE · GUTTA PERCHA · PERMALLOY · COPPER · COPPER
AND COMPOUND. · STEEL WIRES. · SERVING. · CORE. · TAPE. · TAPE. · WIRE.
CONDUCTOR

Fig. 182.—A submarine cable.

arise here which are not found elsewhere. In the first place, the cable must be extremely well insulated, i.e., coated with material which does not conduct electricity. It must be strong, for it is likely to lie across rocks and holes in the sea bottom where it has to support its own weight. Fig. 182 shows a drawing of such a cable. Starting from the inside we have the copper wire which carries the current, then a wrapping of metallic tape made of a nickel-iron alloy, "Permalloy." The effect of this is to increase the speed at which signals can be sent. Outside this is the insulating layer of guttapercha. This insulation must be very sound indeed. Next may follow a layer of brass tape in order to stop the shipworm *Teredo* from boring holes in the cable: over this may be a layer of jute fibre to act as a cushion, then strong steel wires to take the pull when a cable hangs across a cleft in the sea bottom. Finally, a layer of jute fibre and pitch keeps the sea water from corroding the steel wires. So effective is this arrangement that cables have remained forty years in water and come up as good as new.

The signals must be sent down the cable at a great pace if the very expensive cable is to pay its way in fees. Actually, speeds of 2,500 letters a minute have been reached by mechanical senders— no human operator could work a key at this pace! The signals are very faint after the long journey and an amplifier—rather like the valve amplifier of a wireless-set increases them till they will work an inker. Fig. 183 shows such an inker. The inter-

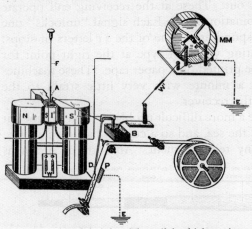

FIG. 183.—A Kelvin inker. The coil A which receives the currents hangs from the thread F, between the poles N, S of a powerful magnet. Its motions are transmitted by a thread to the ink-siphon D. The ink is kept electrically charged by the electrical machine MM. This is necessary in order to prevent the ink gathering in drops on the end of the tube D.

mittent currents (dots and dashes) pass through a coil of wire hanging by a springy thread in the field of a powerful magnet. When a "dot" or "dash" passes, the coil becomes a magnet with its north pole to the big magnet's north pole, and its south pole to the big magnet's

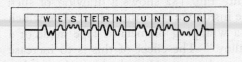

FIG. 184.—The paper tape of the recorder: an upward deflection is a dot: a downward one a dash.

south pole. It is consequently sharply twisted round when the current passes. In doing so, it pulls a thread which deflects a little tube through which ink is trickling on to a moving paper strip.

The difficulties experienced with submarine cables make wireless telegraphy (Chapter XVII) a more popular and cheaper way of sending long-distance messages.

Electric bells are applications of the electro-magnet. The current passes through the coils of such a magnet (A) and so excites the iron core (B). This attracts an iron pole-piece (P) which is attached to a steel spring (S) and has on it a metal rod and ball (R). These fly forward and strike the bell. But the current after leaving the magnet runs through the polepiece and the springs back to the battery. So the polepiece in flying forward breaks the flow of current, the magnet ceases to attract it, and the spring makes it fly back. But as soon as it reaches its first position, the polepiece touches the contact, the current flows again, the magnet attracts the iron and the whole thing happens again. The bell therefore keeps ringing as long as the current flows. The number of strokes per second depends on the distance between the polepiece and magnet and the strength of the spring. Electric horns and buzzers (Fig. 241, p. 405) work in the same kind of way.

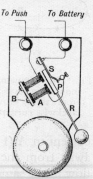

FIG. 185.—The electric bell.

If there is no bell but only the polepiece, spring, magnet and contact we have an *interrupter* used for turning a continuous current into one which is broken anything from ten to a thousand times a second. We shall see that the induction coil uses an interrupter of this sort.

INDUCTION

When a wire is moved either towards or away from another wire carrying a current the first wire has a current "induced" in it.

The reason for this is not susceptible of any simple explanation. Roughly, we may say that when an electron moves along a wire it makes a magnetic field of force round the wire. If this force is *altered* in the neighbourhood of a second wire a current will flow in it. The very simple rule is that if a current is flowing in a wire (A), and a second wire (B) is brought up towards A, then a current will flow in B in the opposite direction to that of the

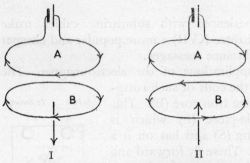

Fig. 186.—Showing the direction of the current induced in loop B when it is (left) drawn away from (right) brought up to a loop A carrying a clockwise current.

current in A (Fig. 186, II). Conversely, if the circuit B is drawn away from the current-carrying wire A, the current in B will flow in the same direction as that of the current in A (Fig. 186, I).

A further point: suppose we have two circuits A and B as before, and start a current in A. This is just as if we had brought circuit B up to A from an infinite distance where it could not feel any effect from the current in A. Consequently, the starting of a current in A causes a current in B in the opposite direction to the current in A, and stopping a current in A causes a current in B in the same direction. You might think this was a way of getting a current for nothing, but the necessary energy is supplied by the first current.

We see then that if we have two parallel wires and a current is started in one, a current is caused to flow in the opposite direction along the other. This principle is used in the induction coil and used to turn low voltage currents into high voltage ones, and also in transformers, chiefly used for turning high voltage alternating current into low voltage current.

The induction coil has a central primary coil of a few turns of thick wire, usually wound as an iron core, and outside this, but not connected to it, the secondary winding of up to a hundred miles of fine well-insulated wire. A current passes through an interrupter —the simplest kind is really an electric bell without any bell, the primary coil acting as the magnet. This stops and starts the current through the primary coil several hundred times a second.

Each time the current is started it induces a current in each of the thousands of turns of the secondary winding and in each of these turns the induced current has a certain small voltage or pressure. All these pressures add up, so that a very great voltage is reached. A hundred thousand volts can easily be attained.

The iron core of the primary coil has a great effect. The coil acts like a magnet and so turns the iron into a magnet. This means that it brings into the right position all the little atomic circuits of the iron for inducing a current, so that not only the currents in the coil but also those in the iron induce currents in the secondary winding.

When the current is broken the circuits in the iron jump back out of position (which is the same thing as switching them

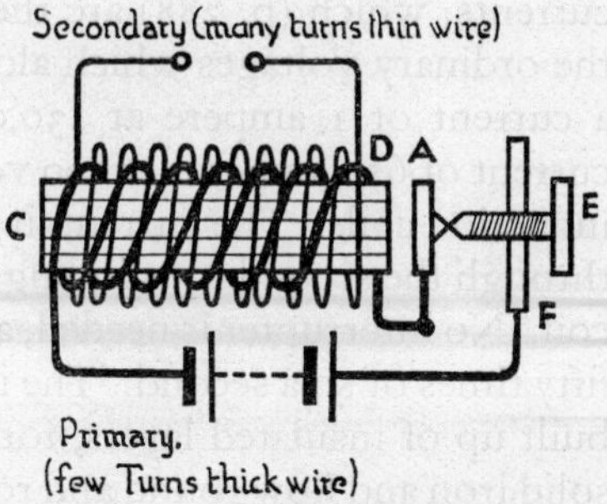

Fig. 187.—Diagram of induction coil. The secondary winding may contain miles of wire.

off, for it is a *parallel* current which causes another to be induced). The stopping of these currents, then, induces a current in the opposite direction in the secondary winding. The current from an induction coil therefore reverses itself hundreds of times a second. Specially pure soft iron is required for the cores of induction coils and transformers. Impure iron does not lose all its magnetism when the magnetising field is cut off.

Induction coils are used chiefly for operating X-ray tubes and for the sparking plugs of cars. The first needs very high voltages indeed, so it is usual to start with a fairly high primary current.

The "electric bell" make-and-break is not much used for these, as sparking is serious when fairly high voltages are put through the primary; so, instead, a mercury interrupter is used. This is a little centrifugal pump which throws a jet of mercury. Each time the rotor turns, the mercury hits a contact and passes the current. The apparatus is usually filled with coal gas so that sparking cannot cause the mercury to be oxidised and dirty.

Most of the current supplied from generating stations is alternating: that is to say it reverses its direction, say, fifty times a second. This if supplied to an induction coil would need no interrupter.

Transformers are used to convert the very high voltage currents, which (p. 288) are the most economical to transmit, to the ordinary voltages which alone are safe enough for use. Thus a current of 1 ampere at 130,000 volts could be turned into a current of 650 amperes at 200 volts. Transformers are really large induction coils. The current, if the voltage is to be lowered, is put through the secondary winding and taken off through the primary coil. No interrupter is needed, as alternating current reverses itself fifty times or so a second. The iron cores have to be very carefully built up of insulated layers, for currents are easily induced in the solid iron and flow round and round in it heating it up and wasting energy. A transformer cannot transform direct current: a serious disadvantage which is the chief reason for the wide use of alternating current.

The Tesla coil works on a principle somewhat similar to that of the induction coil but more complicated. It produces currents which reverse their direction not a few hundred times a second but a hundred thousand or more times. These have great value for medical purposes, because currents of this enormous frequency, though they may have a potential of hundreds of thousands of volts, do not affect the nerves. Their effect on the body is only to heat it as any other conductor is heated by a current. All the ordinary ways of heating the body are rather ineffective. They heat only the surface and the efficient temperature regulation of the body keeps the interior at a steady temperature.

The method of Diathermy consists in passing enormously high frequency currents alternating a million or so times a second through the body. A low voltage current cannot penetrate the body, the resistance of which is several thousand ohms. A high voltage direct or ordinary alternating current is fatal, but a current reversing itself a million times a second penetrates the body, is harmless and merely sets the molecules of the tissues vibrating, and this vibration is, of course, heat. The value of this heat is chiefly to destroy certain bacteria which are very sensitive to it.

If the electrodes applied to the body are two large pads, only a more or less gentle warmth is felt in the tissues between them. If, however, one electrode is a point or knife-edge, the heat is concentrated where it touches the body. The diathermy knife is a loop of wire, connected to one pole of the high frequency apparatus, the other pole being connected to a large moist pad pressed against the body. The "knife" cuts the tissues by burning them locally. This has the advantage that the tiny veins and capillaries are sealed by the heat and that the operation is bloodless.

Very short "wireless" waves can penetrate the body and heat it up, rather like the diathermy current. These are now being developed for medical purposes.

MAGNETS AND CURRENTS

Given then that a wire carrying a current of electricity can induce a current in another wire which is being brought up to it or taken away from it, we can easily see that a magnet will cause a current in a loop of wire which is moved across its pole. A magnet, we said, was a collection of tiny circuits at right angles to its length, and all moving the same way. (Fig. 173.) This is equivalent in effect to a single circuit round the outside of a magnet: this is proved by the fact that a spiral of wire carrying a current behaves precisely like a magnet.

Suppose now a wire loop is drawn down past the face of a north magnet pole. As it leaves the top of each tiny circuit a

current will be induced from B to A (the same way as in the top half of the circuit). As it approaches the bottom of the circuit, a current will be induced from B to A (the opposite way to the bottom half of the circuit). The effect is, then, that a current flows in a wire loop drawn across the direction of the attraction of a magnet. This is an extremely important result, for on it depends

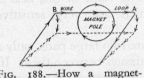

FIG. 188.—How a magnet-pole induces a current in a wire drawn past its face.

the principle of all the dynamos which supply the world's electricity.

The most important application of induced currents is in the dynamo and the electric motor. The principle of these is not very hard to grasp, though the machines in practical use are pretty complicated. Suppose we have a large permanent magnet M and a wire loop ABCD which can rotate between its poles. The ends of this loop we take to a commutator C, two half rings on which slide brushes Br, Br′, which can take the current where it is wanted Suppose the loop is turned anti-clockwise. The molecular ring currents in the magnet pole N

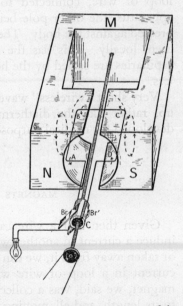

FIG. 189.—The essential parts of the direct current dynamo.

may be regarded as crossed by the wire loop AB. As
the wire comes down from the top of each of these, a
current will be induced from B to A, and as the wire loop
approaches the bottom of each such circuit, a current will also
be induced from B to A. It is not difficult to see that for the
same reasons a current must also flow from D to C. So, while the
loop is turning, a current flows in the direction DCBA. When
the loop has got round to the vertical position there will be no
current flowing for it will not be moving parallel to the magnetic
circuits, but when the loop begins to cross the poles again
current will again flow in the direction DCBA. The half of
the loop which is passing the north pole always has current
in it in the BA direction, and always hands it to the brush Br:
it is easy to see then that a current will go through the lamp
always in the direction indicated as DCBA. The current will
not be continuous but will come in pulses, being greatest when
the loop is horizontal and least when it is vertical. In the
ordinary dynamo the current is continuous because there are
many loops and some are always
passing the magnet.

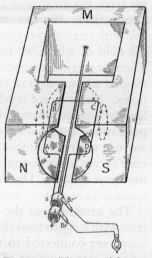

Now suppose we had no commutator but only two slip-rings attached
to our loop (Fig. 190). Now the brush
Br' always takes the current from the
same side (x) of the loop so that
when x is moving downwards past
the north pole it receives a current
in the direction $\overrightarrow{\text{BA}}$, but when it is
rising past the south pole a current in
the direction $\overrightarrow{\text{AB}}$. So this dynamo
would give an *alternating* current
which reverses its direction twice for
every turn the loop makes.

If a current is passed through a
direct dynamo, it will work as a motor.

FIG. 190.—The essential parts
of the alternating current
dynamo.

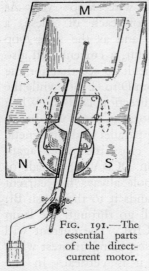

FIG. 191.—The essential parts of the direct-current motor.

Suppose instead of the lamp in Fig. 189 we put a battery and that the electrons are flowing in the direction ABCD. Now the wire AB has a field of force (p. 318) which would repel the N magnetic pole downward. Since the N pole of the magnet is held still, it is the wire that is repelled upward and the loop swings round in a clockwise direction.

Let us see now how these very simple dynamos and motors are elaborated into practicable machines.

Having seen that a loop of wire in a magnetic field can be made to turn electrical energy into mechanical energy and *vice versa*, the next thing is to put this into practice. To begin with, the permanent magnet we have drawn in our simple pictures will not produce a very strong field. We can improve on this with an electro-magnet (p. 319), the field of which we can control. Then we might have more than one magnet and use four or six or more poles. There is not much point in having a powerful machine just to push round a single loop of wire, so

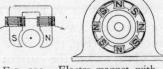

FIG. 192.—Electro-magnet with (left) two poles (right) eight poles as used in motors and generators.

we use a large number of loops wound on an iron core. This core serves to concentrate the field and so add to the power of the motor or dynamo. Direct current machines will be described first, because here motors and generators are almost identical.

The armature, as the moving part is called, is a cylinder of iron with longitudinal slots in which the wire loops lie. The wire loops are connected to the segments of the commutator, there being a large number of these segments instead of two as in our simple machine. The winding of the armature may take many

forms. A simple case of
what is called lap winding
will be described.

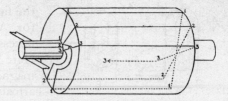

Fig. 193 is a diagram-
matic view of an armature,
the commutator divided
into segments being on the
left. If we follow the circuit

FIG. 193.—Diagram of an armature.

from segment No. 1 we find the current can flow round the armature 1, 1, 1, 1 and then to segment 2, then round loop 2, 2, 2, 2,
and so on. Thus, if the armature is rotated between the poles
of a magnet, an e.m.f. or electrical pressure is generated in *each*
loop and these e.m.f.'s add up to make a large total e.m.f.
Conversely, if an e.m.f. is applied to the brushes, it will send
a current through all the loops in series and each will add its
contribution to the turning force of the machine now acting as
a motor. Notice that there are two separate paths for the current.
It might pass from segment No. 1 round the last loop and so on.
A little consideration will show that these circuits work together.
In the diagram only one loop for each segment is shown. In
practice, the wire might be wound round several times in the
same slot before passing to the next segment.

What has been described is only one of a large number of ways
of winding an armature, but they all agree in taking the current
a number of times round the core.

The field magnets are so shaped that they produce as strong
a field as possible through the armature. In small machines the
"horse-shoe" type is used, wound with field coils round the legs.
In large and multipolar machines the armature is entirely surrounded by a casting with the magnets fixed inside. Each magnet
consists of a cast-steel core, the end enlarged where it faces the
armature and wound with the wire carrying the magnetising
current (Fig. 192).

The method of applying the current to the field magnets
depends on the use to which the machine is to be put.

In a generator we might use a separate current supply to excite

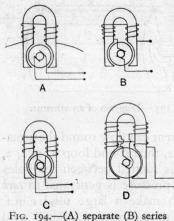

FIG. 194.—(A) separate (B) series (C) shunt (D) compound winding.

the field. This is usually the case for A.C. generators, but is not necessary for D.C. machines. Here we can connect the field magnet either in series with the armature, as in Fig. 194 B, or else in a shunt, Fig. 194 C. Series motors exert a very large pull on starting and so are useful for traction purposes. On the other hand, they must not run with a small load or they would acquire an excessive speed. Shunt motors are better suited for conditions where the load is variable, as they run more or less at a constant speed.

The properties of steadiness and ability to take a heavy load are well combined in the compound motor (Fig. 194, D), in which there are some series and some shunt turns on the magnets. Dynamos are usually compound wound, as it is possible by compounding to supply a constant voltage under varying demand for current.

It may be asked, "Can a generator excite its own field magnets?" The answer is, "Under certain conditions, yes." There is always a certain amount of residual magnetism in the iron cores of the field magnets when the machine is stopped. When the machine starts, its armature runs in this field and so a small current is produced. This passes through the field magnet coils and increases the field, which in turn reacts on the armatures until the full field is produced. This will not happen if the speed is too low and other conditions in the machine are not satisfied.

Alternating current machines offer a greater variety of types, but many of them are described in dealing with D.C. machines. For instance, the simple commutator motor can, with technical modification, be run on A.C. Suppose the current at one instant be flowing through the loop (Fig. 195) as shown. The top of the loop is a north pole and the bottom a south (compare p. 318 and Fig. 177). The loop therefore turns in a clockwise direction. Now the current being alternating, it reverses its direction after a fraction of a second, but since the current through the field magnets also changes its direction the north pole becomes a south one and *vice versa*, and both the armature and the field magnets reverse their polarity. The result is that the force is still in the same direction and the armature goes on turning.

The simple A.C. generator with collecting rings can also be

FIG. 195.—Illustrating the principles of A.C. motors.

used as a motor if supplied with A.C. of the proper frequency and run at the proper speed. Current is passing round the loop (Fig. 195) to give it poles as shown. The loop turns clockwise until its north pole faces the south pole of the magnet. If, at this moment, the direction of the current in the loop is reversed (the field magnets remaining the same) there will be two south and two north poles together; they repel each other and so continue the rotation of the loop. For such a motor as this to work, the current applied to the magnets must reverse itself just as the coil is pulled to face the poles, that is, it must have the *same frequency* as the coil. Synchronous motors built on this principle require auxiliary starting motors to get them in step with the current. The electric clocks run off the alternating current mains depend on this principle. Their synchronous motors can only work in exact time with the pulses of the alternating current and these on the grid system are accurately timed. Consequently the clocks must keep exact time with the master clock at the generating station which regulates the dynamos and is constant within 2 secs. per day.

A very important type of A.C. motor is the induction motor. To understand the working of this, we must understand the nature of the current that drives it. Suppose we have a generator in which we have on the armature a number—say, for example, three *separate* circuits wound in planes 60° apart, as in Fig. 196, and each provided with its own collecting rings. Then as the armature turns there will be generated three different alternating currents which on the average are equal, but each is a third of a revolution period after the next, i.e., they successively acquire their maximum or minimum strength at intervals of one-third period. These three currents are sent out on three wires as a three- (or in general a poly-) phase current. Now, consider a motor with a number of field magnets— any multiple of three as in Fig. 196. The poles 1, 1, 1, 1 are wound with circuit 1 and so on. At the beginning, pole A is a north pole at its maximum strength. The current in A decreases with time and so its pole strength decreases, while that in B is increasing. After one-third period, B is a north pole of maximum strength and then C and so on. Thus the north poles, and in the same way the south poles, pass on from magnet to magnet, and in effect we have a rotating magnetic field. Now consider the armature (Fig. 197) and see the advantage of this type of motor. The armature is self-contained, having no commutator and requiring no external circuit at all. It consists simply of a number of conducting bars joined at the end to conducting discs and having an iron core to concentrate the magnetic field. This is known as a squirrel cage armature. The action is quite simple. The rotating magnetic field induces currents in the bars of the cage and the action of the field on these currents is to produce a force pushing the cage round so as to follow the field. The armature cannot rotate as fast as the field or else no currents would be induced and no force would

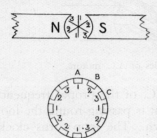

Fig. 196.—Illustrating the induction motor.

FIG. 197.—The squirrel-cage armature.

be exerted. There is always a certain amount of slip between the armature and the field.

The uses of the electric motor are manifold. It is only limited by the need for a supply of current which rules it out for all kinds of locomotion where an electrified track cannot be laid down and for use in places where there is no electric supply— as in mining in remote places. For the rest it is steadily replacing all other kinds of power. It is ideal for small jobs: no other engine works satisfactorily in units of less than 1 h.p.: hence it is ideal for vacuum cleaners, refrigerators and the like. Its current is cheaply carried by a cable—accordingly, factories, instead of having a central engine and expensive and heavy shafting and belting, tend more and more to run their machines each from a separate electric motor. It is alone among engines in producing very little heat, no smell and not much noise. For high speed work it is unrivalled save by the turbine, which we have seen is not suitable for small installations. For low speed work, e.g., for driving rolling mills, the electric motor used to be of little use, but gearing is now so perfect that it is easy to reduce its speed—and so increase the force exerted, to any desired extent.

The electric motor is very efficient and may deliver 95% of the energy supplied to it as useful work. This electrical energy is made at a large efficient generating station which may turn 30% of the energy of coal into work, though 25% is a commoner figure. Accordingly, it is more economical to turn coal into work *via* electricity than to burn it in small steam-engines which rarely or never reach 20% efficiency.

The fact that currents can be induced by moving a conductor of electricity in a magnetic field is the principle of the induction furnace much used for making the finest steel. On p. 336 you saw that it is possible to get a rotating magnetic field. Imagine, then, an armature like the one on p. 136 (Fig. 196, below) lying flat on its side and a crucible of steel standing within it. The magnetic field moving round in the steel produces just the same effect as the steel moving in a magnetic field and consequently currents are induced in the steel. These heat it up and melt it; and since the currents in the steel are in a magnetic field, the steel moves just like the armature of a dynamo, so the induction furnace actually melts the steel and stirs it—a very valuable property. The most remarkable thing about the induction furnace is that it is cold! The rotating magnetic field will only heat something which conducts, e.g., iron or other metal. The story is told—I have it only on hearsay—of an engineer who put his head inside an empty induction furnace and dropped dead for no apparent reason. An autopsy showed that as the result of a war wound he had a splinter of steel harmlessly embedded in an inessential part of his brain. The magnetic field heated this red hot in a few seconds with fatal results.

CHAPTER XI

POWER AND LOCOMOTION

TYPES OF ENGINE

WE have seen that there are four important classes of engine: the water turbine, the steam engine, the internal combustion engine and the electric motor. We can divide these up further and say that there are six great types of engine:

> The water-turbine.
> The steam-turbine.
> The reciprocating steam engine.
> The internal combustion engine with electrical ignition.
> The compression-ignition internal combustion engine.
> The electric motor.

Apart from locomotion these are chiefly useful for the following jobs:

Water-turbines	Generating electricity.
Steam-turbines	Generating electricity. Driving large pumps, etc.
Reciprocating engines	Small generating plants. Pumping engines. Driving shafting for factories of all types. Portable engines for threshing machines, saw mills, etc. Winding engines for collieries.
Internal combustion engine, with electrical ignition	Large gas engines are much used for blowing engines, for blast furnaces, for rolling mills, saw mills and various factory jobs.

| Compression-ignition engines | Chiefly used for generating electricity and heavy pumping work. |
| Electric motors | Almost all the above purposes but particularly adapted to high-speed work. |

It is interesting to consider the way that these engines can be applied to perhaps the most important of jobs, locomotion—e.g., driving ships, trains, buses, aeroplanes, etc.

The water turbine is obviously impossible for locomotion, because a water supply is not a thing one can carry about. The turbine can be used to make electricity and drive a motor, but that is hardly what we are considering here. The five other types of engine are all used in water, road, rail or air transport.

WATER TRANSPORT

What sort of engine does a ship need? A large ship obviously needs a very powerful engine, but all types can be made powerful enough if we choose.

There is no particular advantage in having a light weight engine in a ship, so, except for auxiliaries and racing yachts, we rule out the petrol engine, which is very powerful in proportion to its weight but burns an expensive fuel. The gas engine for obvious reasons is not employed. Electricity, too, cannot be the ship's source of power. It is possible to make electricity by an oil engine or steam engine coupled to a dynamo in the ship and drive the ship's screw by electric motors, but this is not much more than a smooth way of gearing the screws to the steam or oil engine.

We are left, then, with the reciprocating steam engine, the steam turbine and the compression-ignition or Diesel engine. All three of these can be built in big units which can give the great power required, up to 100,000 h.p. or more; and all these are greatly used, which clearly shows that each of the three has some merit for some purpose.

The cargo steamer wants a very economical engine. It does not need great speed, but it wants a reliable engine which can be easily run by a ship's engineer and which will stand up to the heavy strains imposed on it in a small ship. Vibration is not a very important factor. Cargo steamers are not commonly of

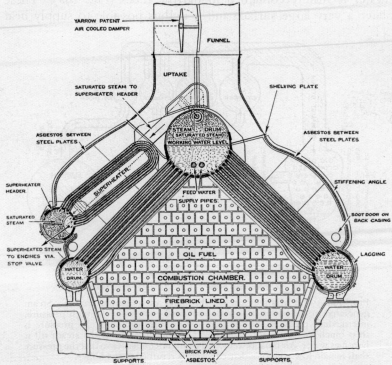

FIG. 198.—The boiler of a fair-sized marine engine. Oil fuel (p. 233) is burned in the combustion chamber and boils the water in the tubes. The steam rises to the top drum and is conducted through the superheater (left) to the engine. The furnace casing has to be fairly light and a poor conductor. Steel plates give strength and lightness: asbestos the poor conduction.

great size. The turbine does best in big installations and consequently the cargo steamer has a reciprocating steam engine or less commonly a Diesel.

The engine of a cargo boat is not so much stinted for size or

weight as is a locomotive engine; consequently trouble is taken
to use the steam as fully as possible, so ensuring economical
working. The boiler is usually of the water-tube type. In order
to take as much of the heat as possible from the furnace, the
water is mainly contained in narrow tubes (Fig. 198). These
have a very large surface and it is thus possible to supply heat

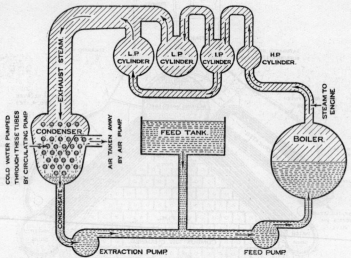

FIG. 199.—The arrangement of the parts of a marine engine. Steam
generated in the boiler (Fig. 198) expands by stages in the high pressure,
intermediate pressure and the two low-pressure cylinders. Its pressure is
then much less than atmospheric. The condenser cools the steam till it
becomes water. Air must be removed from the condenser so that the pressure
shall remain low. The condensed water is returned to the boiler.

rapidly and obtain much steam from a boiler which is not too
large and heavy. The steam passes through a superheater, which
raises its temperature so that it will not condense on leaving the
boiler. It may leave the boiler at some 500 lbs. pressure and a
temperature of about 400° C.—hotter than melting lead. The
steam successively operates the pistons of three cylinders or even
four (p. 265). In this way it can expand enormously. It then
passes to a condenser. Here it condenses to water, which is

returned to the boiler. The marine engine operates under first-rate conditions. There is comparatively ample space for the most economical designs to be used: moreover, the propeller runs at a steady speed.

The engines of a liner present other problems than those to be solved by the designer of the cargo-boat's engines. The expense of running a ship rises enormously with its speed: the resistance of the ship increases as (almost) the cube of the speed. Consequently twenty-seven times as much power is needed to propel a boat at thirty knots as is needed to propel it at ten knots. The cargo boat will, of course, carry nearly twice the cargo in a year if it travels at twice the speed: this probably will not pay if it has to use eight times as much fuel. The paying speed for such boats is 10–15 knots. Liners must get people quickly to their destination: they vie with each other to be the fastest boat. They run less economically than the cargo boat and have a speed of up to 30 knots or even more. Their engines have to be large and have to work without discomfort to the passengers. Consequently a smooth-running type of engine is chosen for liners; on this account designers choose the steam turbine, which even at high speed will not vibrate enough to make its casing quiver. The vibration felt in a liner chiefly arises from the propeller. The turbine, too, is more efficient than the reciprocating engine in units of over 1000 h.p.; the largest liners have engines of 200,000 h.p. Occasionally both types of engine are used. The liner *Olympic* employed reciprocating engines for two of her propellers and conducted the exhaust steam from both into a turbine which drove the central one. This is an economical arrangement, for the turbine is particularly well able to get the last bit of energy from low-pressure steam, while the reciprocating engines have the convenience of being easily reversed.

The battleship presents a third problem. If it is to survive and destroy, it must have greater speed than its adversary. Its weight is enormous: comfort is of no importance. A destroyer is a good example of such a ship. Though its displacement may be only 1350 tons, its engines may develop 44,000 h.p., and can drive it through the water at 38 knots. Here, again, the turbine is usually chosen, for it is best adapted to developing great power in a small space.

The use of oil-engines for craft of every description from yachts to liners is steadily increasing. They have several great advantages. An oil-engine weighs about a third as much as a steam-engine of the same power. It only takes up two-thirds of the space and its fuel takes up less than half the room.

The fact that Great Britain possesses much coal and no oil will for obvious reasons necessitate her vessels being largely run by steam, but there is little doubt that the number of steamships will steadily diminish.

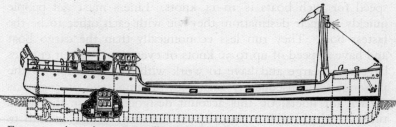

Fig. 200.—A modern coaster illustrating the small space occupied by the Diesel Engine. (Courtesy of James Pollock Sons & Co., Ltd.)

The chief type of engine used is the Diesel (pp. 272-274) one; type is illustrated (Fig. 152). Its remarkable compactness is very well shown in Fig. 200, which shows the very small space taken up in a coaster by its Diesel engine.

LAND TRANSPORT

As soon as we come on land, we find the question of weight bulking large. It matters least in rail vehicles, for the friction of rails is very small. An engine which can pull 10 tons on a level road can pull 40 tons on rails.

It is interesting to see how the stationary steam engine

has to be modified to adapt it for use in a locomotive. A locomotive has to be reasonably compact. Its width cannot exceed
that which will allow it comfortably to clear another such engine
on the next line. Its height is limited by the bridges it must go
under and its length by the sharpness of the curves it must
traverse. Limited in size, it must produce from 1000 to 3000 h.p.,
and must operate with fair economy. Great economy is incom-
patible with limited size and weight. Thus the increase in
efficiency gained by using a condenser (p. 265) and, at most, more
than two stages of compound expansion is hardly possible in a
locomotive.

The essential parts of the steam-engine are the furnace, boiler,
cylinders and pistons, and drive to wheels.

The furnace of a locomotive must be small, but it must supply
great quantities of heat and so burn coal very rapidly. The rate
of burning depends very largely on the draught, i.e., the air supply.
The air supply is drawn into an ordinary furnace by the column
of hot air rising up the chimney stack. The locomotive can have
no stack worth speaking of, consequently it must make its own
draught. The steam as it issues from the cylinder is led into the
base of the smoke-stack: as it rushes upward from the exhaust
pipe E it carries with it the flue gases and so causes a powerful
inrush of air through the firebox. This air enters at the front of
the engine, travels through the hot-air space (Fig 201) above the
boiler tubes and so returns some of the waste heat from the
furnace-casing to the furnace. The most modern locomotives
employ a water tube boiler similar to those used in marine
engines. Figs. 201, 203 show the arrangement of these tubes.
The steam pressure is usually 200–250 lbs. per square inch. As we
saw on p. 262, the higher the steam-pressure the greater the
economy of working. The disastrous effects of boiler explosions
in railway accidents have discouraged designers from using
very high pressures, but a locomotive using 850 lbs. per square
inch pressure has been tried out and found very efficient. The
steam is usually superheated by leading it through strong pipes
heated in the far end of the furnace; thence it goes to the pistons

and cylinders, which work in just the same way as those of the engine described on p. 264. A locomotive requires no gears: it changes its pulling power by altering the cut-off. When an engine is pulling a heavy train up a grade it keeps the inlet valve open during a large part of the piston's travel. The piston is thus exposed to the full boiler pressure for most of its stroke. When travelling at speed on the level or down grade, the cut-off is arranged so that the inlet valve closes early and the expansion of the steam operates the piston for most of the stroke: this, of course, decreases the quantity of steam used and therefore of coal burnt.

The use of two or three cylinders — compound expansion — is sometimes adopted. It makes for economy, but since the low pressure cylinders have to be very large, it adds to the weight and bulk of the engine. It is also less suitable for locomotives which run at uneven speeds than for the steadily running marine engine. The pistons by the connecting rod and parallel rod finally turn the great driving wheels, a process which, since it can be watched in any locomotive, need not be described here.

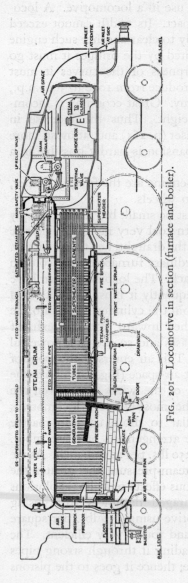

FIG. 201—Locomotive in section (furnace and boiler).

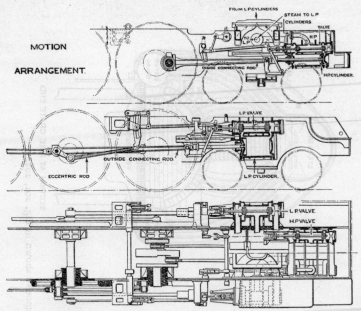

Fig. 202.—How the pistons operate the driving wheels of a locomotive.

The most efficient steam engine is the turbine, and consequently many attempts have been made to use it for driving a locomotive. The obvious difficulties are the very varying speed of the locomotive, the fact that a turbine cannot be reversed and the need to reduce its very high speed of thousands of revolutions per minute to the 300 r.p.m. which is the highest pace of the great 6ft. 6in. driving wheels.

Turbine locomotives have been used in Sweden for some years; the first British turbine locomotive is the recently constructed L.M.S. engine "Turbomotive". The boiler generates steam at 250 lbs. per sq. inch which is superheated to 750° F.

There are two turbines, a forward and a reverse, housed in the position occupied by the cylinders in the orthodox locomotive. Six separate nozzles supply steam to the forward turbine, thus allowing the speed to be controlled. The exhaust steam is not

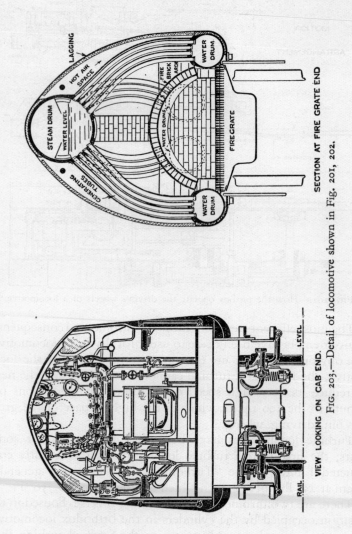

SECTION AT FIRE GRATE END

VIEW LOOKING ON CAB END.

Fig. 203.—Detail of locomotive shown in Fig. 201, 202.

condensed as in the stationary turbine, but escapes via the smoke-stack. The turbines drive the wheels by double helical gears like those in Plate IX (see p. 192). The advantages of such a locomotive are the smooth and steady pull, which, as explained on page 350, is one of the main features of the electric locomotive, the absence of vibration, which further causes a smaller repair cost and a saving of coal, due to increased efficiency, of some 15%. Since there is no condenser, the efficiency is much less than that of a stationary turbine, but it is considerably greater than that of the non-condensing reciprocating engine of an orthodox locomotive.

The railways of the world, with few exceptions—of which the Austrian railways are perhaps the chief—are now run by steam, though it is very doubtful if this will be true in twenty-five years time. Locomotive design has been perfected over a hundred years, and the modern railway engine is a marvel of complexity. But judged by results, it leaves much to be desired. Of the heat produced by burning the coal, not one-twelfth—and often not one-twentieth—is used in pulling the train. The rest disappears in heat losses from the boiler, in hot flue gases from the funnel, in uncondensed steam, and above all in moving a vast engine and tender which may weigh 270 tons. This defect of having to haul 200 tons of engine and tender in order to pull 500 tons of train, with perhaps only fifteen tons of people in it, is, from the engineering point of view, absurd. Apart from this, we have already seen that high efficiency in a steam-engine can only be gained by using several stages of compound expansion (p. 265), an efficient condenser, and various devices designed to rob the issuing gases of as much heat as possible. These devices cannot, for various reasons, chiefly those of bulk and weight, be employed on locomotives, which therefore, though much improved of late years, remain, as engines, inefficient.

Well, then, why not scrap the steam locomotives or why not electrify the lines? Two difficulties stand in the way. First, these systems have not been tried out sufficiently for a company to stake millions on them; secondly the cost of scrapping steam and replacing it would have to be met by borrowing money. The interest on this would probably eat up all the profit that the economy of the change would bring. None the less, the German and American railways are beginning to replace steam by oil, and even in England electrification is spreading.

The electric railway is, of course, already a fact. Numerous lines are electrifying their suburban areas and some are going further afield. The degree of advantage of electricity over steam depends, of course, on what the electricity costs. But, generally speaking, the railway can use cheap slack coal in a power station while it needs good coal for its engine.

A generating station will turn some 30% of the heat of its coal into electricity. Of this, perhaps, 10% is lost in distributing it along the power lines. The electric locomotive turns 95% of its electricity into power, so that at least 25% of the heat of the coal is actually used.

The steam locomotive uses some 7% of the heat of its coal. The economy of two-thirds of the railway's coal is enough to save heavily on the cost of the power stations, etc.

There are several other advantages in the electric railway. The first is rapid acceleration and braking. A steam train increases its speed at about half a mile an hour per second: an electric train at one to one and a half miles an hour per second. This causes a huge saving in suburban trains which stop every mile or so. The reason of this is not a greater power, but a steady pull. The steam engine pulls much more strongly when the piston is at the beginning of the stroke than when it is at the end, so that it really drives in a series of jerks. Moreover, if any locomotive pulls harder than a certain figure, its wheels will slip round and round on the rails while the train stays still. The "jerks," when the pull is strongest, consequently start it slipping.

The electric locomotive can keep up a steady pull just less than the pull which will cause wheel-slip: it also drives on a larger number of wheels; each of these has therefore less pull on it and is less prone to slip. Another advantage is its lightness. The difference in weight between a locomotive and the driving unit of an electric train is enormous.

The electric train goes forward or backward with equal ease. It comes into a terminus platform, discharges its passengers, picks up a new lot and departs. The steam train deposits its load, then has to go out of the station and have its locomotive transferred to the other end, before it can move out again. A station can therefore handle just twice as many electric trains as steam trains.

Two more considerable advantages of the electric train are, first, that it wastes nothing when it is standing still. A steam locomotive burns coal when it is standing about doing nothing. Finally, but not least, the electric train makes no smoke or smell. Some of our London stations, begrimed with smoke, contrast ill with others which are largely used by electric trains and remain clean and bright. If any reader remembers the Crystal Palace tunnel before the line was largely electrified, he will appreciate the point; if he contrasts its present state with a tube railway tunnel, the point will be further emphasised.

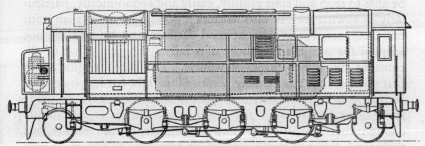

FIG. 204.—A Diesel-Electric locomotive. The shaded area indicates the Diesel engine and generator. The motors drive on the axles.

The locomotive which many believe to be the coming one is the Diesel-electric, which has an oil-engine driving a dynamo and producing a current which drives electric motors geared to the wheels. The obvious advantages are the smooth running and the rapid acceleration of the electric locomotive without the expense of the special track with contact rails. A Diesel engine will turn more than 30% of the heat of the oil it burns into electricity, so that the total efficiency is as high as 25% or even more. Crude oil is burned: the cost of this varies greatly, so that it is not easy to compare its cost with coal. Actually, the fuel for a Diesel-electric locomotive costs only about one-third of that of the coal for a steam locomotive; it must be remembered, however, that the fuel is not the heaviest cost of a locomotive journey. The wages of driver, fireman, guard, ticket collectors, maintenance of permanent way, advertising, etc., add up to far more than the cost of the coal. None the less, other things being equal, the Diesel-electric will beat the steam locomotive for speed, lightness, economy and cleanliness. Moreover, the severe labour of the fireman shovelling coal under most exhausting conditions disappears altogether.

Rail transport is obviously adapted for heavy loads, long distances and high speeds, or some of these. The mere fact of the friction of wheels on rails being about a quarter of that of wheels on a good road gives the former a great initial advantage over road transport. Any vehicle intended for road transport must be able to stop and start rapidly, easily and economically, particularly in towns: weight also matters a good deal more than with rail transport, for at present road surfaces and bridges are not adapted for weights like those of a railway engine. First of all, consider the light passenger vehicle. The petrol-engine takes first place on the road chiefly because it is light for its power and because it is so very easily controlled. For private cars, no other form of transport is of any importance. Steam is not simple enough: there are still one or two steam cars on the market, but their fatal defect is that they require a minute or two to get up steam on starting; while the petrol engine starts instantly—if it is working properly. Electricity involves carrying very heavy batteries, and if the weight of these is to be reasonable, the power available is but small. The oil-engine of the Diesel type is as yet not very suitable for low powers. Units of 60–90 h.p. are made, but the horse-power tax prevents their use.

The motor car presents several problems which do not arise in the locomotive. Its engine works efficiently only at a fairly

PLATE XVII

Section showing (*a*) streamline flow, (*b*) turbulent flow past an aeroplane wing.
(By courtesy of Friedr. Vieweg & Sohn, A.G., Braunschweig, Germany.)

Hawker monoplane with Rolls-Royce Merlin Engine. An example of
streamline form. (By courtesy of *The Aeroplane*.)

PLATE XVIII

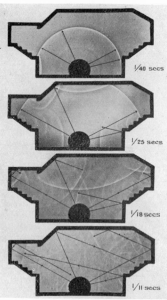

1/40 secs

1/25 secs

1/18 secs

1/11 secs

Sound waves engendered by an electric spark in a model auditorium. Note the manner in which they are reflected. (By courtesy of Dr. A. H. Davis.)

Water-waves, as seen in the tidal wave or eagre in the Trent. (By courtesy of *The Illustrated London News* and the London Electrotype Agency.)

high rate of revolution. It is necessary, therefore, to have gears
to allow of slow running. These gears have already been discussed (p. 194). Moreover, once stopped, the engine is not easily
started—unlike the steam engine or electric motor. It is necessary, therefore, to have a clutch by which the engine can be disengaged from the driving wheels. Finally, motor cars turn
sharply (as locomotives do not). It is necessary then that the
back wheels should be able to rotate at different speeds, for on
a sharp turn the inside wheel may well be going at half the pace
of the outer one. If they were on a single solid axle, they would
have to turn at the same speed, and one or both would have to
slip on the road surface, so rapidly destroying the tyres. The

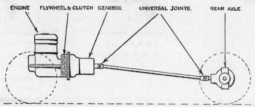

FIG. 205.—The transmission of an automobile.

differential is an arrangement which drives both back wheels
off the single shaft, yet lets them move independently. The
differential is much less easy to comprehend in a picture than on
the car itself, but it is possible to get an idea of its working from
Fig. 206, which shows a simple diagram of a differential. The
shaft G from the gear box turns the differential case A, A, to
which it is geared. The stub axle S thus turns at right angles
to the plane of the paper. On it are two bevel gears E, E free
to rotate. Clearly these move with the stub axle and drive the
side bevels C, C, which drive the wheels. Now on a straight
road the bevels E, E would not rotate *on* the stub axle and the
side bevels C, C would move at the same speed, and the wheels
would also move equally fast. But now let us suppose one wheel
is slowed or stopped. The side gear C, the left, let us suppose,
will slow or stop, consequently the bevel gears E, E will roll on

12

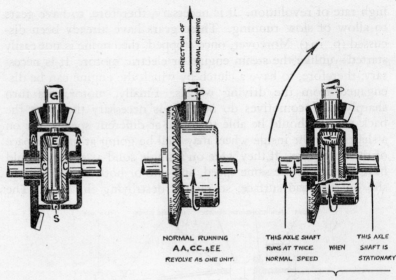

FIG. 206.—The differential gear of a motor-car, looked at from above.

it (like a pinion on a rack), but they still drive the right side bevel (C), which continues to move at twice its former speed, the speed of the stub axle plus that of the rolling bevel gear. Thus the two wheels are both driven independently and one can slow or stop without stopping the other. If they both stop E must stop too; it cannot roll on both at once, for to do so it would have to turn clockwise and anti-clockwise at once.

When we come to the heavy road traffic—'buses, trams, lorries, etc.—there is a wider choice. There are four main systems in use, electric, petrol, heavy oil and steam. The electric system is almost certainly the ideal one, but it requires overhead (or underground) cables, and these cost about £2,750 a mile to erect. The older system was the tram. The current is taken from an overhead wire or underground cable. It drives a motor and returns *via* the rails. Trams have two fatal disadvantages. They cannot get out of the way of traffic nor can they get round an obstruction. Secondly, a tramway track costs £20,000 a mile to lay and a great deal of money to keep in order. Consequently, almost every big town is replacing its trams by trackless trolley

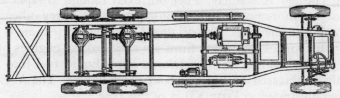

FIG. 207.—The chassis of a trolley 'bus, indicating the very compact character of the power unit.

'buses, which have two overhead wires for the supply and return of the current. These, as stated above, cost about £2,750 a mile, but if the overhead standards were previously used for trams the change-over costs only about £800 per mile. The trolley 'bus system is cheaper than either the petrol 'bus or the tram by about 1d. or 2d. in the shilling. They have several other advantages. They start smoothly, without the jerks and snatching of a clutch: they produce no poisonous carbon monoxide to pollute the air of our streets. Finally, their running cost does not depend on the price of petrol, which in fourteen years has fluctuated between 2s. and 1s. 2d. per gallon. They use electricity made from British coal, which, though it varies in price, does so slowly. They are light, for the motor is small compared with the petrol-motor. Fig. 207 shows how little room it occupies. Finally, they are regenerative. A petrol 'bus climbs a hill and work is done on it in order to raise it. But when it goes down the other side, it is *doing* work and we waste this work by turning it into heat in the brake shoes. The electric 'bus, when it goes down hill at more than, say, twelve miles an hour, drives its motor, which acts as a dynamo and puts electricity back into the power lines! In a hilly district this is very valuable.

Great as are the advantages of the trolley 'bus, its value must be limited to 'bus-work. Long distance 'buses and lorries must

carry their own source of power. The usual recourse is to the
petrol-engine. This has great advantages: petrol can be bought
anywhere and every garage mechanic understands the engine.
But where heavy loads have to be carried long distances, something cheaper is wanted. Fuel oil, even though cheaper than
petrol, has more power in it. Consequently the heavy oil-engine
is coming to the fore. The original Diesel type of engine is too
heavy for lorries, but many firms are now making engines of 50
to 150 h.p., which, like the Diesel, inject liquid fuel into hot
highly compressed air, but which are much lighter. The A. E. C.
engine illustrated in Plate XII is of this type.

AIR TRANSPORT

A craft which is heavier than air and which can yet remain at
a constant height without falling must have some force acting
on it to keep it up. If any object is moved rapidly through air,
a force is felt. Hold a magazine out of the window of a railway
carriage and you will feel that the air exerts a very decided force
on the magazine. This force varies roughly as the square of the
velocity. Thus, it is four times as great at forty miles an hour
and nine times as great at sixty miles as it is at twenty miles an
hour. The aeroplane is lifted by the pressure of the air on an
oblique plane.

Suppose you hold the magazine at an angle of 15° to the
ground (Fig. 208). The
air now strikes the bot-
tom of it and you can
feel that the air is pushing
it *up* as well as *back*.

If you were to let go
of the magazine, it would
be blown away in the
direction F, and so we
can say that the pressure

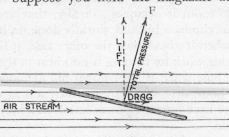

Fig. 208.—Lift and drag on an inclined plane in
an air-stream.

and friction act on the plane in that direction. Now that force has just the same effect as two smaller forces perpendicular to each other, which we call the *lift* and the *drag*.

The wings of an aeroplane are inclined planes like this. The engine and propeller move it along and so make the air-stream which gives the lift. Just as (p. 101) a turbulent flow of water past ships wastes energy, so aeroplanes must avoid wasting their energy in making eddies in the air. So, instead of using a flat plane, it employs a cambered wing of streamline form.

The difference between the excess pressure on the bottom of the wing (Plate XVII) and the low pressure of the partial vacuum on the top is the force which lifts it. The design of the wing has been studied very carefully indeed. Plate XVII shows a section of a wing of an aeroplane, with the airstream flowing past.

The aeroplane consists essentially of a fuselage, which contains the engine, which drives the propeller, and also contains the passengers, etc. The wings provide the lifting force. An undercarriage and wheels allow the machine to take off and land. At the tail is an elevator plane, which, by being moved up and down, can raise or lower the tail and the rudder which, like a ship's rudder, can alter the course to right or left. The elevator plane is operated by a stick control and the rudder by a foot-bar. At the rear of each wing is a hinged flap or aileron. The ailerons are operated independently and so can raise or lower either wing independently, causing the machine to tilt sideways.

The aeroplane can be made to travel "uphill" by inclining its tail-elevator (Fig. 209). This makes increased lift, but as more work is being done also reduces speed. If the course is made too steep, the speed falls and the lift falls off very rapidly, for the lift depends on the pressure of the rapid air stream, which varies as the square of the velocity. The aeroplane is thereby slowed up and begins to drop. This is called stalling and commonly occurs at angles of $15°–18°$. The slotted wing is very effective in preventing stalling. It has the effect of letting air through the wing into the turbulent area behind it and so decreasing the drag which slows the machine down.

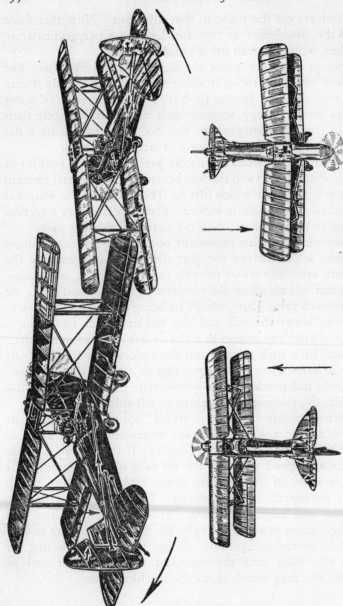

FIG. 209.—(Top left) aeroplane being put into right-hand turn. Joystick to the right pulling right aileron up and left aileron down causing right bank. Right foot pushing rudder bar, pulling rudder to right, thus starting turning influence. (Top right) left-hand turn, as above but reversed. (Lower left) joystick pulled back, elevators up, thus depressing tail and causing aircraft to climb. (Lower right) joystick pushed forward, elevators pulled down, thus raising tail and causing aircraft to dive. (After *The Modern Light Aeroplane*, by courtesy of Messrs. Shell-Mex and B.P., Ltd.)

If the angle of the planes to the ground is decreased, a time comes when the gravitational pull of the earth will supply the power needed to propel the machine. It then "glides" downward, as in Fig. 209.

The pilot who wishes to keep a given course must regulate the aeroplane by the throttle and by the elevator plane controlled by the "stick." It is no good setting the elevator upward (Fig. 209) if the engine is not supplying enough power to make the plane climb: for the machine will turn upwards, lose speed and "stall." If he wishes to fly horizontally, he must keep his engine at a certain speed; for if he increases its speed, the extra stream of air causes more lift and the machine climbs. If he decreases it, the machine turns its nose downward and glides. An aeroplane flying horizontally has practically only one speed, for which the angle of the wings, etc., suits it.

The rudiments of the art of the pilot are to proportion the engine's speed to the elevator lift, and maintain suitable angles to the ground. If air was still, this would be easy. Actually it is full of changing currents. Suppose you are flying at 75 m.p.h. You meet a sudden gust of wind travelling your own way. This momentarily decreases your speed *relative to the air* to 40 miles an hour. Consequently your machine begins to lose lift and you require increased throttle and elevator to make it climb again. The art of flying, then, is anticipating and allowing for the air-currents.

Rising from the ground is not so difficult a matter as landing. The principle is merely to speed up the plane along the ground or water until the airstream exerts enough lift to take it off the ground. Landing is much more difficult. If the pilot approaches the ground too steeply, his speed will increase so much that the shock of meeting it will be dangerous. If he does not approach it steeply enough, he will lose speed so that the machine stalls, drops vertically ("pancakes") and crashes. The art of the pilot is directed to coming down in a curve which levels out to meet the ground gently at a steady and ever decreasing angle. The higher grades of the pilot's art, the manœuvres by which he corrects side slips, loops the loop and so on, are quite beyond the little sketch of the working of the aeroplane which I have tried to give.

The aeroplane engine is designed to turn a propeller or air-screw. This is most commonly mounted ahead of the engine as a "tractor." It usually is of wood and has two blades. The principle

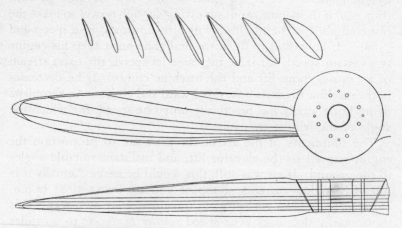

FIG. 210.—The propeller of a modern aeroplane. (Above) Sections at various points between base and tip of blade. (Middle) Plan of blade. (Below) Elevation of blade. (Courtesy of De Havilland Aircraft Co., Ltd.)

is just the same as that of the ship's screw. The inclined surface of the blade is pressed on by the air it displaces. This pressure can be split up into a force hindering the propeller from turning and another force pushing it forward. The first of these forces is wasted: the useful force, perhaps, is four-fifths of the total. The shape of propellers has, of course, been the subject of a vast amount of work and experiment. Fig. 210 shows the appearance of and the shape of sections of a typical propeller.

The engine is required to turn the propeller at a speed which may be 1000 to 1500 revolutions a minute. This is an efficient speed for an internal combustion engine, so no gearing is required, the propeller being directly mounted on the engine shaft.

The only kinds of engine used in aeroplanes are the petrol engine and the Diesel engine. Steam engines are too heavy. The differences between an aeroplane engine and a car engine are not exceedingly great. The working parts, carburettor, valves, etc., are the same in principle, but every effort is made to secure lightness, compactness and reliability.

The ratio of weight to power is the essential point. A man weighs perhaps 200 lbs. per horse-power; a locomotive 100–120 lbs. per horse-power; a stationary gas engine might weigh 80 lbs. per horse-power; while the best aeroplane engines only weigh some 1 to 1.5 lbs. per horse-power.

Many parts which in a car engine are made of steel or cast iron —cylinder heads, etc.—are made of duralumin. The cylinders are of steel instead of cast iron; for steel being much stronger can be made much thinner and therefore lighter. Water-cooling adds weight; consequently, the smaller machines have air-cooled cylinders like motor cycles. These are often arranged radially so that they shall each have their supply of cooling air.

The Diesel engine has now been made light enough for use in aeroplanes. It has the advantage of using a cheap fuel and one that is not easily set alight. Moreover, it is more reliable because there is no electric ignition which, as every motorist knows, is one of the least reliable parts of his engine.

PART III

WAVES

CHAPTER XII

VIBRATION

WHAT IS A WAVE?

EVERYONE knows that sound, light and "radio" are *waves*, but most of us have no clear idea of what this means beyond a notion that the results which sound, light or radio produces arrive at their destinations as a series of pulses. The word "wave" is of course taken from a wave of the sea and the waves on the surface of water are the only kind that the ordinary man can picture clearly.

You are standing on the pier on a fairly calm day. Long ridges of water are seen to be travelling at a few miles an hour towards the shore. All these ridges have roughly the same shape and size and speed.

The eye gets the impression that the water is travelling towards the shore, but in actual fact it is not. In the first place, if the

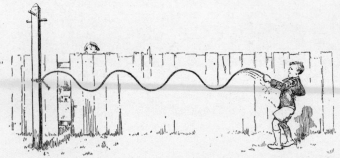

FIG. 211.—The rope moves only up and down: the waves travel to the left.

water was all going inshore, it would pile itself up there into a sort of permanent wave, and nothing of the kind is seen.

More convincingly, watch a floating cork. It lifts on the wave and falls on the trough, but the waves do not carry it along; we therefore conclude that the waves move inshore, but the water merely bobs up and down. If this is difficult to picture, look at Fig. 211: a boy is pulling on a rope and pulling the end up and down. Waves can easily be seen travelling along the rope, which itself only moves up and down.

A single wave of the sea is, then, a distortion of the shape of its surface, a distortion which moves without losing its characteristic shape and without taking the water with it.

The drawing in Fig. 212 may give an idea of how a travelling wave could be generated by particles of water moving straight up and down. In Fig. 212 each letter is supposed to be travelling up to the top, then down to the bottom, without shifting to right or left. As long as they all move in this same way, a wave will be formed travelling from right to left.

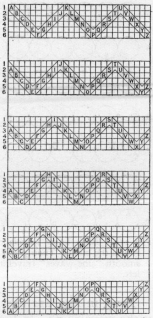

If the particles went up and down at a *steady* speed, the wave would have the form of a saw (Fig. 213, I), but in actual fact they always slow up towards the end of their travel and the commonest wave form is a *sine-curve*, which is the form of wave shown in Fig. 213, II.

If the particles move in circles of the same size at the same speed, a moving wave of the sine-curve type will result (Fig. 214): water waves are the result of a motion of

Fig. 212.—Each letter travels up and down at the same pace: their positions form waves travelling to the left.

FIG. 213.—I, waves engendered by particles moving up and down at a steady speed. II, A sine-curve.

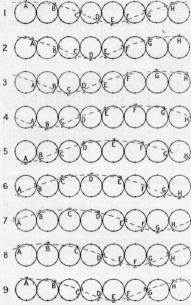

FIG. 214.—Each letter travels clockwise round the circle. Their positions form smooth "sine-waves" travelling to the left.

this kind.[1] It is reasonable to expect, then, that any sort of regularly repeated motion of regularly spaced particles will produce a wave.

Three terms are much in use when discussing waves of all kinds: they are wavelength, frequency and amplitude.

It is not possible to talk much about waves, whether of water, air or energy, without these terms. Plate XVIII illustrates *wavelength*. In a water wave, it is the distance from crest to crest; since light and sound waves have no real crests and troughs, the wavelength is the distance between the nearest places in which the wave is in exactly the same state.

Thus, in Fig. 212 the distance from A to K or from C to M is the wavelength. In Fig. 213, II the distance A B is the wavelength. The frequency is the number of crests passing a point

[1] Actually the particles which make up water waves move in ellipses, not circles.

in a given time, usually a second. It is also the number of times a vibrating particle can go through its complete cycle of movements in a given period. In Fig. 212 it is easy to see that the time for A to get from the top to the bottom and back to the top again is the time taken between the departure of a crest from the spot where A is and the arrival of the next crest at that spot. In Plate XVIII you cannot see the particles, but you could count the waves that pass you in a given time. Suppose the waves were travelling at six miles an hour and their crests were eleven feet apart. There would be $\frac{6 \times 5280}{11}$ or 2880 crests per six miles, so 2880 would pass in an hour.

The frequency of a wave is, then, the speed divided by the wavelength. In this case it is 2880 per hour or 0.8 per second.

The amplitude of a wave is, in the case of a waterwave, half the height from trough to crest. In Fig. 212 (top line) it is half the vertical distance from the level of A to the level of F. In Fig. 214 it is the radius of the circle; in Fig. 213 it is half the height from the top of the crest to the bottom of the trough. In the case of a sound or light wave, there is no real trough and crest of which to measure the height, and the amplitude is the difference of *energy* between trough and crest. This is true of the water wave: at its crest it has the extra potential energy of the tons of water which raise it above its trough.

Water waves are pretty complicated as a rule. It is only in small ripples that the water particles move in neat ellipses. The waves in a storm at sea may be seventy feet high and travel at forty or fifty miles an hour. These great waves are covered with smaller waves, which again

FIG. 215.—How sets of waves may be superposed on one another.

have smaller ripples on their surfaces. Waves with smaller waves on top of them are very common, in fact, universal in sound. We call the big wave the fundamental note, and the little waves overtones.

The breaking of a wave occurs when shallow water is reached. The wave usually breaks when the water in the trough behind it is only as deep as the wave is high. The cause of breaking is that the sand slows down the particles at the *bottom* of their course so that the top of the wave which is unhindered outruns the bottom. Out at sea the wind is usually travelling much faster than the waves and speeds up their tops, so that they over-run the main waves, and form the "white horses" seen in windy weather.

Water waves are the easiest to picture, but actually they are quite difficult to calculate anything about because several different effects (surface-tension, weights of water, depth of water) are concerned. Accordingly, we will say at present very little about how they are made or how they behave, but because they are so easy to picture we will use them to illustrate the much more important waves of sound, radiant heat, light, etc.

VIBRATORS

A sound wave is usually started by a *vibrating* body, and before sound can be understood we must know what is meant by vibrations. The vibrations which cause sound go through their motions 20–20,000 times a second. These are too fast for the eye to follow, so we will look at a few of the more interesting and simple vibrating systems.

A very simple vibrator is an ordinary pendulum. Hang a 5 lb. weight on a yard-long string which is tied to something firm—a stick supported on two chairs, or the curtain rod will do very well. Pull the weight away from the centre. In doing this, you have raised it. Let go of it, and of course it will fall. But it can only fall to where it was before and the only way it can do

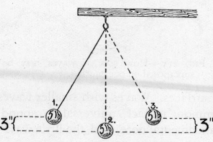

Fig. 216.—A simple pendulum.

that is by swinging back towards the centre. Well, it has fallen
to the centre now: what has happened to the potential energy
you gave it when you lifted it? It has all been turned into energy
of motion (except the tiny bit used to overcome the resistance
of the air). But there is nothing to stop the weight at the centre,
so it goes on until all its energy of motion has been used up in
lifting the weight. If the pendulum were absolutely frictionless
and in a vacuum, no energy would be lost and the weight would
would go up just as far on the left as it did on the right, and the
whole process would continue for ever. This is the simplest sort
of vibration.

At the extremes of the swing the thing that vibrates has
potential energy and no kinetic energy (it is still); at the middle
of its swing it has kinetic energy and (within the limits of movement of the particle) no potential energy. This is not only true
of pendulums but also of springs and many other vibrators.
Tie a bit of elastic (raid a workbox for it) to the curtain rod. A
yard of narrow elastic will do excellently. Hang a half-pound
weight on it, pull the weight down (Fig. 217) and let it spring
back. The weight vibrates up and down. In this case the potential
energy of the stretched elastic (A) becomes the kinetic energy of
the moving weight (B), and as this travels on it
loses speed under the influence of gravity until it
stops at (C), where it has no kinetic energy, but
instead the potential energy due to its height. It
starts to fall, speeds up and is drawn to a stop in the
original (A) position by the elastic force of the
rubber. This would repeat itself *ad infinitum* were
it not that the stretching and unstretching of the
rubber turns energy into heat: the resistance of
the air also has its effect. This idea of a vibration
being the change of potential energy to kinetic and
back to potential again and so forth is very important
and can be applied to every sort of vibration. Think
how it applies to a seesaw, to a violin string, to a
ball allowed to run down the side of a basin.

FIG. 217.—
Vertical vi-
brations of a
weight hung
on a piece of
elastic.

The frequency of a vibration, the number of times it repeats itself a second, is a thing which in some cases is easily calculated. The formula which applies to many cases is: Time of a vibration = $6\frac{2}{7}$ times the square root of the mass (weight) of the vibrating particle divided by the force per unit distance pulling the particle back to the centre.

This sounds a little complicated, but the important part is: *the heavier the thing vibrating, the slower it goes; the greater the pull towards the centre the faster it goes.*

You can try that with your hanging elastic. A heavy weight bounces up and down slower than a light one: broad elastic makes the same weight bounce quicker than narrow elastic. And the pendulum? Will a heavy bob make it move slower than a light one? Try it. You will find it makes no difference at all !

The reason is that the extra mass which *slows* down the vibration also operates as an extra weight increasing the force pulling the bob back to the centre again, and the two effects exactly cancel out. The only thing which influences the time a pendulum takes over its swing is its length. If a pendulum is longer, the bob goes on a less steep path and so speeds up less quickly.

The rule for a pendulum is that the time in seconds for the bob to swing from left to right and back to the left again is $6\frac{2}{7}$ times the square root of the length in feet divided by the number of feet per second by which the speed of a falling body increases each second. Why does this come into it? Well, it is gravity that pulls the pendulum bob back to the centre, so the stronger the force of gravity, the quicker a pendulum vibrates. Timing a pendulum is the best way of seeing how the force of gravity varies from place to place.

The above rule is not quite true, but if the pendulum only swings through a few degrees, it is extremely near to the truth.

The pendulum you made will do very well to test the rule. Time thirty swings. You may find they will take twenty-eight seconds. Now shorten the pendulum to a *quarter* of its length (measured from the support to the middle of the weight). Time thirty swings. They will take *half* the time—fourteen seconds.

Thus, if the length is reduced to one quarter, the time is reduced to the square root of one quarter—a half.

CLOCKS

Since a pendulum's time of swing depends only on its length and the force of gravity, the pendulum has been used for 275 years to make clocks keep time. There is no difficulty in making a clock keep time with a pendulum. Why is it, then, that a clock, though once perfectly regulated, never keeps perfect time, but sometimes runs fast, sometimes slow? There are three chief reasons. First of all, the pendulum rod expands and contracts. Suppose the rod was of steel and the pendulum beat perfect seconds when the thermometer stood at 15° C. On a hot summer day with the thermometer at 30° C. it would be 1.00015 times longer. So the time of swing would be $\sqrt{1.00015} = 1.000075$ times longer. Now, there are roughly 90,000 seconds in a day. Our clock would take $90,006\frac{1}{3}$ seconds to do 90,000 swings, so it would be running $6\frac{1}{3}$ seconds a day slow.

The second trouble is that the time of swing of a pendulum is not quite independent of the amplitude or width of swing. As the clock gets dirty, friction increases, the restoring push on the pendulum gets feebler, and the time of swing a little shorter—so the clock runs fast. Also a newly wound clock pushes its pendulum rather harder than does a clock nearly run down, so making the swing variable. Finally, the resistance of the air depends on the height of the barometer. When pressure is low the pendulum is slowed up less, and so swings in a wider arc.

For astronomical clocks, meant to keep time to a second a year, the most elaborate precautions are needed of which something is said on p. 372.

One has not gone very far before the question arises as to the "standard" of time. All scientific measurements depend only on the *second*, the *gram* and the *centimetre*. If we have these units fixed, every other unit can be calculated from them. Thus, the unit of force is the force that in one *second* will increase the speed of *one gram* of matter one *centimetre* per *second*. The same is true of units of power, pressure, voltage, resistance, anything you like— they can all be expressed in terms of length, mass and time.

The standard gram is a piece of platinum kept in Paris, the standard metre is another piece kept there also, but what is the standard second?

The calendar unit of time is the day, the time in which the earth completes a rotation, and there are 86,400 seconds in a day. This should define what a second is: but the earth is probably not a perfectly constant clock. It is probably running slower and slower as the centuries go on, and it does not even keep perfect time, for it seems likely that one rotation may differ from another by as much as $\frac{1}{250}$th second. The present definition of a second is $\frac{1}{86400}$ of the time between successive returns of the "first point in Aries" to the meridian. To explain this explanation would require several pages, but the effect of it is that a second is $\frac{1}{86400}$ of the time of a rotation of the earth relative to the stars.

FIG. 218.—How the pendulum regulates a clock.

HOW A CLOCK WORKS

The pendulum of a clock is usually hung on a very thin ribbon of spring steel (R). As it swings back and forward, it bears against two pins P and P¹. The crutch (shaded in Fig. 218) which is pivoted at the top therefore swings backwards and forwards with the pendulum. The crutch carries two pallets, T, T′, which engage with the teeth of a ratchet wheel W. This wheel is geared to the train of wheels by which the weights drive the hands. *The hands cannot move unless the ratchet wheel moves too.* In

Fig. 218 the pendulum is not quite yet at the left hand end of its swing. The pallet T has just released the tooth *a*: the drive of the clock makes the wheel fly on until the tooth *b* strikes against the pallet T'. The pendulum finishes its stroke and so pushes *b* back a little in an anti-clockwise direction. This can often be seen in old clocks: in these the second hands visibly recoil at the end of each pendulum swing. The pendulum now starts back to the right. The tooth *b* as it goes back to the position from which it recoiled gives the pendulum a push and it is this push which provides the power that keeps it swinging. The pendulum now travels over to the right and just as tooth *b* has almost escaped from pallet T', pallet T comes in and engages tooth C. This will not be released again till the pendulum gets back to the left hand end of its swing. It is clear now that the escapement wheel can move only one tooth for each double journey of the pendulum. If the pendulum is regulated, as is usual, so that the double swing takes one second, the escapement wheel, which has 60 teeth, will get round once in a minute. (Fig. 218 shows only 30 teeth—for simplicity.) In this case, the escapement wheel may be attached directly to the second hand, the other gears being arranged so that the minute hand goes sixty times more slowly, and the hour hand twelve times slower still.

Fig. 219 gives a good idea of how the escapement is driven. The weight pulls the going-barrel B round. This has attached to it the great wheel C which drives the centre pinion P, which carries the minute hand. This turns once an hour and works a train of wheels, M, N, n, Y, which drive the hour hand round once in twelve hours. The wheels d, D, e, driven by the pinion P, have the right number of cogs to ensure that P turns 60 times slower than the escapement wheel W. The pendulum makes the escapement wheel turn just once a minute: the pinion and the minute hand must then turn just once in 60 minutes, and the hour hand just once in twelve hours!

There are many other (and better) escapements but this one can be seen working very well in most grandfather clocks. A few minutes' inspection is worth an hour's reading in these matters.

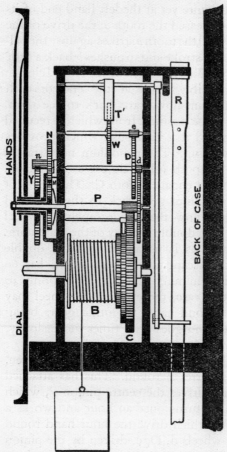

FIG. 219.—Movement of a grandfather clock

The best clocks made are the clocks at Greenwich Observatory. These are rather beyond the power of this work to describe, but roughly speaking, they have a " master " pendulum which *drives nothing* and swings freely in a vacuum. It is compensated for temperature, and kept in a cellar at an even temperature.

This pendulum is kept going by a little push from a falling weight automatically released every half minute. The contact of the weight with the master pendulum makes an electrical signal travel to a second "slave" clock which these signals regulate. These clocks are so accurate that no one knows whether they are not perhaps better timekeepers than the rotation of the earth which provides the standard time by which we check them!

CHAPTER XIII

SOUND WAVES

COMPRESSION WAVES

ANYTHING which moves in air disturbs the air. It pushes the air in front of it and since the air cannot instantly get out of its way, a layer of compressed air is formed in front of the moving object and of rarefied air behind it. The faster the thing moves, the more compressed or rarefied these layers will be.

A compressed layer of gas like this, without anything to keep it compressed, might reasonably be expected to expand again to normal. But as it expands, the molecules fly forward, and (like the pendulum at the bottom of its stroke), they do not stop when the gas has reached its normal state. The molecules fly on and drive before them a new lot of gas which is thus compressed and in turn once more expands. Thus a layer of compressed gas travels outwards. Any actual molecule does not move more than a very short distance, but the compressed layer moves at about a thousand feet a second. This is just like our sea-wave, the water

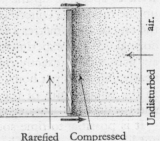

Rarefied   Compressed
air.   air.

FIG. 220.—How a moving object makes a compression wave.

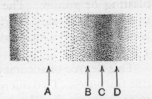

FIG. 221.—A moving compression wave in a gas. A rarefied space behind wave. B Compressed molecules moving back. C Compressed molecules travelling forward and compressing fresh gas D.

373

of which only bobs up and down while the ridge travels on at ten to fifty miles an hour.

An intense sound wave can even be photographed. Plate XVIII shows very admirably how such a wave travels and is reflected. The photograph of a bullet (Plate VI) also shows a sound wave.

VELOCITY OF SOUND

The speed at which such a pulse of compression travels can be calculated. It depends on the force necessary to compress the gas and the inertia of the molecules—the ease or difficulty of setting them moving—which depends on their weight. If all the force went to speeding up the wave and none to *permanently* speeding up the molecules concerned, a pulse of this kind would travel at the rate of 331.5 metres a second in air at 0° C, with the barometer normal. Actual experiments show that the sound travels through air with almost exactly this speed, 331.41 metres per second or nearly 700 miles per hour. The speed varies somewhat according to the temperature of the air, which affects its compressibility, and the amount of water vapour in it, which affects its weight.

It is possible to time sound for oneself though the results are not likely to be accurate because the times are very short. Everyone has seen the ball leave the bat well before he hears the sound of wood on leather, but the interval is not usually as much as a fifth of a second. The most hopeful case, is, when watching blasting or gunfire. The light travels a distance of, say, 5 miles in an immeasurably short time, but the sound will take about 25 seconds, which a stop-watch will time with an accuracy of about 1%.

This degree of accuracy is by no means good enough for scientific purposes. Two microphones several miles apart are employed in accurate work. The sound signal—say from a gun—generates a tiny current in each microphone as it passes and these currents pass round two separate primary coils. These have a single secondary coil surrounding them and are connected to a very sensitive galvanometer.

Each time either telephone receives a sound, and so makes the current flicker, the changing current induces a current in the secondary coil and the spot of light reflected from the galvanometer is deflected across the surface of a piece of travelling photographic paper, which also receives time signals from a standard tuning fork. The distance between the two deflections shows the time the sound has taken to travel the distance between the two microphones.

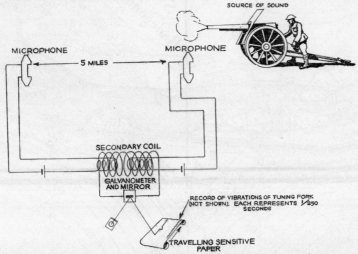

FIG. 222.—The principle of the measurement of the velocity of sound.

An important use of sound in war-time is for determining the position of a gun. A gun can be hidden, but it cannot be silenced. It is not possible as a rule to time the flash and noise, as a ship does to get its distance from a lighthouse (p. 394). One method is to have three or more microphones, say, half a mile apart (Fig. 223). The currents from these are brought to a central station where they operate three galvanometers, each of which throws a spot of light on a film on which a vibrating tuning-fork also throws a wavy trace. A gun fires. The microphones each receive the pulse at different times and send a current to the three galvanometers

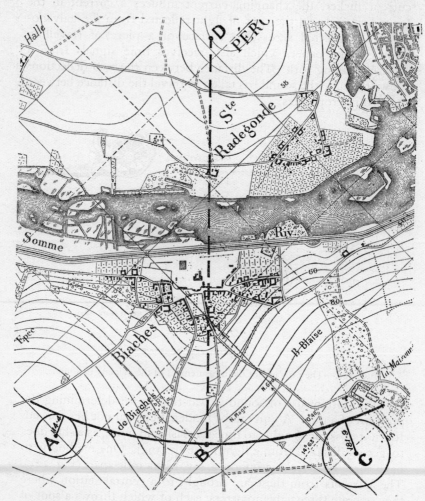

FIG. 223.—Illustrating the method of locating a gun (D) by means of three microphones (A, B, C).   (1:20,000.)

which each deflect their spot of light. By measuring the number of tuning-fork vibrations between each deflection, we find, say, that the microphone B received the sound first while microphone A got it $\frac{78}{250}$th second later, and microphone C $\frac{124}{250}$th seconds later than A.

So when B got the sound, A's sound was still $\frac{78}{250}$th seconds away, that is 114.4 yards away. Similarly, at that moment the sound was $\frac{124}{250}$th seconds, 181.9 yards away from C.

Take the map and draw a circle of 114.4 yards radius round A and another 181.9 yards radius round C. Now, the sound got to somewhere on circle A, to B, and to somewhere on circle C at the *same time*. These two "somewheres" and B must be the *same* distance from the gun and so we have only to find a circle which goes through B and touches the other two circles and the gun must be in the centre of it.

This drawing makes it clear that the gun is 2361 yards away at an angle of 46° E. of N. of B. If the calculations are right, the gunners can now attempt to destroy it by bombardment.

The same principle was used by the Navy for warning ships of the position of submarines. If a vessel saw one, it exploded a charge under water. Several submerged microphones near the shore picked up the sound wave travelling through the water, and a brief calculation showed the precise position of vessel and submarine.

What we call sound then, is a pulse of compression travelling through some material. This is usually the air, but of course sound is carried by all kinds of material. A sound wave in a plank of wood, a rod of steel or a tank of water, is a compression wave just as in air.

These materials are much more difficult to compress than air, so the restoring force is much greater: this should make them vibrate quicker. On the other hand, they are much denser than air, so that more force should be needed to make their particles vibrate at a given speed—consequently, they should vibrate more slowly. In actual fact, the first effect outweighs the second. Steel is 1,200,000 times less compressible than air, and it is 6,030 times more dense. Actually sound travels at just on three miles a second in steel, 14 times faster than in air.

If you apply your ear to a water-pipe while someone hits a distant part of it with a hammer, you may hear three sounds, the one coming through the air, another through the water and another through the steel: unless the pipe is very long, the last two will not be distinguished. Sound is transmitted through an elastic solid with less loss than through air, because less of its energy is wasted in making the molecules move irregularly—i.e., become hot.

If you put a watch on one end of a long table and press your ear against the other, you hear it quite clearly. Sound travels better through ten feet of wood than one of air.

Water-board inspectors look for leaks in this way. They go round at night when no water should be in use and turn the main valves nearly off. By pressing one end of a wooden rod against their ear and the other against a valve, they can hear the whisper of the water going through the chink of the valve to the leak they are seeking.

Since sound is a compression-wave consisting of a crowd of molecules, it can only exist where there are molecules to crowd. Sound cannot travel through a vacuum. If an alarm clock is suspended in a vacuum not a sound will be heard when it goes off, though the hammer may be seen vigorously banging the bell. At the tops of high mountains where the air is much less dense, voices sound weak and the vast deserts of space must be perfectly silent.

WHY SOUNDS FADE OUT

The farther one stands from the source of a sound, the fainter the noise. This is easy to understand if one remembers that a sound spreads out in every direction and it is only the little bit of the wave that enters your ear that can be heard. Suppose someone explodes a cracker 50 feet away from you. A sound wave goes out from the cracker upwards, sideways, forwards and backwards like a dome and when you hear it 50 feet away, the wave has an area of $\dfrac{88}{7} \times 50^2 = 31{,}428$ square feet. Your ear-hole is only about $\frac{1}{20}$th square inch in cross section, so you only get about one fifty-millionth of the total noise. Suppose you were twice as far away. The "dome"-shaped sound wave would have *twice* the radius when it reached you, and so the same amount of sound energy would be spread out to *four* times the area. So you would only get one two-hundred-millionth of the total sound, one-quarter of the sound you got before. This argument applies to sound, light, force or anything you like which spreads out evenly from a point: it is the inverse-square law we met on p. 159.

Now, according to this, sound gets fainter with distance because it is spread thinner and thinner. If we could make sound go in a parallel beam like a car's headlight, or travel down a tube, it would not spread out and so would keep its loudness. This is partly true. By shouting down a megaphone, we get a beam of sound of a sort, and so make sounds carry further; and by speaking down a tube we can make sounds audible for fair distances. However, sound waves always gradually die away by being converted into irregular heat motions of the air, and the only satisfactory way of sending them long distances is to "translate" them into electric currents, light or radio-waves, and send these.

MUSICAL NOTES

Hitherto we have talked about these waves of compression as if they travelled singly; in actual fact it is as difficult to get a single air-wave as a single water-wave. If a stone is thrown into a pool, a group of ripples travels out. In the same way, an explosion in air or the noise of dropping a brick on a pavement sends out a group of air-ripples.

We carry in our heads a complicated little apparatus for detecting sounds—an ear. The structure of it is carefully mapped out on page 891. A membrane is moved by the pulses in the air—

compressions push it in, rarefactions draw it out. This membrane transmits its movements by a bridge of bones to a smaller membrane which is part of a bag of liquid, which is thus caused to vibrate. This liquid contains a second bag of liquid which vibrates with it, and in this latter liquid are a series of nerve-endings which in some way we do not fully understand, are tuned to respond to the various frequencies of the air-waves we can hear and to transmit their message to the brain. We cannot hear all air-waves. What we can hear as sound is a stream of air-waves reaching us at the rate of anything from 20 a second to about 40,000 a second. If the waves are regular (as are the waves in Plate XVIII) we hear a *musical note*; if they are irregular (as are the waves in a choppy sea or the wake of a ship), we hear a *noise*. If the waves reach us at a slow rate, we hear a low note; while a high frequency means a high note.

A very simple experiment will convince you of this. Pull the blunt end of your pencil along a rough piece of regularly patterned material, either a bit of woven material—a hair carpet or piece of canvas or anything with a fine regular pattern, a file or the milled edge of a half-crown. A distinct "note" can be heard and the faster you move the pencil the higher the note. If I do this

FIG. 224.—Sound waves emitted by a shrill whistle.

to my hair carpet, I find that if I move the pencil at the rate of about 4 feet a second, I get a note not far off middle C. The carpet has about 6 strands per inch, so I am causing $6 \times 12 \times 4 = 288$ vibrations a second. Middle C is 261 vibrations per second. A musical note is then a regular succession of pulses. Fig. 224 shows diagrammatically how the notes of a high-pitched whistle travel as a series of spherical waves of compressed air moving outward at 1100 feet a second from the whistle. A very shrill whistle might send out 10,000 waves a second. As they travel about 1100 feet a second they would be rather more than an inch apart. We now see that a musical note is a regular succession of pulses of compressed air. The more rapid the succession, the higher is the note.

Men have had since the earliest times a very clear idea that the highness or lowness—the *pitch* of a note could be measured or at least defined. They have always (or at least for two or three thousand years) had some idea of a musical scale. They realised that certain pairs of notes sounded pleasant when combined while others did not. It is true that some races and cultures regard as in concord notes which others consider to be discords. None the less there is a general recognition that certain intervals such as the octave and the fifth are harmonious. The modern scale took a good deal of working out and is not entirely satisfactory now.

The octaves were soon recognised. It is easy to perceive that you can get the same group of musical effects between, say, middle C and the next higher C, as between middle C and the next lower C. When you come to measure the number of vibrations which correspond to each note, you find that each octave doubles the frequency. Thus, the C's on the piano give the following number of air-pulses a second:

C	65.25
C	130.5
C———	261
C^1	522
C^{11}	1044

The ear has a very clear notion of the *relation* beteen two notes —whether one is the octave of the other. It has no very definite

ideas about the number of vibrations (the absolute pitch) of a
note. Thus the pitch of the various notes has been varied a great
deal in the last two hundred years. Handel's treble C gives 504
vibrations a second. Covent Garden Opera House in 1876
adopted 540, nearly a semitone higher. The present "New
Philharmonic" pitch is 522. The ear cannot judge accurately of
the pitch of very high notes and very low ones become inaudible;
the highest note sounded by the piccolo is 4752 vibrations a
second; the lowest on the organ has 32.7 vibrations a second.

Everyone is agreed that the musical scale shall be divided into
octaves. But the octave itself can be split up into notes in a good
many different ways. The usual method is to consider the octave
as divided into 12 equal semitones, each note vibrating 1.0594
times as fast as the one before it. This system is called the equitempered scale. The octave C to C^1 would then be:

C^1	**522**	
B	492.73	
B♭	465.09	
A	439.07	
A♭	414.42	
G	391.14	
G♭	369.18	Vibrations a second.
F	348.45	
E	328.88	
E♭	310.40	
D	292.98	
D♭	276.52	
C	**261**	

Notes are generally thought to sound in concord when their
vibrations are in the same proportion as small whole numbers.
Thus the C and the C^1 (the note an octave above it) form a perfect
concord, for C^1 vibrates twice for C's once. The interval between
C and G is called a fifth. C vibrates twice while G vibrates three
times. The interval between C and E is called a major third;

here C vibrates four times while E vibrates five times. There is, however, no general agreement about the intervals which are not so simple as these. A composer such as Wagner uses with effect combinations of notes which Palestrina would have called discords: Oriental music combines notes which sound discordant to a Western ear.

The equitempered scale is not the only one. The diatonic scale gives eight notes with frequencies in the proportion 1, $\frac{9}{8}$, $\frac{5}{4}$, $\frac{4}{3}$, $\frac{3}{2}$, $\frac{5}{3}$, $\frac{15}{8}$, 2. The disadvantage of it is that if C is the tonic (by which we mean the note we call 1), we get a certain octave of notes. But if we make G the tonic we get another octave, none of the notes of which is the same as any of those in the scale with C as tonic, which is musically very inconvenient. The equitempered scale is therefore generally adopted.

It is very curious that the ear distinguishes as in harmony the notes which science thousands of years after has shown to have vibrations in simple mathematical ratios. There is no certain explanation of the fact; perhaps we may still believe with Plato that harmony is innate in our souls! The chief explanation put forward is that harmony is the absence of the "beats" mentioned below; these, even when too rapid to be separately heard, are probably unpleasant to the ear.

If two notes vibrate so that their vibrations per second are not in some simple proportion such as $1:2$ or $3:4$, they produce a discord which does not satisfy the ear. Thus C and D sounded together give a dissonant effect. The ratio of their vibrations is 8 to 9.

If two notes are sounded which are just out of tune, a curious effect of "beats" is heard. A piano-tuner tightens or loosens the

BEAT		BEAT		BEAT
SOUND	NO SOUND	SOUND	NO SOUND	SOUND
COMPRESSIONS and RAREFACTIONS COINCIDE	COMPRESSIONS CANCEL RAREFACTIONS			

FIG. 225.—Notes with frequencies in the proportion of 7 to 6 sounded together, illustrating formation of beats. The dark bands may represent compressions, the light ones, rarefactions.

string, till it no longer gives beats with the note of a tuning-fork: it must then be in tune. Fig. 225 shows how these beats arise. Suppose we sound two notes, one vibrating 60 times a second, the other 59 times a second. Once every second the compression waves will reinforce each other and make the sound louder; once a second the waves of one note will exactly fall in the troughs of the other and the waves will cancel out, giving silence. Consequently the sound will rise and fall in "beats" of a second's length.

These can be heard by tuning two strings so that one is a little flatter than the other and bowing or plucking both of them. Most easily, however, they can be heard by listening to the wind blowing through the telegraph wires. If you press your ear to the pole, the beats of the different notes from the wires can often be heard.

We now see what musical notes are and how their pitch depends on their speed of vibration. This is by no means the whole story, however. Hear the middle C on the piano, a tuning fork, a violin, a trumpet, the several stops of an organ. These may all play a note of precisely the same pitch, but a child can distinguish that the sounds are different. The reason is that no instrument plays one single note. If you strike the C string of a piano, it sounds C, which we may call the fundamental, but it also more faintly sounds the C's and other higher notes for seven or eight octaves above. Thus, in addition to the fundamental, the octave, the twelfth, the double octave and the eighteenth are more faintly heard. The fundamental C is just the same for piano, organ or violin, but each of these instruments sounds higher notes too and these are not the same in each case. These notes, higher than the fundamental, are called the overtones or, if they are in harmony with the fundamental, the harmonics. Bells are the most remarkable instruments from the point of view of harmonics. A big bell's fundamental note, the "hum-tone," can hardly be heard; it is the first and higher overtones which we hear. Many of these are discordant with each other, thus giving the bell its peculiar tone.

PLATE XIX

Echo-sounding apparatus. Top right, motor; top left, governor; below, pen and record; bottom, amplifier.

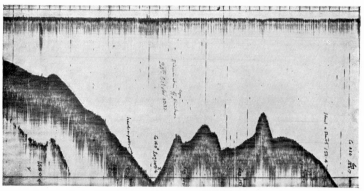

Record of a part of the sea-bottom, obtained by use of the above apparatus. (Both by courtesy of Henry Hughes & Son, Ltd., Fenchurch St., London.)

PLATE XX

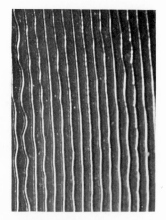

A diaphone.
(By courtesy of Messrs. Chance Bros. and
Co., Ltd., Smethwick.)

Microphotograph of a part of a
gramophone record.

An engineer examining a partly-recorded wax during a session in "His Master's
Voice" Studios. (By courtesy of H.M.V., Ltd.)

Fig. 226 shows very clearly the overtones from a tuning-fork. The pictures were obtained by setting a tuning-fork vibrating so that a bristle attached to the fork just touched a glass plate covered with candle smoke. The plate hung by a thread. This was burned through, whereupon the plate fell past the moving bristle, which scratched a record of its movements in the

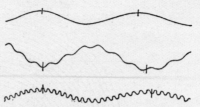

FIG. 226.—Tracing of Vibrations of Tuning fork.
(*a*) Top: Fundamental
(*b*) Middle: Fundamental and Overtone
(*c*) Bottom: Fundamental and Overtone
(Courtesy of Messrs. George Bell & Sons, Ltd., from Dr. Wood's *Textbook of Sound.*)

smoke. Fig. 226 (*a*) shows the pure fundamental. In Fig. 226 (*b*) the fork is giving an overtone of $6\frac{1}{4}$ times the frequency. In Fig. 226 (*c*) the overtone is $17\frac{1}{2}$ times the frequency of the fundamental. It was made to give the different overtones by rubbing it in certain fixed spots with a violin bow.

THE DOPPLER EFFECT

When we say that the thing which determines whether we hear a high note or a low one is the frequency of the sound-waves, we do not really mean the number of waves emitted every second but the number that reach our ears. Suppose (Fig. 227) a siren is hooting at a pitch near that of the middle C, 256 vibrations a second. The compression waves travel roughly 1100 feet a second, so they must be $\dfrac{1100}{256}$ = about 4.3 feet long. Now suppose we shoot past the siren in a car going 110 feet a second (about 75 m.p.h.). If we had stopped still at A or B or anywhere else for a second, 256 vibrations would have passed us. The distance between two waves is $\dfrac{1100}{256}$ = 4.3 ft, so in going the 110 feet from A to B we pass $\dfrac{110}{4.3}$ more waves on their way out-

13

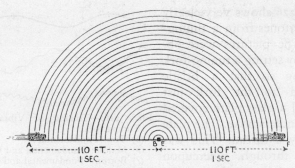

A <----------- 110 FT ---------->< B E<----------- 110 FT ----------->F
1 SEC.　　　　　　　　　　　1 SEC.

FIG. 227.—Illustrating the Doppler effect.

ward, so that the number of waves that reach our ears is $256 + \dfrac{110}{4.3} = 281.6$ in a second and the note we hear is not C but C sharp, a semitone higher. As we rush away from the hooter, we shall find the opposite effect. If we stood still at E, 256 vibrations a second would pass us. But by going the 110 feet to F, we shall be passed in that second by only $256 - \dfrac{110}{4.3} = 230.4$ vibrations, and the note we hear will be about a semitone flat. The phenomenon, called the Doppler effect, occurs with light waves also, and is most important in astronomy; for this reason, it is worth while expressing the results in another way.

The waves are emitted by the siren at the rate of 256 to the second. Their velocity is 1100 feet a second relative to the siren, so they are 4.3 feet apart. But the velocity relative to a car travelling 110 feet a second towards the siren is 1210 feet a second. They are 4.3 feet apart, so $\dfrac{1210}{4.3} = 281.6$ waves will pass the approaching car per second. Their velocity relative to the departing car is $1100 - 110 = 990$ feet per second. So only $\dfrac{990}{4.3} = 230.4$ waves pass the car per second. So, on driving a car at 75 miles per hour past a siren, the note should appear to drop by rather more than two semi-tones. The effect is best heard when a high-speed aeroplane, flying low, passes a spectator. The note of a racing seaplane at 400 miles an hour should show a drop of pitch of about an octave and a half as it passes a spectator.

ECHOES

Sound waves can be reflected, as indeed can all waves. The way in which a wave is reflected is easiest studied in the bath. Start a small wave at the rounded end. It runs to the square end and there piles up against the side. It then starts *back* again without any noticeable loss of size or speed. Remembering that the water-wave particles are bobbing up and down, not travelling along, it is easy to see that, if they are at the top of their travel and touching the side, when they travel down, they must force the particles behind them up; and the wave will travel back the other way.

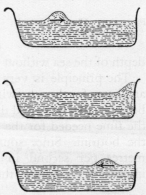

FIG. 228.—How a water-wave is reflected.

The reflection of a sound wave is familiar to everyone as an echo.

I stand at one side of a square of houses and strike two books together with a bang—firing a gun is discouraged in London streets. About half a second later, I hear a similar sound, the echo. The square is about a hundred yards across, so that the sound has to travel 600 feet to get to the opposite wall and back to my ear. Since sound goes 1100 feet a second, I should hear the echo $\frac{6}{11}$ second after the bang.

Fig. 229 shows how a sound wave is reflected. The wave is a layer of crowded air molecules springing apart and so crowding the air molecules ahead of them in turn into a small space. Suppose the "crowded" molecules meet a wall. They cannot

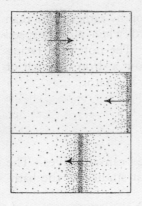

FIG. 229.—How a sound-
wave is reflected.

push it away, so they must spring backward and so crowd the molecules *behind*
them. These again crowd the molecules
behind them and so the wave returns on
its track.

Everyone likes shouting at a wall and
hearing it shout back to him; but beside
this simple pleasure, men of Science
have found one or two uses for
echoes.

ECHO-SOUNDING

The most valuable use of echoes is in
echo-sounding, used to determine the
depth of the sea without the need to lower the line to the bottom.

The principle is very simple. You make a noise under water
and listen for the echo with an underwater telephone. The interval
between the noise and the echo is twice
the time needed for the sound to get to
the bottom. Since sound travels 1440
metres per second in the sea, if the
interval is t seconds, then the depth is

$t \times \dfrac{1440}{2}$ metres. Very pretty; but suppose

the sea is only 10 metres deep. Then
the echo will return only $\frac{1}{72}$ second
after the noise; and to measure this
interval some arrangement will be
needed to time the echo within about
$\frac{1}{1000}$ of a second. Plate XIX shows how
this is done. The motor kept at a constant speed by a governor closes a
switch (between these) which sends
an electrical impulse which discharges a
condenser in the contactor (Fig. 230, C)

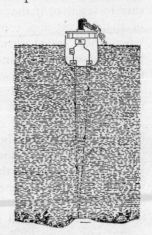

FIG. 230.—Reflection of
sound waves from sea-
bottom. C = contactor,
Tr = transmitter, Re =
receiver, R = recorder.

in another part of the ship. This discharges a big current through an arrangement Tr, fixed to the ship's hull, for sending out sound waves of such very short wave-length that they are inaudible. These waves travel to the sea bottom and are reflected back. A special type of telephone Re, sensitive to very short waves, receives the sound and sends a faint electrical impulse to a large valve amplifier, which converts it into a strong current.

Now to make a record of this. A piece of paper moistened with starch and potassium iodide solution is drawn over a metal support. This paper has the property of becoming coloured when an electric current passes through it. Now a pen (a metal point) starts to move from left to right across the paper each time a signal is sent out. The incoming electric signal causes a current to pass through the pen, paper and metal support over which the latter runs. A dark mark is thus made and the distance the pen has gone before the mark is made depends on the time the signal has taken to go to the bottom and back. The white strip therefore shows the depth of the sea. Plate XIX shows part of a record—practically a section of the sea-bottom. The apparatus is so sensitive that it readily locates wrecks and even shoals of fish; in fact it has given us some very useful knowledge of the depth at which these swim.

The reflection of sound has much importance in determining whether a building has good "acoustic" properties or not. There are many large halls in which it is exceedingly difficult to hear what is being said. St. Paul's, in which one may sit not fifty feet from the priest reading the lesson and be unable to follow the most familiar biblical passage, may be taken as a superb example. Every sound is reflected up and down that vast space so that the air is a confused welter of sound-waves, not an orderly progression. A hall in which it is easy to hear must be so arranged that the sound waves reflected from the walls do not interfere with those emitted by the speaker.

The first way of assuring this is to prevent the sound-waves being reflected. If the walls are hung with tapestry or covered with "acoustic plaster," the sound is mostly absorbed and not reflected. The other method is to design the hall so that the sound-waves, after they have been reflected, either do not reach the audience or reach them so quickly that one word does not interfere with the next. Elaborate carved work as in a Gothic cathedral seems to break up the waves, so also do the walls of an irregularly shaped building such as a theatre. When a modern hall is designed, the architect often makes a model and photographs the sound waves made in it by an electric spark. Plate XVIII shows the way these reflections occur.

MEASURING SOUNDS

The world has grown conscious of late of a growing intensity of noise, and in England the Anti-Noise League is making efforts to reduce some of the worst nuisances such as pneumatic road drills, inadequately silenced motor cycles and the like. One of the chief difficulties in framing legislation against noise has been the lack of a reliable method of measuring how noisy some piece of machinery really is. The best measure of noise is the actual power expended in making the air vibrate, though this is far from perfect because the ear is more disturbed by some notes than others: moreover, a discontinuous noise as of a road drill or a barking dog is more annoying than the continuous roar of traffic. Actually, the energy of sound is very small. A large orchestra doing its worst only expends 70 watts ($\frac{1}{10}$ h.p.) in setting the air vibrating, while the power of a single flute is only about a sixteenth of a watt. It is an amusing commentary on our garrulous species that if all the people in Europe talked at once, the energy would just run a motor-bicycle. Noise-meters of many kinds have been made; some measure the electrical output from a microphone or measure the pressure changes of the sound waves: these are mechanically accurate but have to be compensated to allow for the fact that the ear finds shrill notes most noisy though the low notes commonly have the greatest energy. The simplest "audiometer" consists of a tuning fork which is automatically struck by a blow of definite strength and held as close to the ear as possible. The observer measures the time till the waning noise of the fork just matches the noise to be measured. The fork is first tried against standard noises so that the amount of noise corresponding to each second's lapse is known.

Noise is now measured in *phons*. We first fix a "threshold" taken as the faintest sound that can be heard, then a sound 26% greater than this is said to have a loudness of 1 phon, a sound 26% louder than 1 phon is called 2 phons and so on. A noise of 20 phons is therefore not 20 times 1 phon but $(\frac{126}{100})^{20}$, that is to say 100 times one phon. This "logarithmic" scale of noise has the advantage of discriminating between little noises without representing the big ones by vast numbers.

The following table gives the noise intensities in phons of some noises. It must not be forgotten that the noise here called 100 on our scale of phons has not 10 times the energy of that called 10 but ten thousand million times.

SOME LONDON NOISES (after Davis)

(Expressed as the intensity of a standard note of equal loudness: Noises of two different kinds cannot be compared directly.)

PHONS

110	Noisy aeroplane cabin.
90	Noisy tube trains. Pneumatic drills.
80	Motor horns. Loud music.
70	Loud radio music. Tram, bus or train with windows open.
60	Average music. Average traffic. Interior of train.
50	Conversation. Quiet car passing.
40	Soft radio music. Quiet street. Saloon car.
30	Clock ticking. Quiet suburban street.
20	Quiet garden.
10	Quiet whisper.
0	Silence.

Measurement of these noises may be a first step towards check
ing them. There is no question that pneumatic drills and the
louder cars and lorries could be silenced. The noises of trains and
trams could hardly be much reduced. Such noises as of the
neighbours' radio and barking dogs can be abolished only by the
use of reasonable and urbane behaviour—not a matter for science.

CHAPTER XIV

How Sounds are Made

A VERY great number of instruments are used for making sounds. Some are musical instruments; others, such as fog-horns, hooters and whistles are not. In every case there is *something in the instrument that vibrates* or in some way sets a regular succession of compression waves travelling.

The things used to make noises are:

(1) Sirens and diaphones, which send out a very rapid succession of puffs of air or steam.

(2) Vibrating solids
Vibrating in their natural period
{
Strings, as in the violin.
Rods, as in the tuning-fork and xylophone.
Plates as in gongs.
Membranes as in drums.
}

Not vibrating in their natural period
{
Plates and membranes in motor horns, gramophone sound-boxes, loud speakers, etc.
}

(3) Vibrating columns of air: These may be set vibrating by an oscillating tongue of metal or "reed," as in the clarinet, or by the rush of air over a sharp edge as in the flute or organ pipe.

FOGHORNS AND THE LIKE

The siren and diaphone produce the loudest musical notes we can make. Everyone knows the noise of the factory hooter, which may be heard five or six miles away when the wind is favourable. The factory hooter is always a siren. The fog-horn,

393

which may be heard at distances of twenty miles, is usually a diaphone.

A siren consists of two discs perforated with holes. The lower one is fixed, the upper free to revolve. The holes in the upper disc are at an angle so that the steam makes it turn just as the water turns a reaction turbine. Air or usually steam is forced in below. The upper disk turns, but as it does so, it alternately releases and shuts off the steam according to whether the holes in the moving disc and fixed plate are opposite each other or not. It is easy to see that if the disc has 32 holes and revolves ten times a second, there will be 320 puffs of air a second and the siren will sound the E above middle C.

Fig. 231 shows a factory siren in section.

Sirens give a very good way of finding out how many pulses a second correspond to a particular note. If we connect a siren with

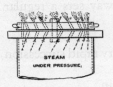

FIG. 231.—Section of a siren.

a revolution counter and drive the moving plate by a governed motor at various fixed speeds, we can easily time it to match a given note and then see how many puffs a second it is giving.

The diaphone (Plate XX) is more complicated. It has a reservoir of compressed air. This works a cylinder and piston like that of a steam engine, but very much shorter. At the start and finish of each stroke the piston rod opens and shuts a valve which allows a puff of compressed air to enter a large horn. If the piston makes 50 strokes a second, the diaphone will give out a hundred puffs of air a second and emit the second G below middle C.

Lighthouses often emit a diaphone note and a light flash at the same time. If a boat sees the flash thirty seconds before it hears the note, the navigator knows that the sound has taken thirty seconds to arrive. Now sound travels about 1100 feet a second (varying somewhat according to the temperature, barometric pressure, etc.); accordingly, he knows he is about six miles from the lighthouse. Sound travels through water much faster than through air, but much more certainly and at a fixed speed. Fog banks, differences of temperature, pressure, etc., hardly affect water. Accordingly modern lighthouses, instead of a siren or diaphone, sound a bell or an arrangement like an exaggerated electric horn under water. Ships are fitted with an under-water telephone or some such arrangement by which the water vibrations can be heard. The lighthouses send out the under-water signal and a light-flash together: the navigator, knowing that light is for practical purposes instantaneous and that sound in water travels about 1450 metres (almost a mile) a second, finds it easy to calculate the ship's distance from the lighthouse.

Sirens and diaphones give an unpleasant note. It is almost all of the same fundamental frequency and lacks the character and richness that the harmonics give to the notes of musical instruments.

VIBRATING RODS—TUNING FORKS

The simplest musical instrument, if it can be called one, is a tuning fork, a U-shaped steel bar. When it is struck, it vibrates, scissor-fashion, and sends out a very pure note with very few harmonics. Its value as a musical instrument is *nil*; its use is to keep in tune and always vibrate at the same rate. The speed it vibrates at depends on two things, the *elasticity* of the steel, which pulls it back into its normal shape, and the weight of the arms, which the elastic force has to set moving.

If you stick two lumps of sealing wax on the tips of a tuning fork, so as to increase the weight of the arms, it will sound flat— i.e., vibrate slower. If it is warmed, the steel becomes a little less elastic, but a change of 20° C. does not make a difference of one vibration a second in a fork tuned to middle C.

To keep a tuning fork going permanently, we can treat it as if it were the arm of an electric bell. Each time the arm moves, it dips a tungsten wire into a pool of mercury. A current passes through the fork, wire and mercury and a small electromagnet which gives the arm a sufficient tug to speed it up as much as the friction of the air, etc., slows it down. An electrically driven tuning fork is not only used as a standard of pitch, but also as a standard of time. A tuning fork can be tuned to vibrate accurately 250 times a second and if a fine point is attached to the end of one bar and is allowed to graze the surface of a rapidly travelling sheet of smoked paper coated with smoke, it will draw a wavy line, each crest being drawn $\frac{1}{250}$th seconds after the one before. Now suppose we want to measure the time a frog's muscle takes to contract.

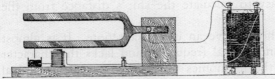

FIG. 232.—Electrically driven tuning fork.

A simple form of the aparatus is illustrated in Figure 456 (p. 855). A drum, covered with smoked paper, rotates about once a second. The muscle is mounted so that when it contracts it lifts a point touching the smoked drum and so draws a white line which represents its own movements. The operator has a large tuning fork, vibrating 100 times a second, to an arm of which is attached a bristle. He holds this so that the vibrating bristle just touches the smoked surface and so traces a wavy line on it, each wave-crest being $\frac{1}{100}$ secs. later than the wave-crest before it. In Fig. 456 the curve of the muscle twitch occupies the space of 11 tuning-fork vibrations and therefore took $\frac{11}{100}$ sec. to complete itself.

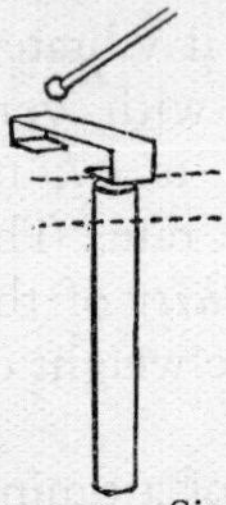

FIG. 233.—Single unit of xylophone. A bar of wood or metal is struck by a hammer and so caused to vibrate over a pot-shaped resonator which intensifies the sound.

There are not many musical instruments made from vibrating rods. The triangle is rather like the tuning fork, but its shape makes it vibrate in a very complicated way, so that it gives a mixture of notes. The xylophone is a set of rods, usually of wood, balanced on two supports. These vibrate up and down. They would make very little noise if there were not under each of them a pot-shaped vessel which we call a resonator.

RESONATORS

Nearly every musical instrument has a vibrating part to make the sound, and a resonator to increase it and modify its tone. Thus, in a violin the strings vibrate and the belly of the violin is the resonator. In a clarinet the reed vibrates and the "horn" is the resonator. So, before we discuss musical instruments, we must say something about resonance.

If you have a tuning fork, best of fairly high pitch, and a tall vase, you can try this experiment. Sound the fork and hold it over the vase while you slowly pour in water. At a certain point the fork will suddenly sound much louder. What has happened is that the air in the vessel is vibrating in time with the fork.

Imagine a very light piston fitting without friction in the neck of a vessel of air I. If you pushed it down, the air would be compressed, II. If you let it go, the piston would

I II III IV V IV VII VIII IX X

FIG. 234.—How a vessel of air could act as a resonator.

spring up like a jack-in-the-box, III, overshoot the mark IV, and vibrate up and down, V, VI, etc., till friction stopped it. Clearly, it would not be the piston (which has no spring in it), but the air which would be vibrating. So the air in a vessel can vibrate by alternately being compressed and expanding. Now if the tuning fork vibrates in the same period as the air in a vessel beneath it, each time the air goes down the vessel, the tuning fork arm gives it a kick behind and sets it swinging strongly. The best resonators have narrow necks; by singing O—O—O—OO into the neck of an empty milk bottle, you can soon find the note at which it sings back again owing to resonance.

The chief task of the designer of a musical instrument is to make the resonance cavity of such a shape and of such materials, that the right harmonics of the vibrator are encouraged and the wrong ones repressed. No one really knows how to do this; if they did, Stradivarius violins would no longer be worth thousands of pounds.

STRINGED INSTRUMENTS

Perhaps the most important set of instruments are the stringed ones. These all have stretched strings or wires as vibrators, and they are set vibrating by striking (piano), by plucking (harp, guitar, harpsichord), or by bowing (violin, violoncello, etc.).

A string is made to vibrate the more quickly by increasing the restoring force, the tension pulling it back; on the other hand, the greater the weight of the string the more slowly it vibrates.

The first of these rules you can easily test by twanging a stretched rubber ring. The more you stretch it, the higher the

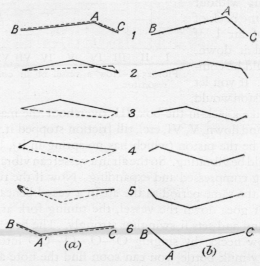

FIG. 235.—The positions taken up by a plucked string as it vibrates. (Courtesy of Messrs. Edward Arnold and Professor Richardson, from the latter's *Acoustics of Orchestral Instruments*.)

note. The second fact you can see used in any piano. The bass strings are wound round with copper wire to make them heavy and slow in vibrating; slackening the tension of strings would have the same effect of lowering the pitch, but would greatly decrease the amount of sound and the brilliance of tone.

In order to play a tune on a string, you must be able to vary the pitch so as to get a number of notes, unless you have one string for each note as in the piano. It is not practicable to alter the pitch by altering the pull on the string. It is possible, however, to alter the length, and this is what is done in the violin and other similar instruments. By fingering, the length of the vibrating string is altered. The tension remains the same, but since the weight of string is less, and the distance the wave has to run along it is less, the rate of vibration is quicker.

A plucked string is pulled into a shape like Fig. 235 (1). Two things happen when it is released. The angle A straightens out and so two angles run up and down the string from end to end in opposite directions.

The string thus at one time or another covers all the positions of the shaded portion of Fig. 236 (1). If you twang a string, you see a figure like this, which is a blurred impression of all the positions a string takes up. Now the string (the picture in Fig. 235 is made from a violin string sounding B″, which makes 995 vibrations a second)

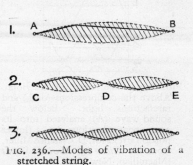

Fig. 236.—Modes of vibration of a stretched string.

goes through all its vibrations 995 times a second. How is it then that the string sounds not only the pure B″, but a whole series of fainter and higher notes—the overtones? The reason is that a string can vibrate in more than one way. It can go through all the positions shown in Fig. 236 (1), but it can also go through all the positions in Fig. 236 (2), or Fig. 236 (3). Now, the speed of vibration depends first on the restoring force, which is the elastic pull of the string (this is the same, however, in whatever way the string is vibrating), and secondly, on the length and weight of the part being pulled back. Now the weight of the string A B is clearly twice that of the part C D; so C D and of course D E vibrate *twice* as fast as A and thus sound the octave. Now, a violin string vibrates in all the ways shown in Fig. 236 *at once* and, to a smaller extent, in several others as well.

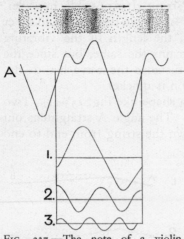

FIG. 237.—The note of a violin. Above the compressions (dark) and rarefactions light.   Below the sound-wave (A) analysed into its component vibrations, 1, 2, 3 (lower portion after Prof. D. Clarence Miller, from his *Science of Musical Sounds* (Macmillan, New York.))

In Fig. 237 (A) we see a curve representing the rarefactions and condensations in an actual sound-wave from the violin sounding B''. The peaks represent condensations of air and the valleys rarefactions. It must not be forgotten that the real wave has *no* humps or hollows. A hump is simply a pictorial way of showing air at high pressure, and a hollow, air at low pressure. The shaded band perhaps gives a better notion of the alternate waves of crowded and rarefied molecules, but for scientific purposes the curve is preferable because it can be treated mathematically. The three curves below (1, 2, 3) show the same thing for the three different waves the string is sending out by vibrating in the three different ways shown in Fig. 236. These three waves all combined make up the curve (A), which is the characteristic shape for a violin note. A piano note would show another and different set of humps and valleys.

A string may be set vibrating in several ways. A harp, banjo, guitar or ukulele is plucked, a piano string is struck with a hard felt hammer; both these ways of sounding a string cause many of the very short waves—high harmonics—to be heard, which give the note a more metallic or bell-like quality. The violin, viola, 'cello and double bass are set in vibration by bowing. The bow is well known to everyone. Its material is horsehair rubbed with resin, which makes it stick more firmly to the string.

A bow sets a string vibrating because it takes more force to overcome the friction between two things relatively at rest than between two things that are moving.

If you sit on a plank and the end is cautiously raised as high as is possible without making you slip, you can sit there as long as you like and the *static* friction will hold you up, but let a slight push start you moving and you will continue to slide, for the *dynamic* friction is smaller and will not stop you.

Now suppose a bow is being pushed across a string. The bow and string move *as one* as long as the static friction keeps them together, but when the string has been forced a certain distance, it slips and the smaller dynamic friction will not hold it. Thus it springs back past its normal position until it has slowed down

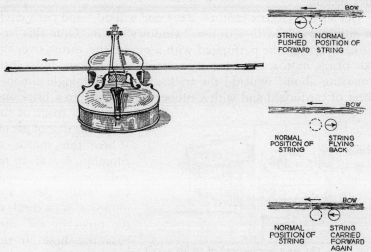

FIG. 238.—How the bow keeps a string vibrating.

enough for the friction of the bow to catch it and carry it forward again.

A bowed string is then pulled by the bow into a shape like Fig. 235 (1). The vibrations excited, run up and down the string rather as shown in Fig. 235 (2, 3, 4, etc.). All this happens too quickly for the eye to see unaided, but there is a simple gadget called the stroboscope which enables us to see a 'cello string in slow motion with waves crawling up and down it in an uncanny fashion. It is an experiment so well worth doing that it may be described here.

We cannot possibly see what happens in each vibration, for the eye combines into a single blur events which succeed each other more rapidly than at intervals of about $\frac{1}{16}$th of a second. Now each vibration is just like the one before it. Imagine the vibration divided into 50 parts and taking place 200 times a second. The stroboscope shows us the first part of vibration (1), the second part of vibration (2), and so on up to the fiftieth part of vibration (50). The eye combines all these glimpses and so sees the whole fifty stages as if they were one spread over $\frac{50}{200}$ths—one-quarter—of a second.

Get a small electric motor—a toy one will do—and cut a circle of stiffish paper with a dozen "windows" in it. Glue this to a cork, which can be perforated with a gimlet and thrust over the axle of the motor. This is not as simple as it sounds, but a little "messing about" will do the trick. Now cut a single slit in a sheet of cardboard and with a rubber band clip it to a brick and stand it in front of the revolving disc of paper. When the motor is running, say at 20 revolutions a second, you will get 160 glimpses a second as the holes in the disc pass the hole in the sheet. Now, suppose

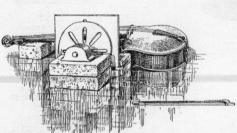

Fig. 239.—The stroboscopic way of seeing a 'cello string in slow motion.

you look at a string vibrating 161 times a second. The first glimpse lasts only for less than a thousandth of a second, so we see the string, as it were, standing still at the beginning of its vibration. When the next glimpse arrives, $\frac{1}{160}$th second later, the string will have done a complete vibration and, since it does this in $\frac{1}{161}$th of a second and $\frac{1}{160}$th second has elapsed, it will have got about $\frac{1}{160}$th of the way through the next vibration. When the next glimpse arrives, the string will have done another whole vibration and $\frac{1}{160}$th of another, so it will be a little further ahead still. So each glimpse shows the string a little further across its path and after 160 glimpses—one second—you will have seen it successively at each stage of its vibration. The eye combines these 160 glimpses and consequently sees the string slowly wriggling once a second.

Now it is necessary that the glimpses should come at nearly, but not quite, the same interval as the vibrations, so the speed of the motor must be suitably regulated. A sliding resistance can be used, but by pressing the axle with a pencil it is possible to regulate it after a fashion. The experiment is well worth doing, though with this simple apparatus it may be troublesome. All sorts of vibrating bodies—tuning forks, strings, drops of water falling from jets—can be observed through the stroboscope.

The vibrating string is by no means the whole of a stringed instrument. The hollow box-like part of a violin or 'cello is its resonator, and without this there would be hardly any sound at all. The string as it vibrates pulls the bridge towards itself and so bends the sounding-board, which is thus set vibrating. Since almost all the sound comes from the belly of the violin, it is most important that it should be so designed that it naturally vibrates with all the frequencies of the fundamental and harmonics of the strings. A bad violin picks out some one or two frequencies of the strings and emphasises them. Practically the whole art of the violin or 'cello builder lies in the building and design of the belly.

VIBRATING PLATES

Vibrating plates are not greatly used as musical instruments.

The only musical vibrating plates are gongs which vibrate in a most complicated way and produce a very rich musical noise so full of harmonics as hardly to represent any single given note.

Bells are really bent plates. They are struck by a clapper, which bends their opening from a circle to an oval. This springs back to a circle, but overshoots the mark and makes an oval pointing the other way and continues to do this until friction makes the vibrations die away.

The vibrations are, like those of a gong, very complicated. As musical instruments, they leave much to be desired, because their harmonics are always discordant to some extent and they

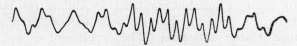

FIG. 240—The curve representing the sound-wave emitted by a bell. It is non-periodic and so emits no definite note. (Courtesy of Professor D. Clarence Miller, from his *Science of Musical Sound*. (Macmillan, New York.))

hardly produce any definite note. Fig. 240 shows a curve drawn from a bell's note. It does not really repeat itself at all. Bells produce sounds of great intensity. As I write this, I can hear St. Paul's striking the hour a mile away; very few musical sounds could carry such a distance.

A plate forced to vibrate in a period which is not its natural one is the foundation of the electric horn. This is practically an electric bell, the spring arm of the bell being replaced by a vibrating plate. In the horn shown in Fig. 241, the current passes first through the contact breaker, then through the coils of an electromagnet. The current energises this. The armature is therefore attracted by the electromagnet and pulls the diaphragm inward. As the armature is drawn to the magnet it presses down the spring which holds the right-hand side of the contact breaker and so breaks the circuit. The electromagnet ceases to attract the armature and the guide spring pushes the latter back again. This lets the contact-breaker close once more and the whole process is repeated. Thus armature and diaphragm fly in and out some hundreds of times a second. The "tone disc" suppresses certain harmonics and encourages others—so modifying the quality of the note.

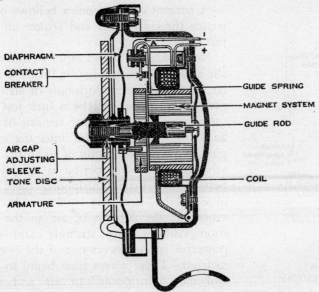

FIG. 241.—An electric horn. (Courtesy of Messrs. Joseph Lucas.)

The plate as it is drawn back and forth by the magnet gives a loud note. The harsh tone of many electric horns is caused by the natural period of the plate being out of tune with that imposed on it by the spring.

WIND INSTRUMENTS

In all wind instruments it is a column of air that vibrates and gives the sound. The simplest of all is the organ pipe which sounds only one note. The organ pipe and the whistle, which is only a very small organ pipe, are worked by the rather mixed and indefinite note which is always heard when air rushes through a slit or jet: this note is used to set a column of air vibrating.

An organ pipe is shaped as in Fig. 242. Some pipes are open at the top, others are closed. The closed ones are the easier to understand.

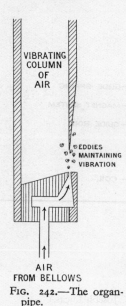

VIBRATING
COLUMN
OF
AIR

EDDIES
MAINTAINING
VIBRATION

AIR
FROM BELLOWS

FIG. 242.—The organ-
pipe.

A current of air from a bellows or fan passes through a slit and strikes an edge just above it.

Now when air blows rapidly from a fine slit against a sharp edge, it forms a regular stream of little whirlpools of air. The pressure in these will be a little less than outside, so a succession of regions of high and low pressure travel into the organ pipe. Now if the column of air in the pipe vibrates in the same period as the interval between the little whirlpools, these will give it the necessary kick to keep it vibrating; the column of air in the pipe soon vibrates very strongly and sends powerful sound waves out of the opening in front. These waves now begin to control the "whirlpools" of air and make them appear at the *right* intervals to keep the air vibrating in the pipe.

The rate at which the air in an organ pipe vibrates depends on its length; an organ pipe closed at the top gives a note with wavelength four times its own length. Thus a closed organ pipe thirteen inches long gives a note with wavelength 52 inches— middle C.

The closed organ pipe gives a poor tone lacking in harmonics. The open pipe as used in most organs gives a note with wavelength twice its length. Thus a 2′ 2″ pipe sounds middle C.

The biggest open pipes used, 32 feet in length, sound a fundamental note of only 16 vibrations a second, which is hardly heard as a note at all. Its harmonics are of course higher and audible as musical tones. The smallest organ pipe is a whistle. If one blows into a key one's mouth represents the organ pipe slit, the edge of the key the edge above the slit and the hollow of the key a closed organ pipe. If the key-hole is half an inch deep, the note sounded will have a two-inch wavelength, which means about 6000 vibrations a second, between 4 and 5 octaves above middle C.

The flute, fife and piccolo are really open organ pipes, of which the effective length can be altered by opening and closing holes in the side. An open hole releases the changes of pressure in the vibrating air and so the resounding column has the length from the mouthpiece to the first open hole.

All other wind-instruments have a *reed*, a tongue of metal or cane made to vibrate by the air blown through it by the player. A "reed" can be seen if the ordinary bulb motor horn is unscrewed.

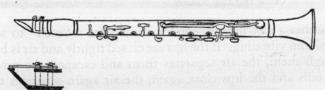

Fig. 243.—The Clarinet, a reed instrument. (Below) Section of reed (white) attached to mouthpiece (black). (Above) The instrument showing keys by which holes can be opened, so shortening the vibrating column of air.

The tongue of the reed vibrates and so sets a column of air vibrating in a tube, and once the air is vibrating it keeps the reed vibrating in the same period as itself. The player's breath just reinforces the reed's motion, so that the vibrations do not die away. The clarinet, oboe, bassoon and saxophone are instruments of this kind. They all have a reed and a tube with holes which, just as in the flute, settle how long a column of air shall vibrate.

"Overblowing" (blowing harder than usual), will cause the air-column to vibrate in two portions at twice the pace—which makes the note an octave higher.

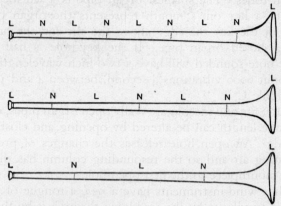

FIG. 244.—Trumpet sounding c, g, c′ (top). The air column vibrates in 2, 3 and 4 portions respectively (*cf.* Fig. 236). At the points N the air is still, and at L, most strongly vibrating; the distance L N in each case is *half* the length of the vibrating column.

The brass instruments employ the lips as a "reed" to set an air-column vibrating. If the lips are closed tightly and air is blown through them, the air separates them and escapes, the pressure then falls and the lips close again, the air again separates them, and so on. When a player blows a trumpet (or bugle, cornet, trombone, tuba, etc.) he presses his lips together with the right degree of tightness to make them vibrate at nearly the *same* frequency as the column of air in the trumpet. It might be

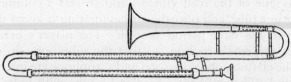

FIG. 245.—The trombone, a trumpet of which the length and characteristic pitch can be varied by sliding telescopic tubes.

thought that a trumpet, since it is a plain tube, could only sound one note. Actually the air can vibrate in it in several different ways, and it can give not only its fundamental note but any one of a limited number of higher harmonics; it is made to do this by the player pressing his lips together with the right tightness to make them sound the harmonic in question.

If a large number of notes is wanted, the length of the tube must be varied. A trombone does this by a slide (Fig. 245), but most brass instruments have valves (Fig. 246) by which the column of air may be made shorter or longer.

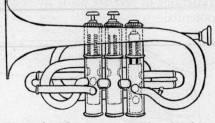

FIG. 246.—The cornet. The length of the vibrating column between mouthpiece and bell is altered by the valves which interpose between them further tubes or "crooks" of various lengths.

REPRODUCTION OF SOUND

All the instruments we have mentioned produce a musical note with a pitch corresponding to the particular period of their own vibrator: string, air-column or the like.

There are a number of instruments—gramophones, telephones, loud-speakers—the object of which is to reproduce sound as exactly as possible. The ordinary musical instrument is designed to vibrate freely in its own period and to resound freely to the most pleasant overtones: the reproducing instrument, on the other hand, must have as little tendency as possible to vibrate or resound—for otherwise it will superimpose its own tone on the music or speech to be reproduced.

Enormous ingenuity has been exerted in producing exact reproduction of speech and music; the result is now very near perfection.

First of these instruments, let us consider the telephone. The instrument consists of a transmitter in which sound-waves cause variations in an electric current. This travels through yards or miles of wire to a receiver in which the varying electric current moves a plate which sets fresh sound-waves in motion.

The telephone transmitter, then, is designed to turn the variations of *pressure* made by sound into variations of electrical potential.

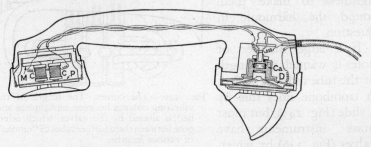

FIG. 247.—Transmitter (right) and receiver (left) of telehphone (courtesy of G.P.O.).

Fig. 247 represents the P.O. pattern of transmitter (right) and receiver (left). The transmitter consists essentially of a thin conical aluminium diaphragm D on which the voice impinges. This disc carries a piston which presses against a number of little grains of carbon (Ca) and a current supplied by a battery passes through these. When these are pressed together, they conduct better than when they are lying loose; consequently each compression wave of the sound momentarily increases the flow of electricity through the whole circuit. An exactly similar current is caused to pass through the listener's receiver, a small permanent magnet (M) attracting a thin iron plate (P). A coil (C) is wound on this permanent magnet so that the currents, as they pass, increase or decrease its magnetism—just as they would magnetise an ordinary electromagnet. As its magnetism increases and diminishes, so its attraction on the plate increases and diminishes and the plate moves backward and forward in time with the variations in current, which again are in time with the speaking voice. Thus the plate of the receiver must vibrate in just the same way as that of the transmitter.

The complicated parts of a telephone service are the exchanges by which any one of some thirty million of the world's telephones can be connected at will to any other.

First of all, in order that we may see how the current flows, let us suppose the connection at the exchange is made. In Fig. 248 is shown the wiring between the two subscribers and the exchange,

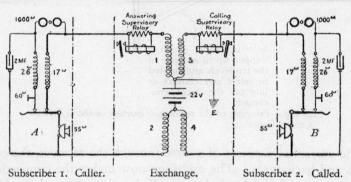

Subscriber 1. Caller.   Exchange.   Subscriber 2. Called.

FIG. 248.—The connections between two telephone subscribers. (Courtesy of the G.P.O.—Crown Copyright).

omitting any indication of the manner in which the subscribers' lines are connected by the operator or automatic relays. The coils, 1, 2, 3, 4 are actually wound on the *same* iron core. This, therefore, acts like an induction coil (p. 000): the varying current in 1 and 2 resulting from the first subscriber's speech induces an exactly identically varying current in coils 3 and 4, and therefore in the second subscriber's circuit. The central battery (22v.) works all the circuits of the exchange. Suppose the left hand subscriber rings up. His receiver hook (above A) rises and completes the circuit to the exchange. The current flows through coil 1 to the relay at the exchange, where it operates the lamp which tells the exchange that it is being called[1]. It then passes over the miles of line between the exchange and the subscriber and passes *via* the 17ω coil through the transmitter and back.

[1]In a manual exchange.

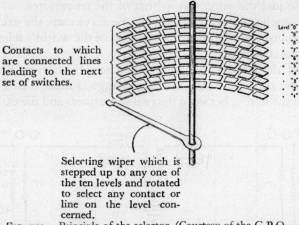

Contacts to which
are connected lines
leading to the next
set of switches.

Level "0"
. "9"
. "8"
. "7"
. "6"
. "5"
. "4"
. "3"
. "2"
. "1"

Selecting wiper which is
stepped up to any one of
the ten levels and rotated
to select any contact or
line on the level con-
cerned.

FIG. 249.—Principle of the selector. (Courtesy of the G.P.O.—
Crown Copyright).

(The current also passes of course through the receiver, the coil
26ω and back again.) The exchange now makes the connection
to the subscriber who is being called and sends an *alternating*
current through his line. Now a direct current cannot cross a
condenser (Fig. 248, 2Mf) but an alternating current can: so
the alternating current passes round the extreme right hand
circuit and causes the bell (not shown) to ring. The called
subscriber lifts his receiver: the hook (above B) flies up and connects
his microphone and telephone circuits to the battery. Now anything subscriber 1 says makes the current in the left hand circuit
vary in time with his voice vibrations: this induces an exactly

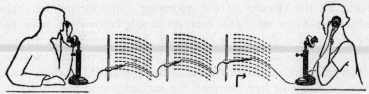

FIG. 250.—How the thousands, hundreds and tens-and-units are successively
selected in the automatic exchange. (Courtesy of the G.P.O.—Crown
Copyright.)

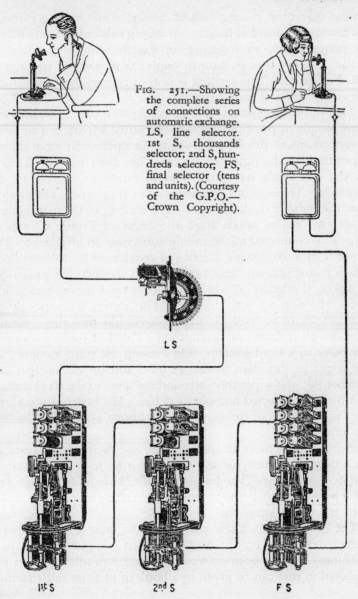

CALLING SUBSCRIBER

CALLED SUBSCRIBER

FIG. 251.—Showing the complete series of connections on automatic exchange. LS, line selector. 1st S, thousands selector; 2nd S, hundreds selector; FS, final selector (tens and units). (Courtesy of the G.P.O.—Crown Copyright).

LS

1st S   2nd S   F S

similar current in the right-hand circuit. This, passing through the receiver, is heard as speech. Anything subscriber 2 says makes *his* current vary, so inducing an exactly similar variation in circuit 1. This after passing through the receiver in circuit 1 is heard as speech. This account is not, of course, the whole story, but it explains the main principles.

The automatic system of connecting any two subscribers is fairly simple in principle, though the actual apparatus employed is very complex. Briefly, a dial sends out a particular set of signals depending on the figure to which it has been moved. Thus 6 on the dial sends six equally spaced pulses of current to the exchange. These pulses operate *selectors* (Fig. 250). Let us suppose the number dialled is 2346. The dialling of the first figure 2 sends two pulses which have the effect of lifting a "wiper" (Fig. 250) connected to the calling subscriber to level 2000. The wiper then moves round a series of contacts until it "finds" one which is disengaged. This latter contact connects the subscriber to a second selector on which are all the lines between 2000 and 2999. His next act is to dial "3." This moves the wiper of the second selector to level 300 and it moves like the other over the contacts till it finds one disengaged. This last contact connects the caller to a third selector. On dialling the third number "4" the wiper of this rises to the 40 level and on dialling the last number "6" the wiper travels round the level to the sixth contact to which is connected number 2346 line. The system for dialling the exchanges is an extension of the above system for dialling the numbers.

Fig. 251 gives more details: LS is the line switch which searches for a disengaged selector and connects it up to the caller: 1st S, 2nd S, F.S., are the Thousands selector, Hundreds selector and Final Selector, which find the individual circuit called and connect with the called subscriber.

The gramophone, a few years ago, was quite a simple instrument to explain. To-day, however, such complicated electrical machinery is used both in recording and reproducing, that the explanation that can be given in a book of this size must confine itself to the simple principles of the subject.

The gramophone record is a crooked groove whose waves reproduce by their sinuosities the compressions and rarefactions of a sound wave. A modern record is made by a very intricate process, the outline of which is as follows:

The music to be recorded is performed in a sound-proof studio in front of a microphone which is a modified telephone transmitter. Just as in the telephone circuit, minute electrical currents are formed which are greatly magnified by a valve amplifier working on the same principle as that of a wireless set (p. 503). The magnified current is then passed into the recording box of the recording machine. Plate XX shows the recording machine as used by the Gramophone Company for H.M.V. records. A turn-table like that of a gramophone—but more heavily built—revolves at an extremely constant speed. On it is mounted a disc of wax. In place of the sound box of the gramophone is a recording box in which the varying currents from the transmitter operate a magnet which pulls a sapphire-pointed needle to right or left in time with the current's pulsations. The recording box slowly moves inward and consequently the sapphire point cuts a spiral line which, however, is not a smooth spiral but is distorted into minute waves reproducing the form of the note. Plate XX shows a microphotograph of part of a gramophone record. As many as six discs may be recorded in order to get a perfect performance. The wax disc is then coated with an extremely fine metallic powder. This enters every groove and recess and makes the disc a conductor of electricity. It is placed in a bath of copper sulphate and connected to the negative pole of a battery, a copper plate being attached to the positive pole (p. 301). In this way a coating of copper is plated on to the disc; when it is thick enough, it is stripped away from the wax and forms an exact mould of its surface; instead of the grooves on the original wax, there are now ridges. From this shell of copper there is made (by plating processes like that already described) a hard steel model exactly like the copper shell. Two of these are mounted in a powerful hydraulic press.

A piece of gramophone record material—a complicated mixture of resins, etc.—is warmed till soft and squeezed between the two steel discs. They are heated by steam, then cooled by water to harden the disc, which can be lifted out when the press is opened. It only remains to smooth the edges and pack it.

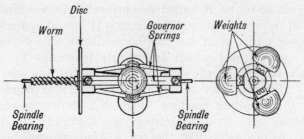

Fig. 252—Governor of gramophone motor (courtesy of Messrs. Decca, Ltd.).

The gramophone on which the record is played consists first of a turntable. This may be driven by clockwork or electricity, but in either case must have its speed very carefully regulated. If the gramophone is to sound the same note as the artist sang, it must obviously turn at the same speed as that of the turntable of the original recording machine. This is accomplished by gearing to the motor a governor (Fig. 252), which consists of three balls hung on springs. As this rotates, the balls are driven outwards centrifugally and so draw the "disc" to the right; the disc operates a brake which slows the mechanism. This governor keeps the turntable moving at any required speed. The sound-box may be either electrical or mechanical. In either case it carries a needle which lies in the groove of the disc and which is moved from side to side as it follows the curves of the sound-track. In the mechanical type (Fig. 253) the needle fits into the stylus-bar which moves on a pivot and is connected at the other end to a springy diaphragm. The motions of the needle are therefore followed by those of the diaphragm, and the air within is set in vibration. The vibrations are rather feeble as yet, so the sound is made to travel through a horn most carefully designed to resound to *all* frequencies. Fig. 254 shows the horn of a so-called hornless model.

The electrical pick-up is now much used. The record sets the needle vibrating in the same way as in the mechanical sound-box, but instead of moving a diaphragm moves an iron armature near the poles of an electromagnet. This alters the magnetisation of the electromagnet and so generates electric currents varying in strength with the motions of the needle and therefore with the curves of the record groove. This current goes to a loud-speaker

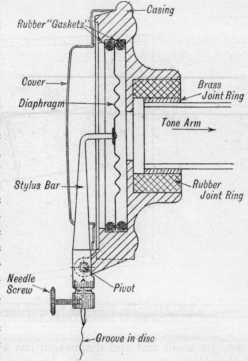

Fig. 253.—Gramophone sound-box (courtesy of Messrs. Decca, Ltd.).

(an amplifier and exaggerated telephone receiver). The advantage of the electrical pick-up is that the needle exerts little force and so there is little wear on the record and hardly any sound of scratching. The quality of reproduction depends entirely on the loud-speaker portion and can be much better or much worse than that given by the mechanical sound-box.

The loud-speaker is an instrument designed to convert into sound electrical impulses, such as are obtained by amplifying a telephone or wireless receiving-set current. The essential of a good loud-speaker is that it should reproduce both high and low notes equally well. Thus, a telephone receiver, for example, will not

14

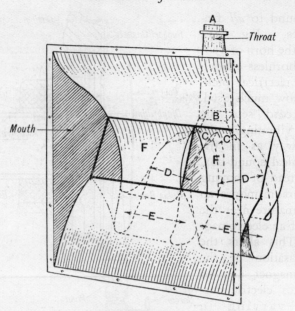

FIG. 254.—The horn of a so-called hornless gramophone.
(Courtesy of Messrs. Decca, Ltd.).

do. Its small and stiff diaphragm has a natural high period of
vibration and so gives a squeaky tone to everything it utters.
The vibrating part of a loud-speaker should therefore have a
natural period of vibration (if any) much greater or much smaller
than the human ear can appreciate and it should respond to high
and low frequencies alike.

The moving-coil loud-speaker has a flat cone of parchment, etc.,
attached to a coil of wire through which the varying current flows.
This coil hangs in a powerful magnetic field. As we have seen
a wire bearing an increasing or decreasing current moves in a
magnetic field, and the greater the variations of the current the
greater the movement. Consequently the coil and cone vibrate in
time with the variations of the current passing through them.
Such an arrangement (Fig. 255) gives an almost perfect reproduction of sound.

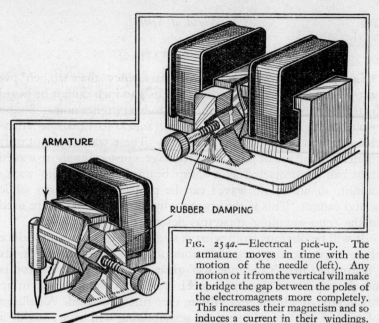

ARMATURE

RUBBER DAMPING

FIG. 254a.—Electrical pick-up. The armature moves in time with the motion of the needle (left). Any motion of it from the vertical will make it bridge the gap between the poles of the electromagnets more completely. This increases their magnetism and so induces a current in their windings. These currents pass to the loud speaker and produce the sound. (Courtesy of *The Wireless World.*)

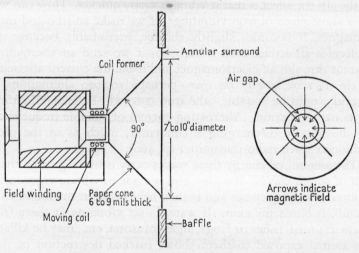

Coil former

Annular surround

Air gap

90°

7" to 10" diameter

Field winding

Paper cone 6 to 9 mils thick

Moving coil

Baffle

Arrows indicate magnetic field

FIG. 255.—The moving-coil loud speaker. (Courtesy of the Oxford University Press and Mr. N. W. McLachlan, from the latter's *Loudspeakers.*)

ULTRASONIC WAVES

Compression waves of greater frequency than 20,000 per second and wave-lengths of less than half an inch cannot be heard by the human ear. Dogs are thought to hear higher notes. Sound waves of higher frequency than this (20,000 to 1,000,000 vibrations per second) are called ultrasonic. These waves are not only interesting but are of practical advantage. Just as the short-waved light can be projected as a sharp beam and long radio waves cannot, so ultrasonic waves can be projected in a beam while sound cannot. This is the reason why ultrasonic waves are used in the echo-sounding apparatus described on pp. 388–389.

It will be obvious from what is said on p. 368, that to produce these very short waves the vibrator must have an enormous "restoring-force," and not too great a mass. The vibrator is usually a piece of quartz or steel. A short column of air in an organ pipe or whistle may vibrate 1000 times a second. A column of steel of the same dimensions set vibrating will have roughly a million times the restoring force and a thousand times the density of the air: the effect is that it vibrates vastly quicker. How can we set a short piece of iron vibrating? If we make an iron rod into a magnet, it becomes slightly shorter, presumably because its molecules all attract each other. So, if we send an alternating current through an electromagnet and make the current alternate *in the vibration time of the iron*—perhaps 100,000 alternations a second would be suitable—the iron core will be kept vibrating in its natural period. Alternating current of suitable frequencies can be got by discharging a condenser, much as in the old-fashioned spark radio-transmitter (p. 500).

The amount of energy these waves carry is much greater than that of sound waves. If a glass rod is made to vibrate vigorously at ultrasonic frequencies and is then held between the finger and thumb, it burns the skin. If water is set vibrating at these frequencies, small fishes or frogs, algæ, infusoria, etc., may be killed. An animal exposed to them shows marked destruction of the blood corpuscles.

Ultrasonic waves are transmitted very much as is light: they cast shadows, can be refracted, readily give interference effect, etc. Their chief practical value is for underwater signalling and echo sounding. An ingenious apparatus, on the same principle as the echo sounder, has been devised by which icebergs can be detected at a distance, even at night or in fog, by their reflecting a beam of ultrasonic waves sent out from a ship.

CHAPTER XV

LIGHT WAVES

ELECTROMAGNETIC WAVES

THE greatest group of radiations or waves is the family of electromagnetic waves which include "wireless-waves," light, X-rays, etc. It is rather important to understand what an electromagnetic wave is. It is not a travelling alteration of the shape of a surface like a water-wave, nor is it a travelling compression of a material like a sound-wave. It is a moving electric and magnetic field travelling at the vast speed of 186,300 miles a second. Let us try to form a clearer picture of this electromagnetic wave. The first thing to grasp is that an electric charge, *when speeding up or slowing down*, causes a magnetic field of force to be produced, and that an *increasing or diminishing magnetic force* likewise induces an electromotive force. It has been proved, by experiment, that the attraction of a magnet is not instantaneous. It travels with the same speed as light (186,300 miles a second). Thus, if a vast electromagnet were suddenly switched on, it would not begin to attract an iron meteor, hanging in space 186,300 miles away, until one second had elapsed.

Suppose we have a rapidly varying electric field such as might

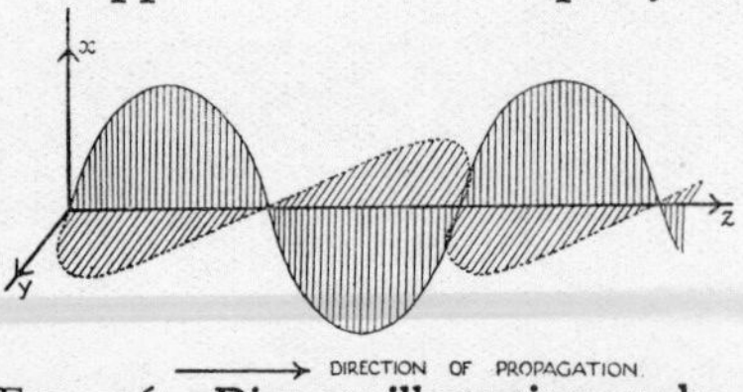

FIG. 256.—Diagram illustrating an electromagnetic wave. The wave-lines are *graphs* showing how the strength and direction of the electric and magnetic forces vary: in the actual radiation there is nothing shaped like a wave.

be caused by an oscillating electric charge. As the electric charge varies, so a varying magnetic field will be produced. Consequently Fig. 256 gives some notion of what is happening in an electromagnetic wave such as light. As the wave travels in the direction z, so the electric field (plain

422

line) rises and falls, while the magnetic field (dotted line) rises and falls in time with it. The direction of the magnetic force is at right angles to that of the electric force. There is really nothing at all going up and down in the wave. The wavy lines are simply graphs showing how powerful the electric and magnetic forces are at each point of their travel. Thus there is, in the wave, a magnetic force rising and falling like a wave and an electric force rising and falling in the same way in time with it. The thing, then, to remember about wireless waves, light, X-rays, etc., is that they are streams of pulses of electric and magnetic force.

Sound-waves require matter to transmit them. Electromagnetic waves pass unhindered through a vacuum. Are these waves carried by anything or can the pulses of magnetic and electric force travel through nothingness? At one time it was considered that force could only act through a material medium of some kind and so an "ether" was invented, filling all space, so that these forces should have something to act upon. No one found any direct experimental evidence that this ether really existed, and though it is very difficult to picture a force acting in emptiness, it is unscientific to invent an "ether" for this reason alone. All attempts to prove the existence of an ether give negative results, a fact which makes us strongly suspect that the "ether" is not there at all.

THE DIFFERENT KINDS OF ELECTROMAGNETIC WAVES

These electromagnetic waves may, as far as we know, be of any wave-length and frequency. The longest we can detect are of the order of some miles, the shortest are as small as the thirtieth part of the diameter of an atom. We group sound waves into a "scale" with the shortest wave lengths and highest frequencies at the top. As we go up the scale, each time the frequency is doubled we say we have traversed an octave.

The frequencies of light waves are much greater than those of sound waves. Since light travels 30,000,000,000 centimetres a second, the number of waves per second (frequency) will be

30,000,000,000 divided by the length of the wave in centimetres. The wavelength is the usual way of expressing the type of electromagnetic wave, but the frequency in cycles (waves per second) or in kilocycles (thousands of waves per second) is often used.

The table below shows the scale of electromagnetic radiations. It extends over some 60 octaves, of which the eye can detect but one. The most important part is near the frequency of light and this part of the scale is reproduced in enlarged form on the opposite page.

ELECTROMAGNETIC WAVES

Type of Wave.	Wave-length A.U. = $\frac{1}{100000000}$ cm.	Frequency (vibrations per sec.)	Source.	Behaviour.
γ-rays	0.03 to 1.4 A.U.	10^{20} to 2×10^{18}	Explosion of the nuclei of atoms.	Invisible. Like very penetrating X-rays.
X-rays	0.5 to 1000 A.U.	6×10^{18} to 3×10^{15}	Bombardment of matter by electrons.	Invisible. Penetrate all kinds of matter. Are not normally reflected or refracted.
Ultra-violet light	25 to 4000 A.U.	10^{17} to 8×10^{14}	Glow of ionised gases and hot bodies.	Invisible. Chemically active. Are reflected and refracted. Affect photographic plates.
Light {blue yellow red	4000 to 8000 A.U.	8×10^{15} to 4×10^{15}	Glow of ionised gas and hot bodies.	Visible. Easily reflected and refracted. Affects photographic plates.
Infra-red and "residual" rays	8000 to 4,000,000 A.U.	4×10^{15} to 7×10^{11}	Radiation from hot bodies.	Invisible. Affect photographic plate very slightly. Do not at all easily penetrate matter.
Hertzian waves	10^6 to 3×10^{14} ($\frac{1}{10}$ mm. to 20 miles)	3×10^{12} to 10,000	Spark discharges. Oscillating valves.	Invisible. No effect on photographic plate. Not easily reflected. Will set electrons moving.
Slow oscillations	3×10^{14} to 3×10^{16} 20 to 2000 miles	10,000 to 100	Coil rotating in magnetic field	Mechanical and heat effects produced.

Wave-length in A.U.	Type of radiation	Trans-mitted by	Effect on photographic plate	Effect on eye	Other effects
2000	Far ultra-violet	Quartz			Not present in sun's rays. Cause serious burns
3000	Middle ultra-violet	Also by Vitaglass		Invisible but destructive in excessive quantity	Present in sunshine. Cause sunburn and in excessive quantity inflammat.on, etc. Produce Vitamin D in skin
4000	Near ultra-violet		Affect ordinary plate		
5000				Visible as violet light / Visible as blue light / Visible as green light	
6000	Light	Glass Down to 20,000 A.U.		Visible as yellow light	Utilised by green plants in converting carbon dioxide and water into sugar and starch
7000				Visible as red light	
8000	Infra-red		Affect specially sensitised plates	Invisible	Produce sensation of warmth

These radiations seem at first utterly different. We cannot perceive waves of radio-frequency at all without some sort of detector. Infra-red rays can be felt as "radiant heat." Light rays can be seen. Ultra-violet rays and X-rays are invisible but make glass and other things glow. The γ-rays of radium are invisible, but will damage the skin exposed to them. What have these rays in common that we group them as "electromagnetic"? Firstly, they are all, as far as we know, generated by *moving electric charges*. Secondly, they travel without any material medium; thus, unlike sound, they travel as well, or better, through a vacuum as through air. Thirdly, they all, as far as we can tell, have the same velocity of about 186,300 miles a second. The great difference between them is due to the fact that they travel in different-sized quanta or packets (p. 433) and these are capable of doing different quantities—and kinds—of work.

Light may be taken as the typical electromagnetic radiation. We are all exceedingly familiar with it, and so we will discuss it first and then go on to talk about the longer- and shorter-waved radiations.

LIGHT

From the explanation at the beginning of the chapter it should be possible to have some notion of what an electromagnetic wave is; the next step is to understand how light is known to be made up of these waves. That light is *travelling* can be clearly seen from the experiments (pp. 430–432), in which its velocity is measured. Now the only things we know that travel are matter and energy. Are light-rays matter? It was thought a couple of centuries ago that they were a hail of tiny particles, rather like the cathode-rays (pp. 293, 294), which of course were then unknown. Well, there is no very obvious reason against this view, provided the particles of light had very little weight. An object like a flash lamp (sealed to prevent evaporation of liquids or escape of gases) does not get measurably lighter as it shines; so evidently, if light consisted of material particles, they would be very small ones indeed.

The chief piece of evidence to the physicist is that light behaves and is generated and moves in a way he can predict from calculations about electromagnetic waves; but as we cannot follow him into these regions, we must be content with something simpler. The most convincing piece of evidence is that two *waves* going the same way can cancel each other out and can make a calm—no wave; but two *particles* going the same way can only make two particles and cannot cancel.

If two portions of light can make darkness, it cannot be made of particles but must be made of waves.

Let us see how two sets of waves can cancel. If we set two trains of waves travelling from places half a wavelength away, the crests of one will be in the troughs of the other and so there will be no wave left!

Plate XXI shows a photograph of ripples on mercury, started by a tuning fork. It is easy to see that where a crest meets a trough no wave is to be seen. Now we cannot repeat this with two lights instead of the two tuning fork styles, because two lights do not keep in step like the arms of a fork; but we can show it if we use two portions of the same light.

INTERFERENCE

The simplest way of showing that this can be done is to blow a soap bubble and look at it in light of a single colour. Instead of seeing films of colours, the bubble is seen to be mottled and striped in black and the colour of the light used. The whole film is equally illuminated with light. Yet in some parts of the film no light is seen.

You can see this for yourself by blowing a soap bubble in front of a gas fire and then throwing several pinches of salt on the red-hot radiants. This gives yellow sodium light which is almost all of a single wavelength. A better sodium light is made by heating in a Bunsen burner a piece of asbestos string, previously dipped in strong brine and dried.

A simpler way of showing this is to press together two pieces of plate glass. Irregular dark and light bands and stripes can be seen, though there is nothing there but two pieces of transparent glass and a film of transparent air between.

On the wave theory the light is a succession of troughs and crests, really maxima and minima of electric or magnetic force. In Fig. 257 the light rays are shown as striped bands, the dark

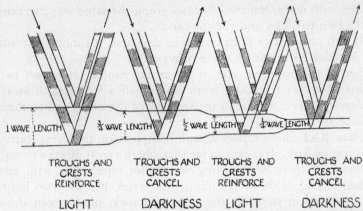

TROUGHS AND CRESTS REINFORCE   TROUGHS AND CRESTS CANCEL   TROUGHS AND CRESTS REINFORCE   TROUGHS AND CRESTS CANCEL

LIGHT   DARKNESS   LIGHT   DARKNESS

FIG. 257.—Interference. Light is reflected at full strength when reflected from films of certain thicknesses but extinguished when reflected from others[1].

parts representing troughs and the light parts crests. These rays are reflected at the top of the film and at the bottom of the film, and if these are $\frac{1}{4}$ or $\frac{3}{4}$ or $1\frac{1}{4}$ wave-lengths apart, no light will be reflected.[1] If the film surfaces are o, $\frac{1}{2}$, 1, $1\frac{1}{2}$, or a whole number of wave-lengths apart, the troughs and crests will reinforce each other and the light will be reflected. For thicknesses of fractions of a wavelength like $2\frac{3}{8}$ wavelengths, the light will be partly reflected and partly not. A soap bubble looks coloured in white light because this is a mixture of lights of all wavelengths, each wavelength causing in our eyes the sensation of a particular shade of colour. If the film at a particular place is of the right thickness to "interfere" with, say, yellow light, this will be destroyed, but the other coloured lights will not be affected and the mixture of all colours but yellow reflected back to the eye, give it the sensation of violet. As the soap bubble changes in thickness, so the colours change too.

This interference gives us a way of measuring the wavelength

---

[1] This indicates the *principle* of interference in its simplest form. Actually the matter is complicated by there being a change of phase (e.g. from trough to crest) on reflection. This actually reverses the above results, films of $\frac{1}{4}$, $\frac{3}{4}$ wavelength, etc., giving brightness and those of $\frac{1}{2}$, 1, $1\frac{1}{2}$, etc., giving darkness.

of light, because the thinnest film which causes interference is half a wave-length thick. An ingenious way of measuring this film is by means of Newton's rings. A weak spectacle lens of about 1 metre radius of curvature (i.e., as much curved as the surface of a ball, 2 metres in diameter) is laid on a glass plate and the light of which the wave-length is to be measured is made to shine on it. The film of air between the lens

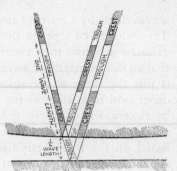

FIG. 258.—Why Newton's rings are formed. (*See footnote* p. 428).

and plate gets thicker as we go outward from the centre, and a little geometry enables us to calculate the thickness of film at any given distance from the centre—in the above instance the thickness of the air film in centimetres will be $\frac{1}{200}$th of the square of the distance from the centre. Thus, at 1 cm. from the centre, the film will be $\frac{1}{200}$th cm. thick; at 1 mm. from the centre it will be $\frac{1}{2000}$th mm. thick. When a lens and plate are illuminated thus, a neat set of concentric light and dark circles is seen, and by setting up the arrangement so that it can be viewed with a low-power microscope, the innermost ring can be measured; and for sodium light and a lens of 1 metre radius of curvature is just over a millimetre in diameter. Hence it can be calculated that the film of air is 0.00001473 cm. thick at this point and the wavelength of sodium light is four times this figure, 0.00005893 cm. The use of this for testing lenses is described on p. 474. These phenomena of interference cannot be explained by any theory in which light is regarded as a material particle. They prove that light must be a wave-motion, but they do not prove it to be an electromagnetic wave-motion. Light cannot be a kind of wave depending on the motion of matter as do water-waves, because it travels through a vacuum.

The first piece of evidence that light is an electromagnetic wave is that the velocity of light is the same as the electromagnetic waves made by a moving electric charge in a wireless transmitter. The velocity of light is slower in any transparent medium like glass or air than in a vacuum, and the amount of slowing up that an electromagnetic wave would display can be calculated, and is just the same as the amount of slowing up of light. Several other odd facts such as the alteration of the frequency of light by electric and magnetic fields show that it must be electromagnetic. The strongest evidence, however, is that calculations based on the hypothesis that light is an electromagnetic wave explain perfectly the way it is reflected and refracted and also its dispersion—the way it is scattered by particles and bends round very small obstacles.

THE SPEED OF LIGHT

It is very important to be able to measure the velocity of light accurately because a great deal of the force of the arguments for the theory of Relativity depends on it.

There are several good ways of doing this: Michelson's method will be described here. Its accuracy may be judged by the fact that the apparatus as described here proved that light travels faster than 299,792 and slower than 299,800 kilometres a second! First of all it must be realised that when a ray of light hits a mirror at an angle it "bounces" off (i.e. is reflected) at the same angle, much as a billiard ball bounces off the cushion (p. 453). Michelson sent an intense ray of light (Fig. 259A) through a fine slit on to an octagonal mirror which could be made to spin at a speed which could be varied and could be read off on a revolution counter. If the octagonal mirror is not moving, the ray of light is reflected by two more mirrors along the path 1, 2, 3, 4, and there strikes a big concave[1] mirror which reflects it to another concave mirror (5) twenty-two miles away! This mirror is very accurately set so as to reflect the ray to a little fixed mirror (6) and then (7, 8) all the 22 miles back again to the

---

[1] Used because, if the ray shifts, a concave mirror will still reflect it in the same direction.

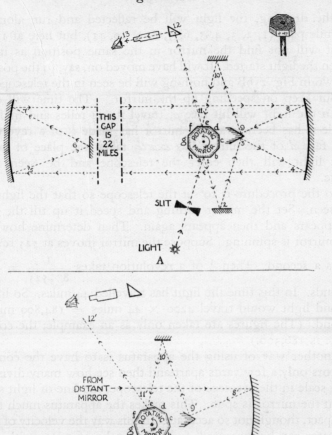

FIG. 259.—Michelson's apparatus for determining the velocity of light.

other concave mirror. From this it goes *via* two more mirrors (9, 10) back to the octagonal mirror (11) which reflects it into a telescope. This is set so that the eye sees the slit, after its light has travelled this long journey, as a line of bright lying on an illuminated scale (marked on the eyepiece of the telescope). Now set the mirror spinning. As it goes past the position shown in the drawing, the light will be reflected and run along its 44-mile path (1, 2, 3, 4, 5, 6, 7, 8, 9, 10, 11), but here at 11 the light will not find the mirror in the same position as it had when the light started. It will have moved on, say, to the position shown in Fig. 259B and nothing will be seen in the telescope.

But keep on speeding up the mirror. The time will come when the light will hit face *a*, travel its 44 miles and find that while it has been away the mirror has made $\frac{1}{8}$ of a revolution and face *d* of the mirror has *exactly* taken the place of face *e*. The light will then enter the telescope and be seen once more.

So the procedure is to set the telescope so that the light can be seen. Set the mirror turning and speed it up till the light disappears and then appears again. Then determine how fast the mirror is spinning. Suppose the mirror moves at 525 revolutions a second. Then $\frac{1}{8}$ of a revolution takes $\dfrac{1}{8 \times 525} = \dfrac{1}{4200}$ seconds. In this time the light has travelled 44 miles. So in one second light would travel 4200×44 miles $= 184,800$ miles a second. (The figures are taken only as an example; the correct value is 186,300.)

Another way of using the apparatus is to have the concave mirrors only a few yards apart and then see how many divisions on a scale in the eyepiece of the telescope, the line of light shifts when the mirror is spun. This makes the apparatus much more compact, though not so accurate. In this way the velocity of light in water can be measured, for a long tube of water with glass ends can be put so that the light goes through it. Consequently it can be shown that light travels more slowly through water than through air.

As light is an electromagnetic wave, one should be able to get it by making an electric charge vibrate. But its frequency is something like 10^{15} waves per second, and we have not yet found a way of making an electric charge vibrate so quickly. The shortest waves made in this way are of wavelength about 0.01 cm.—five thousand times as long as light waves: they are long heat-waves and have much of the character of light without, however, being able to affect the eye.

QUANTA

A remarkable discovery without which we should know very little about the way light is given out by atoms, especially atoms of a gas, is the quantum theory of Planck. The essential point is that when vibrating electric charges radiate electro-magnetic waves, these are always given out *in separate "packets"* called quanta, consisting of a few hundred or a few thousand waves. A quantum of energy is not a fixed thing like an atom or electron, but its size depends on the number of vibrations the electric charge makes every second. The best way of measuring the size of the quantum is by the rule that the total energy of the quantum in ergs is 6.55×10^{-27} times the number of vibrations per second. This number is called Planck's constant. A quantum is such a small packet of energy that even a feeble source of light like a candle gives out 3×10^{19} quanta per second. The stream of quanta from a candle is so rapid that there is no way of seeing that the light comes in quanta at all.

This quantum theory enables us to calculate correctly a number of things about light and heat which could not be worked out correctly before, though most of these cannot be treated without mathematical reasoning quite out of the depth of this book. It does, however, help us to understand how light is produced.

HOW GASES GLOW

The greatest puzzle that the quantum theory unravelled was the explanation of the very odd sort of light that glowing gases produce. Glowing gases are familiar to us in neon advertising signs and those brilliant blue-green mercury lamps which illuminate many arterial roads.

Simpler examples are the brilliant red, blue and green flames seen in fireworks and, easiest of all to study, the yellow flame seen when ordinary salt is heated in a gas burner. If you throw a tiny pinch of salt on to the glowing fireclay of a gas-fire, this yellow flame is very easily seen and is due to the vapour of the sodium in the salt, glowing in the gas flame.

Now if you measure the wavelength of any of these kinds of light (best with a spectrograph, p. 463) you find that, unlike the light from an electric filament or a red-hot poker, the light is only of a few wave-lengths. Nearly all of the yellow sodium light is of one wave-length, 5893 A.U. (frequency 5.09 × 10^{14}), whereas the electric filament lamp emits light of every frequency we can measure.

The neon lamp gives visible light of a dozen or so main frequencies, the mercury arc lamp of only four. How is it, then, that the light from a glowing gas is "tuned" to a few fixed "light-notes"?

Now the atoms in a gas are not moving over any fixed or regularly repeated path. They are merely dashing about from place to place in a quite confused fashion, colliding frequently. The average time between two collisions in a gas is far longer than the frequency of any light wave, so we should expect (as we find) that most gases do not glow when they are heated. Air at a red heat or hotter gives out no glow at all and the oxyhydrogen flame gives only a slight blue glow although its temperature is probably 2500° C.; a piece of solid held in the same flame gives a blinding white light.

Why, then, do some gases glow? The answer is that the atoms are not vibrating but something like a vibration is going on *inside them*.

An atom, we have seen (p. 27), has a small heavy kernel of positive electricity and round it a cloud of light negative electrons. The work of Niels Bohr and others has proved that these electrons are grouped according to the amount of potential energy they have got. In different kinds of atoms the nucleus may have from one to ninety-two electrons grouped round it, and these are grouped, we believe, in layers rather like the coats of an onion. Fig. 260 shows the grouping in an atom of strontium, an element whose vapour glows brilliantly red. We may number these 1, 2, 3, 4, 5, etc., from the inside. Each group can only contain a limited number of electrons, but the electrons can move from one group to another if this latter has less than its full complement of electrons. Thus the electrons in the fourth ring of the strontium atom (Fig. 260) could jump to the fifth. But, since the positive nucleus attracts the negative electrons, some work must be done to pull them from an inner group to

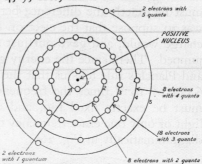

FIG. 260.—Diagram of a strontium atom. The positions of the electrons (small circles) are not meant to be exactly indicated. The essential feature is the existence of electrons in concentric groups having different energies.

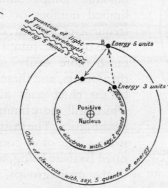

FIG. 261.—When an atom absorbs energy from collisions, electrical forces, etc., its electrons are caused to jump from positions where they have smaller potential energy (A) to positions with considerably greater potential energy (B). Intermediate states are not possible. When the electron jumps *back*, to a position of less energy (A), the energy lost appears as a quantum of light.

an outer one. This work must be supplied from outside: thus in the neon-tube it is the electric energy that moves the electrons to their new places; in a red firework it is the energy of the collisions between the strontium atoms. Now, when an electron has been moved from an inner group to an outer group and then jumps *back* from an outer group to an inner group, its potential energy—the possibility of doing further work—becomes *less* and this energy appears as light. Now the point of this theory is that the energy of an electron in, say, group 4 has some fixed value, and after it has hopped back to group 3 its energy has another fixed value, so that the energy given out must be exactly the difference between these. Bohr's great step was to suppose that the electron behaved as a vibrating electric charge would, and gave out just one quantum of light when it jumped. Then, since the energy given out in each jump is fixed and Planck's rule tells us that the energy of a single quantum is 6.554×10^{-27} times the frequency, the frequency of the light must be exactly fixed too, and each electron-jump will cause light of only one exact frequency to be given out. This is shown diagrammatically in Fig. 261.

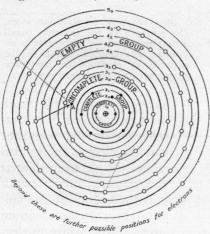

FIG. 262.—Diagram of a sodium atom emitting light. Electrons are shown as ◉ while possible but unoccupied positions for electrons are shown as O. The electrons in complete groups 1_0, 2_0, 2_1, remain undisturbed. The odd electron A (3_0 group) moves to a position in one of the outer groups when the sodium atom takes in energy. When it jumps back it gives out a quantum of light of fixed wave-length. Only certain jumps are possible. Some of these are indicated by arrows. The heavy arrow indicates the particular jump which gives the well-known sodium light.

Now there are only a certain number of possible places for electrons in the atom, so there are only a limited number of possible jumps and a limited number of light frequencies it can emit. Some of these jumps are much more easily made than others, and these will be the chief ones made, which still more limits the possibilities. The matter is made a little more complicated by there being, within the main groups, subgroups whence jumps can be made, but the principle is the same. Fig. 262 illustrates the manner in which a sodium atom can emit light of many different frequencies.

MAKING LIGHT

Light is always produced when an electron vibrates very rapidly or shifts its place in an atom, and this is the only way of making it we have yet found!

There are two chief ways of making light. The first is to make a solid very hot: this is done in bright flames, like those of a candle or oil-lamp, in incandescent gas burners and in ordinary electric filament lamps.

The second way is to displace the electrons of the atoms of a gas; when they jump back they emit light. This is done in the neon-advertising signs and in the mercury vapour lamps. The electric arc produces its light in both ways.

A solid, such as an electric light filament or a kitchen poker, emits heat-rays at the ordinary temperature; as it is heated up it emits waves of shorter and shorter wavelength until at about 500° C. it begins to produce, as well as heat-waves, the longest light-waves—red ones. As the temperature rises, the red gradually shifts to "flame" colour, to yellow, to white, and finally to a bluish-white. The higher the temperature, the greater the proportion of the energy that is given out as light and the smaller the proportion given out as heat; however, at any temperatures we can reach, most of the energy of the hot substance is wasted as heat. Consequently efforts are always being made to raise the temperature of the things we use as lights.

The most ancient form of light is the lamp or candle. Here a substance containing hydrogen and carbon is made to burn. Now, burning is the act of combining with oxygen—in this case the oxygen of the air. The liquid oil or melted wax climbs up the wick and the heat of the flame turns it into vapour. Part of this vapour burns to the gaseous carbon dioxide and steam, and in doing so splits the big molecules of the wax-vapour into hydrogen atoms and bits of solid carbon.[1]

---

[1] The splitting is not probably so simple as this, the molecule probably first breaks into groups of atoms, which then split up further.

The hydrogen burns to steam and the carbon is made "yellow-hot" in the flame and gives out the light. When it gets to the edge of the flame where oxygen abounds, it burns, forming carbon dioxide gas.

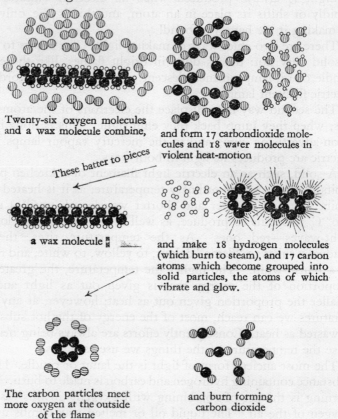

Twenty-six oxygen molecules and a wax molecule combine,

and form 17 carbondioxide molecules and 18 water molecules in violent heat-motion

These batter to pieces

a wax molecule

and make 18 hydrogen molecules (which burn to steam), and 17 carbon atoms which become grouped into solid particles, the atoms of which vibrate and glow.

The carbon particles meet more oxygen at the outside of the flame

and burn forming carbon dioxide

This explanation, with small differences, holds for the lamp which chiefly differs in requiring an artificial draught to burn up all the carbon in its big flame. If the flame is too big for the amount of air, the lamp smokes and we find the carbon on the ceiling.

But why does the particle of carbon emit light? It is a mass of carbon atoms, each made up of electrons and the violent battering by the molecules of the hot gas sets the atoms vibrating strongly. Now, the atom-centres are about 10^{-8} cm. apart and we might not be far out if we thought they travelled about 10^{-9} cm. each time they vibrated. The glowing carbon atoms would be expected to have an average velocity of about 3×10^5 cm. per second, so they should complete their vibrations in about 3×10^{-15} second, and should give light waves of about this frequency. Light travels at 3×10^{10} centimetres a second, so each wave would be $3 \times 3 \times 10^{10} \times 10^{-15}$ cm. long $= 9 \times 10^{-5}$ cm. This would be a little more than the wave-length of red-light (about 8×10^{-5} cm.), but since different atoms are moving at different speeds and other factors, such as the distance they travel, are not accurately known, the agreement is not bad. The light from a hot body is a mixture of all kinds of wave-lengths, from long heat waves upward to light or ultra-violet light. It is only in such a mixture of wave-lengths that we can see colours. Light of only a few wave lengths makes colours look entirely different, the mercury lamps now used on arterial roads show this well.

It is not easily possible to get more light from a lamp or candle by making their flames hotter. The oil produces a fixed amount of energy, which is used up in light and in heating the incoming air and the outgoing gases. The only possibilities seem to be, first, to heat the air before it comes to the lamp. This would mean that since the air started hot, the heat which would normally be put into it would go to heat the flame hotter and so make more light be given out. I do not know if this has been tried! The other way would be to supply pure oxygen instead of air. The flame would not then have to heat up the useless nitrogen of the air and so would get far hotter. The lamp would of course have to be re-designed, for either of these expedients would be dangerous and ineffective if applied to the ordinary oil-lamp. Actually, the best answer to the problem of getting light by burning things is the *incandescent mantle*. This can be used with an oil flame (as in the Aladdin lamps) or with a gas flame, as in the ordinary incandescent burner. The principle in each case is to give the flame so much air that it burns up all the carbon before it has a chance to glow. This gives a hot blue flame which plays upon a mantle, a thimble-shaped network of a mixture of thorium and cerium oxides. These oxides glow in a peculiar way, emitting a greater proportion of rays of light-frequency than anything else does. A wire-gauze mantle in the gas flame would not give a hundredth of the light.

A gas mantle can be made in two ways. In one, "ramie fibre," obtained from a plant of the nettle family, is knitted into a long "hose," which is cut into lengths and sewn up to make the closed end. The fabric is soaked in a strong solution containing thorium and cerium nitrates with nitrates of beryllium and calcium and magnesium which strengthen the mantle.

The wet mantles are squeezed in a kind of mangle, dried on glass shapes and burnt off, leaving the fragile skeleton of thorium and cerium oxides. The skeleton is dipped in a kind of celluloid solution to give it strength enough to travel; this is burned off when the mantle is first used.

In the second method artificial silk is used and may be even better than ramie fibre.

No one has ever satisfactorily explained why this mixture of thorium oxide with a little cerium oxide should shine so brilliantly. It may be that the gas and air molecules actually combine on the cerium oxide surface and so impart their energy directly to it.

The hotter the flame, the better the light from the mantle. The best light is obtained by using high pressure gas, which can be mixed with much air without "popping back." It is possible to get a light of 27 candle-power for an hour from a cubic foot of gas on this system, whereas 18 c.p. would be good in a low-pressure gas mantle. The incandescent mantle is less and less used indoors, as it is much less convenient than electric filament lamps; all the same, it remains a popular way of lighting streets because of the convenience of having single lights of very high power and because of the cheapness of gas as a source of energy.

FILAMENT LAMP

The necessary portion of a filament lamp is a fine thread of conductive material which is heated by the passage of an electric current. The desirable thing about such a thread is that it shall bear heating to the highest temperature possible, because as the temperature is greater, so the percentage of the energy turned into light becomes greater too. The first electric lamps (Fig. 263) had filaments made of carbon. These were poor in comparison to the filaments of the modern lamp because they could not be heated above about 1750° C. without turning into vapour. The vapour was indeed slowly formed at this temperature, and condensed on the glass, cutting off the light.

The next stage was to discard carbon altogether and use a metal which had a very high melting point—above 2000° C.—and which would not turn into vapour. Metals with high melting points do not vaporise at all quickly. Their atoms are far heavier than those of carbon and so do not fly off so easily. First of all, osmium, a rare metal like platinum, was tried, then tantalum—another rare metal. They were improvements on carbon, but were very expensive. Another metal, tungsten (p. 72) had long been known. Its melting point was known to be tremendously high and it seemed most suitable for filaments, but it could only be obtained as a powder which could not be melted into a bar and drawn into wire. However, a way of doing this was discovered. The metal, made from wolfram—an ore found largely in Australia—is obtained as a fine dark grey powder. To turn this into a bar of tungsten, it is packed into a steel box and squeezed solid by tremendous force from a hydraulic press. This makes it into a very brittle bar, which can just be handled without breaking. Now this bar is placed in an atmosphere of hydrogen—the oxygen of the air combines with hot tungsten—and heated by a powerful electric current which makes the powder-grains stick together and make a metal rod. Then an ingenious machine heats it white hot and hammers it vigorously in a vacuum, and

Proportion of electrical energy turned into light.

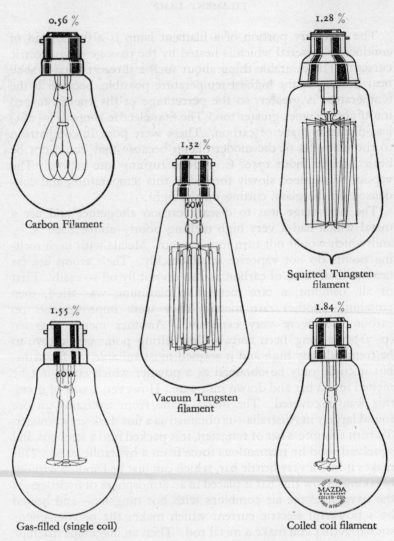

0.56 %

Carbon Filament

1.28 %

Squirted Tungsten filament

1.32 %

Vacuum Tungsten filament

1.55 %

Gas-filled (single coil)

1.84 %

Coiled coil filament

FIG. 263.—Lamps and their efficiencies. (Courtesy of Messrs. Mazda, Ltd.)

finally squeezes it into a solid rod. Next this is drawn into wire in the way illustrated in Fig. 19. The dies have to be made of diamonds; nothing else could stand the strain, and even these become worn in time. In the most modern type of lamp this tungsten filament is wound into a coil and this is coiled on itself. This process makes the hot filament cool much less quickly; consequently the same quantity of electricity makes it far hotter than a straight filament and as we have seen, the hotter the wire the greater is the proportion of electricity which is turned into useful light.

The spiral is cut into lengths and supported, as shown in Plate XXI. The lamp is then as completely evacuated as possible and argon or some other gas which does not affect tungsten is allowed to enter it.

The older lamps had their filaments in a vacuum, Now water evaporates more rapidly in a vacuum and so does tungsten. The only limit to the temperature to which you can heat the filament is the temperature at which tungsten turns into vapour appreciably. This thins the filament and finally breaks it. By filling the lamp with gas, the tungsten evaporates less and can safely be made hotter.

The modern filament lamp is unchallenged for domestic lighting. For street-lighting it competes in a fairly even contest with high-pressure gas-mantles and electric gas-discharge lamps.

WHY GASES GLOW

It is believed that the method of lighting which is likely to displace all others is lighting by glowing gas. We have already seen that an atom of gas emits light (pp. 435, 436) when an electron in the atom jumps from a "place" where it has much energy to a place where it has little. Very well, then; if an atom is to emit light, an electron must jump from a higher group to a lower group. Since there are only a limited number of "places" in each group, one must be vacant for this to happen; and heat or electricity is able to make a gas glow by turning electrons

out of their usual places and so making vacant spaces for the
other electrons to jump into. Suppose a gas is made very hot;
an electron absorbs energy from the force of the collision of the
heated atoms and hops to a higher group or even right out of
the atom. Immediately another electron in a higher group hops
into its vacant place, and in doing so sends out a quantum of
light. Electrical forces too (as in the neon-tube) may drag an
electron out of its place and allow another electron to jump back
into the vacant seat and so send out light.

It is the attraction of the nucleus that keeps the electrons in
the atom. Accordingly, those electrons in the innermost ring near
the centre of the atom are very difficult to force out, and they
can only be ejected by the gangster's method of bombarding
them with a stream of high-speed electron-bullets.

When one of these electrons is removed, an electron from the
second ring jumps instantly into the vacant place. Since the
jump means a big energy change, the frequency $\dfrac{E}{6.55 \times 10^{-27}}$
is very high and instead of light we have the very short wavelength X-rays. Less brutal but still vigorous treatment may
remove one of the second rank electrons. When its place is filled
from the third rank, a rather less violent energy change occurs and
the light frequency is less—we get ultra-violet rays. The third
rank electrons are fairly easy to displace[1], and when their places
are refilled no very great energy changes occur. These fairly small
energy changes give out the waves we call light, having wavelengths from 3600 to 7600 A.U. Now there are ninety-two kinds
of atoms. They all have the same sort of electron grouping as
the sodium atom (Fig. 262), but they have from one to ninety-
two places filled and their nuclei have very different attracting
powers. The result is that while each element gives out light
of certain fixed wave-lengths, the wave-lengths are different
for each. Any light can be sorted out into wave-lengths by
the spectroscope (pp. 463, 464), and by examining these wavelengths we can tell what kind of atom gave them out and how

[1] We are here considering a fairly small atom, e.g., sodium or neon.

vigorously it was being "excited" by electricity or by the heat-motion of the surrounding atoms. Thus, we can examine the light from a star, so far away that the light we see started on its journey before civilisation existed, and has travelled at 186,300 miles a second ever since. This light will probably contain the same set of wavelengths as we find in the light from glowing sodium vapour on earth; if so, we know that the incredibly distant tempest of glowing gas at the star's surface contains sodium! In this way we have found out that all the stars contain some of the same elements as the earth, and that there is no evidence that any of the stars contain elements not known on earth.

We now have some idea how a glowing gas emits light of a few fixed wavelengths; though neither we nor anyone else understands how an electron's jump in the atom causes a quantum of light to spring from the atom. However, we are in a position to see how the neon tube, the discharge lamp and the arc lamp give their light.

GAS DISCHARGE LAMPS

Gas discharge lamps are familiar to us all as the brilliant neon advertising signs and as those intensely brilliant blue-green mercury lamps which are now becoming so familiar.

The advantages of the gas discharge lamps are their showy colour and high efficiency. Fig. 264 shows clearly that the best gas discharge lamp can give about four times as much light for a given amount of electrical energy (and therefore money!) as the best filament lamp. Their disadvantage is the fact that a white light is not obtainable—at least without giving away most of the efficiency. The cold cathode tubes, e.g., neon signs, require a high tension electric current and so cannot be plugged straight in to the ordinary mains.

We have already seen that if an electron in an atom jumps from one state to another, a quantum of light is produced. The wavelength, i.e., the colour, of this light depends on the difference between the energy the electron has before and after its jump. Since an electron has only a few possible jumps, a particular

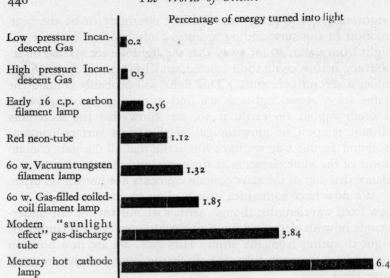

Percentage of energy turned into light

Low pressure Incandescent Gas	0.2
High pressure Incandescent Gas	0.3
Early 16 c.p. carbon filament lamp	0.56
Red neon-tube	1.12
60 w. Vacuum tungsten filament lamp	1.32
60 w. Gas-filled coiled-coil filament lamp	1.85
Modern "sunlight effect" gas-discharge tube	3.84
Mercury hot cathode lamp	6.4

FIG. 264.—The above table shows what proportion of the energy supplied to various lamps is turned into useful light. The incandescent gas-lamps are much more valuable than would at first appear, for electrical energy as supplied for lighting costs from 3 to 15 times as much as its equivalent in heat energy.

kind of atom can only give out a few "colours" of light. Thus the jumping electron in the sodium atom gives out yellow light, those in the neon atom give red light, those in the mercury atom give mainly green and violet light.

There are two chief kinds of gas discharge tube, the cold cathode and hot cathode type.

Fig. 265 shows a diagram of one of the red neon-tubes which are so much used for advertising and display. It has two electrodes usually of iron—and is filled with neon gas at a pressure of about 6 mm.—about $\frac{1}{120}$th of the pressure of the air. A tube

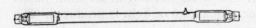

FIG. 265.—Cold cathode gas-discharge electric lamp (neon tube). (Courtesy of The General Electric Co., Ltd.)

commonly requires about 3000–4000 volts to keep it running, but up to 10,000 volts to start the discharge. The mains current has therefore to be transformed (p. 328) to high voltage and some device has to be adopted to give a high voltage when the tube is first switched on and a lower one later. The tube works in just the same way as the discharge tubes described on page 293, and glows for the same reason. But where air glows with a feeble blue light, neon with its different pattern of electrons glows with a brilliant red light.

One might think that these tubes would last for ever, but actually their life is not much more than a year's continuous work. If you read pp. 286, 293 again, you will realise that in a tube of this kind positive ions are always bombarding the negative electrode. This seems to knock off atoms of metal which deposit on the walls of the tube and entrap atoms of the gas. The gas thus gradually disappears.

These discharge tubes can be made to give many brilliant and beautiful colours. Pure neon gives a red light at higher pressures, up to $\frac{1}{20}$th of atmospheric pressure, and an orange light at lower pressures. The addition of mercury vapour gives a brilliant blue. If instead of neon nitrogen is employed, a beautiful pale apricot light is produced. Carbon dioxide gives almost a daylight white, helium a "heliotrope-white." The brilliant greens are obtained by use of mercury vapour in a tube made of fluorescent uranium glass which shines brilliantly green when ultraviolet light falls on it.

These cold cathode tubes are admirable for fashioning into long ornamental patterns, lettering, etc., but are handicapped for interior lighting by the need for high voltages. Till recently they have all been less efficient than filament lamps. The hot-cathode tube gives much more light per foot and also runs at low voltages, and is the most efficient lamp known. The secret is to emit electrons from the cathode. These will then ionise the gas and make it conduct.

For really brilliant lighting suitable for roads, etc., the vapour of sodium or mercury is employed. Sodium gives an intense yellow light of only one single wavelength, which makes everything look yellow or brown—for the things illuminated can only reflect the yellow light they receive.

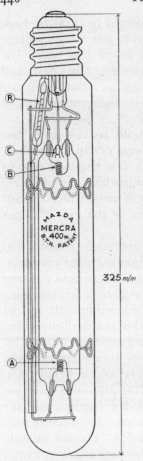

325 *m/m*

FIG. 266.—The Mazda
Mercra Lamp.
(Courtesy of Messrs.
Mazda Ltd.)

Fig. 266 shows the Mazda Mercra lamp, which consists of two glass envelopes, the space between the inner and outer envelope being a vacuum which, on the principle of the vacuum flask, causes the inner tube, once heated by the current, to remain at a high temperature. The inner tube contains an inert gas (e.g. argon) at about $\frac{1}{120}$ of atmospheric pressure and also some liquid mercury. When the alternating current is switched on, it first passes back and forth between the electrode C and the filament B, providing ions and electrons that enable the main arc to strike between electrodes A and B.

To prevent the main arc flowing between B and C a resistance R is incorporated. As the lamp warms up more and more of the mercury turns into vapour and an intense arc-like discharge passes between the two electrodes A and B.

As the current is alternating, these are alternately the anode and the cathode. The electrodes are heated by the arc current and emit electrons (c.f. p. 286). The mercury atoms glow as a consequence of their electrons being displaced and falling back (c.f. p. 435). The glow is exceedingly brilliant because much energy (400 watts) is concentrated in quite a small column of vapour instead of being spread over a long tube.

The mercury vapour lamps are extremely efficient and give, in their present form, a light which shows up colours fairly well. Their chief fault is a lack of red rays which causes any bright red

PLATE XXI

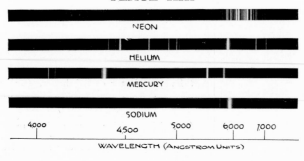

NEON

HELIUM

MERCURY

SODIUM

4000   4500   5000   6000   7000

WAVELENGTH (ANGSTROM UNITS)

(*Above*) The spectra of Neon, Helium, Mercury and Sodium. (*Below*) A continuous
spectrum. (By courtesy of G.E.C., Ltd.)

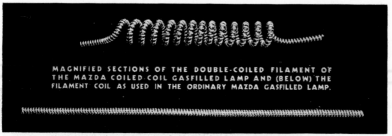

MAGNIFIED SECTIONS OF THE DOUBLE-COILED FILAMENT OF
THE MAZDA COILED-COIL GASFILLED LAMP AND (BELOW) THE
FILAMENT COIL AS USED IN THE ORDINARY MAZDA GASFILLED LAMP.

The coiled coil filament. (By courtesy of Messrs. Mazda, Ltd.)

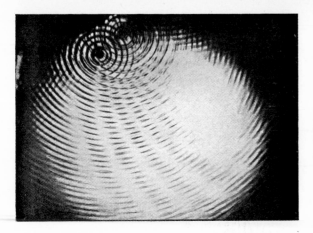

Mercury ripples set
in motion by two
points attached to a
tuning fork. Note
interference. (By
courtesy of the
*Philosophical Maga-
zine* and Messrs.
Taylor & Francis.)

PLATE XXII

(*Above*) Projector of lighthouse. (By courtesy of Messrs. Chance Bros., Smethwick.)

(*Centre*) Part of line spectrum (lithium carbonate in arc between copper poles) taken by quartz spectrograph. (By courtesy of Messrs. Adam Hilger, Ltd.)

(*Below*) All metal quartz prism spectrograph. (By courtesy of Messrs. Adam Hilger, Ltd.)

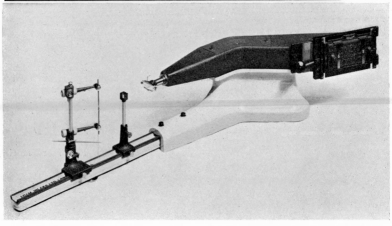

object to appear of a curious brown-red tint. They give, however, so much light for so little money that this defect is tolerated. The electric arc has already been explained and something has been said of its use for welding and furnace work. As a means of lighting, it

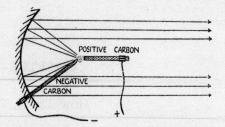

FIG. 267.—An arc as illuminant for a cinema projector.

has the great advantage of giving a small point of intensely brilliant light. Fig. 267 shows its use in the search-light of a cinema projector. The arc is struck so that the positive "crater" which emits most of the light faces into the reflecting mirror which—like the motor headlight mirror, concentrates it into a parallel beam which passes to the film (Fig. 300, p. 482).

The light of an arc lamp is too cold and brilliant for indoor lighting and needs too much attention; and it is disappearing even from the streets. But it keeps its position for projectors such as this, because it is very small and very brilliant.

CHAPTER XVI

How Light Travels

FROM the practical point of view, the important thing about light is the way it travels in straight lines—rays—and the way the direction of these lines is altered by reflectors and lenses. A ray of light such as enters a darkened room through a pin-hole in the blind, is a stream of electromagnetic waves done up in the packets we call quanta. The waves are so small compared with any distances we can see that we can treat a ray of light as if it travelled, when undisturbed, in a perfect straight line. A big long wave can easily bend round corners—this is familiar with wireless waves and with sound waves. Short wireless waves of a few metres are badly hindered by an interposing hill, while light waves of .00005 cm. bend round things so little that rather special apparatus is needed to show that they bend round them at all. That they do bend a little is shown by the fact that the edge of a shadow or the image on a screen or in a camera is never absolutely sharp. The light rays always spread a little each side of their course.

SHADOWS AND ECLIPSES

Shadows are made where light is stopped by something which will not transmit it. The shape of a shadow is easily made out if we remember that light goes in straight lines. Suppose we have a point of light (unobtainable—an arc lamp at a distance comes near it) and a circular plate. If light travelled in absolutely dead-straight lines, there would be a cone-shaped area behind the plate where there was absolute darkness. A screen would receive a shadow which might be a circle or an ellipse (or a parabola or a hyperbola) according to its position.

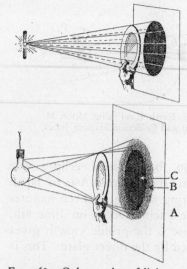

The edge of the shadow is not sharp like a razor edge because the light-source is not a point and because a little light gets round the corner. Most sources of light are by no means points. If we have a white electric bulb and let it throw a shadow of a dinner plate on a wall, we see a fully lighted part A, a half-lighted part B, the penumbra, and a dark part C, the full shadow or umbra. The most interesting shadows are those of the earth and the moon. The moon goes round the earth once a lunar month (29.53 days) and the earth and moon together go round the sun once a year (365.24 days). As 29.53 has no

FIG. 268.—Only a point of light can give a sharp-edged shadow· a large source of light gives a shadow grading from full light to darkness.

exact relation to 365.24, the two do not keep time and the earth, moon and sun go through all possible relative positions within their orbits. Now and again the moon gets between the sun and the earth, or the earth gets between the sun and the moon. In the first case we get an eclipse of the sun, in the second an eclipse of the moon. The moon is, oddly enough, almost exactly the right size and distance to screen the disc of the sun. The result of this is that unless you stand in the line through the centres of the sun and moon and look exactly head-on at the moon, you see the sun round the corner of it; and from only a very small bit of the earth can you see the sun entirely obscured—a total eclipse. The rest of the earth sees a bit of the sun showing round the corner of the moon—a partial eclipse. Partial eclipses are common enough. The dates on which they will occur can of course be calculated, and are to be found in almanacks such as Whitaker's. Total eclipses are pretty rare. There will not be another in

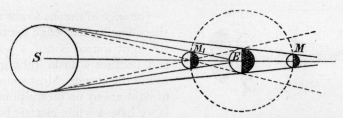

FIG. 269.—Moon M₁ eclipsing Sun S: Earth E eclipsing Moon M.
(Courtesy of Messrs. Edward Arnold and Professor Spencer Jones,
from the latter's *General Astronomy*.)

England until August 11th, 1999, but a total eclipse was
visible along a line stretching from Greece across Asia to Japan
on June 19th, 1936, while one lasting as long as seven minutes
will be visible in Peru and on the Pacific Ocean on June 8th,
1937. The real interest of an eclipse is the profile view it gives
of the surface of the sun unobscured by the direct glare. This is
illustrated in Plate XXXVII.

Eclipses of the moon are commoner because the earth's shadow
is much larger than the moon. The moon in a partial eclipse,
when it is in the penumbra of the earth's shadow, looks coppery-
red; and even in the umbra of the earth's shadow it does not
entirely disappear for the earth's atmosphere illuminated by
sunlight scatters enough light to reveal the moon's surface.

The calculation of the date and place of an eclipse can be very
accurately performed, for all the factors affecting the paths of
the earth and moon are very accurately known. It is possible to
work out when and where an eclipse will occur and, still more
interestingly, when and where they have occurred in the past.

Thus in Amos viii. 9, we find: "And it shall come to pass in
that day, saith the Lord God, that I will cause the sun to go down
at noon, and I will darken the earth in the clear day." Now the
only eclipse in the Near East at anything like the period at which
this prophet was writing was on June 15th, 753 B.C., which
dates the prophet and the events he mentions very accurately.
In the *Odyssey* there is a passage which is taken to indicate that
there was a total eclipse on the day Odysseus returned. There was

an eclipse which was total in or near Ithaca on April 16th, 1178 B.C., which date is in very fair agreement with historical evidence, which points to about 1200 B.C. for the sack of Troy.

A complete catalogue and set of maps of every eclipse from 1207 B.C. to A.D. 2161 has been published.

REFLECTION

We have already seen how water-waves and sound-waves can be reflected from a flat surface. Light waves too are reflected from any smooth surface, though things vary a great deal in their power of reflecting light. Thus, where polished black glass may reflect only a hundredth of the light falling on it, a silver mirror may reflect twenty-nine thirtieths. A dead-black surface is one that reflects no light at all. Black velvet is the nearest approach. Since it reflects no light, it is really only visible by contrast with other objects. Very effective stage disappearing-tricks are done by lowering a black velvet cover over a person standing in front of a black velvet curtain. The best reflectors are of metal. The reason why metals reflect light so well is that they are quite opaque and take a high polish.

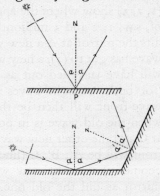

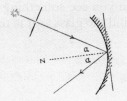

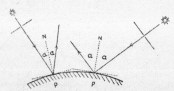

There is one very simple rule that tells us where light will go when it is reflected. It behaves like a perfect billiard ball hitting a perfect cushion. It bounces off at the *same* angle as it bounces on. A more scientific way to put

FIG. 270.—How light is reflected from surfaces of different shapes.

it is to say: Suppose the light-ray hits a mirror at some point P. Imagine a line PN drawn from P, "normal" to the mirror, that is, at right angles to it if it is a flat mirror, or at right angles to a flat surface touching it at the point P, if it is a curved mirror. The arriving light makes the same angle (a) with the line as does the departing light. Fig. 270 gives a good notion of how to apply this rule.

The reason why light obeys this law about reflection is supposed to be that each bit of the wave front starts a new wave as soon as it meets the reflector. Suppose the continuous black lines (1, 2, 3) show where the approaching wave has got to at intervals of, say, 1, 2 and 3 millionths of a second. As soon as the wave hits the mirror at A a new wave A' starts out. When the original wave has got to (3), a new wave will just be starting at B; wave A' will have travelled out as far as the old wave has travelled in (for both are light waves and go at the same speed). The new wave-front will then be the dotted line (5). In the same way, when the old wave is in position 4, a new wave will be starting at C and the other new waves will be at A'' and B'. So the wave-front will be A', B', C (line 6). It is easy to see (or to prove by geometry) that the new wave makes the same angle with the mirror as did the old one.

When you see something in a flat mirror, it appears to be as far behind the glass as it is really in front of it. The reason of this

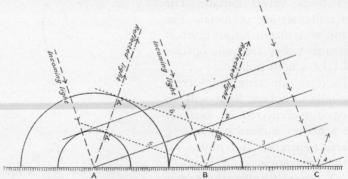

FIG. 271.—Illustrating the reflection of a beam of light.

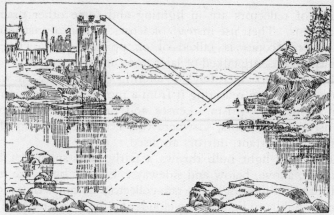

FIG. 272.—Why the reflection in water appears the same size as the object, but upside down.

is that the eye judges where a thing is by the angle and direction of the rays that come to it and takes it for granted that all rays have come straight to it in the ordinary way. It sees the tower in Fig. 272 beneath the water because the reflected rays make the same pattern on its retina or sensitive screen as a tower upside down beneath the water would make. This book has hardly the space to talk about the odd effects that reflections from mirrors can give. The kaleidoscope is perhaps worth mention, for it is easy to make and rather amusing. It consists of three rectangular mirrors set together to make a regular prism (Fig. ooo); any ray which comes out of the top opening to the eye will have been reflected from all three mirrors. So, any object inside it will appear to be repeated three times symmetrically at angles of 120°. But these reflections will appear to be repeated too, so any object is seen reflected dozens of times in a perfectly symmetrical fashion.

Looking at oneself in the glass is a universal pleasure: but the most interesting examples of

FIG. 273.—The Kaleidoscope.

the use of reflectors are in lighting and some other practical applications. Their use instead of lenses in optical instruments such as telescopes is talked of on pp. 496, 497. The very curious mirages are talked of later, too, under refraction.

There are two chief ways of altering the direction in which light is going—by reflecting it from a mirror or by refracting it with a lens or a prism. Lenses and prisms are much more expensive than mirrors, so where very accurate directing of the light is unimportant, mirrors are used.

An electric light bulb throws a fairly even sphere of light around it, above, below and sideways. Electric bulbs are much used for street-lighting. The rate-collectors do not wring money from the public to light up the clouds and the house-tops. Every ray of light that does not reach the street is as bad as so many shillings thrown into the sea. It is therefore imperative to throw the light on to the road. Most of my readers will be familiar with the little system of mirrors shown in Fig. 274. This catches much of the light which would otherwise illuminate the air or the lamp-post base and throws it on to the road.

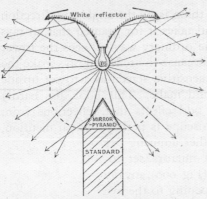

FIG. 274.—The action of the reflectors of a street lamp in directing into the illuminated area rays which would otherwise be wasted.

Motor-car headlights are designed to illuminate the section of road ahead of them for as great a distance as possible. The chief reason why light grows fainter as we get away from the source of it is that the beam of light gets wider, so that the same light has to cover a greater area. Thus, the total output of light given by a naked lamp is, at a distance of 200 yards away, spread all over a spherical area of about five hundred thousand square yards. If a reflector concentrates the light into a 20 yard circle, the same quantity of light now covers 300 square yards and is therefore sixteen hundred times as strong. If the light could be made to travel as a beam of *parallel* rays, it would

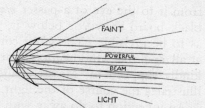

Fig. 275.—Reflection from the parabolic mirror of a motor-car headlight.

never spread out at all and would remain equally bright for miles —except in so far as mist and dust would stop it. The ideal beam for a headlight is a parallel beam to give distance, and also a fainter general illumination, so that the neighbouring objects such as the sides of the road can be seen.

Exactly this effect can be gained by a perfect "parabolic" mirror and a point-light inside it. A parabolic mirror is so curved that every ray from the focus is thrown in the same direction. Actually, no mirror is perfect and all lights have some size, so the best we can get is an approximation to the ideal.

The parabolic mirror cannot be made good enough for the lighthouse beam, which must carry for ten or fifteen miles: for these, a system of lenses and prisms is employed: these are described on page 476.

Fig. 276.—The non-reflecting shop-window. (Courtesy of Messrs. Sage & Co.)

A simple application of reflection which is becoming important is to the shop window. The reflection of the bright clouds, housetops, etc., from the surface of the window makes it difficult to see the darker interior. The modern shop often has a window curved as in Fig. 276. The window is so curved that any rays which are reflected from it to the eye of a passer *must* have come from the dead-black board above or below it; these, of course, are so faint as to be invisible. The gazer consequently cannot see the glass at all and the window does not seem to be there! Fig. 276, kindly supplied by Messrs. Sage & Co., the manufacturers, illustrates the course of the light.

An invention to do away with the maddening reflection from the glasses of the pictures in galleries is badly needed. The curved glass is hardly possible because the eye has become used to looking on the picture and frame and surrounding wall as a single unit.

REFRACTION

Light travels fastest through a vacuum, a tiny bit slower through air and decidedly slower through water or glass or any transparent liquid or solid. The result of this is that a ray of

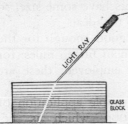

FIG. 277.—A ray of light is bent when it enters a glass block.

light turns sharply when it goes from air to glass, or from glass to water, or from any medium to any other medium. Fig. 277 shows a beam of light travelling through air into glass. Why does the slowing of light make it bend? Look at the diagram (Fig. 278). Suppose each of the points in the row on the wave front arrives at the glass surface, say, 10^{-11} seconds after the one before. In this time, light travels, through a vacuum, a distance of 3 mm. Suppose the wave-front begins to enter a thick plate of glass, and that in this glass the speed of light is half what it is in air. Then, when point 4 has reached the glass, point 3 will have been going through it for 10^{-11} seconds, point 2 for 2×10^{-11} seconds, etc., up to point 0, which will have been travelling through the glass for 4×10^{-11} seconds. Well, in glass the light goes $1\frac{1}{2}$ mm. in 10^{-11} seconds, so the circles of $1\frac{1}{2}$, 3, $4\frac{1}{2}$ and 6 mm. show where the waves will have got to and WF will be the new

wave front. Look at it
another way: o goes further
in glass and a shorter distance in air than 4. Since
travel is quicker in air, 4
catches up on o.

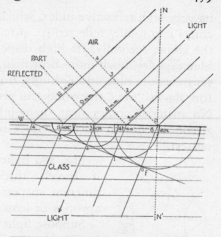

Thus, on going *from* a
material where light goes
more quickly *to* one where
it goes more slowly, the
light slews towards the
"normal" to the surface
(NN¹). The way we
measure this change is to
imagine a circle half made
of the material and to let
a ray come across it through

Fig. 278.—Why light is bent when it
passes from air to glass.

the centre. If we draw two lines parallel to the material's surface
from the normal to the place where the ray cuts the circle, then
the length of the long one (*a*) divided by the length of the short

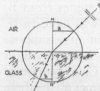

Fig. 279.—If light is
bent as illustrated
here on passing
from air to glass,
then $\frac{a}{b}$ is the refractive index of
the glass.

one (*b*) is called the *refractive index*, and tells
us how much the material bends light. All
this matters quite a lot. On it depends the
working of lenses, and therefore of cameras,
telescopes, microscopes, cinemas, etc.

The refractive index gives a useful way of
recognising gemstones and indeed most
transparent things. The discovery of "synthetic diamonds" was recently announced. A
few days later, the London Chamber of Commerce announced that the "synthetic diamonds" had a refractive index of 1.725; that of

diamond is 2.4175. The stones were stated to be white spinels,
complicated silicates, and, though beautiful, lacked the permanence,
brilliance and fire of the diamond. The brilliance of the diamond
and the reason it cannot be imitated by glass or anything else is, first,

its very high refractive index, which ensures that the light which enters it is totally reflected (p. 461) several times before it leaves the stone; secondly, its high dispersion, which means that the blue rays are much more bent than the red. Thus, the diamond separates the blue and red light from the white light and therefore shows "fire," the wonderful play of colour seen in the stone. No material comes near diamond for refractivity. The gem zircon, zirconium silicate, with a refractive index of 1.9 comes nearest.

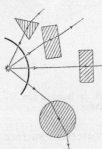

FIG. 280.—How light is bent when it passes through pieces of glass of various shapes.

Fig. 280 indicates how light is bent when it travels through transparent solids of different shapes; we shall come back to this apropos of lenses.

Suppose light is coming out of a solid or liquid into air. Let us suppose, for example, we are shining a light through the bottom of a glass basin full of water (Fig. 281). The refractive index is 1.333 or $\frac{4}{3}$, which means that for any one ray a must be $\frac{4}{3}$ of b. If the light shines from A it will travel out along the path A'. But suppose it shines from B. If a' is to be $\frac{4}{3}$ of b' the ray will have to be along the water surface. But now suppose we move the light to C; a'' cannot be $\frac{4}{3}$ times b'', for there is no room in the circle for so long a line, and actually the light is all *reflected* down again through the bottom of the basin.

You can easily observe the same thing with a glass

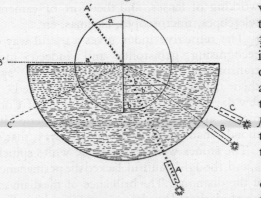

FIG. 281.—Illustrating total reflection.

FIG. 282.—Total reflection from a glass of water.

of water. You can only see *up* through the surface at certain angles (Fig. 282). This total reflection is used for several purposes. It gives a perfect mirror which can never tarnish as a metal mirror does and which has no colour and reflects 100% of the light. It is

used in prismatic binoculars (Fig. 313) to bend the light rays on themselves. It is also used in the glass reflectors used as pavement lights for basements. Fig. 283 shows how these reflectors throw the light into the room they illuminate.

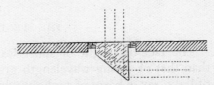

FIG. 283.—Total reflection utilised in a pavement light.

A very curious effect due to refraction and total reflection is the mirage. Air, like every transparent substance, slows light up, and the denser the air the more it slows it. Now cool air is denser than hot air at the same pressure, so as light passes obliquely from cooler air to hotter it is bent away from the normal (as when it travels from water to air (Figs. 281, 282).

Now suppose a man is riding over a baking desert plain. The air next the ground will be hottest and the air above cooler.

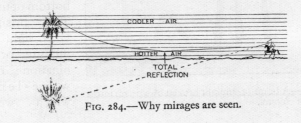

FIG. 284.—Why mirages are seen.

So a ray of light, say, from a palm tree is gradually bent until the angle at which it enters the hottest air is so small that it is totally reflected. It then rises till it meets the eye. Consequently the eye sees an inverted tree like a reflection in water (Fig. 284). The sky, too, is reflected from the layers of hot air and the bright reflection so simulates water that desert travellers find it hard to believe they are not really looking at a lake.

In India it is extremely difficult to do any accurate surveying by day, for the rays of light from the object observed to the theodolite are bent and the results are variable and unreliable. Consequently surveyors work at night when the air is cool and use bonfires or lamps as their points for observation.

THE SPECTRUM

The fact that light of short wavelength is more slowed up than that of a long wavelength gives us the spectrum. If a ray of light, say, a beam of sunlight which has passed through a hole in a shutter falls on to a screen, a white spot of light will be seen. Now, put a prism between the hole and the screen. The white spot of light disappears and a band of colour takes its place. At the top the light is violet shading through indigo, blue, green, yellow and orange, down to red at the bottom of the strip. The prism has taken light of the mixture or combination of all wave-lengths which we call

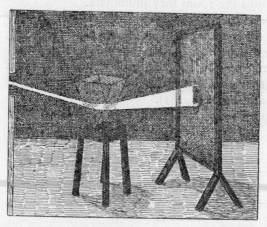

FIG. 285.—A beam of sunlight broken by a prism into a band of colours.

"white" light and sorted these out, bending the shortest wave-lengths most, and the longest least. The above arrangement is not a very good one because the light spot is big and the colours overlap. The arrangement in Fig. 286 is better. The light from a fine slit is focussed by a lens so that the light, if no prism were there, would form a sharp image of itself at B (just like the image in a camera). But the prism bends the light; and as light of each wavelength is bent to a different extent, as many images of the slit as there are wave-lengths appear on the screen. But if the slit is illuminated by white light or the light from any glowing solid like a filament lamp, the light will contain every wavelength and so the images of the slit overlap to make a band of colour—red, orange, yellow, green, blue, indigo and violet. In Fig. 286 only blue and red are illustrated for the sake of simplicity. But suppose instead of the light

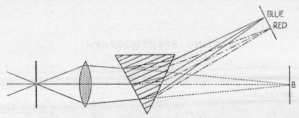

FIG. 286.—The principle of the spectroscope.

from, say, a filament lamp, we look at the light from a neon tube. By no means all wavelengths are here. The light is almost all of wavelengths 7245, 7174, 6506, 6402 and 6266 A.U. Consequently, for each of these wavelengths an image of the slit would be formed and the result when photographed is like Figure 000, each of the lines being an image of the slit made by light of some exact wavelength.

The spectrograph is a refinement of the simple apparatus shown in Fig. 286. Fig. 287 shows a modern spectrograph as used for photographing spectra. At the left-hand is the slit and in the brass tube are the lenses for focusing it. Then follows the prism. The photographic plate is set out at an angle to the tube

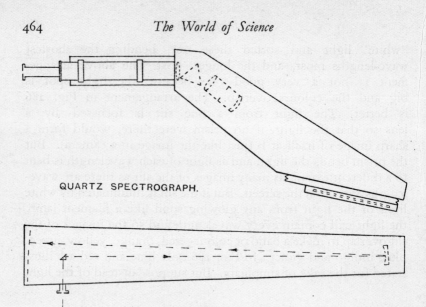

QUARTZ SPECTROGRAPH.

GRATING SPECTROGRAPH.
"EAGLE" MOUNTING.

RESEARCH DEPARTMENT.

ADAM HILGER, LTD., LONDON

FIG. 287.—Optical arrangement of Spectrographs. The quartz spectrograph above operates on the simple principle indicated in Fig. 286. A quartz prism transmits ultraviolet light: glass would not. A system of several lenses ensures accurate focusing. The photographic plate is slanted in order to separate the lines widely. Below, use of a grating in a spectrograph. Light enters below *via* a slit and is reflected to the grating which is ruled on a concave mirror. It separates the lights of different wave-lengths as described on p. 471 and focuses them as lines in a photographic plate at the left-hand end. (Courtesy of Messrs. Adam Hilger, Ltd.

in order to make the spectrum as long as possible and so separate the lines widely.

Instruments of this type enable the position of the lines to be charted to an accuracy of one in a million. Every kind of atom gives a particular set of lines which has been accurately charted. Thus the lines of neon are as in Plate XXI: sodium vapour on the other hand gives its light almost all of the wavelength, 5893 A.U.

Its spectrum consists, then, of one brilliant line (actually a double line) and a number of fainter ones. The spectrum of an element is a sort of signature by which it may be recognised whenever it gives out light.

An amazing amount of information has been gained by the spectrograph. First of all, it is our chief informant as to what the stars are like. As already mentioned on page 444, the spectrum of a star shows the familiar lines we know in the spectra on earth: these tell us the kind of atoms the stars contain. Secondly, spectra change as the temperature rises. The spectrum of sodium vapour in an electric arc ($3000°$ C.) shows more lines than the spectrum of sodium vapour in a gas flame (c. $1800°$ C.). By matching the spectra of the sodium vapour in the stars with the spectra obtained under different conditions on earth, we can get an idea of how hot the surface of a star is. But the information does not stop there. A magnetic field shifts the electrons in an atom slightly and so gives their "jumps" rather different energy. Different energy means different wavelength and the result is that an atom in a magnetic field shows two lines where it showed one before. The spectrum of the sun shows these split lines and we thus know that there is a big magnetic field on the sun's surface. The spectrum tells us still more. We worked out (p. 385) that if an observer approached a siren rapidly, its note sounded sharp (frequency increased), and when he went away from it the note sounded flat (frequency decreased). The same is true of the light from a star. Suppose we are receding from a star at 100 miles a second. It emits in the second, let us say, 10^{15} vibrations of a certain kind of light, say, that which we can see as the D-line in the sodium spectrum. These vibrations are spread out over 186,300 miles and would reach us in a second were we not receding. But as we are departing at 100 miles a second, only 186,200 miles of vibrations instead of 186,300 reach us. The light is therefore only of a frequency $\dfrac{1862}{1863}$ of what it would be from a sodium atom on earth. The practical result is that we can see the sodium line in the star's spectrum, a little shifted towards the red end where the bigger wavelengths and smaller frequencies are. We can measure the position of a spectral line with the accuracy of one in a million. It is quite easy then for an astronomer to find out whether we are receding from a star or approaching it: these results are of course very important in deciding how the various parts of the universe is moving.

On earth the spectroscope is also useful. It is the most delicate way of detecting minute traces of certain elements. If we want to be sure that some potassium chloride does not contain any sodium chloride, we pass electric sparks through a solution of it. If we do not see the D-line of sodium, we know the potassium chloride is exceedingly pure. Several new elements have been discovered by finding unknown lines in the spectrum of a mineral. Many more abstruse uses for it have been found: it has been the chief means of finding out how the electrons are grouped in the atom. Once Bohr had got at the principle of electron-jumps giving out light-quanta, it was easy to measure the wavelengths of the light appearing as lines in the spectra of the atoms, to calculate from this the energy of the jumps and find out how many different jumps were made. This has been our chief way of mapping the interior of the atom.

The rainbow is obviously a spectrum caused by the different colours in white sunlight being split up by raindrops, but it is not obvious why it should appear as a "bow." You only see a rainbow when the sun is fairly low in the sky and behind you. Suppose a ray from the sun enters a drop of rain (Fig. 288): it will be reflected and emerge. As it comes out, the red and blue rays will go at different angles. If there has been

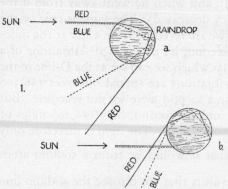

FIG. 288.—How raindrops split up white light.

one reflection, the red will be lowest and the blue will be highest, the reverse being true if there has been two reflections in the drop (Fig. 289). This explains the double rainbow, in which both single and double reflections occur. The result is, a spectrum with red at one side and blue at the other. Actually, the colours overlap and so the rainbow is not quite a true spectrum. Why is it a bow? The colours will be seen where the sun is at such an angle that the drop and you make the correct angle for the re-flection (about 42° 50'). Consequently, *all* drops which make this angle with you and the sun will give the colours and clearly these will lie in a circle.

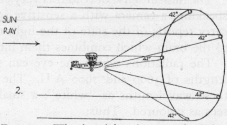

FIG. 289.—Why the rainbow is an arc of a circle.

If you stand on the ground, the part of this circle which is below you will be cut off, though from an aeroplane a complete circular bow might be seen. If the sun is higher than 42° 50' in the sky, no rainbow can be seen from the ground.

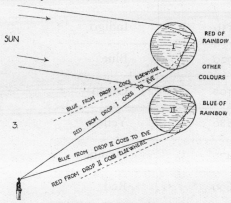

FIG. 290.—How each raindrop contributes one particular colour to the bow seen by any one person.

The eye cannot take in the red and blue rays from the *same* drop because they are yards apart by the time they reach the ground. Fig. 290 shows how each drop contributes a par-ticular colour according to its height, so forming the "bow." The secon-dary bow often seen outside the other is due to the double reflections, as in Fig. 288. It is easy to see that the ordinary bow will have red inside and blue outside, while the secondary bow will have the colours in the opposite order.

COLOUR

The human sense of colour is very curious. The eye is, roughly speaking, a camera with a sensitive screen at the back. Nerves carry reports of the state of the light on each part of this screen to the brain which combines them into a picture.

The radiations which the eye can see lie between the wavelengths of 3600 and 7600 A.U. The eye sees a mixture of all these wavelengths as "white": a small range of wavelengths it sees as coloured. Thus:

Light of wavelength	*is seen as*
Less than 3600 A.U.	Invisible
3600–4300	Violet
4300–4550	Indigo
4550–4920	Blue
4920–5500	Green
5500–5880	Yellow
5880–6470	Orange
6470–7600	Red
More than 7600	Invisible

Now the only difference between, say, red and blue light is a difference of wavelength: yet "red" and "blue" are so different that a man who had seen "blue" but had never seen "red" could never be made to understand what "red" was like. With sound there is a *steady* change of pitch as the wavelength shortens. Anyone who had heard C and its octaves C″ and C‴ would have a fair idea what C⁗ would sound like. But the colours corresponding to different wavelengths seem to have nothing in common.

Another very curious thing is that a mixture of wavelengths may give the same sensation as a single one. A mixture of blue and yellow light of wavelengths 4700 A.U. and 5700 A.U. looks green: a light of wavelength 5000 A.U. also looks green. Light of 7000 A.U. looks red, so does a mixture of all the visible lights except green (4920–5500)! We have really no idea how colour-vision works though we know very well what wavelengths of light give certain sensations.

You might think that a red neon-light and a piece of red cloth must both give the same red light and therefore give the same sensation to the eye. This is not necessarily true. The neon light gives light of wavelengths between 7245 and 6266, which therefore seems red. But the cloth has white light—red, yellow, green, blue and violet all mixed—shining on it. It may absorb—retain and turn into heat—the yellow, green, blue and violet and let the red light pass on. But it equally well might keep the greenish-blue component of the light and let the red-yellow-indigo-violet mixture pass on. This, we also see as "red."

For this reason, if we mix blue and yellow light we get a quite different result from that obtained when we mix blue and yellow paints. Suppose we focus a patch of yellow (5740 A.U.) light on a screen and focus a patch of blue light (4820 A.U.) on top of it, the light from the screen has wavelengths 5740+4820 A.U., and appears to us as *white*. If we mix yellow paint and blue paint, they appear green. The reason of this is that the yellow paint absorbs and destroys all the white light except the yellow light and a little *green* and red: the blue pigment absorbs and destroys all the light except blue and a little *green* and violet. So between them they absorb and destroy everything except the green wavelengths. Two coloured lights, which, if mixed, give white, are said to be "complementary." The following gives a list of these colours. If we mix light of colour A and colour B, we get white. If we take colour A from white light we get colour B and vice versa.

A.	B.
Red.	Greenish blue.
Orange.	⎰ Shades of
Yellow.	⎱ violet.
Greenish yellow.	Violet.
Green.	Purple.

If you stare steadily at a bright colour for some time, your faculty for seeing that colour gets tired out and if you look at a white wall you see a patch of the complementary colour, which is simply plain white less the colour you are now unable to see.

INTERFERENCE COLOURS

It is well known that colours are often seen where there is no coloured material at all. Soap-bubbles, oil-films on water, mother-of-pearl are all examples of these colours. We find they are always connected with very thin films of material and it is natural to suppose they are the result of interference. Fig. 257 shows how the thin film of liquid in a soap-bubble reflects light of a certain wavelength in some parts and destroys it by interference in another. Suppose the film at some point is 5400 A.U. (.000054 c.m.) thick. This is just a wavelength and a half of violet light, and so violet light reflected at that point will be extinguished. But the other wavelengths in ordinary white light will not be extinguished, because the film is not $\frac{1}{2}$ or $1\frac{1}{2}$ or $2\frac{1}{2}$ times their wavelength. Accordingly, the light reflected is white without violet which appears yellowish green. Since the soap-bubble varies in thickness, every colour will have some place where it is extinguished by interference and so every possible complementary colour appears somewhere on the bubble. The colours of oil films on water have the same origin. Mother-of-pearl is a pile of very thin layers of calcium carbonate (marble) laid on to the inside of the oyster shell. These are so thin that they cause interference like a soap-bubble.

Interference is used in a very valuable arrangement called the diffraction grating which is now often substituted for the prism of a spectroscope, as being suitable for very short and very long waves, which do not easily go through glass. It is not very difficult to understand its principle. A diffraction grating is simply a piece of glass ruled by a diamond point with, say, 15,000 lines to the inch. This, naturally, is difficult and expensive and most gratings are casts from these originals. Imagine in Fig. 291 (*a*) a grating with 14,000 lines to the centimetre with yellow light of wavelength .000058 cm. shining on it. The waves

Yellow light of wavelength .000058 cm.   Blue light of wavelength .00004 cm.

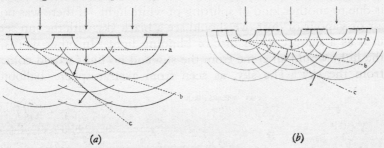

(*a*)   (*b*)

FIG. 291.—Diagram to show why light is bent when it passes through a grating. Note that the longer the wavelength the more it is bent. The scale is about 10,000 times actual size.

pass through the little apertures and spread out in new ripples as they go. Now, the direction of a ray of light is the perpendicular to the wave front (like that of a water wave); so the ray of light will go first of all straight on (*a*). But the lines (*b*) and (*c*) are also lines of wave fronts. So the light will split up into several rays travelling in directions which depend on the fineness of the grating, and the wavelength of the light. Now, Fig. ooo (1) is a representation 10,000 times magnified, of what happens when yellow light (5800 A.U.) passes through a grating. Fig. ooo (2) shows what happens when deep blue light 4000 A.U. does the same. It is easy to see that the blue light is less deflected than the yellow. This is just like the action of the prism (p. 463), except that this deflects the shortest waves most and the grating deflects them least. The rays of different wavelengths are deflected through different angles and so will appear as a spectrum.

Any regular pattern, if fine enough, will act as a grating and so split white light into its component colours. The brilliant colours of the peacock's tail and iridescent beetles and dragon-flies and the wings of the brilliant blue Morpho butterfly (which are made into jewellery) are simply due to fine ribbings and markings which make them into diffraction gratings. There is no colouring matter or dye there at all: the peacock splits up white light to get its colours!

The fact that the sky is blue and that dawn and sunset are red, is due to another kind of splitting of white light. If there was no air or vapour or dust, we should see a black sky with the sun set in it as a sharp circular disc of blinding light. In other words, the light would all come from the sun and no light would come from the sky. The sky, as seen from a stratosphere balloon

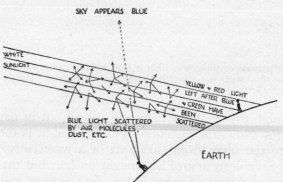

FIG. 292.—Why the sky is blue and dawn and sunset are red and yellow.

14 miles up appears nearly black. The sky gives out light because the sun's rays are scattered by dust particles, by water droplets and even by the tiny irregularities of density resulting from the movement of air molecules. Light waves fall on these particles and the illuminated particles send out new light in every direction. Now it can be proved that short waves are much more easily caught by particles than long waves. Actually the blue part of the sun's radiation is sixteen times as easily scattered as the red. Consequently the light that comes from the sky at an *angle* to the sun's rays is mostly the scattered blue rays: while rays which have passed through a great length of air, as at sunset or dawn, are robbed of their short waves, only the red being left. Since the long red rays are the least scattered by particles, they have the best fog-piercing powers and red neon-lamps are used at aerodromes to show the way to incoming planes. These are much more easily visible than white lights and do not make the fog into an opaque luminous wall.

The red and yellow fog-lamps used by cars have the same purpose, but the loss of light counterbalances any advantage due to their superior penetration.

LENSES

Lenses are pieces of transparent material of which the surfaces are parts of spheres or planes. The surface of a lens may be said to have a *radius* of curvature which is the radius of the sphere of which it is part. As lenses are an essential part of every optical instrument—microscope, camera, telescope, etc.—it is worth seeing how they are made. The glass for a lens is kept melted in a large crucible for a long time so that tiny air-bubbles and specks of solid can settle out, and great care is taken to see that it is perfectly mixed so that every part of the glass shall be able to bend light as much and as little as every other. The charge of glass is made into thick sheets and these are cut into bits. Very often as much as two-thirds of a charge of glass has to be rejected as imperfect. The glass is then cut by grinding-wheels, fed with car-

borundum powder, roughly to the shape of the lens and ground to
something near the finished shape. The lenses are then stuck with
pitch on to a round knob, which is spun round and round, while a
hollow cup-shaped tool is rocked backwards and forwards across
it. The tool is fed with fine polishing powder and water and in an
hour and a half all the lenses are ground to parts of spheres of the
same radius as the tool.

The lenses are tested by pressing them on to a glass shape
which would exactly fit a perfect
lens. If the lens exactly fits the
shape, no Newton's rings (p. 429)
can be seen. If it is very nearly a
fit, about two rings can be seen
showing the lens is not more than
two wavelengths of light ($\frac{1}{2000}$th
centimetre) in error, and this is
usually the best aimed at. The
worst fault of a lens is that it
should be distorted—not a perfect
sphere—in this case the Newton's
rings will not be circular but have
some irregular shape.

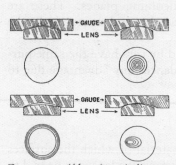

Fig. 293.—(Above) grinding a
number of small lenses. (Below)
testing lenses by use of Newton's rings.

The effect of a convex (bulging)
lens is to make light rays either
converge more or diverge less.
If a lens is hollow on one side and
bulging on the other, the sharper
curve overcomes the effect of
the other. Fig. 294 shows clearly why this must be. The
course of the light rays is drawn out on the principle of
"a/b" (Fig. 279) being always the same for any particular material.
The drawing shows too that a beam of parallel rays, falling on
the *central* part of a convex lens, will be brought to a single point
of light at the focus. The rays from the outer part of a thick
lens are not properly focussed: this effect, called spherical aberration, is the reason why "stops" are always used in optical

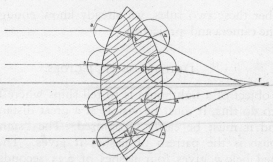

FIG. 294.—Why a thick lens brings to a focus parallel rays which fall near its centre but not those which fall near its edges. This effect is called spherical aberration.

instruments to remove them. If the rays which fall on such a lens are converging, they will come to a point nearer to the lens than the focus (Fig. 295 (2)). If they are diverging fan-wise, they will either come to a point further away than the focus (Fig. 295 3), or if the source of the light is at the focus (4), the light will become a parallel beam or if the source of light is nearer than the focus they will diverge (5). This state of affairs is important to grasp as the action of the camera and the magnifying glass depend on it.

Now it is pretty clear that all the rays which go through the *centre* of the lens go on in the same direction unchanged, and we can also see from Fig. 295 that all the rays which are parellel to the axis of the lens go to a point called the focus. The more sharply the lens is curved, the nearer to it is the focus. If we

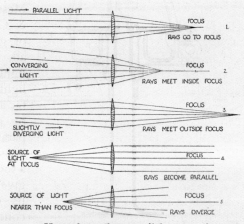

FIG. 295.—How a lens affects parallel, converging and diverging light-rays.

remember these two rules, we already know enough to understand the camera and projector.

LIGHTHOUSE PROJECTORS

The object of a lighthouse is to tell ships where they are. In order to do this, it must be visible at a great distance—even in fog; and it must be easily recognised. The "signature" of a lighthouse is the pattern of flashes it gives. Thus the light described below gives four flashes of 0.23 seconds with three short dark intervals of 2.43 seconds and a long dark interval of 11.43 seconds. A lighthouse, which stands where it is buffeted by the waves, is usually a tower of masonry of great weight and strength; however, the essential part of it is the lantern. Fig. 296 shows a small lighthouse lantern made by Messrs. Chance Brothers & Co. It has several points of great interest. First of all, it is necessary that a lighthouse should send a light which should carry as far as possible, and we saw on p. 457 that a beam of parallel rays could do this. This lantern has in its centre a 500-watt lamp. This would give no great visibility on its own, but when it is concentrated by lenses and prisms into beams, each

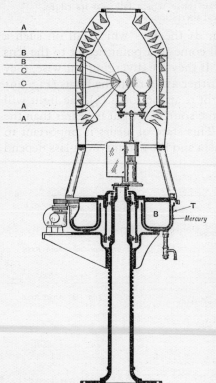

FIG. 296.—Lighthouse lantern (courtesy of Messrs. Chance Bros & Co.).

of these shows 608,000 candle-power and the light, if on a high enough place, can be seen 38 miles away in clear weather. There are two lamps; for a lighthouse must never be extinguished. If the filament breaks in the centre one, the spare is automatically brought into use. A lens can only give a narrow beam because of the spherical aberration already mentioned, but the lighthouse supplements its lenses by prisms at such an angle that the effect of refraction and total reflection sends the beams which fall on them in the same direction as that sent out by the lens. Thus ray A is reflected by a prism, ray B is refracted by a prism, and ray C refracted by a lens, but all go in the same direction as the line from the light to the middle of the lens. As there are four panels, this arrangement gives four beams.

The lamps remain still, but the lantern with the lenses and prisms turns round every twenty seconds. The four beams turn with it and therefore, as they pass a ship, they are seen as four flashes of 0.23 seconds, with three short dark intervals of 2.43 seconds and a long dark interval of 11.43 seconds.

Each lighthouse has a different arrangement of beams. It is essential that it should turn very steadily and very easily despite the fact that it is necessarily heavy. The ingenious notion of floating the lantern on mercury is employed. A trough T is filled with mercury and the hollow base (B) of the lamp floats on it! Mercury is so dense that very little of it will suffice to float the heavy lamp support. The turning is done by an electric motor and this is supplied by two generating sets of petrol-engine and dynamo—two, because one must always be ready if the other breaks down. Ships depend on the light for a warning of danger; it must never fail.

THE CAMERA

In understanding the camera, a few very simple experiments will help. Cut a hole in the side of a cardboard box and put a strong lens in it—the lens from the eye-piece of an opera glass will do very well. Bend a piece of card so that it stands upright

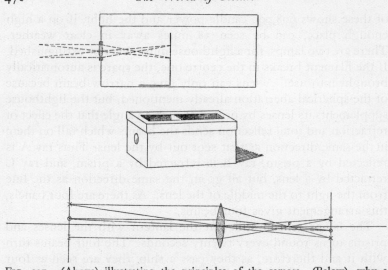

F<small>IG</small>. 297.—(Above) illustrating the principles of the camera. (Below), why a camera gives a reversed image.

behind the lens and can be slipped backwards and forwards. Point the arrangement at a distant object—say the trees or housetops seen through the window. Now move the cardboard slide back and forth till you see a clear picture on it. The picture is upside-down and left-to-right. You can see that if you had a sensitive plate instead of the cardboard and kept all light away except what came through the lens, it would be a simple camera. Now point the thing at some near bright object, say a vase on the table. To get a clear picture you must move the card back considerably. The further the object from the lens, the nearer is the image. Fig. 298 shows why the camera must be lengthened to take a near object: the nearer the object, the more the rays diverge and the less the lens makes them converge. This is the reason why a camera must have some arrangement (usually light-proof bellows) by which the plate can be placed near the lens for distant photography and far from the lens for close photography. Actually, no difference is noticed beyond about 50 feet; so a fixed camera will take sharp photographs at all

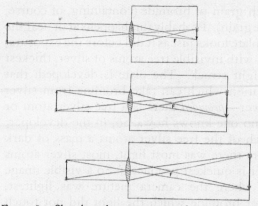

distances beyond this.

This is the principle of the camera. A practical camera has many refinements. First, it has a shutter which allows light to enter for a very short fixed time. Secondly, it has a stop which cuts off more or less of the outside of the lens.

FIG. 298.—Showing why a camera must be made longer if near objects are to be photographed.

Thirdly, it requires a focusing arrangement, and fourthly some contrivance for changing plate or film without exposing it to the light.

The sensitive plate or film is a very remarkable thing of which by no means everything is yet known. The coating of the plate is gelatine in which are suspended tiny crystals of silver bromide, a substance whose molecules are made of one atom of silver and one of bromine. The silver bromide particles have sensitive specks of silver sulphide on them: the sulphur comes from the gelatine, which is not merely a way of sticking the silver bromide to the plate. Now, when light reaches the plate, it strikes the silver bromide particles and in some unexplained way increases the energy of one, two or many molecules of silver bromide on each grain, so that they fly to bits and leave a few

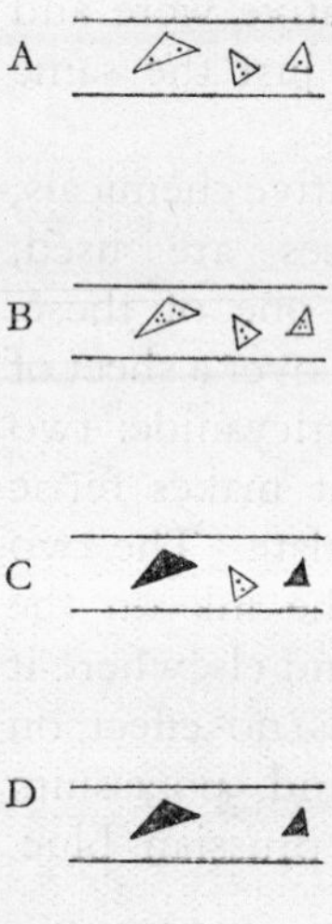

A

B

C

D

FIG. 299.—A sensitive film. (A) Crystalline grains of silver bromide. (B) The two outer grains have been exposed to light and contain numerous free atoms of silver. (C) Development reduces these latter grains to metallic silver. (D) Fixing removes the unchanged bromide grains but leaves the silver.

atoms of silver on each grain of bromide (containing, of course, millions of atoms to the grain). Probably this happens at or near the sensitive specks. The plate looks just as it did before the exposure, but it is really freckled with invisible free atoms of silver, thickest where the strongest light struck. The plate is developed: that is, immersed in a solution which can take bromine from silver bromide and leave silver—*provided* there is a free silver atom or two to lead the way, no one knows how. So, in the developer, there forms round each of the free silver atoms a mass of dark coloured silver. Where there was most light, most silver atoms were formed and silver is quickest produced. So a visible image or negative, darkest where the camera picture was lightest, remains. But the silver bromide which the light did not touch still persists and would slowly blacken in light. Accordingly, we fix the negative by putting it in something which will combine with and dissolve silver bromide very quickly, but silver only very slowly. "Hypo," sodium thiosulphate, is used. This leaves on the plate only clear gelatine and a dark silver image. Since hypo does very slowly combine with and dissolve silver, it must be well washed out—if this is not done, the negative will fade.

The process of printing on gaslight paper makes a positive with dark parts where the clear parts of the negative were and vice versa. Its developing and fixing works on just the same principle as that of the photographic plate.

Silver bromide and iodide are the only *rapid* sensitive chemicals, but several dozen other photographic processes are used, mostly for printing. The blue print process is one of these. In making a blue-print of a tracing, this is stretched over a sheet of paper containing ferric oxalate and potassium ferricyanide: two chemicals which do not affect each other. Light makes ferric oxalate lose carbon dioxide and make ferrous oxalate. The two sheets are exposed to a brilliant light: where the ink on the tracing protects the ferric oxalate, it is unaltered and elsewhere it becomes ferrous oxalate. Now ferric oxalate has no effect on potassium ferricyanide, but ferrous oxalate and potassium ferricyanide in presence of moisture, turn into prussian blue.

PLATE XXIII

(*Left*) Diseased tobacco leaf. The diseased patches can be rendered visible by photography in infra-red light but not in normal light. (*Right*) The Cuillins, Isle of Skye, (*above*) taken by normal light, (*below*) by infra-red rays. (*Left:* By courtesy of Mr. F. C. Bawden, of the Potato Virus Research Station, Cambridge; both by courtesy of Messrs. Ilford, Ltd.)

PLATE XXIV

Photograph taken in the dark by the infra-red heat rays from two electric irons. (By courtesy of Messrs. Ilford, Ltd.)

An alteration in a cheque invisible by ordinary light (*above*), but clearly shown in ultra-violet light (*below*). (By courtesy of British Hanovia, Ltd., Slough.)

$$\underset{\text{Ferric oxalate}}{
\begin{array}{c}
\text{O} \quad \text{O} \\
\| \quad \| \\
\text{O}\!-\!\text{C}\!-\!\text{C}\!-\!\text{O}
\end{array}
}$$

Ferric oxalate

$$+ \text{O}=\text{C}=\text{O} + \text{O}=\text{C}=\text{O}$$

Ferrous oxalate
and carbon dioxide

Accordingly, when the print is done, it is washed in water and turns bright blue except where the black lines of the tracing have protected it. The finished print is in white on a blue ground.

The magic-lantern or cinema projector is a camera. The screen is the plate. The whole room is the box of the camera. The lens of the projector is the lens of the camera, and the slide or the cinema film is the object being photographed.

Fig. 300 shows the arrangement of light, film, lens and screen. The principle of a projector is simple enough: the practical difficulty is that all

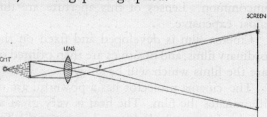

FIG. 300.—Course of light in projector.

the light on the screen has come from the film or slide. Now the film may have an area of about $1\frac{1}{4}$ square inches and the screen of 12,000 square inches; and in this case the film must be ten thousand times as brightly lit as the screen. Consequently, if the image on the screen is to be clear and bright, torrents of light must be poured on the film or slide. Light cannot be got

16

without heat rays and it is far from easy to prevent films from
being overheated in a projector. With inflammable films this
would be a real danger were it not that films are run through the
projector so quickly that they have not much time to heat up.

MOVING PICTURES

The cinema camera is a camera which takes some sixteen
successive pictures every second. The film is moved *step by step*
across the back of the camera proper. Each time the film stops,
a shutter between the lens and film opens, and an exposure is
made; before it moves on, the shutter closes. The effect of this
process is to take a negative of the familiar cinema film consisting
of successive pictures of a scene, each showing it as it appeared
$\frac{1}{16}$th second after the last one. Obviously the exposure cannot
be more and must be less than $\frac{1}{16}$th second. Accordingly, brilliant
lighting must be employed to get the best effect. Press cameras
have to be operated in dull weather. These have remarkable
lenses almost as big as the picture they take in order to admit
plenty of light. f 3.5 is the least aperture used, and f 1.5 is not
uncommon. Lenses of this aperture are difficult to make and
most expensive.

Cinema film is developed and fixed on the same principle as
ordinary films, and positives are then printed on similar film: these
are the films which will be shown.

The cinema projector has a powerful arc or other light which
illuminates the film. The heat is very great and if the film stops
it is likely to catch alight; on account of this fire danger a fireproof
projection room is used. The projector has two continuously
moving "feed sprockets" which wind the film off and on to
the spools; these keep a free loop of film in the projector. This
film passes through the gate, which defines the edge of the
picture and holds the film flat and at the right distance from
the focussing lens, which of course works on the same principle
as appears in Fig. 300. The essential part of the mechanism is the

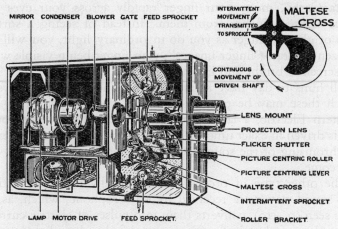

MIRROR   CONDENSER   BLOWER   GATE   FEED SPROCKET

INTERMITTENT MOVEMENT TRANSMITTED TO SPROCKET

CONTINUOUS MOVEMENT OF DRIVEN SHAFT

MALTESE CROSS

LENS MOUNT
PROJECTION LENS
FLICKER SHUTTER
PICTURE CENTRING ROLLER
PICTURE CENTRING LEVER
MALTESE CROSS
INTERMITTENT SPROCKET
ROLLER BRACKET

LAMP   MOTOR DRIVE   FEED SPROCKET

FIG. 301.—Small cinema projector. Note condenser lens to direct light on to film, blower to cool film by air blast. (From material kindly supplied by Messrs. Ross, Ltd.)

intermittent sprocket and shutter. The intermittent sprocket is made to stop and start by the ingenious "maltese cross" movement (inset); each time the wheel revolves, the pin on it will turn the maltese cross sharply and then leave it still till the pin comes round again. The maltese cross drives the intermittent sprocket and this pulls the film past the gate step by step. So that the audience shall not see a blur when the film moves a rotating "flicker shutter" cuts off the light when the sprocket is pulling the film along. So the screen has on it a still picture for, say, a twentieth of a second, then a moment of darkness, then another slightly different still picture, and then another moment of darkness. The audience does not see this, for the nerve endings of the eye take about $\frac{1}{8}$ of a second to *stop seeing* a picture that has vanished. So the eye sees four or five cinema-pictures at once and blends them together, seeing the step by step differences between them as a steady glide. If you want to convince yourself that cinema pictures are discontinuous, next time you are in a cinema and can bear to take your eyes off the Prime Minister or

Greta Garbo, move your finger rapidly across your eyes and about eighteen inches from them. Instead of seeing a sort of strip of ghostly finger as you do in ordinary light, you will see a dozen separate "finger-images"; your finger being visible when the screen is bright and invisible when it is dark.

All films to-day have sound effects. There are two ways in which these may be produced. In the system typified by the Western Electric, a large gramophone record plays the sound and is driven in exact time with the film: the problem of the exact synchronising of the sounds and movements has been very well overcome.

The other type of process is scientifically more interesting. The sound-waves are received by a microphone, which, as we have seen (p. 410), converts them into pulses of electric current. The pulses of electric current are amplified and made to work a neon-tube. This glows alternately brightly and faintly as the pulses of current traverse it. The light of this lamp is focused on a strip of film beside the picture and so makes a record of the sound-wave in bright and dark lines. As the film passes through the projector, the light from a lamp is directed through the film and on to a photo-electric cell which passes a current when light shines on it but does not do so in darkness. So as the bright and dark bands are focused on to this, pulses of current flow through it, which when led through a loud-speaker reproduce the original sound.

The photo-electric cell is an interesting arrangement and can be made to do many amusing tricks. It is a glass bulb containing some of the metal potassium (or

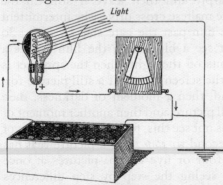

Fig. 302.—When light falls on the potassium (black) in the glass bulb, it ejects electrons from it. The positive ring attracts these, thus a current flows.

rubidium). Light knocks out electrons from this. It is easy to see from Fig. 302 that when light acts on the potassium and ejects electrons from it, these will flow to the positive electrode which attracts them. These electrons will travel to the battery (or to earth), while electrons from the battery will take the place of those ejected from the potassium. In fact, a current will flow and a sensitive galvanometer in the circuit will detect it.

The photo-electric cell is an "electric eye" and has found very many uses. It is very difficult to measure the brightness of light exactly by any means which employs that fallible instrument the eye. But a photo-electric cell gives an easily measurable current which depends on the brightness of the light which shines on it. It can be used for many simple inspection jobs. Suppose cans with dark labels are to be packed in cases, and are travelling along a conveyor to the packing room. A photo-electric cell will "see" the bright unlabelled can and its current can operate a switch which makes a machine remove it.

MICROSCOPES

The reason why a lens magnifies will be more clearly seen when we realise what the eye is. The eye is simply a camera. Fig. 303 shows its chief parts. The "iris" is a stop to regulate the amount of light. It opens automatically in a dull light thus giving more light but worse definition. If you look at print in a room so dark that you can only just see it, it looks blurred because the worst parts of the lens—round the

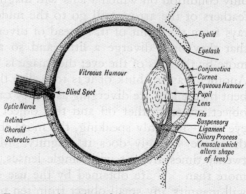

Eyelid
Eyelash
Vitreous Humour
Conjunctiva
Cornea
Aqueous Humour
Blind Spot
Pupil
Optic Nerve
Lens
Retina
Iris
Choroid
Suspensory
Sclerotic
Ligament
Ciliary Process
(muscle which
alters shape
of lens)

FIG. 303.—A section of the human eye (*see* pp. 894–899).

edge—are in use. In brilliant light, the iris closes to perhaps $\frac{1}{6}$ of the area and we see distinctly. Behind the iris is a lens of elastic, gristly and perfectly transparent material. This lies in a ring of muscle which by contracting can make the lens more nearly a sphere. This makes it bend the light more and so focus near objects clearly. When the muscles relax, the lens becomes thinner and less curved and so can focus distant objects. At the back of the eye is the retina, a sensitive screen about which we do not understand much; more is said about it on pp. 894–899. It is full of nerve-endings which report to the brain whether light is falling on them or not and so inform it of the picture which the lens throws (upside-down and right to left!) on the screen or retina. Now the size an object appears to be obviously depends on the space its image fills on the retina. Look at Figure 304 and imagine the lens L is

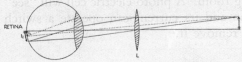

RETINA

not there. The object is giving out diverging rays of light. These go to the eye and form an image I_1. The dotted lines show how the

FIG. 304.—Why a convex lens magnifies.

light goes. But there is actually a lens between the eye and the object, the object being nearer to the lens than its focus; this is the only condition on which a lens will magnify. The rays from the feathers of the arrow still go to the middle of the eye, but the rays from the point of it, instead of diverging a lot, are bent so that they only diverge a little and so are bent inward much more by the lens of the eye; the image is therefore much bigger. Another way to think of it is to realise that the rays after being bent by the lens are diverging as if they came from a much larger object rather further off and this object is, in effect, what the eye sees. Roughly speaking, the more sharply a lens is curved, the more strongly does it magnify. Magnifications of about twenty times are got with single lenses, but usually powers of more than ×6 are obtained by the use of a microscope which will magnify any small object from ten to about three thousand times. Bigger magnifications could be reached, but they are not useful because a light wave can only show up distinctly an object of more than $\frac{1}{3}$ of its length and an object of this size can be seen very distinctly if magnified 1000 times. Actually a magnification of 650 brings out all possible detail; higher powers show no more, they merely make the object larger but less distinct. If ultra-violet light with, say, $\frac{1}{4}$ the wave-length of light is used, things four times as small can be seen, but the work is difficult—firstly, because this ultra-violet light does not penetrate glass and therefore all lenses have to be made of

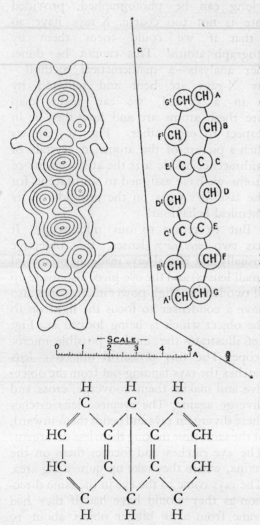

Fig. 305.—(Left) The contours indicating the average number of electrons at each point in an anthracene molecule. The electrons will be most frequent where there is an atom, so if the figure is considered as a mountain-map the peaks are atoms. (Right) The interpretation of the contours as a chemical formula, a picture of the molecule a hundred million times magnified. (Below) The formula as usually printed. This is the same as the right hand figure but seen from a different angle. (Courtesy of Professor J. M. Robertson, from *The Crystalline Structure of Anthracene* in the Proc. Roy. Soc., Vol. 140.)

rock crystal, which is very hard and expensive to grind; secondly, because ultra-violet light is invisible and has to be recorded on a photographic plate. In this way a thing .00004 cm. long can be photographed, provided the grain of the plate is not too coarse. X-rays have so small a wavelength that if we could focus them by lenses we could photograph atoms! This cannot be done, but by using Fourier analysis—a mathematical method— to calculate the way X-rays are bent and reflected by the layers of atoms in a crystal, we can really map out a picture of where these atoms are and how they lie in respect to each other. Fig. 305 shows such a picture of the atoms in crystals of anthracene, beside it is the arrangement of atoms we have assigned to anthracene for the last fifty years on the grounds of its chemical behaviour!

But to return to our microscope. It has two *necessary* lenses, the objective (usually but not always made up of several small lenses) and the eye-piece also made up of two lenses. High-power microscopes also have a condenser to focus the light on to the object which is being looked at. Fig. 306 illustrates the simplest possible microscope. The tiny powerful objective lens catches the rays fanning out from the objective and makes them converge, cross and diverge again. The eyepiece lens catches these divergent rays and bends them inward, at the same time making them less divergent. The eye catches and focuses them on the retina, where they take up quite a big area. The rays come to the eye in the same direction as they would have had if they had come from a *far* bigger object about 10

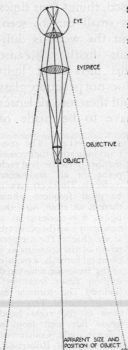

FIG. 306.—The principle of the microscope.

inches away, and this imaginary object is what the eye thinks it sees! Suppose the bacterium or whatever object we are looking at is made to look a thousand times as long and a thousand times as broad: it then will seem to have a million times the area. So the light from that bacterium is spread over the area of a million bacteria and will of course be a million times fainter. For this reason, if a high power is being used, an intense spot of light is usually focused on to the object; if this is not done, it looks faint and dull and details cannot be perceived.

A very small change indeed of the distance of the objective from the

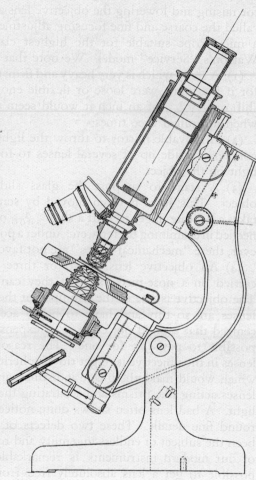

FIG. 307.—A modern microscope (Messrs. W. Watson's "Service" model, kindly supplied by the makers).

object will alter the angle of the rays so that they no longer diverge into the eyepiece at the correct angle to be converged again into the eye. Consequently, delicate arrangements for raising and lowering the objective lens are needed—these are called the coarse and fine focusing adjustments. Fig. 307 shows a microscope suitable for the highest class of work, Messrs. Watson's "Service" model. We note that it has:

(1) A stand which is very heavy and firm; this is most necessary, for if the joints were loose or flexible enough to let the object shift only $\frac{1}{1000}$ of an inch it would seem to shift a whole inch when magnified 1000 times.

(2) A movable mirror to throw the light on the object and a condenser made up of several lenses to focus a spot of intense light on the object.

(3) A stage to support the glass slide which carries the object. This stage is often moved by screws and racks, for it takes a delicate finger to shift a slide $\frac{1}{5000}$ of an inch at once as is needed in examining bacteria, etc., under a power of $\times 2000$. However, these "mechanical stages" are not favoured by all biologists.

(4) An objective lens. Two or three of these are usually carried on a nose-piece, so that they can be rapidly changed. The objective is one of the triumphs of the lens-maker's art; the lenses are so tiny and have to be so accurately mounted and centred that a good objective is an expensive article; it is quite possible to pay £20 for one. The reason for having several lenses in the objective is to get rid of spherical aberration (p. 475), which would make the image indistinct, and also to prevent the lenses acting like prisms and separating the colours of the white light. A bad lens often shows quite noticeable coloured fringes round fine details. These two defects of the simple lens have been the subject of endless ingenuity and research; the perfection of our modern instruments is remarkable, but it is not yet possible to get a lens absolutely free from these faults. The objective has to be very near the object, which can only be covered by the thinnest slip of glass.

(5) A tube to carry the lenses, shifted up and down by the coarse and fine adjustment. The coarse adjustment is only a rack and pinion very accurately and delicately made. The fine adjustment allows the objective to be raised or lowered by

distance as small as $\frac{1}{10000}$ of an inch. The tube which holds the lenses rests on an L-shaped lever, the long end of which is supported by a collar which can be moved to left or right by a screw. A *whole* turn of the screw moves the collar only $\frac{1}{250}$ which moves the short end of the lever less than $\frac{1}{500}$ of an inch.

(6) An eyepiece fitting into the top of the tube. This is made from two lenses and a stop between them.

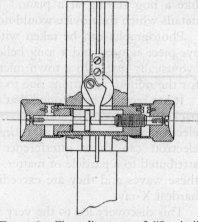

FIG. 308.—Fine adjustment of "Service" microscope. (Courtesy of Messrs. W. Watson & Sons, Ltd.)

It is easy enough to use the microscope. The object is put on the slide and the objective racked down almost to touch it. The mirror and condenser are adjusted until a good light is seen in the eye-piece. The objective is then racked up by the coarse adjustment till the image appears. The fine adjustment is then used to get *exact* focussing and a perfectly sharp picture.

This is well enough for a fairly low power and easy objects, but when we are trying to make out the exact appearance of bacterium's inside at the very limit of the microscope's power, great skill is needed. The light must be exactly focused by the condenser. The object (probably under water) is covered with a thin glass of exactly calculated thickness. A drop of cedar oil is allowed to run between this glass and the objective lens and between the condenser and slide. This prevents total reflection of valuable light rays (and has other advantages). Light of only one wavelength is sometimes used to prevent the formation of colour fringes. The eye itself makes a great difference. The novice sees the image in a microscope clearly enough but finds it very difficult to interpret it. All the things he sees are unfamiliar and he feels like a hog staring at a piano. The expert sees and interprets details which the novice would not notice.

Photographs can be taken with the microscope. A different eye-piece is used and a long bellows-camera attached where the eye usually goes. In a town microphotography is very difficult, for the minute vibrations due to traffic blur the image seriously.

It has recently been found that the electron itself behaves like a packet of exceedingly short waves, though they are probably not electromagnetic waves, as is light or the X-rays. Thus, the electron can show interference effects which can hardly be attributed to a particle of matter. We can calculate the length of these waves and they are exceedingly minute—shorter than the hardest X-rays.

This discovery led to the very recent and promising invention of the electron microscope which may very possibly be developed to give us vastly greater magnifications than the ordinary light-microscope. Streams of electrons cannot of course be focused by lenses but they can be deflected by electric or magnetic fields and it has proved possible to deflect a beam of electrons streaming from the cathode of an X-ray tube by passing them through wire coils carrying a current and therefore giving a magnetic field. These magnetic fields can make the beam of electrons converge and diverge just as lenses make light rays come to a focus or spread out. Fig. 309 shows an electron microscope. It is like an ordinary microscope inverted and with coils for lenses. The whole thing is enclosed and kept at a high

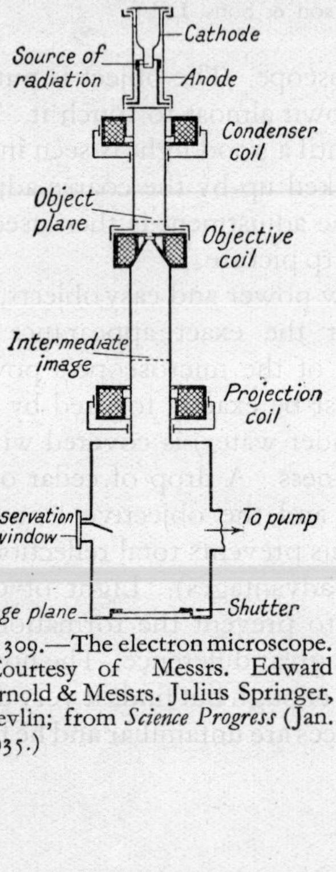

FIG. 309.—The electron microscope. (Courtesy of Messrs. Edward Arnold & Messrs. Julius Springer, Revlin; from *Science Progress* (Jan. 1935.)

vacuum. High tension current is applied to the anode and cathode, and just as in the X-ray tube (p. 516), electrons stream from the cathode. The condenser coil focuses them on to the object to be magnified. Another coil acts like the objective of a microscope and a third (projection) coil like the eyepiece, focusing the electron beam, so that it gives an image on a photographic plate. The advantage of this technique is that an electron behaves like a wave of exceedingly minute length.

As we have seen, the ordinary light microscope cannot give a sharp picture of anything smaller than a third of the wavelength of the light it uses, that is, the limit of visibility remains at about .00004 cm., however great the magnification. But the tiny electron-waves might theoretically give a sharp image of an object only 1.6×10^{-8} mm.—about the size of a large atom! This has not yet been achieved, but there is no doubt that the electron microscope offers a possibility of taking a photograph of a molecule!

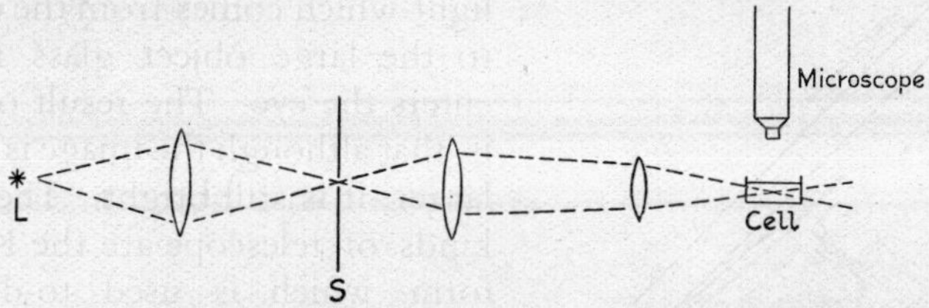

FIG. 310.—The principle of the ultramicroscope.

The ultramicroscope enables us to see—after a fashion—particles which are too small to be seen with the ordinary microscope. Its principle is that, as has already been explained on p. 472, very minute particles can *scatter* light. If an intense beam of brilliant light is directed sideways into a liquid under a powerful microscope, none of the rays can enter the objective unless they are turned aside. Now if a liquid such as a "solution" of colloidal silver is used, every tiny metallic particle in the liquid will scatter some of the light and will be seen by the microscope as a dancing speck of light. Their shapes cannot be discerned; actually, the particle is not seen at all, but its position is marked by the tiny halo of light it scatters. The Brownian movement of these tiny particles is fascinating to watch: they do not roll and tremble under the buffets of the water molecules as do the particles in Indian ink: they dart and dance under the ceaseless hail of blows. Here is a true perpetual motion.

TELESCOPES

The telescope is designed to enable us to see distant objects more clearly. The principle on which it works is, roughly speaking, that the rays from a distant object are bent by the lenses to such an angle that they diverge slightly and so fill the whole of the retina of the eye instead of converging and being focussed on to a tiny patch of it. It is important to note that the rays from a distant object enter a lens (or mirror) much larger than the pupil of the eye. All the light which comes from the object to the large object glass finally enters the eye. The result of this is, that although the image is made larger, it is still bright. The chief kinds of telescope are the Kepler form which is used to-day in small astronomical and all ordinary small telescopes, and the Galilean telescope which is often used in opera glasses.

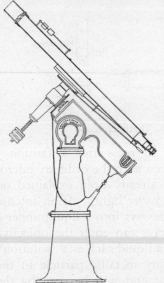

Reflecting telescopes with mirrors instead of lenses are used for astronomical telescopes.

Fig. 311 shows an astronomical refracting telescope made by Messrs. W. Watson. In its simplest form the ordinary astronomical refracting telescope

FIG. 311.—Astronomical refracting telescope. (Courtesy of Messrs. W. Watson & Sons, Ltd.)

is just two lenses. The object glass receives the nearly parallel rays which it brings to a focus. The light diverges from this and the eye-piece lens brings it to an angle at which the eye can focus it into a large image, which you can see will be upside down. This does not matter, for stars and planets have, after all, no "right-side-up." The principle and the course of the light is like that of the microscope, but instead of a powerful tiny objective designed to converge rapidly diverging rays, it has a weak lens which converges rays, already nearly parallel, from a distant object. The objective is of large diameter so that as much light as possible may be collected. The actual telescope as used, has a large objective which may be 3 inches in diameter (as in Fig. 311), or as much as 3 feet in the largest telescopes. This lens is built from two different lenses made of different glasses in order to prevent the prism effect and avoid colour fringes. At the other end of the tube is the eye-piece, made up of several lenses. The mounting is very heavy and solid because any vibration is magnified. A counter-poise takes the strain of the pivot. Graduated circles show the astronomer the angle his instrument is making with the star he is watching. The terrestrial telescope (Fig. 312) is like the one we have studied except that it has a pair of lenses in the centre which turn the image the right way up. It has a sliding tube for focusing purposes.

An astronomical telescope needs very little

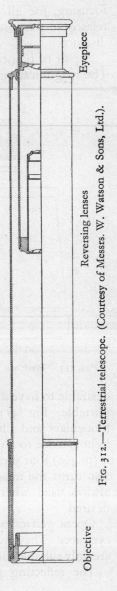

Eyepiece

Reversing lenses

Objective

Fig. 312.—Terrestrial telescope. (Courtesy of Messrs. W. Watson & Sons, Ltd.).

focusing, for all the things it is used on are so far off that, for telescopic purposes, they may be considered to be at the same distance.

A pair of binoculars is a combination of two small telescopes. The magnification of a telescope depends on its length, so it is

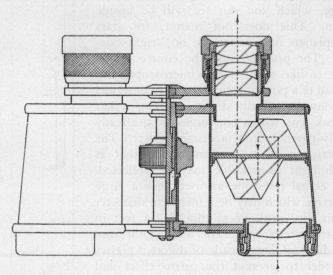

FIG. 313.—Prismatic binoculars. (Courtesy of Messrs. W. Watson & Sons, Ltd.)

desirable to have a long instrument. But a long instrument is not portable. Fig. 313 shows a pair of Messrs. Watson's prismatic binoculars and illustrates the ingenious method by which the light is made to go a long way in a short tube by totally reflecting it (p. 460) four times from the backs of two prisms. This process also turns the image the right way up. Prismatic binoculars are always used where a magnification of more than about 6 is desired.

Opera glasses often have a convex object glass and concave eye-piece. They give a brilliant image and occupy little space, but. are only suitable for small magnifications.

The reflecting principle is preferred for large astronomical telescopes. To see faint distant stars, it is necessary to collect a wide field of rays and concentrate these into the pupil of the eye or on to a photographic plate. Very large lenses are much harder to make than very large mirrors, so when a telescope of eight feet in diameter is constructed, a mirror replaces the lens. There are other reasons for preferring the mirror. Thus it is at the bottom of the telescope and is better protected from draughts than a lens. Changes of temperature are fatal to good work because the lens or mirror expands unequally and loses its carefully contrived shape.

Fig. 314 shows one pattern of reflecting telescope.

The parallel rays from a star enter it and, since the mirror is a concave one, they are concentrated on to a small oblique mirror which throws them into the eyepiece at the side.

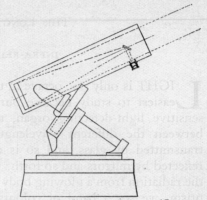

FIG. 314.—Reflecting telescope. (Courtesy of Messrs. W. Watson & Sons, Ltd.)

CHAPTER XVII

THE LONG WAVES

INFRA-RED RAYS

LIGHT is only one octave in the scale of radiation. It is the easiest to study because our bodies possess in the eye a sensitive light-detecting organ, able to discriminate roughly between the different wavelengths. Light, too, is perfectly transmitted by glass, and so is easily concentrated by lenses, reflected by mirrors and so forth. If we sort out the spectrum of the radiation from a glowing body (say, a gas mantle) with a glass prism, we see a band of colours, violet, indigo, blue, green, yellow, orange, red—but beyond the place where the red light ceases, nothing appears.

If, instead of a glass prism, we use one made of transparent rocksalt, we find that a long strip beyond the red light is *hot*. A delicate heat detector is a thermocouple: in its simplest form, it consists of wires of different metals joined, one join being kept cold: an electric current is produced depending on the temperature of the hot join. If it has several such junctions it is called a thermopile; by using a very sensitive galvanometer to detect the electricity, we can thus make a far more sensitive heat-detecting instrument than any thermometer. A good instrument will show an increase of temperature of a millionth of a degree.

If we make a spectrum with a rocksalt prism as described above and move a thermopile along it, we find that there is a long hot region beyond the red end of the visible spectrum. These infra-red rays extend from 8,000 A.U. to about 1,000,000 A.U., about five "octaves." These waves are invisible: when they fall on anything, they warm it. They can be refracted and reflected just like light but there is a good deal of difficulty in handling them, because very few materials let them through. They can now be photographed and infra-red photography is important because these long waves are not scattered by dust or mist. Thus, a photograph taken by infra-red rays is brilliant and sharp. Plate XXIII shows two views, one taken in ordinary light, the other taken through a screen which shuts out ordinary light, a plate sensitised to infra-red rays by certain dyes, being used.

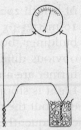

Fig. 315.—The principle of the thermo-couple. When the two junctions are at different temperatures a current flows. The right-hand junction is kept at a constant temperature, the other is used as a thermometer.

Many objects which reflect ordinary light in the same manner and therefore look alike, reflect infra-red rays differently. Plate XXIII shows the detection of "mosaic disease" in a tobacco-leaf while it is yet invisible to the eye.

A striking result is the possibility of taking a photograph in a dark room! Plate XXIV shows a photograph taken of a tea-cup taken in total darkness by the rays from two hot electric irons! Several hours' exposure is needed. It should be possible to take photographs in dark rooms with these specially sensitised plates provided that a sufficient exposure were given, for infra-red rays are always being emitted by every object.

The "residual rays" are of even longer wavelengths; they can be reflected from rock-crystal which transmits the ordinary infra-red rays. They are not at present of practical value. Only slightly longer than these, however, are the shortest waves of "radio-frequency."

RADIO

Electromagnetic waves of frequency from a few inches up to a mile or more can be generated by moving electric charges, and are of vast importance as the means of transmitting wireless telegraphy, telephony and television. For these purposes, waves

of length 200—2,000 metres are most suitable: the short waves of
10 metres or so are rather easily screened by intervening hills or
buildings, but are likely to be important for television. The most
obvious difference between wireless waves and light, is that the
former are able to pass through (or round) all ordinary obstacles.
Light is stopped by most kinds of matter because light waves are
of about the right frequency to set an electron moving in an atom:
consequently, the light is used up in setting these in motion. A
wireless wave is so much slower that it is quite "out of tune" with
ordinary matter, and therefore passes through it without affecting
it or being affected by it.

The principle on which wireless waves are generated is to set
electrons surging back and forth in a wire, the aerial; the number
of times they swing along the wire every second can be altered in
various ways. As we have already seen on p. 422, an electric
charge moving back and forth will cause an electromagnetic
wave of the same frequency (speed of vibration) as the motion of
the charge. The simplest device which can make an electron
rush backwards and forwards from 30,000 to 3,000,000 times a
second, is the old-fashioned spark transmitter. Fig. 316 shows it
in a very simple form. Wireless waves are generated by an
electron moving back and forth along a wire. The frequency
of the wave depends on the time of travel.

Suppose the induction coil is set to work. It crowds electrons

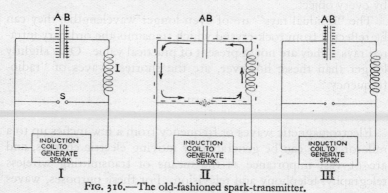

FIG. 316.—The old-fashioned spark-transmitter.

into the left-hand side of the apparatus and draws them out of the right-hand one. The attraction of the positively charged plate (B) of the condenser assembles a great multitude of electrons on the negative plate (A) (Fig. 316, I). As the electrons accumulate on the left, a time comes when their mutual repulsion is too great and they leap the spark gap and rush round the wire to B. (Fig. 316, II). But, just like a pendulum falling, they over-reach themselves and pile up at B. (Fig. 316, III). They then repel each other as badly as before and so rush back across the spark gap to A. The electrons thus rush back and forth along the wire and, in doing so, will generate a wave. Now the frequency of this wave will depend on the number of journeys the electron will do each second: i.e., on the time they take for each journey from A to B.

This time depends first on the capacity of the condenser. By this we mean the number of electrons it will take before they get to such a degree of overcrowding and repulsion that they repel each other back again. Naturally, the bigger the condenser plates, the more electrons they will hold and the nearer the plates, the more they will hold (because it is the attraction of the positive plate keeps them there and the shorter the distance, the greater the attraction). Well, the greater the capacity of the condenser, the longer it will take to fill and empty; so by using a *variable condenser* (Fig. 317) we can alter the vibration time of the circuit. In a variable condenser the area of the *effective* part, where the positive and negative plates face each other, is altered by turning the milled head. Included in the circuit is also an inductance I. This is a simple coil: as the electrons speed up round one turn, they tend to induce a current in the opposite direction in the next turn and so oppose their own motion. An inductance then slows down the vibrations. So by varying the size of the condenser and the inductance, we can, in theory, at least produce

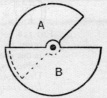

FIG. 317—The principle of the variable condenser. The effective part of the condenser is where A and B overlap: the extent of this is alterable by turning A. (Courtesy of the University Tutorial Press, from Hutchinson's *Wireless, Its Principles and Practice.*)

oscillations of any wavelength we like. Actually, the spark transmitter is out of favour because it emits a great number of harmonics, waves of multiples of the main frequency and these interfere with other users of the radio.

All modern wireless telegraphy and telephony is based on the thermionic valve. The three-electrode valve is the foundation of all forms of radio apparatus. In its simplest form it has a plate P, a perforated grid G and a fine filament F in a high vacuum.

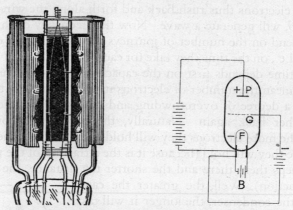

Fig 318.—(Left) The interior of a triode valve. Part of the outer (solid) plate and of the grid of spirally wound wire is cut away, exposing the filament. (Right) The parts of a valve shown diagrammatically. (Courtesy of the University Tutorial Press, from Hutchinson's *Wireless: Its Principles and Practice*.

The metal filament is coated with some material which emits electrons when hot, usually calcium or barium oxide, and it is kept hot by a small current (from the battery B). The plate and filament are connected to the terminals of a high tension battery. Suppose the grid is electrically neutral (Fig. 319, A)— not connected to anything. The positive plate will attract the negative electrons and they will flow from the filament to the plate. In other words a current will flow through the circuit, P, G, F.

Suppose, however, the grid is given a small negative electrical charge (Fig. 319, B). It will repel the electrons which try to get through its meshes and since these are very near the grid and a very long way from the plate, a small negative charge on the grid will repel them much more than the big positive charge on the plate will attract them. So, if the grid has a negative potential of about 6 volts, no current flows; if it is neutral, current flows easily. If it is positive, current flows still more easily for the grid charge hauls the negative electrons through the meshes. Once they are through, the positive plate pulls them in. The point, then, is that *a little change in the charge on the grid of a valve makes a big change in the current that flows through it.*

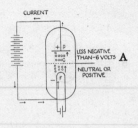

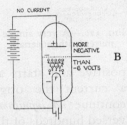

Fig. 319.—Action of triode valve, electrons represented as small circles.

The manufacture of valves is of course a most skilled busi-ness. The merit of a valve is (1) that the filament should emit plenty of electrons, this is ensured by coating it with various oxides (e.g., barium oxide) (2) that the grid should have the utmost repelling force for a given charge on it. This is done by making it of the finest metal gauze so that electrons must come very near to it in order to pass through. (3) There must be as perfect a vacuum in it as possible. If gas is present in appreciable quantities, it will ionise (p. 286), and the positive atoms will bombard the filament and damage it.

The modern radio transmitter is a very complicated arrange-ment. It has to produce waves of very great power and of practically fixed wavelength. We shall do best to see how a simple valve transmitter works, so at least grasping the principle of large-scale transmission. A battery B is connected through an inductance coil I to the plate of the valve P, and also to the fila-ment F. Current will flow in this circuit if the grid is neutral or

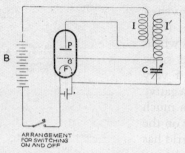

FIG. 320.—A very simple valve-transmitter (without aerial).

positive, but not if it is more negative than, say, 6 volts (see Fig. 319). But as soon as current flows in the inductance coil I, it induces a current in the opposite direction in the coil I'. This makes the grid negative and stops the first current. But stopping the first current in I induces a new current in the other direction through I'. This makes the grid positive and starts a new current in I which again induces a current the original direction in I'. This process will continue *ad infinitum*, the current of electrons in I' being reversed hundreds of thousands of times a second. The number of times a second the electrons run back and forward in I' depends on the slowing of the current by the inductance itself: but it can be regulated by putting across the circuit a variable condenser (C) which has to be filled and emptied of electrons each time the current changes. By altering the capacity of this condenser, the time of oscillation can be altered. The electrons, running up and down this coil I' and the wires which feed it, would generate electromagnetic waves, though rather feeble ones. In order to radiate electromagnetic waves of considerable power, the coil I' is allowed to induce currents in a *third* coil (A) (Fig. 321), which is connected to earth and to an aerial wire. By altering the length of this coil, it is possible to make the aerial and coil (A) of the right length for the free electrons in them to surge from end to end in *time* with the reversing current in the coil I'. This little current keeps

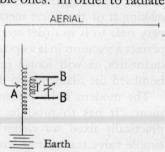

FIG. 321.—How the waves generated by the valve are radiated by the aerial. BB, connections to grid and filament.

the electrons vibrating strongly, just as the light push of the escapement of a clock (370) keeps a big pendulum vibrating.

It is important to grasp that the electromagnetic waves induced in the aerial have a frequency of 300,000 to several millions per second. We wish to use these waves to express by their variations sound waves with a frequency of 100 to 10,000 a second. During the time of a single sound wave from 30 to 100,000 electromagnetic waves will be transmitted. Thus, if you are transmitting music and you want to send a musical note of 1,000 vibrations a second by means of radio waves which vibrate perhaps a million times a second, you must switch the latter off and on a thousand times a second: so sending out pulses of five hundred waves each, $\frac{1}{2000}$th of a second apart, thus:

500 waves	500 waves	500 waves
each lasting	each lasting	each lasting
$\frac{1}{1000000}$ sec.	$\frac{1}{1000000}$th sec.	$\frac{1}{1000000}$ sec.

$\frac{1}{2000}$ sec. $\frac{1}{2000}$ sec. $\frac{1}{2000}$th sec. $\frac{1}{2000}$th sec. $\frac{1}{2000}$th sec.

Now, we already know that a telephone transmitter into which a musical note of 1,000 vibrations a second was played would send pulses of electric current a thousand times a second, so that, if we connect a telephone to the grid of a valve (D, Fig. 322), the valve will let a single pulse of current through at every sound vibration. This pulse will reach valve E and start oscillations in I and I' and so set the electrons swinging in the aerial. Accordingly, the arrangement in Fig. 322 would make a simple transmitter. The telephone gives currents +—+—+—+— etc., in time with the sound waves. Valve D turns these into stronger pulses of direct current +, +, +, +, +, +, still in time with the sound waves. Each pulse sets the current in the two coils I and I' oscillating at some very high frequency as long as the pulse lasts.

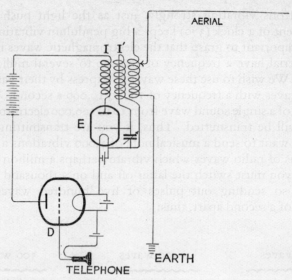

FIG. 322.—The simplest transmitter for wireless telephony.

The current in I′ is an alternating one thus:

no current	current oscillating for time of 1 sound wave	no current	current oscillating for time of 1 sound wave	no current etc.

These oscillating currents set electrons surging in the aerial: this sends out trains of waves of the same frequency, and each train of waves corresponds to a single sound wave.

In order to receive the wireless waves, the first thing is to catch your waves. To do this, you may regulate your aerial length till the electrons in the wire will surge back and forth along it about a million times a second. This can be done by a coil of variable length like the one in Fig. 321. However, a more usual method is to attach a variable condenser so that you can slow or quicken the surge of electrons by giving them a bigger or

smaller condenser to fill.
The electromagnetic waves,
when they reach the aerial,
set the electrons in it
swinging in time with
themselves, say, 1,000,000
swings a second. The
process of getting the aerial
to the right period is called
"tuning." Suppose we fit
up a circuit as in Fig. 323.
The aerial currents surging
back and forth make an

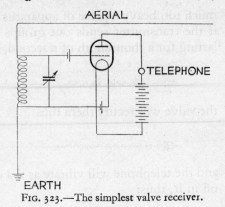

FIG. 323.—The simplest valve receiver.

alternating current in the circuits on the left of the valve. The
current going through these can be represented thus:

FIG. 324.

This current makes the grid alternately positive and negative.
To the grid is connected a small battery which just keeps it
negative when no alternating current is being sent in by the
aerial. When the grid is negative no current flows from filament
to plate but when the aerial sends a pulse of positive current to the
grid strong enough to weaken or reverse the negative current
from the battery, a current will flow from the filament *via* the
grid to the plate. The result is, that instead of the alternating
current, we have in the circuit through filament plate and telephone a succession of currents mainly in the same direction, each
a little more than half a sine curve.

FIG. 325.

Now, a succession of electric currents lasting a millionth of a
second at intervals of a millionth of a second, affects a telephone
receiver like a smooth continuous current, for a telephone is

much too heavy a piece of apparatus to vibrate at this speed. So, if the transmitter sends out groups of waves, thus, each group lasting for a thousandth of a second,

the valve will rectify them thus:

and the telephone will vibrate as if a current was switched on and off in it, thus:

off for 1000th sec.	on for 1000th sec.	off for 1000th sec.	on for 1000th sec.	off for 1000th sec.

which will make its diaphragm vibrate five hundred times a second and generate a sound of 500 waves a second.

We have talked throughout as if the sound wave was like this:

FIG. 326.

and therefore gave a similar current in the microphone or telephone and caused electromagnetic waves like this:

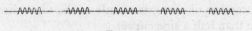

FIG. 327.

to be sent out. In actual fact the pressure wave of a sound is more like this only more complicated in form.

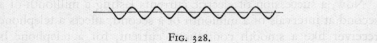

FIG. 328.

and the telephone currents are thus

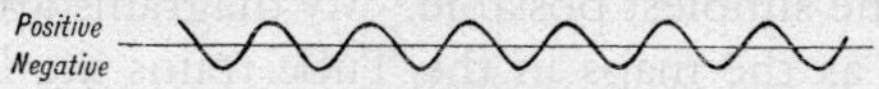

Positive
Negative

FIG. 329.

This makes a current like this in the rectifying valve circuit

FIG. 330.

and a varying current in the aerial which sends out a wave like this, reproducing the form of the original *sound* wave in a pattern of electromagnetic waves.

FIG. 331.

This is the wave that is picked up by the detector aerial. After passing through the detector valve (p 507) it has the form shown below,

FIG. 332.

the lower negative halves being much reduced in amplitude with the result that pulses of rapidly interrupted current, varying in the same way as the original sound wave are produced. These after amplification operate the telephone or loudspeaker.

No wireless set is as simple as the ones I have described. The most important additions are the use of more valves to increase the currents from the aerial to the rectifying valve, and the currents from this valve to the telephone or loud speaker. The way in which a valve is used to increase a current is explained on pp. 502, 503.

But since it is not very easy to understand any wireless set, I have kept to the simplest possible. My diagrams are about as like the real thing as the maps in the Tube trains are like the actual system. But if you grasp how a sound wave can be translated into electromagnetic waves and these back to sound, you will at least be in a position to begin to understand "how wireless works."

Television—the process of making a scene enacted in one spot visible at another by the agency of radio signals—is a far harder problem than broadcasting. A single train of sound-waves will convey to the ear all it can hear. The complex sounds of a railway station, for example, can all be reproduced by the single vibrating plate of a loud-speaker or sound box. It is otherwise with light. In "viewing" the image on the retina of the eye, the brain appreciates a *pattern* of stronger and weaker light-waves *all perceived at once*. Wireless signals entering an aerial can only give one signal at a time; they are either coming in or not coming in, and that is all there is to it. They can give any pattern of signals one after the other, but not at the same time. Accordingly, television has to divide the picture into lines and spots and show each part with a single signal. If a whole picture is shown, one part at a time, but all within a twentieth of a second, the eye will see it as a whole because the first part will not have faded from its retina until the last part has already made its impression.

This presents a formidable task which, however, has already gone far towards being solved.

The working of a television transmitter and receiver is more than this book can describe. However, we shall get a hint of the principles if we imagine a picture, say a film, at the transmitting station. Now suppose it divided into an imaginary gridiron of lines as at A. Make a thin light beam travel along all those lines from X to Y, 25 times every second and let the light spot be focussed on to a photo-electric cell (p. 484) which allows a current to pass proportional to the brightness of the light that falls on it. When the beam is traversing a dark part of the film, the photoelectric cell will let little current pass: when the beam goes through a light part, a bigger current will pass. So during each $\frac{1}{25}$th of a second, the photoelectric cell will send out a current which varies from strong to weak in just the same way as the part of the film then scanned by the beam, varies from light to dark. Now this varying current can be made into a wireless signal just in the same way as the varying current of a microphone.

The receiver has a beam of light which flashes over a screen and moves in just the same pattern as that in which the transmitting beam moves. This beam is made (by other signals) to keep *exact time* with the transmitting beam. So, if the transmitting beam is at Q

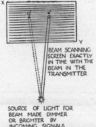

PHOTOELECTRIC CELL

TRANSMITTER TURNING THE CURRENTS FROM THE CELL INTO RADIO WAVE SIGNALS

AERIAL

LENS

X

PICTURE ON SCREEN

Y

BEAM SCANNING THE PICTURE BY MOVING OVER THE WHOLE ZIG-ZAG. IN $\frac{1}{25}$ SEC.

X

Y

BEAM SCANNING SCREEN EXACTLY IN TIME WITH THE BEAM IN THE TRANSMITTER

SOURCE OF LIGHT FOR BEAM MADE DIMMER OR BRIGHTER BY INCOMING SIGNALS

FIG. 333.—Diagram illustrating simplest principles of television.

at any instant, the receiving beam will be at the corresponding spot Q'.

Now the television signal is received like any ordinary wireless signal, but instead of working a telephone, the electric currents produced by the set—which, of course, are identical with those produced by the photoelectric cell in the transmitting station— are used to make the receiving beam fainter or brighter. Thus, if the transmitting beam is passing a dark bit of the picture at Q, the receiving beam will be at Q' and the faint signal will make it dim. If the transmitting beam is on a light bit at R, then at that moment the receiving beam will be at the corrresponding spot R' and will be made bright by the strong wireless signal it has just received. Accordingly, every bit of the receiving screen will be illuminated strongly or weakly, once in $\frac{1}{25}$ second and the little bits of dark and bright illumination will be combined by the eye into a single picture. This should explain how a *still* picture at the transmitting station is received by the set.

Now suppose that each $\frac{1}{25}$ second a *new* slightly different picture is transmitted from the station. Clearly these will blend (as in the cinema) and we shall see on the screen a moving picture.

Television will certainly develop rapidly though probably more slowly than did broadcasting. The technical difficulties are much greater: none the less, remembering what broadcasting has become in 15 years, I shall be surprised if most of us do not see the 1950 Derby in our homes.

CHAPTER XVIII

The Short Waves

ULTRAVIOLET radiation is the name given to the rays of wavelengths from about 500 to 3,900 A.U. These numbers are chosen because radiation of greater wavelength than about 3,900 A. U. is visible to the eye and is called "light," while radiation of 500 A.U. and shorter behaves like X-rays. Actually, ultraviolet light and X-rays overlap. The same rays can be obtained by spark and arc spectra and from X-ray tubes. The ultraviolet rays of very short wavelength are difficult to investigate, for they are stopped by ordinary transparent substances so that prism-spectrographs cannot be used. Gratings can hardly be ruled fine enough, while the crystals (p. 518) used to diffract X-rays are too fine. Ultraviolet light of wavelength longer than 1,850 A.U. can be refracted by lenses or prisms of fluorite or rock-crystal. The rays of wavelengths 2,000—3,900 A.U. are, therefore, best studied and most used, and are what we ordinarily call ultraviolet rays.

Ultraviolet rays are usually produced at the same time as light. Thus, a white-hot body gives both kinds of radiation. The sun sends out great quantities of ultraviolet radiation but since it is more easily scattered even than blue light, the earth receives little or none when the air is hazy. However, a certain amount of light of wavelength down to about 3,000 A.U. gets through. An arc lamp is a rich source of these short radiations, particularly an arc between poles of iron. Most artificial sources of light are seen through glass which only lets through the waves longer than 3,400 A.U. An ordinary glass filament lamp or discharge tube therefore, gives very little ultraviolet light.

Moreover, daylight received through glass windows contains very little ultraviolet. The new "Vita" glass will transmit rays down to 3,000 A.U., and so passes almost all the shortwave light which reaches us through the air.

In practice, we require ultraviolet light free from ordinary light. The best way of producing it is to use a mercury vapour lamp (p. 448) made of silica—fused rock crystal—instead of glass. The brilliant light produced is of many wavelengths, but if it is allowed to pass through a sheet of dark glass coloured by nickel oxide, the light is excluded while much of the ultraviolet rays pass on.

Ultraviolet light affects the photographic plate much more rapidly than ordinary light and generally has more effect on chemical compounds.

One of the most interesting things about ultraviolet radiation is its effect on living things. It is very destructive to the human eye. Snow-blindness is an irritation of the eye resulting from the ultraviolet waves of sunlight reflected from snow. Most things absorb ultraviolet light completely and so cannot reflect it.

The carbon arc and still more the iron arc are very dangerous to the eye. In electric arc welding deep blue shields are always employed. Ultraviolet light causes the skin to become pigmented and it is the ultraviolet light in sunlight that causes the skin to become brown. The story of the way vitamin D is made by ultraviolet light shining on plant and animal foods is a remarkable one, and is told in Chapter XXXVIII. It is very generally believed that good health and resistance to infection results from exposure to this light. The artificial sun-lamps now widely used enable us to become brown in winter.

Ultraviolet light is very destructive to bacteria and low forms of life which have no opaque skin to protect them. Water can be sterilised without affecting its flavour by running it through a tube containing a quartz mercury arc. A certain amount of trouble is caused however by films forming on the tube and obstructing the light. The most interesting feature of ultraviolet light is the way it causes *fluorescence*. When shortwave light shines on certain materials, they give out light of a longer wave-length. The shortwave light supplies energy to the molecules which they give out again as long-wave radiation. Some things fluoresce in ordinary light. Fluorescence is very well seen with a weak solution of red ink (eosin). If a tumbler of this is held up to the light, the unchanged light coming through is pale pinkish-yellow. The solution, however, *gives out* light in all directions, and seen from the side, it appears bright green. Ammoniated quinine gives the same effect. Looked through, it is colourless, but seen sideways, a pale luminous blue. Now, ultraviolet light makes many things fluorescent and this looks very striking, because the ultraviolet light is invisible, while the light given out by the fluorescent substance is usually blue-green but may be red or violet. In the Natural History Museum at South Kensington there is a remarkable exhibit: a case of minerals with an ultra-violet lamp above. When this is switched on, the case remains dark while the minerals fluoresce and glow with varied coloured lights. This is not only a scientific curiosity, for many things which look exactly alike to the eye can at once be distinguished because they fluoresce differently in ultraviolet light. Mixtures of other flours with wheat, margarine in butter, chicory in coffee can be readily detected. In medicine, ring-worm is easily discovered, for the fungus that causes it fluoresces with a brilliant green light!

A most remarkable use is in detecting forgeries. Writing which has been erased, usually leaves traces behind. Plate XXIV shows a bearer cheque from which the amount has been skilfully erased, and another inserted. The photograph in ordinary light shows nothing, but in that taken by ultraviolet rays, the altera-tions are easily visible.

Writing which has been erased from ancient manuscripts may often be read by ultraviolet light. A remarkable use of it is in the detection of stains of blood and of other animal fluids. The photographs of Plate XXV speak for the new weapon in the hands of the police.

The use of fluorescent glass in the green "neon-tubes" is mentioned on p. 447.

X-RAYS

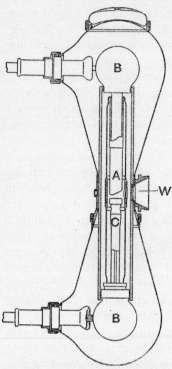

FIG. 334.—A modern X-ray tube. The outer casing is of metal and is connected to earth, so avoiding danger from the high-tension current. The X-ray tube proper is the innermost tube. It is of chrome-iron, and in it the cathode C and the anode and anticathode A are fixed. The rays generated at the slanting face of A pass out as a beam through the window W. The balls B, B, by their rounded surface avoid brush discharges, the upper one takes up and radiates away the considerable heat generated in A.

The rays of wavelength 500 A.U. and less are easily obtainable and are called X-rays. They are produced, when anything, usually a piece of some hard infusible metal is bombarded with electrons. The violent blows of the flying electrons drive the electrons of the atoms of the metal out of the "places" near the nucleus. When the electrons from the outer places fill up these vacant spaces, they make a jump to a position of much lower potential energy: consequently, a great deal of energy is given out in the quantum of radiation emitted. Now, a big quantum means a high frequency and short wavelength. To get very short X-rays we bombard metals whose electrons are very difficult to dislodge and whose places will be filled with the greatest emission of energy. Such metals are tungsten or molybdenum.

Since in generating X-rays very high tensions are used, there is danger from shocks. A typical modern X-ray tube, as shown in Fig. 334, is, however, completely shock-proof and ray-proof. The whole outer tube is made of metal which is connected to earth, effectually preventing the possibility of its earthing itself through the user. A high tension current of electrons then enters and passes to the heavy metal cathode C. The anode has a very large globe of metal attached to it, so that the heat produced is radiated away. Tubes to give very powerful discharges have a water-cooled anode. The tube is highly evacuated and the electrons have to leap the gap to the anode A and bombard the slanting face of it. Its atoms give out the rays which pass through the window W, which is of glass, to the exterior.

X-rays have four great uses. First, they penetrate materials with light atoms and are stopped by materials with heavy atoms. Thus they penetrate flesh easily, but bone less easily. X-ray photographs are shadow pictures, not images focussed by a lens. They are taken by placing a photographic film (wrapped in black paper to keep ordinary light out) on one side of the patient and directing X-rays on his other side. The X-ray picture is an invaluable aid in the treatment of any injury to a bone or joint. Soft parts are more difficult to X-ray. The intestinal tract is fairly easy, for if the patient eats a great deal of the harmless barium sulphate, this coats his stomach and intestines, and, as it stops X-rays, a good shadow-picture can be taken. Lipiodol is a harmless oil containing the heavy element iodine. By letting a little of this trickle into the lung and the air cavities, we can get a picture of these. Plate XXVI shows the elaborate "tree" of air passages in the lung outlined with lipiodol. The ribs and collarbones are clearly seen.

The second use of X-rays is a similar one. The shortest-waved X-rays easily penetrate steel, and it is possible to spot a hidden crack in a weld or casting by an X-ray photograph (Plate XXV).

The cancer-cell is destroyed by X-rays of the right wavelength. Sometimes, the whole of a small growth can be destroyed by X-rays: sometimes portions remain and start a new growth, but in almost every case, there is at least a great temporary improvement. Curiously enough, while X-rays are used for the treatment of cancer, they may also cause it. A short exposure is perfectly harmless: but many of the early workers with X-rays, who did not know the danger, contracted a very slow but intractable skin disease, which made them martyrs to the science of radiology which has saved the lives of thousands of others. To-day, X-ray tubes are heavily screened with lead so that no rays can go elsewhere than where they are needed. The old X-ray tube diffused a wide beam of rays which were apt to stray. The modern type sends a directed pencil of rays where they are needed.

Finally, X-rays have done an enormous amount towards making us understand what solids are. In the earlier chapters of this book, I said much about the way in which the atoms and molecules of solids are arranged. Almost all this information was found out by use of X-rays.

To understand this, turn back and read the sections about interference of light and about diffraction gratings. When a beam of light of a single wavelength shines on a soap film, the film appears dark and light in patches owing to interference. This occurs because a soap film is about as thick as a light-wave is long. Now a crystal is built of layers of atoms and these are about as far apart as the wavelength of X-rays. Accordingly, the layers of atoms in a crystal cause interference in X-rays. X-rays have various wavelengths but if we use a potential of about 50,000 volts and a molybdenum target (A in Fig. 334), the X-rays are nearly all of the same wavelength. This wavelength was found (by an interference method) to be 0.712 A.U. or .0000000712 cm. Suppose we shine this molybdenum radiation on a crystal, which consists of layers of atoms regularly spaced. Then, if the X-rays strike the crystal at one or two particular angles, all the waves reflected from these layers will have their crests together and troughs together while at other angles the troughs and crests will not coincide and the light will interfere. The result is that a crystal reflects X-rays very strongly at certain angles and very feebly at others.

If you look at Fig. 335 you can see that if you knew at which angles X-rays were reflected from crystals, you could tell where the layers lay, for, like light and all radiation, X-rays are reflected back at the same angle at which they come off. Thus, if a lamp is at A, a hidden mirror at B and the spot of light at C, you know the mirror must be in the position p not q or r.

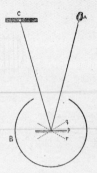

Secondly, we can tell how far apart the layers are if the wavelength of the X-rays is known; on the principle that if all the layers are to reflect a beam so that all the crests of the reflected rays reinforce each other, these layers must be an exact whole number of wave-lengths apart, measured along the track of the beam. Fig. 336 shows that only for certain values of the angle (A) at which the X-rays strike the crystal will a powerful reflection take place: it is not difficult to see that knowing the wavelength

Fig. 335.—How the angle of reflection shows the position of the reflector.

and the angles at which the powerful reflections appear the distances between the layers of atoms can be worked out.

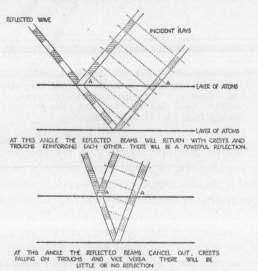

REFLECTED WAVE

INCIDENT RAYS

A A → LAYER OF ATOMS

→ LAYER OF ATOMS

AT THIS ANGLE THE REFLECTED BEAMS WILL RETURN WITH CRESTS AND TROUGHS REINFORCING EACH OTHER. THERE WILL BE A POWERFUL REFLECTION.

A A

AT THIS ANGLE THE REFLECTED BEAMS CANCEL OUT, CRESTS FALLING ON TROUGHS AND VICE VERSA THERE WILL BE LITTLE OR NO REFLECTION

FIG. 336.—Showing that a crystal, consisting of layers of atoms, will reflect X-rays at certain angles, but not at others.

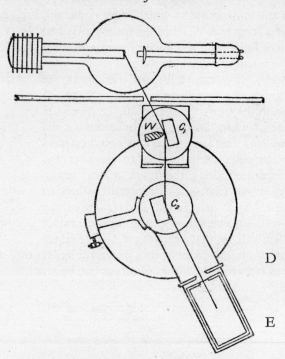

D

E

FIG. 337.—Diagram of X-ray spectrometer for study
of reflection of X-rays from crystals. (Courtesy of
Messrs. Geo. Bell & Sons, Ltd., and Professor
Bragg, from *The Crystalline State*.)

Fig. 337 shows a simple type of X-ray spectrometer. The
X-ray tube supplies the rays and these fall on a crystal C_1. The
rays reflected from this are of a single wavelength only. C_2 is the
crystal under study, mounted on a revolving table with a pointer
to show the angle it makes with the beam. D is a slit and E an
"ionisation chamber" which conducts electricity if X-rays pass
into it. If we move the crystal and chamber till a powerful
reflection goes into the chamber, it is easy to measure the angle
at which the reflection comes.

Now we find as we move the crystal, quite a number of layers of atoms which can reflect the X-rays, and by figuring out where the layers would come for a particular arrangement of atoms, we can work out which of the many, but not unlimited arrangements is found in the crystal being examined. Fig. 338 gives a notion of some of the layers of atoms in a rocksalt crystal. It is easy to see

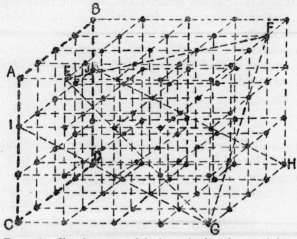

FIG. 338.—Showing some of the layers in the salt crystal from which X-rays can be reflected. Dots represent sodium and chlorine ions: ABCD, EFG, IJGH, are some of the possible reflecting planes of atoms.

that when we know from the angles of the X-ray reflections where the layers lie and how far they are apart, we can easily settle where the actual atoms must be in order to form such layers.

There are other methods of using X-rays to discover crystal structure. We saw on p. 471 why a fine-ruled "grating" bends light at certain fixed angles which depend on the wavelength and the fineness of the grating. Now a crystal, with its regular lines of atoms, acts like a complicated grating ruled in several directions at once.

Accordingly, since the "rulings" (the distances between the lines of atoms) are about as small as the wavelength of X-rays, a crystal splits a beam of X-rays into several beams which when

17*

allowed to fall on a photographic plate, give a pattern of spots. The mathematician, from the pattern, can deduce the kind of grating which would give it. Plate XXVI shows a "Laue" photograph of a hexagonal (six-sided) crystal. The spots can be seen to have a sort of six-fold symmetry. The reflection method perfected by the Braggs is generally preferred because the pattern of atoms in the crystal cannot by any means always be calculated from the pattern of spots.

X-ray analysis is becoming very important because it is the only certain way of finding out how the atoms and molecules of a solid are arranged.

RADIOACTIVITY

Shorter still than the X-rays are the gamma-rays emitted by radium and the other radioactive elements. More will be said about these remarkable substances in Chapter XIX; for the present, a brief sketch of their very odd behaviour will be enough. There are some 40 radioactive elements: many of these are however identical in all respects except their radio-active behaviour and the weight of their atoms. Thorium, which is contained in gas-mantles, is radioactive, but so feebly that it was known for 70 years before anything odd was noticed. Radium is the best example. It is very rare—rich ores do not contain more than some 50 milligrammes per ton—it is difficult to extract and it is in great demand for treatment of cancer. Consequently, its price is very high indeed—£10 per milligramme (nearly £3,000,000 an ounce) is asked. Radium is a metal, but it is used in the form of its compound with chlorine or bromine. This radium bromide is what is sold as "radium." When pure, it looks very much like ordinary salt, but several very odd things are noticeable about it. It shines in the dark; it is always a little warmer than anything round it. It rapidly fogs a photographic plate even though the plate is wrapped in lead sheet thick enough to keep out X-rays —let alone light. Fluorescent substances shine brilliantly when brought near it. It ionises the air near it and makes it conduct electricity slightly. It turns glass dark-coloured and alters many chemicals merely by contact with them. It burns the skin very severely if left close to it for long.

Most of these phenomena could be explained if radium were giving out a very potent kind of X-rays all the time, and this is actually true—though it is by no means the whole fascinating story, which was worked out in the early years of the century by the Curies, Rutherford, Soddy and many others.

Every atom has a minute heavy positively charged nucleus with a cloud of electrons round it. Radium is no exception to this rule, but its atoms have unstable nuclei. The nucleus of the radium atom is a heavy and complicated affair with some 226 protons, and neutrons packed into an extremely minute space. We know practically nothing about the interior of the nucleus; we do not know if the particles are still or moving, and we can only make guesses as to how they are arranged. But sooner or later, the life of every radium atom ends by its nucleus exploding. If you could point to a particular radium atom and say "When will it explode"? we could not say, any more than I could point to a particular baby in a crèche and say when it will die. But, just as I could say with confidence that, barring changes in the national health, half those babies will be dead in 57 years time, so I could point to a gram of radium and say, "Half those atoms will have exploded in 1600 years time." A radium atom, on the average lasts 1600 years. No one knows why its nucleus may last 1600 years and then suddenly explode. One could picture the protons, etc., in the nucleus jostling about until they got to a position with so much kinetic energy that the nucleus flew to bits like a bursting flywheel. But considering the vast speeds and minute distances of the parts of an atom, it is difficult to picture a condition of affairs so improbable that the nucleus should reach it only once in a thousand years or so! A uranium nucleus may last 8,000,000,000 years, and presents an even worse problem.

Anyway, the thing that happens to radium is that the nucleus of each atom explodes after a sufficient time and that in 1600 years half the nuclei in existence now will have burst.

A gram of radium chloride, say, a saltspoonful, contains about 24×10^{20} radium atoms and so 12×10^{20} will burst in 1600 years. Fifteen hundred years is 3×10^{10} seconds, so that $12 \times 10^{20} \div 5 \times 10^{10}$ that is 24,000,000,000 radium nuclei burst every second in that dwindling gram of radium. This is the average speed; at the beginning when nearly all the radium is still there some 52,000,000,000 nuclei burst every second.

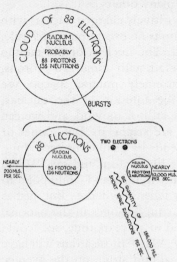

FIG. 339.—What happens when a radium atom bursts.

What happens when the radium nucleus bursts? The radium atom shoots out the nucleus of a helium atom (which we call an alpha-particle) at the enormous speed of 10,000 miles a second, and at the same time emits a great deal of energy in the form of a quantum of very short electromagnetic rays. These we call gamma-rays.

The remainder of the radium nucleus gathers all its electrons but two about it and makes an atom of radon, an entirely new element—actually a gas.

This, in turn, changes to another element, and by a series of 9 changes the element radium finally becomes the homely and permanent substance—lead.

This habit of bursting explains the odd behaviour of radium. It is always warm because the recoil of the atoms of radon it produces jostles the unexploded atoms into quicker motion. The rays it gives out are of two kinds—the so-called alpha-rays which are a stream of high-speed helium-nuclei and not rays at all, and the gamma-rays which are true radiation. It shines in the dark because it fluoresces under the action of its own radiation. Both alpha-rays and γ-rays affect a photographic plate.

Most radioactive elements—including radium—give out beta-rays, which are a stream of electrons travelling at enormous speeds—up to 99.8% of the speed of light. These behave much like the cathode-rays mentioned on pp. 293–294. The source of these electrons is not certain. They are in some cases knocked out of the atom by the alpha-particle: in other cases they seem to come from the nucleus itself.

The chief uses of radium are, first, in medical work and secondly in luminous watches. For medical work, the γ-radiation is useful, for it has a remarkable effect in killing cancer cells. If radium can be got near enough to most kinds of cancer cells, it will kill them and will not kill the surrounding cells of the body.

There are three main difficulties: Firstly, there is not much radium in the world, and so powerful beams of γ-rays cannot be obtained. Secondly, cancer cells often migrate to distant part of the body and set up fresh sources of trouble. Thirdly, there is no way of applying radium to a deep-seated growth—e.g., in the stomach or liver. The usual method of procedure is to seal up the radium in needles and stick these into the growth or to seal up the radio-active gas radon in tiny glass "seeds" and insert these.

The use of radium in luminous paint brings us to the question of phosphorescence.

There are three main difficulties: First, there is not much less well understood. In the scientific sense a phosphorescent thing is one which after being exposed to light, shines in the dark. The best known is the luminous paint made from calcium sulphide intimately mixed with about 2% of salt and a trace of some metal like copper or manganese. This, after being exposed to a bright light shines with a soft violet radiance which dies out in the course of some hours. Evidently, it can store light and dole it out again; but how it does it, no one knows. Luminous watches are painted with phosphorescent zinc sulphide containing a trace of radium. The radium rays make the zinc sulphide fluoresce and the watch shines whether it has been exposed to light or no.

Fire-flies, glow-worms, many fish, decaying wood, etc., shine with a cold light, but this is not phosphorescence in the scientific sense but "chemi-luminescence," light emitted as the result of some chemical reaction. An odd phenomenon is tribolumin-escence, the production of light when certain crystals are rubbed. Rub two lumps of sugar together in a very dark room and you will see it.

Neither X-rays nor γ-radiation can be reflected and refracted in the same way as light: accordingly, they cannot be used in optical instruments like microscopes and telescopes. That they are electromagnetic waves like light however, is clear from their resemblance to it in almost every other particular.

The reason they are not reflected at smooth surfaces as light is, is first that every surface is made of atoms, and therefore even the smoothest polished metal has irregularities much larger than a wavelength of X-rays. It has recently, however, been found that X-rays can be reflected in the same way as light by a metal surface at a grazing angle to the beam. Secondly, the X-rays and γ-rays penetrate deeply into all kinds of matter and are absorbed within it. They cannot be refracted by a lens because the atoms of the glass diffract the rays as a grating diffracts light.

There is no very certain means of measuring the wavelength of the shortest γ-rays. A fair idea can be gained from the thickness of matter, say lead, which they will traverse before they lose half their strength. Short wave X-rays are more penetrating than long-wave X-rays, and γ-rays are much more penetrating than short X-rays: they are, therefore, much shorter still and we believe them to have wavelengths from 0.1 to 0.005 A.U. A few years ago it was found that extraordinarily penetrating rays were travelling to the earth from the upper air. They manifest themselves by ionising gases—knocking off their electrons, but this property was the only reason to believe them to be electromagnetic waves. Their very great penetrating power made it appear that their wavelength was as little as 0.00008 A.U. However, the present belief is that these cosmic rays from outer space are positive electrons, about which at present we know very little.

We have now been up and down the scale of electromagnetic

radiation. Radio-frequencies, the shorter Hertzian waves, residual rays, infra-red radiation, light, ultraviolet radiation, X-rays, and gamma rays.

What have all these in common? They all travel with the same speed as light—as far as has been tested. They all move in straight lines except when reflected or refracted; they can all curl round something smaller than their wavelength. They require no material medium (like air) through which to travel. They all produce electrical effects, either setting electrons in motion as do wireless waves or knocking them out of metals like light or out of gas molecules like short-wave radiations.

There are several instances where a thing behaves both as a collection of waves and as a particle. A quantum of light is clearly made of waves—otherwise it could not show interference, diffraction, and so on. But it behaves like a particle in being emitted as a unit and in keeping to itself and not spreading out like a sound wave.

An electron is, on the other hand, recognisably a particle. It has appreciable mass. Its velocity varies and is not the same as that of light. It is deflected by an electrostatic field or by a magnet. Yet it can produce interference effects and thus behaves like a wave or a collection of waves.

PART IV

CHEMISTRY

CHAPTER XIX

Particles, Atoms and Elements

THE ULTIMATE PARTICLES

BEFORE surveying the science of Chemistry—the study of the way in which atoms are put together into molecules—it is well to try to build up a clear idea of what we know about the constitution of an atom.

We have evidence that every atom is built up of far smaller particles than itself: thus every atom contains the minute and very light *electrons*, for these can be obtained from it when it is ionised (pp. 285, 293). Secondly, we know that a hydrogen atom divested of an electron consists of a single, minute, positively charged particle, nearly 2,000 times heavier than an electron: this we have called a *proton*.

In addition to these two other kinds of particle have recently been elicited from matter. When the metal beryllium or its compounds is bombarded by the α-particles from radium, it is found to emit particles which have almost the same mass as a proton but which have no electric charge at all. These are called *neutrons*. Finally in the penetrating "cosmic" rays which reach us from outer space are found positively-charged particles with only the same weight as an electron. These are called *positrons*: they are also produced when artificial radio-elements emit their radiations and when very shortwave X-rays act on matter.

These four kinds of particle are the only materials from which atoms could be built up. The hypothesis has been put forward plausibly enough that there exists a fifth type of particle, a

528

"neutrino," which has no charge and a mass comparable with that of an electron, but there is no direct experimental evidence for it. Summarising all this, we can say that the following four ultimate particles have been experimentally demonstrated:

	Mass[1]	Electrical charge[2]
Protons	1.008	$+1$
Neutrons	1.008	0
Electrons	0.00054	-1
Positrons	0.00054(?)	$+1$

The earlier theories, built up when only protons and electrons were known, gave the atom an outer cloud of electrons—certainly correct—and an inner minute nucleus made up of protons and electrons. Now there are very grave difficulties in believing that anything as small as the nucleus could contain such light particles as electrons. The common-sense man naturally feels that the lighter the particles the smaller they should be, but this is not true for electrical charges, the mass of which increases the more closely the charge is concentrated into a little space.

Now we believed (before neutrons were known) that *because* the nucleus of a sodium atom has a mass of 23.00 units and a charge of $+11$ units, *therefore* we can only suppose it to be built of:

23 protons	*Mass 23*	*Charge* $+23$
12 electrons	*Mass negligible*	*Charge* -12
	Mass 23	*Charge* $+11$

We can now believe that the sodium nucleus is made of

11 Protons	Mass 11	Charge $+11$
12 Neutrons	Mass 12	Charge 0
	Mass 23	Charge $+11$

The same arguments apply to all atoms except that of hydrogen.

So if we say that atoms are made of protons and neutrons only, we can account for the minuteness of the nucleus and be none the worse.

[1] The unit is $\frac{1}{16}$ of the weight of an oxygen atom.
[2] The unit is the charge on one electron.

But here is a trouble. We can get neutrons from the nuclei of certain atoms by bombarding them with α-particles, etc.: we can get electrons (β-rays, p. 525) from the nuclei of others. Are there, then, protons, neutrons and electrons in the nucleus? Not necessarily: it is thought that the nucleus contains only neutrons and protons, but that occasionally the transformation

Neutron $\longrightarrow$ Proton $+$ Electron
Mass 1   *Mass* 1   *Mass c.* 0
Charge 0   *Charge* +1   *Charge* —1

may occur so causing an electron to be expelled from the nucleus, the proton remaining behind.

The positron probably plays no part in the atom. It is very short-lived, probably combining with an electron and emitting a quantum of very short-wave radiation and possibly also a neutrino.

Photographs of the trails of the electron, positron and proton appear in Plate XXVII.

ATOMS

The atom itself we have already discussed fairly fully: our main conclusions were that:

(1) It is very small and light, a million million atoms make too small a lump to see.

(2) It is entirely made of very light negatively charged electrons, comparatively heavy neutrons without electrical charge and comparatively heavy protons with a positive charge.

(3) There are as many electrons as protons, so the whole thing is electrically neutral.

(4) The protons and neutrons are all in the nucleus at the centre of the atom. The nucleus is tiny even compared with the atom; it has a positive charge and almost all the weight of the atom is centred in it.

(5) The electrons are arranged in "groups" outside the nucleus (pp. 435–436). When an electron jumps from one group to another, it takes in or gives out a quantum of radiation—light or X-rays. The electrons may be revolving in orbits but there is no certain evidence of this.

Chemistry is chiefly concerned with the way the atoms of elements join up in twos, threes or dozens to form "molecules" of compounds: the outside electrons of the atoms are the things that bind the atoms together. "Molecule," it will be remembered, is the term applied to a collection of two or more atoms firmly bound together by electrical forces.

We realise then that physicists have good reason to believe that all the matter in the universe is made up of atoms, and that these atoms are composed only of three things, electrons, protons and neutrons. About these particles, little is known beyond their weights, their sizes, their electric charges, and the peculiar manner in which they seem to be both particles and waves.

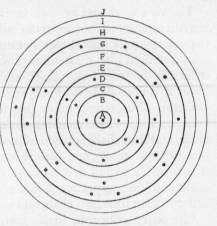

FIG. 340.—Diagram of a copper atom.

A. Tiny nucleus with 29 protons and 34 neutrons. It weights 4,000 times as much as the rest of the atom put together and has a large positive charge.

B.C.D.E.F. Complete groups of electrons (18 in all) which can only be detached by very vigorous treatment—in electric arc, X-ray tube, etc.

G. A group of ten electrons from which one can quite easily be detached. This is one of the two electrons which copper can lose when it forms a compound with another element.

H. Incomplete group of 1 electron. This is easily detached by strong heat, chemical reactions, etc. This electron is very loosely attached: it can come off and travel from atom to atom. This is why copper conducts electricity well.

I.J. etc. Possible positions to which electrons can jump when the atom is heated strongly.

The atom is not, of course, flat like this picture. The electrons are grouped in shells like the coats of an onion.

The view of matter as made of electrons, protons and neutrons is rather remote from everyday affairs, because matter contains these very firmly bound together into atoms which are themselves usually united into molecules. If you want to find out about the difference between say, "lime" and "chalk," it is not helpful to know that both these materials are made of protons, neutrons and electrons. But, if you know that lime is entirely made of molecules, each of which contains one calcium atom and one oxygen atom; and that chalk is made of molecules each of which contains one calcium atom, one carbon atom and three oxygen atoms, it is possible to tell first what substances can be obtained from chalk and lime respectively, and secondly what must be done in order to turn lime into chalk and *vice-versa*.

Chemistry concerns itself, first, with finding out the proportional number and kind of atoms in all the different materials of which the world is made, secondly, with finding out how to turn one kind of molecule into another kind. The chemist's task is made simpler by the fact that there are only ninety-two different possible patterns of atom. Everything that the chemist has tested can be broken up into atoms and only ninety different kinds have been found. Now, a material with only one kind of atom in it is called a Chemical Element, and since it is almost impossible[1] to turn one kind of atom into another kind, it is impossible to get anything out of a chemical element but itself. Take an example. Copper is an element. It is simply a mass of closely packed copper atoms. Take a pound of copper, heat it to a white heat, pass huge electric currents through it, do anything you like to it, you can't get anything out of it but one pound of copper. Suppose you make it red hot in ordinary air; it changes to a sort of black "scale" or rust. Even this has got nothing new *out of* the copper: all that has happened is that the oxygen in the air has combined with it and made copper oxide. If you heat this "scale" in hydrogen, you get all the copper back again. Fig. 341 shows what happens to the copper when heated in the air.

Actually not only the top layer of atoms but a million or so of

[1] But see pp. 544, 551.

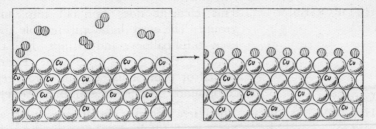

FIG. 341.—What happens to copper when heated in air.

Copper atoms (marked Cu) and   ⟶   Layer of copper oxide molecules on
oxygen molecules (shaded).   the surface of the copper.

the under-layers combine with the oxygen: a penny is at least ten million atoms thick.

Water, on the other hand, is not a chemical element because you *can* get something else than water out of it. If you pass an electric current through water, it gives the gases hydrogen and oxygen.

Well, then, the chemist finds he can extract from the things

FIG. 342.—Water molecules (left) can be changed to hydrogen and oxygen molecules (right). Small sphere = hydrogen atom, large sphere = oxygen atom.

in the world only ninety different materials which cannot be broken up into anything simpler. Some of these are common; some rare: and just to clear our ideas up as to what sort of things these fundamental elements are, a list of them is given below.

ELEMENTS

Every single thing in the world, yourself included, can be broken up into some few of the elements in the list which follows and, given a fine enough technique, could be made from them. These 90 elements are not entirely unlike each other: they fall into groups of five or six elements which resemble each other, often very closely.

HYDROGEN

This element does not fall into any group. The very light inflammable gas used to fill balloons and airships. Half of ordinary coal gas is hydrogen. Every animal or plant must contain hydrogen compounds. Water is one-ninth hydrogen.

Group o.
HELIUM
NEON
ARGON
KRYPTON
XENON

These five elements are all gases and they are remarkable because they are the only elements whose atoms will join up neither with themselves nor with any other kind of atom. Helium is a very light gas and won't burn, so is useful for air-ships. Neon is used in lamps (p. 447). Argon is used to fill electric bulbs and krypton and xenon are so rare as to be useless!

Group I A.
LITHIUM
SODIUM
POTASSIUM
RUBIDIUM
CÆSIUM

These elements are metals but are very soft and easily melted. Their atoms show a most violent tendency to join up with any atom except the atoms of another metal. The result is, they burn in air— combine with oxygen. They will even turn the hydrogen out of water and take the oxygen.

The elements themselves are not of much use, but the compounds of sodium and of potassium with other elements are very important indeed, including salt, soda, saltpetre, etc.

Group II A.
BERYLLIUM
MAGNESIUM
CALCIUM
STRONTIUM
BARIUM
RADIUM

Another lot of metals which are not important except when joined up to other elements. They all burn very easily: Most people have seen the brilliant white flame of magnesium. Calcium com- pounds are very common. Lime, chalk, marble, plaster of paris are examples.

Group III A.

BORON
ALUMINIUM
GALLIUM
INDIUM
THALLIUM

Borax and boracic powder contain boron. Aluminium everyone knows. Gallium and indium are both rarities—no one has found any use for them. Thallium was recently used in medicine but is very poisonous and unreliable.

Group IV B

CARBON

This element is familiar as diamonds, as graphite (pencil-lead), as charcoal, soot, coke, etc. It is, with hydrogen, oxygen and nitrogen, the element absolutely essential for life. Its atoms link with themselves and other atoms to form a prodigious number of compounds, the study of which is called Organic Chemistry. It is not a metal.

SILICON

Pure silicon is something of a rarity but compounds of silicon form a great part of almost all rocks. It is the second commonest element.

GERMANIUM

A rarity.

TIN

Everyone knows this metal, which is the surface coating of "tin cans."

LEAD

Needs no introduction.

Group V B

NITROGEN

This is a gas which makes up four-fifths of the air. Its compounds such as ammonia and nitric acid are extremely important. Every living thing contains combined nitrogen. The gas itself is not important except for making these compounds.

PHOSPHORUS

A peculiar element which exists in two forms, red and white—both of which are all phosphorus. The reddish brown stuff on the *outside* of a match-box is partly red phosphorus. All living things contain a proportion of phosphorus. Some of its compounds are important artificial manures.

ARSENIC

This is a greyish metallic looking stuff. The arsenic with which people poison their relations is a white powder—a compound of this and oxygen. The chemist calls it arsenious oxide.

ANTIMONY

A grey, rather brittle metal. It is used for ornamental objects and, mixed with copper and tin, for typemetal.

BISMUTH

A pinky-white metal of not much importance. Some of its compounds are used as medicine.

Group VI B
OXYGEN

Oxygen makes up one-fifth of the air. Without free oxygen no animal or plant— except a few bacteria—could live and no fire could burn. Its atoms combine with others very easily. Eight-ninths of water is oxygen, as is more than half of most rocks. It is the commonest element in the world.

SULPHUR

Everyone has seen sulphur as yellow sticks or powder. It can be made into beautiful amber-coloured crystals, and also into a soft transparent elastic mass like rubber. Its compounds are important —sulphuric acid, plaster of paris, iron pyrites—to name but a few. All living things contain a little sulphur.

SELENIUM

This looks rather like black sealing-wax. Its interest is its sensitiveness to light: in a bright light it conducts electricity;

	in the dark it does not: it can therefore be used like a photoelectric cell (p. 485).
TELLURIUM	This is a rarity.
POLONIUM	A radioactive element: no one has yet got enough of it to see, though its rays can be detected and measured.

Group VII B.

FLUORINE	A yellow gas: its atoms combine with others so easily that it corrodes or ignites almost everything it touches.
CHLORINE	A yellowish green gas with a very strong smell. It is very destructive to the lungs. It is used for bleaching and various odd jobs in the chemical trade. Ordinary salt is more than half chlorine.
BROMINE	A dark-red liquid which gives a brown vapour with a powerful smell. It is only used in the chemical industries.
IODINE	A black shiny solid which when warmed gives a beautiful violet vapour with a most irritating smell. Dissolved in alcohol, it is a good disinfectant.

Group III A

SCANDIUM
YTTRIUM
LANTHANUM
Fourteen 'rare-earth' elements not important enough to be named here.
ACTINIUM

All rather rare and unimportant metals. The so-called 'flint' in a petrol-lighter is made of an alloy of rare-earth metals.

Group IV A

TITANIUM
ZIRCONIUM
HAFNIUM
THORIUM

Not very uncommon but not very important elements.
The oxide of Thorium is used to make gas-mantles.

Group V A.

VANADIUM ⎫ Rather rare metals. Tantalum is ex-
NIOBIUM ⎪ ceedingly hard and if it was less rare,
TANTALUM ⎬ might be useful for tools. Vanadium is
PROTOACTINIUM ⎭ used for alloying with steel.

Group VI A.

CHROMIUM Till recently, the metal was a rarity, but now is familiar. Everyone knows its blue-white lustre. It does not tarnish and is so hard that it is not easily scratched. Some of its compounds are useful pigments.

MOLYBDENUM Rather rare. It is difficult to fuse. The bit of wire which supports the filament in an electric light bulb is often made of molybdenum.

TUNGSTEN Very hard, very strong and melts only at the terrific temperature of 3360°C. It is used chiefly in filament lamps (p. 441) and X-ray tube targets.

URANIUM The metal is not used for anything, but its compounds give a fluorescent yellow-green colour to glass. It is the "parent" of most of the radio-elements (p. 546).

Group VII A.

MANGANESE The metal is uncommon, but steel always contains a little. Potassium permanganate contains manganese.

MASURIUM There is only scanty evidence that it exists. No one has yet got enough to see!

RHENIUM This is a novelty; rather like tungsten, but very rare.

Group VIII.

IRON Needs no introduction. Its compounds are very common. The higher animals cannot exist without it.

COBALT	Is a metal—not much used. Blue glass and china are coloured by cobalt.
NICKEL	Is well known as nickel plating. A hardish white metal which does not tarnish much.
RUTHENIUM RHODIUM PALLADIUM OSMIUM IRIDIUM PLATINUM	All hard grey-white heavy metals. Palladium is sometimes used for jewellery. Platinum and iridium are useful because they—with gold—are the only metals which are not tarnished even at a red heat, and are not affected by most chemicals. They are both rare and very expensive.

Group I B.

COPPER	Is well enough known. It is valued because it is tough and an excellent conductor of electricity.
SILVER	Is valued for its beautiful colour and its tradition of worth.
GOLD	Was the first metal known. It was valued for its beauty and the fact that it is untarnished and imperishable. This artificial worth makes it too expensive for most useful purposes.

Group II B.

ZINC	Is well known as zinc sheeting and perforated zinc. Galvanised iron is coated with zinc.
CADMIUM	Is a rather uncommon metal but is occasionally used for plating iron.
MERCURY	Is the only metal liquid at ordinary temperatures. It is chiefly used in scientific apparatus.

To this list one or two "radio-elements" which have a transitory existence must be added.

Each of these elements is made of only one kind of atom and

one of the greatest triumphs of the Bohr (and succeeding) theories of the atom is, that they explain in a beautifully simple way how the elements are related to each other.

THE DIFFERENT PATTERNS OF ATOM

From arguments concerned with spectra, etc. (pp. 433 *ff*), we come to the conclusion that a typical atom is like this

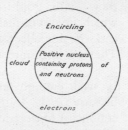

Now, a neutron[1] has no electric charge and a whole atom has no total charge: so it must contain just as many positive protons as negative electrons. So, a typical atom is

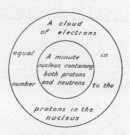

Now, each of the ninety-two elements has a different number of outer electrons. The lowest number is possessed by hydrogen which has just *one* electron, revolving round a nucleus consisting of one proton and no neutron. The highest is Uranium which has

---

[1] An alternative theory is that the nucleus contains only protons and electrons If throughout the following pages you put "a proton and an electron," instead of a neutron, you will have the older theory, the objections to which have been recounted on p. 529.

in its nucleus ninety-two protons and 146 neutrons, and *ninety-two* electrons outside. Accordingly, we can make a list of the atoms in order of the number of electrons they have. This number is called the Atomic Number. The electrons in an atom, we have seen, are ranged in groups (pp. 435, 531), and the number of electrons in each group is limited. If, then, we make a list of the elements in order of their atomic number (number of electrons in their atom) and start a new line from each element which has all its groups filled with electrons and none partly filled, we get the chemist's Periodic Table which appears below. This rather odd-looking list has several remarkable things about it. First, each vertical column contains five or six elements which are very much alike. Thus, column o contains the inert gases which can only be distinguished from each other by their spectra and their density. Secondly, the number of the column which contains a particular element, is related to the number[1] of other atoms with which one atom of that element will combine.

Each place in this table corresponds to a definite atomic number, i.e., to a definite number of electrons in the outer part of the atom of the element which occupies it. The number of positive protons must be definite too —for the whole atom is neutral—

[1] There are a few exceptions to this rule in groups VII and VIII.

Atomic numbers	Ia	IIa	IIIa	IVa	Va	VIa	VIIa	VIII	Ib	IIb	IIIb	IVb	Vb	VIb	VIIb	0
1–2	1 Hydrogen															2 Helium
3–10	3 Lithium	4 Beryllium									5 Boron	6 Carbon	7 Nitrogen	8 Oxygen	9 Fluorine	10 Neon
11–18	11 Sodium	12 Magnesium									13 Aluminium	14 Silicon	15 Phosphorus	16 Sulphur	17 Chlorine	18 Argon
19–36	19 Potassium	20 Calcium	21 Scandium	22 Titanium	23 Vanadium	24 Chromium	25 Manganese	26 Iron 27 Cobalt 28 Nickel	29 Copper	30 Zinc	31 Gallium	32 Germanium	33 Arsenic	34 Selenium	35 Bromine	36 Krypton
37–54	37 Rubidium	38 Strontium	39 Yttrium	40 Zirconium	41 Niobium	42 Molybdenum	43 Masurium	44 Ruthenium 45 Rhodium 46 Palladium	47 Silver	48 Cadmium	49 Indium	50 Tin	51 Antimony	52 Tellurium	53 Iodine	54 Xenon
55–86	55 Caesium	56 Barium	57–71 Lanthanum & fourteen rare earths	72 Hafnium	73 Tantalum	74 Tungsten	75 Rhenium	76 Osmium 77 Iridium 78 Platinum	79 Gold	80 Mercury	81 Thallium	82 Lead	83 Bismuth	84 Polonium	85 ——	86 Emanation
87–92	87 ——	88 Radium	89 Actinium	90 Thorium	91 Protoactinium	92 Uranium										

GROUPS

The Periodic table of elements.

but the number of neutrons may vary. We call an atom
with 82 outer electrons an atom of the metal lead. An atom of
lead, then, always has 82 electrons and 82 protons; but there are
no less than eight *isotopes* of lead, different kinds of lead the atoms
of which have the same number of electrons and protons but
different numbers of neutrons. The diagram shows——

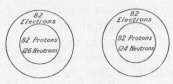

FIG. 343.

the two most abundant kinds of lead atom. The first weighs
208 times as much as a hydrogen atom: the second 206 times as
much. The outer electrons are identical in arrangement and
number. Since the behaviour of a material depends almost
entirely on its outer electrons, these different kinds of lead only
differ in the weights of their atom and their densities and are called
isotopes.

These differences are so small that the chemist does not bother
about them. For his purposes, these differences occasioned by
one or two extra neutrons do not exist, and there are ninety-two
possible patterns of atoms only.

When discussing spectra (p. 435) it appeared that the electrons
were arranged in groups which were limited in the number of
electrons they could contain. This number is usually 8. In an
atom most of the electrons are in groups which already contain as
many as they are able to hold. The electrons in these
complete groups are generally firmly held. But in most
elements, there are a few electrons which are not in a completed group, and it is by reassorting these that atoms bind
themselves together.

Now the chemist is chiefly concerned with making new substances by binding atoms into new molecules and these few outer

electrons which do the actual binding are therefore particularly important to him. As an example of the arrangement of electrons, we may look at the figure of the copper atom (p. 531). We can see that there is one electron (group H) which is conspicuously a member of an incomplete group, and which is very easily detached. Every atom—except an atom of one of the Group o gases—has from 1 to 7 electrons which can be easily detached. The number at the head of each group in the Periodic Table (p. 541) is the number of these loose electrons. So the list tells us in a compact way how many loose electrons belong to each kind of atom. Now it is by these loose electrons that atoms join themselves up into molecules. How is this done? Well, first of all one atom may present its loose electron to another. If we heat some sodium in chlorine gas it burns vigorously. A sodium atom has one loose electron, a chlorine atom has seven. Sodium gives

One Sodium atom one outer electron		One Chlorine atom seven outer electrons		One Sodium ion no outer electron (one + charge)		One Chloride ion eight outer electrons (one − charge)
	+		→		+	

When packed into a crystal form common salt

up its loose electrons to the chlorine atom which now has eight, and as we have seen a group of eight electrons is usually a complete one, very symmetrical and not easily broken up. But the sodium atom has given away a negative electron, so it has a positive charge: the chlorine has taken up an extra negative electron, so it has a negative charge. Consequently, the sodium "ion" and the chlorine "ion" attract each other strongly and pack themselves into a crystal of salt, with a structure as shown in Fig. 16.

There is another important way of linking by loose electrons: namely by sharing them. If an atom, say a carbon atom, has four loose electrons and another, say an oxygen atom, has six loose electrons; the carbon atom can give each of two oxygen atoms a *share* of two of its electrons and receive a share of two of the oxygen atoms electrons in return. The sharing is nearly always done so as to give all the atoms concerned a share of eight electrons, the favourite and particularly stable number. If we suppose that the shared electrons move round both nuclei concerned we could represent this way of combining thus:—

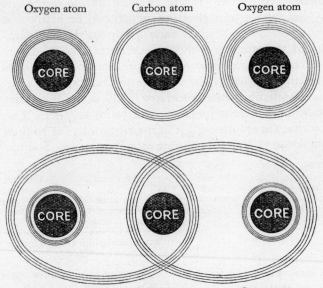

FIG. 344.—Diagram of carbon dioxide molecule. By the core is meant the nucleus and any completed groups of electrons.

All molecules are held together as a consequence of their atoms having given away or shared their outer electrons.

TRANSMUTATIONS

If we grasp clearly the idea of the list of elements on pp. 541 we are in a position to understand radioactivity (already mentioned on pp. 522), which did perhaps more than anything else to stimulate us to learn about the structure of the atom.

Let us recall again that the position of an atom in the list—

its number from the beginning—is simply the number of electrons outside its nucleus. Each of these electrons has a unit negative charge; so, since the whole atom has no charge, the nucleus must have as many positive charges as there are electrons.

Now the nucleus of the atom is probably made of protons and neutrons only: each proton has a positive unit charge and neutrons have no charge. So, the nuclear charge of an atom is the number of protons in it.

Remember now that the number of the element in the Periodic table is simply the number of electrons in its atom and that this is the same as the number of protons.

Suppose we found out a method by which we could take a proton out of the nucleus. The positive charge of the nucleus would become one unit less. It would therefore lose a single negative electron from its outer rings and become the next lower element in the table. Thus, if you could pull a proton out of the mercury atom it would become a gold atom! Actually, we cannot do this, for all our forces are too feeble. We can no more break up the mercury nucleus with ordinary forces than we can open a salmon tin with a feather. We might be able to break up an occasional mercury nucleus by shooting alpha-particles or protons at it, but as a method of making gold, it would be much less good than trying to kill rabbits by dropping bricks on them from an aeroplane in the dark. Given enough bricks and enough time, you would hit a rabbit occasionally, but it would be very slow work.

Now radioactive elements have atoms of which the nuclei, on their own and for no reason that we have yet fathomed, shoot out either a packet of two protons and two neutrons (an alpha-particle), so decreasing the positive charge of the nucleus by two units, or turn one of their neutrons into a proton and an electron which is shot out as a beta-particle, thus increasing the positive charge on the nucleus by one unit. As explained above, when this happens, an atom of a new element must be formed. Thus radium (No. 88) is always shooting out these alpha-particles and changing into an inert gas called radium emanation (radon) (No. 86).

No one could pick on a radium atom and say, "You will lose your alpha-particle on Friday week," no more than you can lay your hand on the shoulder of an old gentleman in the tube and say, "You will die on the seventh of January, 1946." But we know with great accuracy that half the radium atoms in a gram of it will have exploded by the year 3523 and that half the gentlemen of sixty-five alive in 1935 will be dead in 1946.

This half-life period is the best measure of the speed at which a radio-element vanishes. Some of these elements are half gone in a millionth of a second, others in minutes, months, years or millions of years. We obviously cannot directly measure the very long or the very short periods, but a rule called the Geiger-Nuttall relation has been found to apply to the many cases that can be tested and is therefore believed to apply to the others. It depends on the fact that the shorter time an element lasts, the harder it shoots out its alpha-particles. If we measure the range of these—the distance they get before the air stops them—and call this r, then their half period is proportional to $r^{53.9}$, a very curious relationship indeed. If one radio-element can shoot its a-particles through 3 cm. of air and another through 6 cm., then the first lasts $(6 \div 3)^{53.9}$ (about sixteen thousand billion) times as long as the second.

These radio-elements are slowly disappearing. They have not totally disappeared because they are continually being made from two elements, uranium and thorium, with half-life periods of about 5,000,000,000 and 13,000,000,000 years respectively. There is evidence that the earth is only about two or three thousand million years old, so that most of the uranium and thorium in it must have come from the sun, and we think it likely that they were made there. We have very little evidence indeed, but it seems possible that heavier nuclei could be built up from lighter ones at the huge temperatures and pressures which prevail in the interior of the sun.

At any rate, in the half-pound of uranium oxide, that you can buy from the chemist for 10s., about two million atoms break up every second. You notice nothing; for what are two million atoms among the six hundred thousand million million million in the half-pound? Moreover, the explosions are rather feeble.

If you put a piece of uranium oxide on a photographic plate in the dark, you would soon see something was happening, however, for in a few days it would print its own image by the rays it emitted.

A powerfully radioactive element like radium is a very different matter; its remarkable behaviour has already been described in Chapter XVIII.

There is a regular family tree of radioactive elements, each one transmuting itself into the next. This process goes on until uranium or thorium ends up as lead!

The tables which follow show how this happens.

Each element turns into the one below it. On the left of the arrow is the time in which half the element above it is transformed into the one below it. On the right the signs α, β, γ mean that alpha-particles, beta-particles or gamma rays are emitted. The number on the left of the element is the atomic number, its place in the Periodic table (p. 541), that on the right is the weight of its atom (the unit being $\frac{1}{16}$th of the weight of an oxygen atom. Different elements may have the same atomic number.

Take for example element 86. We find three different radio-elements, Actinon, Radon and Thoron, all apparently element 86. The atoms of these are isotopes like the lead atoms in Fig. 343, that is to say, they have the same pattern of electrons and the same *charge* on the nucleus; but they have different *numbers* of neutrons in the nucleus. These elements are, as a result, precisely alike except in their half-life period and to a very minor extent in their density.

Two or more elements, too, may have atoms of the same weight, good examples being Radium B and Radium C. In this case, however, there is no resemblance at all, for the weight of an atom hardly affects its other properties.

Thorium Series

90 Thorium, 232
1.31×10^{10} years ↓ α
88 Mesothorium I, 228
6.7 years → —
89 Mesothorium II, 228
6.2 hours ↓ β+γ
90 Radiothorium, 228
2.02 years ↓ α (β)
88 Thorium X, 224
3.64 days ↓ α
86 Thoron, 220
54 sec. ↓ α
84 Thorium A, 216
0.14 sec. ↓ α
82 Thorium B, 212
10.6 hr. ↓ β+γ
83 Thorium C, 212
1 hour ↓ β — α → 81 Thorium C'', 208
84 Thorium C', 212
10^{-11} sec. ↓ α   3.1 min.
82 Lead, 208 ← β+γ

Actinium Series

89 Uranium Y, 230
25.5 hrs. ↓ β
87 Proto Actinium, 230
12,000 years → —
89 Actinium, 226
20 years → —
90 Radioactinium, 226
19.5 days ↓ α(β)
88 Actinium X, 222
11.4 days ↓ α
86 Actinon, 218
3.9 sec. ↓ α
84 Actinium A, 214
$\tfrac{1}{500}$ sec. ↓ α
82 Actinium B, 210
36 min. ↓ β+γ
83 Actinium C, 210
2.15 min. ↓ α — 81 Actinium C'', 206
84 Actinium C', 210
$\tfrac{1}{2}$ sec. ↓ β+γ   β+γ 4.71 min.
82 Lead, 206 ←

Uranium Series

92 Uranium I, 238
4.67×10^{9} years ↓ α
90 Uranium X₁, 234
24.6 days ↓ β
91 Uranium X₂, 234
1.15 min. ↓ β (γ)
92 Uranium II, 234
2×10^{6} years ↓ α
90 Ionium, 230
69,000 years ↓ α
88 Radium, 226
1,580 years ↓ α(β,γ)
86 Radon, 222
3.85 days ↓ α
84 Radium A, 218
3 min. ↓ α
82 Radium B, 214
26.8 min. ↓ β+γ
82 Radium C, 214
19.5 min. ↓ α — β+γ → 81 Radium C'', 210
84 Radium C, 214
10^{-6} sec. ↓ α   (β+γ) 1.4 min.
82 Radium D, 210
16.5 years ↓ β
83 Radium E, 210
5.0 days ↓ β
84 Polonium, 210
136 days ↓ α (γ)
82 Lead, 206

?

All the elements numbered:	Apart from period of change and rays emitted are exactly like:
81	Thallium
82	Lead
83	Bismuth
84	Polonium
85	No such element known
86	Radon
87	No such element known
88	Radium
89	Actinium
90	Thorium
91	Protoactinium
92	Uranium

The most important of these radio-elements is radium, the separation of which in a pure state has already been described. The long period elements are abundant, but only feebly radioactive. The very short-period elements, on the other hand, are so rare as to be unobtainable in visible quantities, though they are intensely active and produce most energetic rays. Radium is a useful compromise. It is very active and not too rare to be separated. Ionium might be useful, but it is an isotope of thorium and so exactly like it that it cannot be separated from it. Mesothorium I and Protoactinium have also been separated in a fairly pure state, but radium holds the field. Most of the transitory radio-elements have never been seen at all. They are recognised by their rays only.

All three series end up as lead, and the lead atoms produced are of different atomic weights, according to whether they came originally from uranium, thorium or actinium. Consequently, we can gauge the age of a rock by seeing how much of its uranium has been turned to lead; and actually estimate the age of the earth (pp. 741, 742).

Only the heaviest atoms—those with 208 or more protons and neutrons in the nucleus—break up in this way, with two exceptions, namely, the very common element potassium and the very rare elements samarium and rubidium. The radioactivity of these exceptions is exceedingly feeble and it is not yet possible to be sure that it is quite the same thing as the radio-activity of radium.

We can now cause artificial radioactivity in a great number of elements. If we project a stream of neutrons at the element, some of the nuclei of its atoms take in one or more of the neutrons. The new nucleus is unstable and within a few minutes or hours breaks up again, shooting out α-particles or electrons together with short-wave gamma rays. This process turns them into a new element and is a real transmutation. Actually, only the minutest quantities are transformed, but the rays show us what is happening. At present it does not offer a practical way of making gold, though there is no theoretical reason why the metal should not be made in this way, given a large enough supply of neutrons.

Elements can also be transmuted by shooting alpha-particles or protons at them. Occasionally a nucleus is struck and the atom of that element is transformed into another. Thus if the α-particles from a radioelement pass out into an atmosphere of nitrogen, occasionally one will hit the nucleus of a nitrogen atom and be swallowed up by it, ejecting a proton at the same time.

The nucleus of a nitrogen atom
has: 7 Protons + 7 Neutrons
The α-particle has: 2 Protons + 2 Neutrons
_____
9 Protons + 9 Neutrons
The ejected proton represents a loss of: 1 Proton
_____
The final atom has: 8 Protons + 9 Neutrons

In other words its atomic number is 8, and its atomic weight 17, and it is "heavy oxygen." We have transmuted nitrogen to oxygen. Dozens of different transmutations have been accomplished by such means. But it is important to remember that these transmutations are affairs of a few dozen atoms only. We can only detect them because we can photograph the tracks of the colliding atoms and particles. This can be done because an electrically charged particle, when it moves rapidly (p. 287) ionises the air, i.e., knocks electrons off its atoms. So the track of a proton is marked by a line of wrecked atoms. Now if the air is super-saturated with moisture, tiny droplets of water will form round each ion and the track of the proton will be marked by a thin line of cloud, which can be photographed.

Plate XXVII is a photograph of the transmutation already mentioned! The radiating lines are the tracks of α-particles from a radio-element. One of these hits a nitrogen atom, ejects a proton (fine track) while the atom struck and changed into oxygen is driven forwards (coarse track), cannons off another atom and comes to a stop.

Plate XXVII shows the tracks of positrons and electrons in a magnetic field. The fact that some are deflected to the left and some to right shows that we have both positive and negative particles. That the former could not be α-particles or protons is shown by the degree of curvature of the tracks. They are deflected to the same extent as the electrons: we conclude that the particles have the same speed and mass and size of charge as electrons, differing only in that their charge is positive.

CHAPTER XX

COMPOUNDS

MOLECULES

WE have seen that there are ninety-two different kinds of
atoms, and consequently, ninety-two kinds of stuff which
we call elements, each of which has only one kind of atom in it.
Iron, copper, sulphur, hydrogen—these are elements, but what of
the hundreds of thousands of different kinds of stuff that are not
elements? The chemist divides them up into "pure compounds"
and "mixtures." Pure compounds, with which the chemist is
chiefly concerned, contain only one kind of molecule, but two or
more different kinds of atoms. Thus, water is a collection of
molecules, each made of one oxygen atom and two hydrogen
atoms. Absolutely pure water contains nothing but these
molecules; no pure water has ever been made, but the best may
have only one foreign molecule among a million water molecules.
Again, the molecule of rock-crystal (silica) is simply made up of a
silicon atom and two oxygen atoms.

Now, to say that water is a compound of hydrogen and
oxygen atoms is a very different thing from saying it is a mixture
of the gases hydrogen and oxygen. In a mixture of hydrogen and
oxygen made by simply bubbling the two gases into the same
vessel (p. 123), there are loose hydrogen molecules and oxygen
molecules bumping about at random. The *mixture* is obviously a
gas (since hydrogen and oxygen are both gases): it may contain
any proportion of hydrogen and oxygen which may happen to
have been put in: it will behave like oxygen (you could breathe
it) and like hydrogen (it would be very light): you could get the

oxygen out easily, e.g., by cooling the gas to – 190° C, when oxygen would liquefy and hydrogen would not, and you could get the hydrogen out by passing it through a porous tube, which hydrogen penetrates four times as quickly as oxygen. The *compound* water does not contain oxygen molecules or hydrogen molecules and so is not in the least like hydrogen or oxygen. It contains oxygen and hydrogen *atoms*, but these are bound together so

Molecules of pure ELEMENTS
oxygen   hydrogen

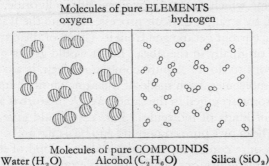

Molecules of pure COMPOUNDS
Water (H$_2$O)   Alcohol (C$_2$H$_6$O)   Silica (SiO$_2$)

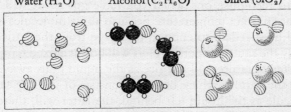

Molecules of a MIXTURE of alcohol and water

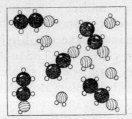

FIG. 345.—Diagram of the arrangement of the atoms and molecules in elements, compounds and mixtures. The diagram shows the sizes (× 30,000,000) and arrangement of the atoms correctly, but the atom itself must not be thought of a round ball with a definite surface! (p. 27).

*18

tightly into water molecules that they can only be got apart again by rough treatment such as the use of electricity or heating its vapour, steam, to a white heat.

In the case of rock-crystal, which contains silicon and oxygen atoms, it is not at all easy to get the gas oxygen from it, though, actually, it is rather more than half oxygen! The chemist can do it by putting it into hydrofluoric acid—a compound of hydrogen and fluorine which turns it into a gas, silicon fluoride, and water. He could, by a rather difficult process, separate the water, and by an electric current get oxygen from it—some of the oxygen which had been originally in the silica. But it would give a good man a week's work to do it. A pure compound, then, is a collection of identical molecules, each made of the same number and the same kind of atoms arranged in the same way. A mixture is a collection of different kinds of molecules. Fig. 345 should give an idea of what we mean by a pure compound and by a mixture.

Since a pure compound contains only one kind of molecule, it is easy to recognise one when you have got it. It will melt (or freeze) at an exact temperature because all its molecules are alike, and will be speeded up enough to escape from the lattice (p. 69) at exactly the same temperature. It will boil at a fixed temperature, and the temperature will not rise as the liquid boils away. This is because the vapour which boils off consists of just the same kind of molecule as the liquid left behind; the latter will, therefore, be unaltered and will boil at the same temperature. Lastly, when once we know how the molecule of a pure compound is made up, we can calculate what proportions of the different elements the compounds contains. Take the bright scarlet sulphide of mercury, the pigment vermilion. The molecule of this contains one atom of mercury and one of sulphur. A mercury atom weighs 200.6 units,[1] and a sulphur atom 32 units. So, a vermilion molecule contains 200.6 units of mercury and 32 units of sulphur, and weighs altogether 232.6 units. So, exactly $\dfrac{200.6}{232.6}$ of the

[1] The "unit" is one-sixteenth of the weight of an oxygen atom. Grams are far too large a unit for weighing atoms.

molecule is mercury. But the vermilion is entirely made of these molecules and so $\frac{200.6}{232.6}$ or 86.2% of it must be mercury.

If the chemist wants to know if a specimen of vermilion he has made or purchased is pure, he uses this fact. He takes an exactly

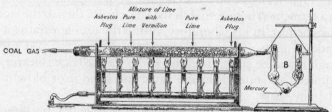

FIG. 346.—How the chemist discovers the proportion of mercury in vermilion.

weighed amount of the vermilion and mixes it with pure lime. He heats the mixture in a glass tube (Fig. 346) through which a gentle stream of coal gas is running. The lime takes the sulphur from the vermilion. The mercury turns into vapour which is carried over more pure hot lime to remove any remaining sulphur, and condenses to liquid mercury in the weighed tube (B), which contains some gold leaf, which has an extraordinary power of collecting mercury vapour. By weighing this tube (B) he finds the weight of mercury in it. If his vermilion is pure the mercury from it will be just 86.2% of the weight of vermilion he started with.

PURIFICATION

The chemist has many ingenious devices for getting pure element or compounds out of mixtures. He gets the pure compound sugar out of sugar-cane juice, pure salt out of sea-water, pure sulphur out of the rough ore. The central idea of all these tricks for separating pure compounds is to find something the pure compound will do that the other things in the mixture will not do—or *vice versa*. We cannot do better than look at a few examples of his craft both in the laboratory and the factory.

The two simplest methods to understand are distillation—used to separate things of different boiling point—and crystallisation—used to separate things which dissolve to a different extent in water. First, let us see how the chemist would separate pure alcohol from a fermented liquor, first in the laboratory, then in the factory.

The chemist, in his laboratory, ordinarily uses apparatus which is made of glass. Very few chemicals affect glass, you can see through it and be sure it is clean, and once the trick is learnt, it is not difficult to soften it in the flame and bend it or blow it into almost any shape.

He joins his various bits of apparatus together by means of corks and rubber tubes, both of which stand up to chemicals pretty well. Metal apparatus is not much used. For a few purposes, platinum is necessary, but a platinum vessel the size of a large thimble costs £5. So most chemists have to do without it. Sometimes, silica, pure white sand, is melted into a glass and blown into apparatus. This is pretty expensive but, unlike glass, stands sudden heating without fear of cracking.

Suppose then, our chemist wants to separate alcohol from wine, which for his purposes may be thought of as water, alcohol and a number of solids which won't evaporate. He will base his efforts on the fact that alcohol, when heated, boils at 78° C. while water boils at 100° C. You might think that if you heated a mixture of alcohol and water, the alcohol would start to boil when 78° C. was reached, that it would then all boil off and that the water would be left behind. But, unfortunately, the alcohol and water do not boil independently. The mixture begins to boil at 85—90° C. and both water vapour and alcohol vapour come off. Still, the vapour is richer in alcohol than the original liquid, so by boiling the liquid we start our separation. If we cool this vapour, the water molecules turn back to liquid more readily than the alcohol molecules—as we should expect, since it takes a higher temperature to turn water into vapour. So, by cooling the vapour, which we get by boiling the liquid, we can condense out a liquid with more water and less alcohol in it than the vapour, leaving this still richer in alcohol. By doing this continuously we can make alcohol with only about 15% of water in it.

To perform this distillation as he calls it, the chemist wants something to boil his wine in, something in which to condense most of the water out of the vapour, something in which to turn the alcohol vapour back to liquid, and something in which to catch the alcohol.

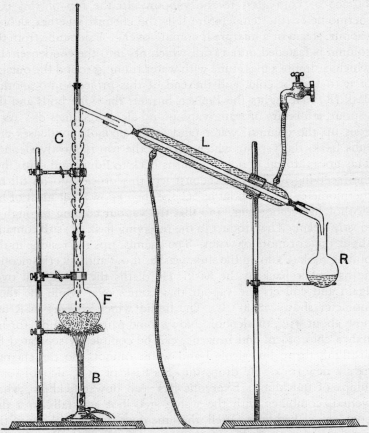

FIG. 347.—Fractional distillation.   Laboratory method.

He puts the wine in a flask (F), a sort of bottle made of thin, strong glass of very even thickness. He supports this on a stand and sits it on a piece of stout wire-gauze, under which is a Bunsen burner (B)—a simple arrangement for burning a mixture of gas and air (already mentioned under the heading of the gas-mantle p. 440).

In the top of the flask is a cork in which he has bored a hole, which is of the right size to grip the fractionating column (C), a tall glass tube of some irregular shape which exposes a big surface of cold glass to the vapour. In the top of this is a thermometer (the temperature tells the chemist whether alcohol vapour, steam or a mixture is coming over). A side tube from the column is fastened into a cork which fits into the condenser (L), which is simply a glass tube with water running round the outside of it to keep it cold, and the end of this projects into another flask (R). He lights the Bunsen burner: the wine boils and the vapour, a mixture of water vapour and alcohol, comes off. As it goes up the column, water (and some alcohol) condenses and runs back: the vapour which gets to the top is mostly alcohol. This goes into the condenser, turns back to liquid and drips into the receiving flask. The chemist lets this process go on till his thermometer shows about 90° C.: he then knows that most of his alcohol has come over, and that the vapour coming through is mostly steam. The product in the receiving flask (R) still contains about 15% or more of water. The chemist tips the residue in the boiling flask (F) down the sink, washes it out and puts the alcohol he has made back in the flask! He distils the alcohol all over again and collects the vapour that comes over while the thermometer shows 78–81° C. The liquid which collects in R has now about 95% of alcohol. Now, some pairs of liquids, for instance chloroform and benzene, can be completely separated by distilling them, but alcohol and water cannot. So the chemist tries a new trick. He drops into his flask of 95% alcohol some lumps of quicklime. Everyone has seen how quicklime, when wetted, combines with the water, gets hot and falls to a dry powder—slaked lime. Well, the lime does the same thing to the water in the alcohol. After two or three days, the chemist distils the mixture of alcohol and lime. The lime, combined with all the water, remains in the flask and 100% pure alcohol passes over into the receiver.

On the factory scale, the principle is just the same. In the diagram below, the column A represents the boiling flask of

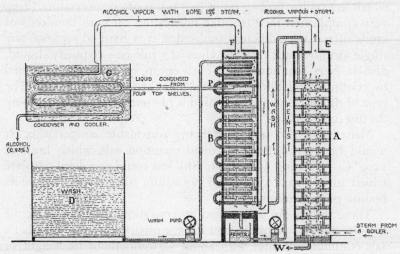

FIG. 348.—A Coffey still. The weak alcoholic liquor "wash" is pumped to the top of the column A. The wash runs down this, and steam is blown up it. The steam evaporates the alcohol. The mixture of alcohol vapour and steam passes up the tower B. Here most of the steam condenses (incidentally heating the wash. The uncondensed vapour is about 85% alcohol.

figure 348; here the mixture of alcohol and water (wash) is heated by steam. The column B is the fractionating column, the tubes in G are the condenser. The fractionating column B is simply a succession of shelves with tubes so arranged that the alcohol vapour and steam have to bubble through the water and alcohol which have already condensed. This is a very efficient arrangement indeed, and actually produces 85% alcohol from a fermented "wash" containing only 5 or 6% of alcohol.

This distillation method enables a chemist to get almost any liquid in a pure state. He has only to distil it repeatedly, rejecting everything which boils more than a degree or two away from the boiling point of the liquid and, if he has enough material, he will probably get a pure compound in the end. Of course, there are plenty of difficulties; thus, substances whose molecules break up near the boiling point—e.g., olive oil—cannot easily be purified by distillation, though the trick of lowering the pressure, which lowers the boiling point (p. 119), is often successful. From very complicated mixtures like lubricating oil with hundreds of kinds of not very different molecules, it is hard to separate any single kind by itself. But the chemist's rule is:—to purify a liquid, distil it. Now that liquid air is fairly cheap, gases are often purified by cooling them till they liquefy and then distilling them. The type of distillation apparatus used is of course very different from the one in figure 347.

Many solids do not boil at any reasonable temperature. It would be very difficult to distil common salt, which boils at 1490° C.—a strong white heat. Still less could one distil saltpetre which turns into oxygen and potassium nitrate long before its boiling point is reached.

These things can be purified by crystallisation. The principle is quite simple. Suppose you have a mixture of, say, Glauber's salt (sodium sulphate) with about a twentieth of its weight of ordinary salt. You can dissolve 20.25 grams of Glauber's salt and no more in 100 cubic centimetres of cold water (10° C.) and a considerable amount of common salt as well. But you can dissolve 65 grams of Glauber's salt and a large amount of common salt in the same amount of warm water at 30° C. So take 65 grams of your mixture containing 61.75 grams of Glauber's salt and 3.25 grams of common salt, and dissolve it in 100 c.cs. of warm water at 30° C. or more. Now let it cool to 10° C. The water will still dissolve the 3.25 grams of salt but will only dissolve 20.25 grams of Glauber's salt. So, the odd 41.5 grams (61.75–20.25) of the latter appears as pure crystals without any salt! The chemist would probably do the operation as in Fig. 349. He would warm up the salt mixture and water in a beaker, a strong thin glass tumbler with rounded corners (A). He would leave this to cool with a "clock-glass" over it to keep out dust (B). He would then

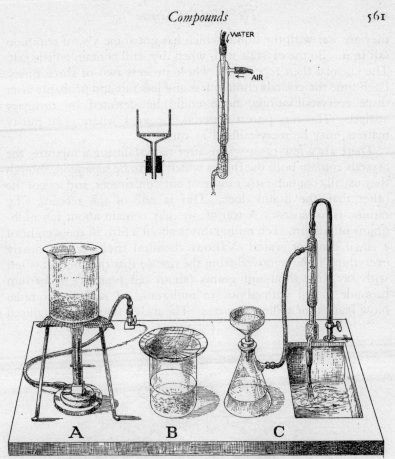

FIG. 349.—Purifying a substance by crystallisation.

suck the liquid away from the crystals with the clever little gadget shown inset in Fig. 349. The jet of water mixes with air in the conical tube and carries it away as a froth of bubbles. This reduces the air pressure in the filter flask (C). The affair at the top of this is a kind of china colander, covered by a filter paper, which is a sort of strong thin porous blotting-paper. The pressure of the air pushes the liquid through into the flask and the crystals stay behind on the paper. The crystals are pure Glauber's salt: but they are wet with the liquid which has got some 3 % of common salt in it. So the crystals will, when dry, still contain a little salt. The chemist then repeats the whole process two or three times. Each time the crystals contain less and less salt and probably after three recrystallisations, none could be detected by ordinary analysis. The very purest material, for work where great purity matters, may be recrystallised 15 times.

There are a few cases where after recrystallising a mixture, the crystals contain both the things which are to be separated, though they usually contain rather more of one constituent, and less of the other than the liquid does. This is one of the reasons why radium is expensive. A ton of ore may contain about ten milligrams of radium. Ten milligrams is about a fifth of the weight of a small drop of water! Various chemical tricks enable nearly everything to be removed from the ore: so that the chemist is left with say, five thousand grams (about ten pounds) of barium bromide mixed with about 10 milligrams of radium bromide. Now begins the tedious process. The mixed salts are crystallised

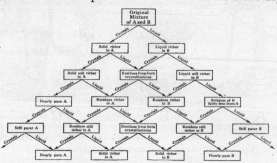

FIG. 350.—How fractional crystallisation is carried out.
A = radium bromide   B = barium bromide.

in much the same way as our impure Glauber's salt. The crystals will contain a little more radium than the original and the liquid a little less radium. The crystals are crystallised again, giving a new lot of crystals richer in radium, and a liquid poorer in radium, and this has to be repeated many times. Fig. 350 shows how the crystals from one process are mixed with the liquid from another, so that the material is gradually sorted out into pure radium bromide and barium bromide. As the radium bromide and barium bromide look precisely alike, it is very necessary to test them at every stage to see how the process is getting on. This is not difficult because the rays from the radium reveal its presence very readily by ionising the air and making it conduct electricity.

This crystallisation method is usually easy: it is only a very few things that need such a lengthy treatment as radium, and needless to say anything that requires all this skilled labour is expensive. But such things as salt, sugar, soda, Epsom salts, copper sulphate, quinine, tartaric acid, saltpetre—to name but a few out of thousands—are easily purified by two or three such crystallisations. On the large scale, in the manufacture of chemicals, chemists use enamelled pans like large coppers holding a hundred or so gallons of liquid. The solution in them takes two or three days to cool, consequently, the molecules have time to arrange themselves as very beautiful crystals. Common soda is crystallised in this way, and forms noble arrays of crystals like great lances of ice. But the public prefers its soda crushed, and it is only here and there in a 7 lb. bag of soda that you can pick out recognisable crystal fragments.

The troublesome things to purify are those that won't boil and won't dissolve in water, alcohol or anything else. Copper oxide, metals like iron or platinum, silicates like mica, organic things with huge fragile molecules like keratin (the material of hair) or cellulose, the material of cotton wool, are the really difficult things to purify. The only way to get them pure is either to remove everything else from them, or to make them from pure materials. We can only get pure cellulose by soaking cotton fibres in various chemicals which we hope will destroy or dissolve every kind of molecule except that of cellulose. Pure copper oxide we can make by crystallising the blue salt, copper sulphate, till it is quite pure, and contains atoms of no other metal than copper. Then we can turn this into pure copper by passing an electric current through it, and then heat the pure copper in lots of pure oxygen. In this way, we can get material which has nothing but copper and oxygen in it.

"Pure" is a relative term in chemistry. No one has ever seen a pure material. If "pure copper" has only one iron atom to every ten thousand copper atoms, it is very pure indeed. Our standard of "perfectly pure" material is a material in which we can find no impurities. Nobody believes that any of our materials are perfectly pure, *i.e.*, have no other molecules in them but those of the material we want.

This survey has given us a rough idea of how the chemist purifies his materials. If you look at a chemical catalogue, you will find that you can buy about 5,000 different pure substances. Well, all these must have been made out of something and the only things man can start with in making his chemicals are air, water, plants, animals and the rocks. From these, the chemists make a few hundred pure materials, and build these up into the five thousand chemical substances you can buy and the two hundred thousand you have to make for yourself if you want them. Such familiar things as most of the metals, as nitric acid, aspirin, chloroform, benzene, most of the drugs we take, almost all our dyes, existed nowhere on earth till the chemist began his work. The two great tasks of the chemist are *analysis*—splitting up substances to see what elements and molecules they contain—and *synthesis*, building up simpler molecules into more complicated ones.

FORMULÆ

Chemical formulæ are a bit of a bugbear to the amateur. H_2O is commonly known to mean "water"; but things like $C_6H_5.CO.NH.C_6H_4.CH_3$ and names like

ι-2 : 2 : 6-trimethyl- Δ^5-*cyclohexenyl-γη-dimethyl-*$\Delta^{\beta\delta\zeta\theta}$-*nontetraene*,

put the public off. The chemical formula is a very harmless affair: the chemical names look horrible because they are really a sentence in code. The name tells the chemist who knows the code what atoms there are in the molecule, and where each of them is! We speak of the man next door as Bill Jones. This merely labels him. The chemist could do this if he wanted to. He might call the compound amphiblose or discorin, or something euphonious. But he prefers to give it a name which explains it; which is as if we called Bill Jones, *The-fellow-with-red-hair-who-lives-at-42-Acacia-Street-and-is-a-bank-clerk*. If the substance with the long name comes into common use the chemist gives it a "trivial" name which people can pronounce and remember. Thus, 2-phenylquinoline-4-carboxylic acid, a drug used for treating gout and sciatica, receives the simple name of Atophan.

The formula is just a shorthand way of saying what atoms there are in a single molecule of the substance. Each element has a symbol—an abbreviation—which stands for one of its atoms. This symbol is usually the initial of the element; in some cases the initial of the Latin name for the element is taken. Where several elements share an initial, a second small letter is appended.

A FEW SYMBOLS

Element	Symbol for an atom of the element
Hydrogen	H
Boron	B
Carbon	C
Nitrogen	N
Fluorine	F
Neon	Ne
Sodium (*natrium*)	Na
Magnesium	Mg
Aluminium	Al
Silicon	Si
Phosphorus	P
Sulphur	S
Chlorine	Cl
Bromine	Br
Iodine	I
Potassium (*kalium*)	K
Calcium	Ca
Barium	Ba
Iron (*ferrum*)	Fe

Element	*Symbol for an atom of the element*
Copper (*cuprum*)	Cu
Nickel	Ni
Silver (*argentum*)	Ag
Gold (*aurum*)	Au
Zinc	Zn
Mercury (*hydrargyrum*)	Hg

A little number after a symbol tells the number of that kind of atom in the molecule. A molecule of alcohol is arranged like this, the black balls being carbon atoms, the little white ones hydrogen atoms and the shaded one, an oxygen atom.

The symbol for a carbon atom is C, for a hydrogen atom is H, and for an oxygen atom is O. So if we want to show how the atoms in alcohol are arranged, we can print the formula

$$
\begin{array}{ccc}
\text{H} & \text{H} & \\
| & | & \\
\text{H—C—C—O—H} \\
| & | & \\
\text{H} & \text{H} &
\end{array}
$$

If we are not anxious to show the arrangement of the atoms, we put the formula as C_2H_6O, meaning by it that a single molecule of alcohol contains two carbon atoms, six hydrogen atoms and an oxygen atom. One other way of writing the formula remains. When alcohol is treated with chemicals, it behaves as if it was made of three bits or groups of atoms, CH_3, CH_2, and OH. So we often write

$$
\begin{array}{ccc}
\text{H} & \text{H} & \\
| & | & \\
\text{H—C—C—O—H} & \quad\text{as}\quad & CH_3.CH_2.OH \\
| & | & \\
\text{H} & \text{H} &
\end{array}
$$

Fig. 366 shows pictures of the molecules of several substances and their formulæ. To find out the formula of a complicated unknown substance—say a drug someone has extracted from a tropical plant or the body of an animal—is a very difficult job, and is much beyond the scope of this book. Roughly, you first find out what elements are in it, then what is the weight of each of them, then (knowing the weight of each kind of atom) the number of atoms of each kind. Then comes the really difficult part. Given a formula like $C_4H_7ON_3$, it is the chemist's job to find out that the atoms, which might be arranged in dozens of different ways, actually have, let us suppose, this particular arrangement:[1]

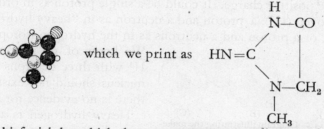

which we print as

$$HN=C \begin{matrix} & H \\ & | \\ & N—CO \\ & | \\ & | \\ & N—CH_2 \\ & | \\ & CH_3 \end{matrix}$$

The chief trick by which these arrangements are discovered is to do things (*e.g.*, heating the substance or boiling it with acids) which may knock the molecules to bits: from these bits you may be able to separate substances of which you already know the formulæ. These formulæ, then, probably are parts of a jig-saw puzzle which when solved gives the formula of your molecule. Another method is to say, "If the formula is so-and-so, we ought to find that it can be made when certain specified substances are cooked up together." The experiment is tried and may be successful.

However, determining formulæ is work we can leave to the professional: if we carry away the notion that C_9H_7N is the formula of a substance which has, in every one of its molecules nine carbon atoms, seven hydrogen atoms and a nitrogen atom, it is enough for now.

[1] Throughout Part IV of this book carbon atoms are represented as black, oxygen as diagonally shaded, nitrogen as stippled, hydrogen as white, others as spheres labelled with the appropriate symbol (p. 565). Their sizes are in general thirty million times greater than those of the actual atoms.

CHAPTER XXI

HYDROGEN

WHAT we call an atom of hydrogen is an atom which has only one electron. Its nucleus must, therefore, have a single positive charge. It could be a single proton as in ordinary hydrogen (H^2): a proton and a neutron as in "heavy hydrogen" (H^1), or a proton and 2 neutrons as in the hydrogen isotope H^3. We know of no reason why H^4 with three neutrons in its nucleus should not exist: but there is no evidence for it.

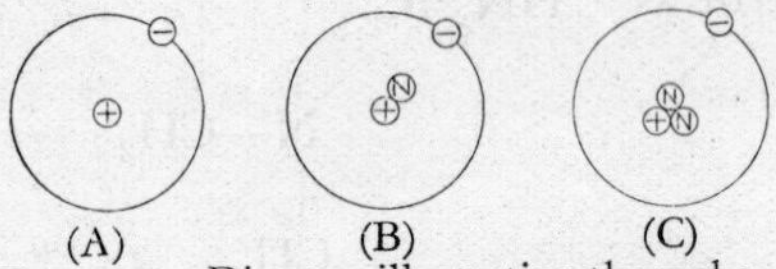

FIG. 351.—Diagram illustrating the make-up of (A) the ordinary hydrogen atom (B) the H^2 isotope (C), the H^3 isotope: electrons are marked –, protons +, and neutrons N.

Heavy hydrogen is a very new discovery, and the exceedingly rare H^3 still newer. One hydrogen atom in about 6,000 is of the heavy H^2 variety, and one in 100,000,000 of the H^3 type.

Hydrogen atoms will only remain single for a very small fraction of a second and then link up with their neighbours into pairs which we call hydrogen molecules. In these, two nuclei share two electrons. It is not known just how the sharing is done but Fig. 352 gives a possibility —each electron rotating round both nuclei. At any rate we know that hydrogen gas as we make it consists of pairs of hydrogen atoms.

There are at least twenty quite good ways of making

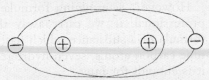

FIG. 352.—A possible but very conjectural arrangement for a hydrogen molecule (H^1_2). The symbol + indicates a proton, the symbol – an electron.

hydrogen gas. Let us consider a very simple one which gets the hydrogen from the cheapest compound in the world—water.

Make coke white hot and blow steam over it. Carbon and steam give the gases carbon monoxide and hydrogen, a process we have already described on p. 255. This gas is then mixed with more steam and led over a mixture mainly consisting of iron oxide, whereupon the carbon monoxide and the steam give the gases carbon dioxide and hydrogen.

We have now a mixture of carbon dioxide and hydrogen. Compressed carbon dioxide dissolves easily in water, hydrogen does not: so by compressing the gas and forcing it through water, we dissolve out all the carbon dioxide and leave hydrogen.

This is the chief commercial method. It gives us, by the way, a very good chance to show what a chemical equation is. We will show what happens to the steam and coke by a picture

$$C + OH_2 \rightarrow CO + H_2$$

The equation says just the same thing as the picture, but in type! The second stage in which carbon monoxide and steam giving carbon dioxide and hydrogen may be figured

$$OC + OH_2 \longrightarrow CO_2 + H_2$$

The iron compounds over which the hot gases had to be passed do not figure in this picture because they are *unchanged*. It is not at all uncommon in chemical work to find that two substances will only react chemically—re-assort the atoms in their molecules—in presence of some third substance, which is apparently quite unchanged.

A substance of this kind is called a *catalyst*. It is not really known how a catalyst does its work. Sometimes it may combine with one of the substances and make a compound which the other substance breaks up again.

Thus call the two substances A and B; their compound which we want to make, AB; and the catalyst C. Without the catalyst A does not combine with B, but with it we may find that A and C gives AC and then AC and B gives AB and sets free C to react with A once more. Thus a little C can make any quantity of A and B combine. But more often it would seem that the catalyst absorbs the gases on to its surface and so brings their comparatively widely spaced molecules into very close contact so that they have a greater opportunity to combine. Be this as it may, these catalysts are of huge importance. Hydrogen, ammonia, nitric acid, sulphuric acid and many important chemicals are made by means of them, and the "enzymes" by which living things perform almost all the peculiar chemical operations of their cells are catalysts also.

The steam-and-coke method serves very well for commercial purposes.

In the laboratory (or the home), certain metals and certain acids can be used to give hydrogen. Zinc and hydrochloric acid (spirits of salt diluted with water) or dilute sulphuric acid (battery acid) are best used; the acid produces with water the "ion" H_3O^+ with a positive charge, that is to say, with one electron fewer than the four single atoms H, H, H and O would have. Zinc gives its two spare electrons to two of these ions which break up into water and hydrogen atoms which at once turn into molecules. The zinc turns into zinc ions which dissolve in the water.

So, starting from pure sulphuric acid and zinc,

(1) Dilute the acid and so make a molecule

$$\begin{array}{ccc} H_2O & & [H_3O]^+ \\ & + H_2SO_4 \longrightarrow & + [SO_4]^{--} \\ H_2O & & [H_3O]^+ \end{array}$$

of it into two hydroxonium ions with an electron lacking and a sulphate ion with two extra electrons.

(2) Put in the zinc. Its atom gives its two loose electrons to

the hydroxonium ions and turns them into water **and** hydrogen atoms which then form molecules. The zinc is left as an ion which combines with six water molecules.

$$Zn + [H_3O]^+ \longrightarrow Zn^{++} + 2H_2O + H + H$$
$$[H_3O]^+$$

$$H + H \longrightarrow H_2$$
$$Zn^{++} + 6H_2O \longrightarrow [Zn(H_2O)_6]^{++}$$

The solution left behind after the zinc has given its electrons away, contains zinc ions (combined with six molecules of water), and an equal number of sulphate ions probably each combined with one molecule of water. If the solution is boiled down, these become near enough to be attracted by each other, and pack themselves into a beautifully regular pattern and appear as crystals of the salt zinc sulphate.

We can write its formula as

$$[Zn.6H_2O]^{++} [SO_4.H_2O]^{--}$$

or more simply as $Zn\,SO_4.\,7H_2O$.

The chemist makes his hydrogen in the ingenious apparatus called a "Kipp" from its inventor and shown in Fig. 353.

The liquid is a mixture of an acid (not nitric acid) and water. The solid is zinc, best in the irregular lumps made by pouring molten zinc into water.

Turn on the tap. The pressure of acid pushes the hydrogen out, and the acid rises on to the zinc. A steady stream of hydrogen is then produced. Turn off the tap, and the hydrogen as fast as it is produced collects

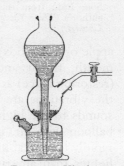

FIG. 353—Kipp's apparatus.

in the middle bulb and forces the acid back into the upper bulb—and after a few seconds no acid remains on the zinc

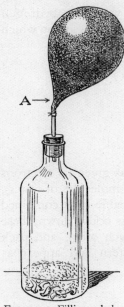

A→

and the action ceases till more hydrogen is wanted, and the tap is turned on again!

Figure 354 shows a balloon being filled with hydrogen. A rubber cork is best, but a good sound one made of ordinary cork does very well. It is as well to coat the bottom of the cork only with hot candle-grease.

Suppose we have some hydrogen—say a cylinder of it—how should we tell it from air? It is colourless like air and invisible. If you let some escape, it would not poison you, though you could not live in pure hydrogen. In fact, as long as you were careful not to strike a light and so cause a shattering explosion you could live in an atmosphere of four parts of hydrogen and one of oxygen, instead of in ordinary air (4 parts nitrogen to one of oxygen), and would only notice one curious difference: your voice would sound shrill! The reason of this is interesting. The voice is generated by vibrating membranes in the larynx (Adam's apple or voice-box), and is intensified by the air vibrating in the mouth, throat and nose. Hydrogen has the same elasticity (restoring force) as air has, but it is much lighter so that (p. 368) the vibrations are much quicker and a cavity filled with it resounds to the higher frequencies in the voice. If you fill a toy balloon with air, it sinks slowly: filled with hydrogen, it rises rapidly to a great height. The reason why a balloon, full of a gas lighter than air, rises has already been explained: the question arises as to why hydrogen is so light. Actually, a cubic foot of hydrogen has about a fourteenth of the weight of a cubic foot of air. One of the most important laws in chemistry tells us that equal volumes of gases, under the same conditions of temperature and pressure, contain the same number of molecules.

If a cubic foot of oxygen contains a billion billion molecules at say, 15° C and a pressure of 15 lbs./square inch, then a cubic foot of hydrogen will, under these same conditions also contain a billion billion molecules. But a hydrogen molecule contains two protons, while an oxygen molecule contains 32 protons and neutrons (the electrons are so light that they can be left out): consequently, an oxygen molecule is 16 times as heavy as a hydrogen molecule. So a cubic foot of oxygen (a billion billion heavy molecules) is sixteen times as heavy as a cubic foot of hydrogen (a billion billion light molecules).

Air is a mixture of one part of oxygen, 16 times as heavy as hydrogen, with four parts of nitrogen, 14 times as heavy. Consequently, air is fourteen and two-fifth times as heavy as hydrogen. The lightness of hydrogen makes it the usual thing for filling balloons and airships. Helium is not much less light, and is non-inflammable. It is therefore more useful where enough can be obtained.

Since a hydrogen molecule is very light, it must move very fast. All molecules at the same temperature have the same energy— *i.e.*, hit equally hard. Consequently, the light ones move fastest. This high-speed motion makes it very difficult for a hydrogen molecule to be slowed down enough to liquefy or freeze (p. 72, 136): it liquefies only at –252° C. The only gas more difficult to liquefy is helium.

The most obvious difference between hydrogen and air is that in air or oxygen hydrogen burns with a very hot and almost invisible pale blue flame. Burning is simply a chemical change— an alteration of the way atoms are linked together—which takes place with so much energy that much heat and light are given out. A hydrogen molecule *at the ordinary temperature* can bump an oxygen atom millions of times a second for many years without altering either of them. But at a red heat, the molecules are moving faster and collide harder, and the atoms in them are twisting and wriggling more vigorously. So, a hot hydrogen molecule bumps a hot oxygen molecule and they link up and make a molecule of hydrogen peroxide H_2O_2.

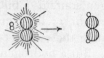

This bumps a molecule of hydrogen and so forms two molecules of steam.

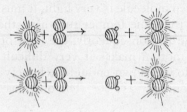

These have got in them all the extra energy which the reshuffling of the atoms provides, and so they shoot off with an extra dose of energy. When either of them hits an oxygen molecule they hand on this energy to it, which makes it ready to combine with the next hydrogen molecule it hits and form more hydrogen peroxide and water.

But since each oxygen molecule produces *two* steam molecules which start *two* oxygen molecules reacting, it is evident that the number of molecules combining *doubles* in the time interval taken by the process just described, which is less than a millionth of a second, and continues to double itself in each succeeding millionth of a second.

So, clearly, hot oxygen and hydrogen will combine in an extremely short time and, moreover, turn all their chemical energy into heat and work in this short time. This means an explosion. If you put a match to an open jar containing a mixture of oxygen and hydrogen, a deafening bang is heard and if the jar does not break, a faint dew of moisture is seen upon it; this is the water formed.

A gas explosion like this travels as a wave. The first lot of gas to burn produces much heat and suddenly and violently expands. This compresses the gas in front of it and heats it up until it too explodes. The result is a wave of compressed gas like a very violent sound wave (but twice as rapid) travelling outward. · After the explosion is over, the wave travels on as a sound wave and is ultimately heard as the noise of the explosion.

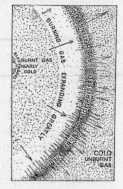

Fig. 355.—How an explosion wave is propagated.

Hydrogen combines with lots of elements beside oxygen. We will leave these till we talk about the elements in question, but a list of them will give some idea of the important compounds concerned.

ELEMENT	COMPOUNDS WITH HYDROGEN ONLY.
Carbon	All the compounds in oil and petrol. The two simplest examples are methane CH_4 (firedamp) and acetylene C_2H_2.
Nitrogen	Ammonia NH_3.
Oxygen	Water OH_2: hydrogen peroxide O_2H_2.
Sulphur	Hydrogen sulphide H_2S (the poisonous part of sewer-gas).
Chlorine	Hydrogen chloride HCl, which dissolved in water gives hydrochloric acid.

Besides these, there are a host of compounds which contain hydrogen and two or more other elements, and these include almost everything of which the bodies of plants and animals are made.

Hydrogen combines in two very different ways. Some

hydrogen compounds like firedamp, "methane" (CH_4), or ammonia (NH_3) stick to their hydrogen atoms pretty firmly: but another class called "acids" very easily exchange hydrogen atoms for other atoms.

ACIDS

The idea of an "acid" is not very easy to grasp. Think of a few of the acids you have met. There is sulphuric acid, an oily transparent liquid which destroys clothes and skin, and most other things it is dropped on: there is citric acid, used in lemonade powders: there is boric acid, the boracic powder used for dusting sore places, etc. Not much in common between these. An acid is really a compound containing hydrogen which, when the

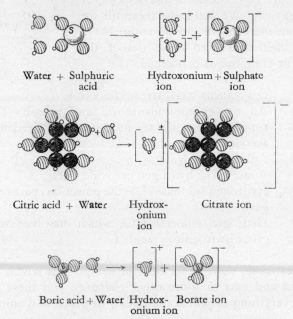

Water + Sulphuric   Hydroxonium + Sulphate
      acid   ion   ion

Citric acid + Water   Hydrox-   Citrate ion
               onium
               ion

Boric acid + Water   Hydrox-   Borate ion
               onium ion

Fig. 356.—How certain acids ionise. For explanation of symbols see note p. 567.

PLATE XXV

(*Left*) Bloodstained cloth. (*Centre*) Same washed and photographed in ordinary light. (*Right*) Same as centre, but photographed by ultra-violet light. (By courtesy of Dr. F. W Martin, Medico-Legal Department, University of Glasgow.

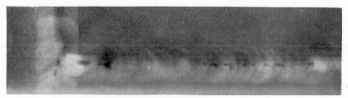

X-ray picture of an oxyacetylene weld showing cavities and blow-holes.

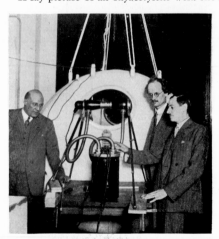

The sphere of Professor Piccard's stratosphere balloon being examined by X-rays for defects. (Both by courtesy of Messrs. Philips Metalix, Ltd.)

PLATE XXVI

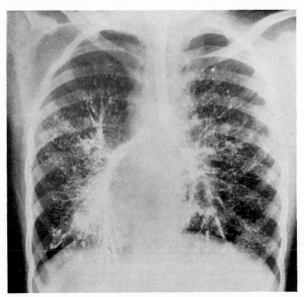

Radiograph of the chest showing "bronchial tree" outlined by lipiodol. (By courtesy of the authorities of St. George's Hospital, London.)

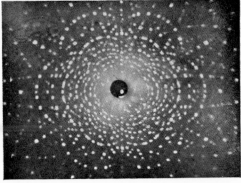

Laue X-ray diffraction photograph of a crystal of nepheline. Note the hexagonal symmetry. (By courtesy of the *Mineralogical Magazine*.)

compound is dissolved in water is in some measure detached as a hydroxonium ion H_3O^+.

Sulphuric, citric and boric acid are alike in giving this H_3O^+ ion when dissolved in water. They differ in that where a certain weight of sulphuric acid gives a million ions, the same weight of citric acid gives 16,000 ions and of boric acid but 25.

We call sulphuric acid a strong acid, citric acid a weak acid, and boric acid a very weak acid.

COMMON ACIDS

ALL THESE GIVE H_3O^+ WHEN DISSOLVED IN WATER

STRONG ACIDS

Nitric acid	"aqua fortis"
Sulphuric acid	"oil of vitriol"
Hydrochloric acid	"spirits of salt"

WEAK ACIDS

Acetic acid	The acid in vinegar.
Tartaric acid	Used in baking-powder. The acid in sour wine.
Citric acid	The acid in lemon juice.
Oxalic acid	"Salts of lemon," very poisonous.
Acetyl-salicylic acid	Aspirin.

VERY WEAK ACIDS

Boric acid	"Boracic powder."
Carbonic acid	"Soda-water."

19

So really all acids when mixed with water are just solutions of hydroxonium ion H_3O^+ and of some other ion which from the point of view of its acid properties usually does not much matter. Acids without water (or some other solvent like water) just do not act as acids at all ! So, if we want to know how acids in general behave, it is enough to know what hydroxonium ion does.

First of all, it tastes sour. You can try that with the strong sulphuric acid if you stir a drop or two into a tea-cup of water. A stronger solution would be dangerous. The tastes of acetic acid (in vinegar), of citric acid in lemon juice, are familiar enough. For the very weak acids, carbonic and boric, the sense of taste is not sensitive enough to detect the sourness. It is a pretty general rule that anything which tastes sour (not bitter) has an acid in it. Unripe fruit, sorrel leaves, lemons, cranberries, aspirin, all contain acids and taste sour.

Hydroxonium ion is not poisonous unless a great deal is present, in which case it irritates and finally destroys and liquefies the substance of the throat and stomach. Consequently, if you drink any of the strong acids mixed with only a little or no water, you will die a slow and painful death. Weak acids, and strong acids mixed with fifty or so times their weight of water, are harmless unless the other ion or the unbroken acid molecule is poisonous. Thus, oxalic acid is very poisonous, though a weak acid, and the most rapid of poisons, prussic acid, is so weak as to be hardly an acid at all.

Secondly, hydroxonium ion will take electrons from suitable metals and turn them into ions and itself into water and hydrogen. This has been explained under the making of hydrogen (p. 570). This will not work with some metals (platinum, gold, silver, mercury, copper): it works best with magnesium and second best with zinc. Actually, the hydrogen comes off very slowly unless the acid is a fairly strong one.

Finally, hydroxonium ion H_3O^+ and hydroxyl ion OH^- combine and form water H_2O. The things which give hydroxonium ion are acids and those which give hydroxyl ion are called alkalies or bases. So acids combine with alkalies to give water; and the remaining ions when the solution is boiled down pack themselves into crystals and are called a salt.

Consider some caustic soda. The molecule of this is a positively charged sodium ion bound by electrical attraction to a negatively charged hydroxyl ion (Fig. 357, I). Dissolve it in water and the ions wander off freely, a bodyguard of water molecules screening them from each other's attraction (Fig. 357, II). Dissolve some hydrochloric acid in water (Fig. 357, III). It changes to hydroxonium ion H_3O^+ and chloride ion Cl^-—a chlorine atom with an extra electron. Mix the two solutions. Hydroxonium ion and hydroxyl ion give water (Fig. 357, IV), and the chloride ion and sodium ion Cl^- and Na^+ are left. Now, a mixture of sodium ions, chloride ions and water is just a solution of common salt, and if you boil the solution dry you get small crystals of sodium chloride built out of ions of sodium and chlorine (p. 47).

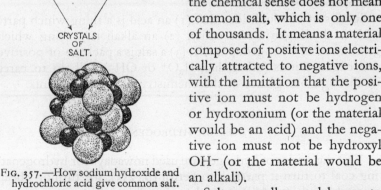

FIG. 357.—How sodium hydroxide and hydrochloric acid give common salt.

Any acid and any alkali or base give a salt and water. A salt in the chemical sense does not mean common salt, which is only one of thousands. It means a material composed of positive ions electrically attracted to negative ions, with the limitation that the positive ion must not be hydrogen or hydroxonium (or the material would be an acid) and the negative ion must not be hydroxyl OH^- (or the material would be an alkali).

Salts are well enough known to all of us. The following table tells us the formulæ of a few salts and shows the acids and metals (or alkalies) they can be made from.

SALTS

Common name.	Chemical name.	Formula.	Made from	
			Acid	Alkali or Base.
Common salt	Sodium chloride	NaCl	Hydrochloric HCl	Caustic soda NaOH
Glauber's salt	Sodium sulphate	Na_2SO_4	Sulphuric H_2SO_4	Caustic soda NaOH
Saltpetre	Potassium nitrate	KNO_3	Nitric HNO_3	Caustic potash KOH
Plaster of Paris	Calcium sulphate	$CaSO_4$	Sulphuric H_2SO_4	Calcium hydroxide or lime $Ca(OH)_2$
Marble	Calcium carbonate	$CaCO_3$	Carbonic H_2CO_3	Calcium hydroxide or lime $Ca(OH)_2$
Lunar caustic	Silver nitrate	$AgNO_3$	Nitric HNO_3	Silver oxide Ag_2O
Blue vitriol	Copper sulphate	$CuSO_4$	Sulphuric H_2SO_4	Copper oxide CuO
Corrosive Sublimate	Mercuric chloride	$HgCl_2$	Hydrochloric HCl	Mercuric oxide HgO
White vitriol	Zinc sulphate	$ZnSO_4$	Sulphuric acid H_2SO_4	Zinc oxide ZnO

Some sort of rough idea that (1) an acid is a thing which parts with its hydrogen atoms easily; (2) an alkali is a thing which gives away an OH^- group easily; (3) a salt is a package of positive and negative ions (other than H_3O^+ or OH^-) will do to carry us through our glance at the chemistry of other elements.

USES OF HYDROGEN

Vast quantities of hydrogen are used nowadays for hydrogenating coal to turn it partly into petrol (p. 253); for turning cheap uneatable oils (p. 630) into clean fats for making margarine— for hydrogenating lubricating oils (p. 235), and for turning nitrogen into ammonia (p. 647).

CHAPTER XXII

AIR AND OXYGEN

OXYGEN

OXYGEN is the most abundant element in the world. The air is one-fifth oxygen, all the vast wastes of the sea are eight-ninths oxygen and the rocks we walk on contain between a quarter and half their weight of oxygen. I look round this room—metals excepted, I cannot see a thing which does not contain oxygen. Skin, cotton, wool, brick, glass, china, wood, paint, ivory, all contain oxygen.

It is characteristic of oxygen that it combines with most things very readily if they are heated and once an oxygen atom has combined with another kind of atom, it is not easy to tear it away from its companion. The chemist calls it a reactive element—one which readily forms compounds.

An oxygen atom has a nucleus with eight protons and eight neutrons in it.

TWO OXYGEN ATOMS

Six electrons in outer layer.   Six electrons in outer layer.

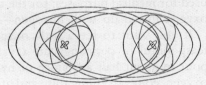

Eight electrons in outer layer.   Eight electrons in outer layer.

OXYGEN MOLECULE

FIG. 358.—A diagram illustrating how two oxygen atoms might form an oxygen molecule. Like all pictures of the insides of atoms, it is not to be taken too literally.

581

Round this circulate, first, two 1-quantum electrons, then six 2-quantum electrons. The arrangement with least energy is the ring of eight electrons. Accordingly, an oxygen atom tries to get two electrons by combining with other atoms. It can do this by combining with another oxygen atom, two electrons of each being shared by the other to give at least a share of eight to each.

One can make oxygen in twenty or more ways, but the only industrial method is to get it from the air. It may seem odd not to get it from water, which is eight-ninths oxygen, instead of from air, which contains only a fifth. The trouble is that when a ton of hydrogen and eight tons of oxygen combine and make nine tons of water, they give out a great deal of heat—about equivalent, in fact, to 50,000 horse-power hours. It follows, then, that to get those eight tons of oxygen back, we must spend at least those 50,000 horse-power hours of energy, and energy costs money. The air is simply a mix-up of oxygen molecules and nitrogen molecules. If a trick can be found to separate these, as we might separate peas and beans, the oxygen can be got without spending much energy. The trick has been performed. Air is liquefied as described on p. 136, and the liquid air is distilled in an apparatus which works on much the same principle as the petroleum still illustrated on p. 234. Oxygen boils at —186° C. and nitrogen at —195° C., so by very careful design of the apparatus, liquid oxygen can be left in the still while the more volatile nitrogen passes out of it. The oxygen is chiefly used for medical purposes; for the majority of chemical purposes, oxygen mixed up with nitrogen—i.e. air—does very well.

If you want to see a little oxygen, a simple way is to put a teaspoonful of permanganate crystals in a medicine bottle and pour in about half an ounce of hydrogen peroxide. Bubbles of oxygen come frothing out, and if you lower a burning match on a wire into the bottle, you will see the brilliant way in which things burn in oxygen. Pure oxygen looks and smells and tastes exactly like air. It is absolutely necessary for the life of any animal or plant more complicated than a bacterium. Pure oxygen, however, is a slow poison to mammals and causes inflammation of the lungs; for medical purposes, where the lungs are not doing their work properly, a mixture of air and oxygen is often administered to patients and has saved many lives. The very interesting subject of oxygen and breathing is taken up again in Chapter XXXVIII. Oxygen and indeed all gases dissolve slightly in water. Water contains eight-ninths of its weight of oxygen atoms all combined with hydrogen atoms but, if pure, no oxygen molecules. Animals need oxygen *molecules* for their breathing, consequently in pure water a fish drowns as quickly as a man. All ordinary water contains dissolved oxygen, which the fish extracts by means of its gills. Sewage absorbs oxygen and so very foul rivers will not support the life of fish.

COMBUSTION

When most things are heated in oxygen—or air—they combine with it. The only things which will stand heating in oxygen without reacting with oxygen are the "inert gases" like neon; fluorine, chlorine, bromine and iodine; platinum, gold and silver and the things which have already combined with as much oxygen as they can, such as stones, fireclay, quartz and lime.

To describe what happens to things when they are heated in air or oxygen really needs a volume to itself.

First, consider the elements. These are divided into non-metals and metals. Of the common non-metals, hydrogen, we know, burns to water. The flame of hydrogen burning in oxygen is one of the hottest in the world and temperatures of 2500° C. have been reached with it. It is not of much practical use, as the electric arc is cheaper and as hot. Carbon exists as diamonds, as graphite and as charcoal. In diamond, the carbon atoms are all chemically combined; it slowly wastes away when kept at a white heat in oxygen. Graphite does the same thing, but the very porous charcoal burns quickly with a white and brilliant light. In each case the gas carbon dioxide is produced; but it is possible (p. 254) to get carbon monoxide. Nitrogen does not burn in oxygen, but if made very hot it gives the gas nitric oxide. This is a commercial way of making nitric acid (p. 647).

Sulphur burns with a violet flame and gives the gas sulphur dioxide, familiar as the fumes of fireworks.

The metals are all (except platinum, gold and silver) affected by oxygen. A few will burn in air. Everyone has seen magnesium ribbon burning. If you blow a little aluminium powder into a flame, it burns with a bright flash.

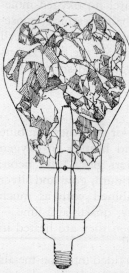

An interesting application of this is the Sashalite flash lamp. This is designed to give a sudden brilliant flash for press-photography, etc. It is a bulb (Fig. 359) filled with oxygen at low pressure and containing a mass of crumpled aluminium foil—"silver paper." The passing of a current heats a filament which ignites a composition which, in turn, fires the aluminium. Its great advantage over the old flash powder is its smokelessness.

Iron burns too, as you can easily see when steel is ground on a carborundum wheel. If you drop a pinch of iron filings into a flame, you can see it burn with pretty branched sparks. Other metals like lead or nickel do not easily burn but, if kept at a red heat in air, slowly change into the oxide.

Fig. 359.—Sashalite flash lamp.

In every case, the metal forms a compound with oxygen called an oxide. The white ash from burning magnesium is magnesium oxide, the scale from burning iron is one of the several iron oxides, the black brittle stuff which is left on a copper wire which has been made red hot is copper oxide.

The things which we burn for practical purposes are compounds of carbon and hydrogen, as coal and oil, or of carbon, hydrogen and oxygen as spirit, wood, paper, fats, etc. In every case, if there is enough air or oxygen, when these things burn, they produce carbon dioxide and water.

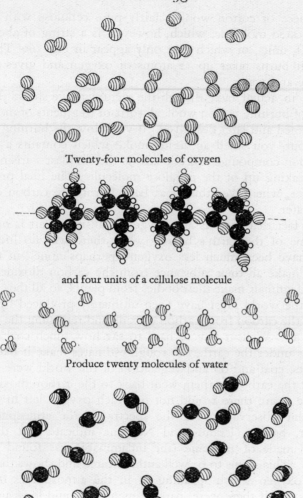

Twenty-four molecules of oxygen

and four units of a cellulose molecule

Produce twenty molecules of water

and twenty-four molecules of carbon dioxide

FIG. 360.—What happens to the molecules when cotton wool
burns. The black spheres represent carbon atoms, the grey
spheres oxygen atoms, the white spheres hydrogen atoms.

19*

A piece of cotton wool is fairly pure cellulose with a very complicated molecule, which, however, is a string of about 200 $C_6H_{10}O_5$ units, of which four only appear in Fig. 360. This unit when it burns takes up 12 atoms of oxygen and gives carbon dioxide and water.

But, in actual fact, though the picture above shows the final result of burning cotton wool, all sorts of fragments of molecules are formed and later destroyed. If you blow the burning cotton wool out, you smell an acrid smoke which contains a variety of carbon compounds—acetic acid is the simplest—arising from the breaking up of the cellulose molecule. The final products, however, when everything has been burnt, are carbon dioxide and water.

The fact that there is any oxygen at all in the air is odd. At the time of the earth's history when there was no life, there must have been much less oxygen—perhaps none—in the air. Plants make all their substance from the carbon dioxide of the air, and animals make their bodies from plants, so all the coal and oil in the world must have been ultimately produced by plants taking the carbon from carbon dioxide and returning the oxygen to the air. Well, it is very hard to say how much coal and oil there is under the earth, but rough estimates make it likely that if all the coal and oil and vegetation of the world were burned so that the carbon in them went back to the carbon dioxide that it came from, there would not be much oxygen left in the air.

Recent observations of the spectra of the atmospheres of Jupiter, Saturn, Uranus and Neptune indicate that they are mostly made of methane (the inflammable gas found in coal mines). This seems to be well authenticated and shows that there is no oxygen worth speaking of in the atmospheres of these planets, for if there were, passing meteors would long ago have caused a huge gas-explosion and turned the methane into carbon dioxide.

CHAPTER XXIII

Carbon the Lifegiver

CARBON CHAINS

THE atoms of the element carbon have the power of linking themselves into long chains, rings and nets. Chains of more than 3 or 4 atoms of the same kind cannot be made by any other element except carbon. Consequently carbon forms complicated compounds having larger molecules than those of any other element. These compounds are all-important to us, for it is of them that our bodies are made.

We shall have more to say of the carbon compounds in our bodies in Chapter XXXVIII; for the present, we may look at a few of the simpler but important materials containing carbon.

Carbon itself occurs as two very different kinds of crystals, diamond and graphite. A diamond crystal is made of carbon atoms all chemically combined in a 3-dimensional

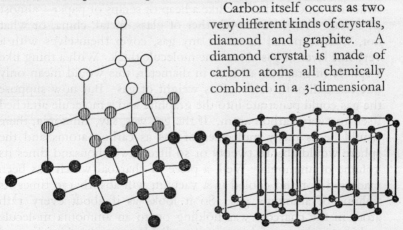

Fig. 361.—Structure of diamond (left) and graphite (right). The spheres represent carbon atoms.

net of hexagons (Fig. 361). A graphite crystal is a pile of flat nets of carbon atoms, the atoms in each net being chemically combined—linked by sharing their electrons—while the individual nets are only held together by rather feeble electrical attractions.

Both diamond and graphite are very difficult to affect by chemicals because the carbon atoms are already as fully combined as possible except just at the surfaces and edges and only a very small proportion of the atoms are at the edge. But there are several other materials which are nearly all carbon, notably charcoal (made by heating wood in a vessel from which air is excluded), lampblack, coke, etc. Charcoal made by heating sugar in a closed vessel is almost pure carbon. The X-ray pattern shows that, like graphite, its atoms make hexagonal nets, but that these nets are probably very small and jumbled together irregularly. The result of this is that these small "nets" have a great many edges where chemicals can get at the carbon atoms. Consequently, charcoal burns quite easily and is slightly affected by some acids which do not affect diamond or graphite to any extent that we can measure. A very curious property of charcoal is its power of absorbing other things, which may be simply due to its very open porous structure which makes it—like a heap of scraps of paper—almost all surface. All surfaces whether of glass, metal, china, or what not, when exposed to air or any gas, cover themselves with a very fine layer of gas about one molecule thick. With a thing like a sphere of graphite an inch in diameter, this would mean only one ten-millionth or so of its weight of gas. But now suppose the gas could penetrate into the graphite and a molecule attached itself to every carbon atom. If the gas was, say, ammonia, there would be as many molecules of gas as carbon atoms and the sphere would absorb twenty or so litres, two thousand times its volume of ammonia. Well, a piece of charcoal which has been made red hot and cooled in a vacuum will absorb 170 times its volume of ammonia gas. So it looks as if about every 12th atom in the charcoal was holding on to an ammonia molecule and we might guess (on not too reliable grounds) that charcoal was a jumble of nets of carbon atoms of such a size that every atom in 12 or so was an edge atom capable of holding on to a gas molecule. This behaviour of charcoal is most useful in making and regulating high vacuums (p. 204). It is also greatly used for making sugar white. Sugar-cane juice is of a brownish tint and the brown stuff is some compound with a huge molecule (which we have not yet learnt how to map out). The manufacturer filters the juice through charcoal, which absorbs this brown stuff and lets the colourless sugar solution pass on. When the charcoal has absorbed all the colour it can, it is made red hot. This turns the brown colouring matter, etc., into more charcoal, and this charcoal can be used over again. If you boil a little diluted beer or port wine with powdered charcoal (the material made by charring bones is the best) it will take all the colour out of the liquid.

Carbon is a rather unreactive substance. Charcoal from old fires lighted by the primitive Sinanthropus man perhaps a million years ago remains unchanged, though any metal but gold would have corroded to a shapeless mass of rust. Now carbon (in the form of graphite) is one of the very few things which resists chemicals and also conducts electricity well, consequently it is used very greatly for anodes in electrolytic cells such as those described on p. 691 for making aluminium. To make these anodes a rather interesting process is employed. The anodes are moulded out of ordinary powdered carbon with a little tar to stick it together. They are baked hard and packed in coke dust in a large box-shaped furnace. A very large electric current is sent through this which makes the whole thing white hot. The effect of this is to turn the anodes into graphite—probably as a result of the little networks of carbon atoms linking with others to form bigger ones.

CARBON MONOXIDE

Carbon forms two well-known compounds with oxygen—both gases. It is rather interesting to see how very different they are, in spite of their both being made of nothing but carbon and oxygen.

The two gases are carbon monoxide and carbon dioxide. We have already seen how carbon monoxide is produced when air is blown through red hot coke (p. 254), or when steam is blown through white hot coke. If any ordinary fuel, oil, petrol, gas, coke, coal, etc., is burned with a full supply of air, only carbon dioxide appears in the gases produced, but if air is deficient, or burning is imperfect as in a coke fire with a poor draught or the exhaust of an idling motor engine, carbon monoxide is produced. Chemists have several ways of making pure carbon monoxide, but the important thing from our point of view is its use as a fuel and its dangers. We have already written in Chapter IX of its practical use for running gas engines.

Pure carbon monoxide looks like air and has only a faint smell not unlike that of onions. It is often said to be odourless because the observer has been afraid to take a good sniff of it. It would not be dangerous if it smelt like chlorine or ammonia, but it poisons many people every year because they do not notice it in time. Carbon monoxide does its deadly work because it combines with hæmoglobin—the stuff which makes our blood red. The function of hæmoglobin is to carry oxygen from the lungs to the rest of the body. But the carbon monoxide molecule takes up the position on the hæmoglobin molecule that the oxygen molecule should occupy and so suffocates the body from within. It has been calculated that air containing one or two parts of carbon monoxide in ten thousand is dangerous if breathed for many hours. Now coal gas contains from one-tenth to one-third carbon monoxide and motor-exhaust may contain several parts of it per hundred. Coke fumes may contain up to 20% of the gas. All these are therefore poisonous. Coal gas is to-day the commonest way of committing suicide; occasionally, a broken main lets enough gas into a house to poison the sleepy occupants. Motor-car exhaust is not dangerous in the open air, but it may leak into a closed car and cause faintness and even death, and it is most dangerous to run a car in a closed garage. Most people know the dangers of the coke-bucket, but in southern countries deaths sometimes occur through taking the pans of smouldering charcoal, used for warming rooms, into bedrooms with closed windows.

Carbon monoxide burns with the beautiful blue smokeless flame which may be seen playing over a bright fire of glowing coals. When it burns, its molecule takes another atom of oxygen and forms carbon dioxide, as is illustrated in Fig. 139, p. 254. It will also combine with the gas chlorine and forms the deadly poison-gas carbonyl chloride or phosgene which is far more deadly than carbon monoxide.

CARBON DIOXIDE

Carbon dioxide presents an entirely different picture. It is a kindly and beneficent substance. It feeds the green plants of the world and is harmless to man unless a great deal is breathed. It has dozens of uses in industry; dissolved in water it gives soda water; solidified, it gives the Drikold which keeps ices cold; it is used in making washing soda and a good many other chemicals. Finally, it is a strong stimulant to breathing, a mixture of oxygen and a little carbon dioxide being quite the best thing for reviving the partly suffocated.

The air contains a little carbon dioxide—in the open country about 3 parts in 10,000. Every breath man and animal exhales, every bit of coal, oil or gas burnt, sends carbon dioxide into the air. The coal that the world burns, alone sends seven hundred and fifty cubic miles of carbon dioxide into the air each year. Yet the proportion does not increase, first, because the ocean of air is so vast, and secondly because countless myriads of leaves on land and of tiny green algæ and diatoms in the sea, are turning the gas to starch, sugar and cellulose on which men and animals will feed.

Carbon dioxide is made, as we have seen, by burning carbon and all the fuels containing it, but in this way we get it mixed up with air. When it is wanted pure, waste furnace gases containing 10% or more of the gas, a little oxygen and a great deal of nitrogen are compressed and forced into water. The water dissolves the compressed carbon dioxide very easily, making a sort of super-soda-water containing very little of the nitrogen etc., in the fuel gas. When the pressure is released, the carbon dioxide bubbles out of the water again. It is compressed again and then liquefies easily (which any impurities like nitrogen do not) and can be forced into cylinders.

This is the cheapest way of making it. The easiest is to drop a piece of soda into vinegar! The laboratory way is to use the apparatus shown in Fig. 353, putting marble chips in the centre bulb instead of zinc. Marble is calcium carbonate —a regular arrangement of calcium ions and carbonate ions. The hydroxonium ions from the acid and the carbonate ions produce carbon dioxide gas and water, while the calcium ions and chloride ions remain dissolved in the water (Fig. 362).

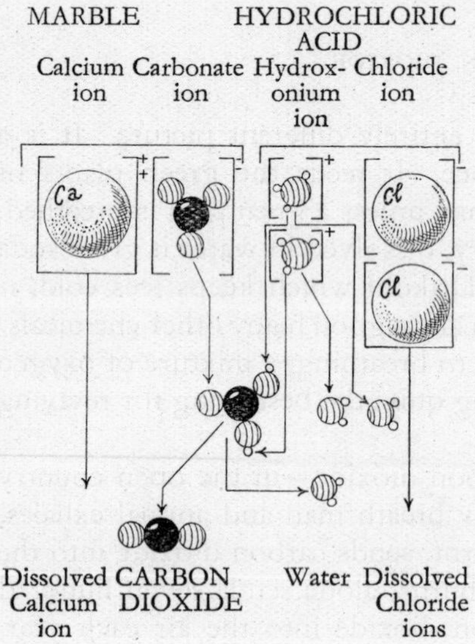

MARBLE   HYDROCHLORIC
                     ACID
Calcium Carbonate Hydrox- Chloride
   ion   ion   onium   ion
                     ion

Dissolved CARBON   Water Dissolved
Calcium DIOXIDE   Chloride
ion   ions

FIG. 362.—How marble and hydrochloric acid give carbonic acid, which breaks up into carbon dioxide and water.

It is colourless and invisible like most gases. It has the slight smell and taste we all know in soda-water. Water dissolves it a good deal more freely than most gases and the solution is a very feeble acid. Carbon dioxide will not burn because it can't combine with any more oxygen. Every atom has a limit of combining power. It takes two electrons to hitch an oxygen atom to anything—its 6-group of electrons has to be made up to 8. Carbon has four "spare" electrons, not in a complete group already, so it can hitch up to one oxygen atom by using two of these or to two oxygen atoms by using all its four; but it can't hitch to three oxygen atoms unless it borrows some electrons as it does in the CO_3 ion, where the calcium atom supplies a couple.

Most things will not burn in carbon dioxide because they would have to get the oxygen for their burning away from the carbon. Only a very few atoms (magnesium is an example) are energetic enough to do this. Consequently, carbon dioxide is a useful fire extinguisher. It is not of much use by itself because the draught of the fire carries it away, but a foam of bubbles filled with carbon dioxide is the best way of putting out oil fires.

In a foam extinguisher an acid solution (often of alum) is pumped through one limb of a Y-shaped tube, while a solution of soda is pumped through the other. Some slimy substance such as liquorice is often added, so that the foam produced shall last. The two solutions meet, mix and produce bubbles of carbon dioxide: these pass out as a foam through a nozzle attached to the third limb of the Y-shaped tube.

Just look back a moment. We have talked of two gases, carbon monoxide and carbon dioxide, both made of oxygen and carbon and nothing else. They don't differ as, say, a weak whisky-and-water differs from a strong one, but they are quite as different as whisky-and-soda is from café-au-lait. Carbon monoxide burns because the carbon atom has spare electrons with which to hold an oxygen atom—carbon dioxide does not because its carbon atoms have used up all their electrons. Carbon monoxide is poisonous because it has spare electrons by which to link itself to the blood-pigment; carbon dioxide stimulates breathing because—well, because the body has evolved a regulator which detects an undue amount of carbon dioxide in the blood and quickens the breathing to breathe it out again. There is a sensible reason for all the differences between these gases; most of these reasons we know, but we can't put many of them in simple language.

ORGANIC CHEMISTRY

A whole department of Science—Organic Chemistry—is given up to the compounds of carbon. The name Organic Chemistry dates from a century back, when it was believed that carbon compounds such as sugar, alcohol, uric acid, etc., could only be made by the help of an organism—animal or plant. The great majority of organic compounds can now be made by starting with the simple elements, carbon, hydrogen, oxygen and nitrogen; none the less, the name "organic" is still fairly appropriate because the bodies of animals and plants are chiefly made up of these "organic" compounds of carbon. Moreover, the source of very many of our organic compounds are such plant products as sugar, starch, wood, vegetable acids, turpentine, etc.; and the most important source of all—coal tar—is derived from coal, the mummified remains of ancient swamps and forests.

Organic chemistry is very highly systematised. The organic chemists in the last hundred years have learned to predict with some accuracy how a new molecule containing carbon atoms is likely to behave, and they have developed ways of building up or synthesising almost any possible kind of molecule.

One of their most interesting and important tasks is finding out how the molecules of the drugs, dyes, perfumes, etc., found in plants are constructed, and then building up those molecules from cheap and common compounds. A good example of this work is given by the case of indigo. Fifty years ago, the valuable blue dye indigo was made chiefly in India from the indigo plant. The material was expensive and not very pure, various brownish substances being mixed with it. Then the chemists got to work on indigo. They broke it up by heat. They broke it up by treatment with nitric acid; they applied every kind of chemical trick to it and so split its molecules into a number of materials with simpler molecules. These latter molecules were already known to have certain structures and by a sort of intelligent piecing together, it was settled that the indigo molecule had a structure of carbon atoms, hydrogen atoms, oxygen atoms, and nitrogen atoms linked up into the pattern which the chemists express thus, and which is pictorially represented in Fig. 363, VIII.

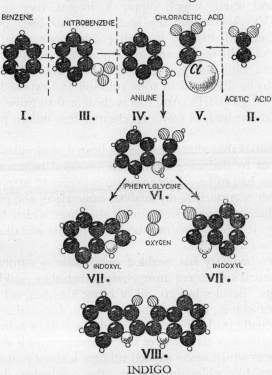

H   H
C   C
HC   C—CO OC—C   CH
HC   C   C—C   C   CH
C   NH   NH   C
H   H

The Molecule of Indigo

BENZENE   NITROBENZENE   CHLORACETIC ACID

I.   III.   IV.   V.   II.

ANILINE   ACETIC ACID

PHENYLGLYCINE
VI.

INDOXYL   OXYGEN   INDOXYL
VII.   VII.

VIII.
INDIGO

FIG. 363.—How the chemists build up the complicated
molecule of indigo. (See footnote, p. 567 for symbols
employed.)

Then the chemists began to work on making a substance with these molecules from quite simple and cheap materials. It took a long time to find the way but, finally, several possible ways were devised and one proved to be an even cheaper way of making it than by getting it from the plant.

They start with benzene (I), which is very cheap and gives the necessary hexagons of carbon atoms, and with acetic acid (II), which is also made very cheaply by distilling wood. The benzene they mix with nitric acid and sulphuric acid and obtain a yellow almond-smelling oil, nitrobenzene (III). This, with the help of iron and water, which supply hydrogen, they turned into aniline (IV). Meanwhile the acetic acid has been boiled and chlorine bubbled through it, giving chloracetic acid (V). This is heated with the aniline and gives phenylglycine (VI). This is then melted with caustic potash and gives indoxyl (VII). This has only to be dissolved in soda solution and exposed to air to turn into indigo (VIII). And this is cheaper than growing indigo plants? Curiously, it is so much cheaper that indigo planting is extinct.

It is remarkable that these complicated molecules were all mapped out by deducing from their chemical behaviour where these atoms had to be. There was no prospect of mapping them in any other way until X-ray analysis came along and proved the organic chemist exactly right in all the cases which have been tested. Fig. 305, p. 487, shows the X-ray picture and the chemical formula for anthracene.

Organic chemistry has enabled us to make a number of important natural substances more cheaply than they could be made from plants. Besides indigo, oil of bitter almonds, oil of cinnamon, oil of cloves, and camphor are examples of things which are now usually made in chemical works instead of being grown. But a far more important side of this synthetic work is the making of substances which never existed till man learned to make them. Anæsthetics like chloroform and ether, valuable drugs like sulphonal, aspirin, phenacetin, salvarsan, amyl nitrite; explosives like nitroglycerine and "T.N.T.", poisons like mustard gas; all the novel dyes which make our modern dresses far more varied and brilliant in colour than those of any other age—all these are new substances which could never have existed without the organic chemist's syntheses.

HYDROCARBONS

The skeleton of a molecule of an organic compound is nearly always a chain of carbon atoms. The chain may be straight or branched, or very commonly may return on itself as a loop. A carbon atom has four electrons in its outer group, so it can attach itself to four other atoms. When two atoms are linked in a compound, they each share the other's electrons and a pair of shared electrons is symbolised by the organic chemist as a line —. Thus, the molecule of the gas ethane (contained in natural gas) is something like this: the big black sphere being a model of a carbon atom and the little white one of a hydrogen atom. The organic chemist calls the carbon atom C and the hydrogen atom H and writes the structure as:

$$
\begin{array}{ccc}
\text{H} & & \text{H} \\
| & & | \\
\text{H—C} & \!\!\!\!—\!\!\!\!— & \text{C—H} \\
| & & | \\
\text{H} & & \text{H}
\end{array}
$$

Since the carbon atom has four spare electrons, it can share with four other atoms and unlike most other atoms it always uses all its four spare electrons. So, in the formula of an organic compound, every C atom has four "bonds," as we call them, linking it to other atoms. The four linkages are not arranged like a flat cross but are as far as possible away from each other. Thus, methane is not II but I:

None the less, organic chemists usually write their formulæ in the flat style II, because the solid style I is so difficult to draw or print from type.

The simplest organic compounds have only carbon and hydrogen atoms in their molecules. An enormous number of hydrocarbons are known and it is worth describing them rather fully just to show what a variety of things can be made out of only

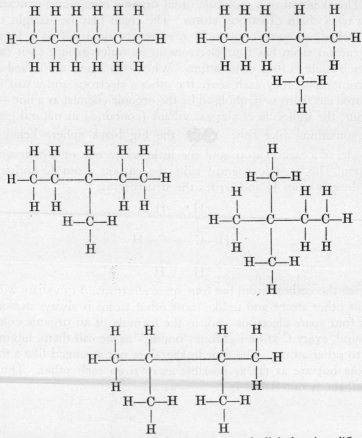

Six carbon atoms and fourteen hydrogen atoms can be linked up in 5 different ways. Each of these five is a picture of the molecule of a *different* substance.

two kinds of atoms. These hydrocarbons (not the same as carbohydrates!) are of three chief types. First, the ones that have straight chains where the carbon atoms are linked to each other by a single pair of electrons. These are called the paraffin hydrocarbons. There are an enormous number of these. Page 598 shows that a molecule containing six carbon atoms and fourteen hydrogen atoms can be linked up in 5 different ways; while a molecule containing thirteen carbon atoms and twenty-eight hydrogen atoms can be made up in 802 ways. Doubtless, 802 different oils of formula $C_{13}H_{28}$ could be made if enough organic chemists worked at the problem for long enough, but as they would only differ in boiling point and freezing point by a few degrees and in density by a few parts per thousand, the work will not be done till there are more organic chemists and fewer problems for them to tackle. These 802 "isomerides" (as we call compounds with the same set of atoms differently arranged) of formula $C_{13}H_{28}$ are all called tridecanes, though we have exact ways of naming each one so as to define the arrangement.

The four simplest hydrocarbons are all gases. They include methane, CH_4, the firedamp found in mines, ethane C_2H_6, propane C_3H_8, and butane C_4H_{10}, and are all found in natural gas (p. 228), which is an important fuel in the U.S.A.

The next five are liquids much like petrol, which (p. 000) contains a good deal of them. They are called pentane (C_5H_{12}), hexane (C_6H_{14}), heptane (C_7H_{16}), octane (C_8H_{18}) and nonane (C_9H_{20}), and each of them, like hexane (p. 598) can exist in several different forms. The next seven ($C_{10}H_{22}$ to $C_{16}H_{34}$) are contained in petrol, paraffin oil and gas oil. The remaining paraffin hydrocarbons with more than sixteen carbon atoms are waxes. Paraffin wax—candle grease—is a mix-up of paraffin hydrocarbons with twenty or so carbon atoms. The biggest hydrocarbon molecule has a chain of sixty carbon atoms.

These hydrocarbons are used as fuels as we have already seen (p.233)and paraffin wax has various uses—as an insulator, for waterproofing paper, etc.—but they are rather inert substances on the whole. They are very little affected by chemicals and the chemist does not bother much with them. The gas ethylene deserves a passing glance. It has the formula C_2H_4, its two carbon atoms linked by two electron pairs, thus:

as it is commonly written. It is not very important in itself, but this double link comes in many important compounds. There are a great many other hydrocarbons with straight chains and double links, but they are not important.

Acetylene C_2H_2 has its carbon atoms linked by 3 electron pairs.

This arrangement is one which is unstable, probably because the electrons in the 3 pairs repel each other, and their orbits, like bent bows, have a great store of energy. The result is that acetylene is very reactive—combining with most things—and

that when compressed it is a high explosive! It is not safe to
send it about compressed into cylinders like oxygen or hydrogen.
Instead, it is dissolved under pressure in acetone just as carbon
dioxide is dissolved under pressure in water to make soda-water.

Acetylene has some com-
mercial importance because
when burned in oxygen it
gives an intensely hot flame
by means of which steel
can be welded. Fig. 364
shows an acetylene blow-
pipe. Acetylene enters at B,

FIG. 364.—The oxy-acetylene blowpipe.
Oxygen enters at A, acetylene at B.

oxygen at A. It would be most dangerous to store mixed oxygen
and acetylene: in the blowpipe they are only mixed the moment
before they burn at the nozzle.

Everyone knows that acetylene is made from calcium carbide
and water. Calcium carbide itself is made in rather an interesting
way. Coke and lime are fed into a furnace through which a big
electric current flows. Coke conducts electricity and is heated
white hot by the current;
the liquid calcium carbide
runs out at the bottom of
the furnace.

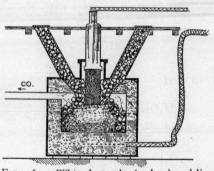

FIG. 365.—White hot coke (carbon) and lime
(calcium oxide) change into calcium carbide and carbon monoxide.

The calcium carbide is
not by any means pure
and it is the traces of
other gases like phos-
phorus hydride and silicon
hydride that make acety-
lene smell so foul. The
pure gas has not much
smell, and what it has is
not unpleasant. When it
is made on the large scale the odorous gases are taken out by
means of chemicals which combine with them and not with
acetylene.

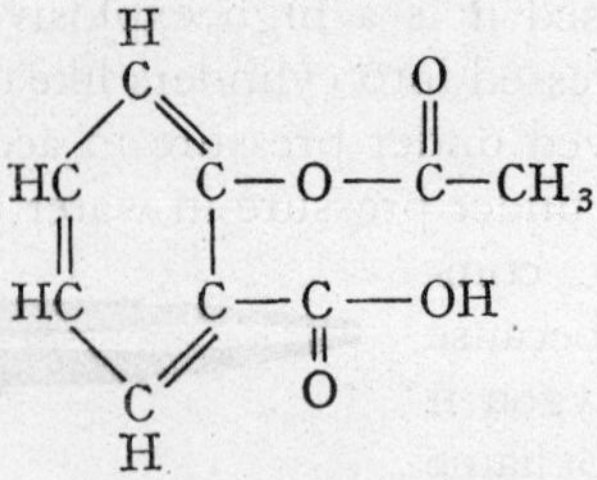

Aspirin

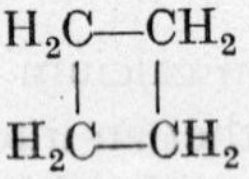

Cyclobutane

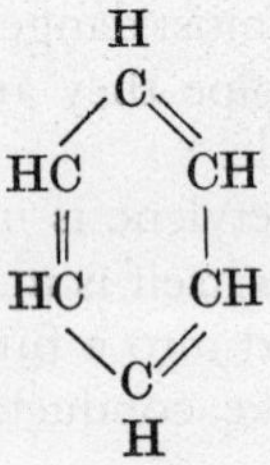

Benzene

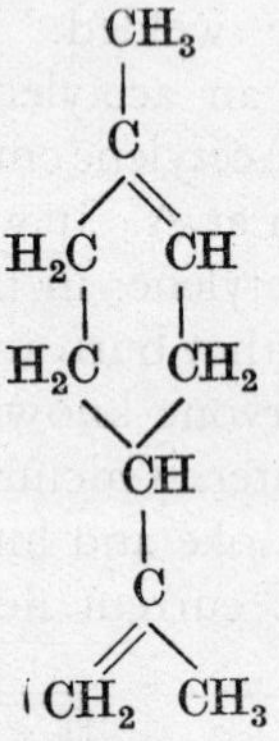

Oil of lemon

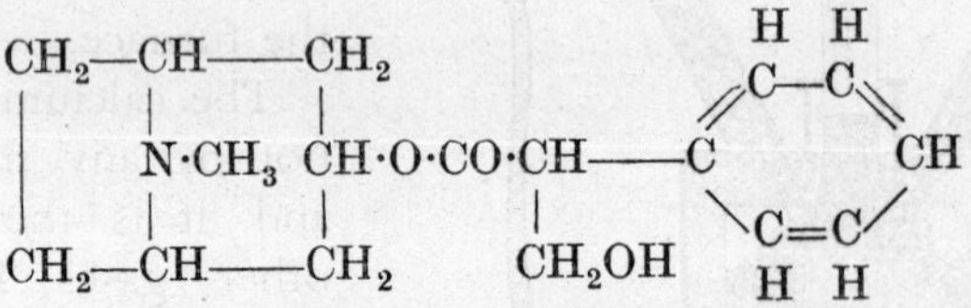

Atropine, the poison of deadly nightshade

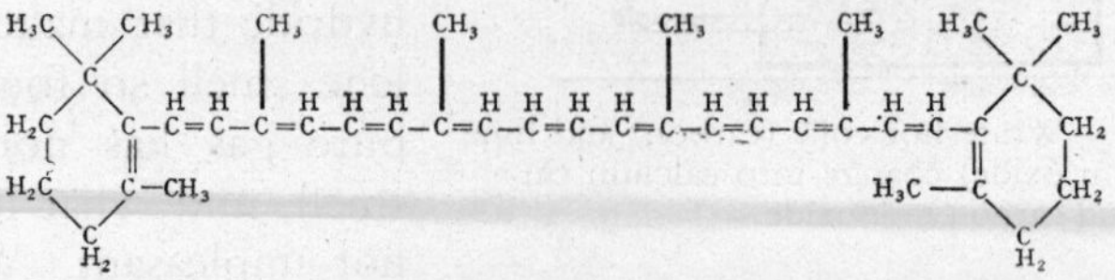

Carotene, the orange-yellow substance in carrots

FIG. 366.—The molecules of some of the hundreds of thousands of ring-compounds of carbon. Most of these rings are made up of 6 atoms, but one example of a 4-ring is shown.

The majority of hydrocarbons have rings of carbon atoms. Rings of 3, 4, 5, 6, 7, 8 or more carbon atoms are known, but the ring of 6 is overwhelmingly the commonest. It does not seem clear why 6 is commoner than 5, but if you remember that the electron pairs which link carbon atoms are inclined at 109° to each other, it is not very difficult to see that in the 3 and 4 membered rings the links must be pulled out of their usual place, while in the bigger ones they can take their natural positions, particularly if the rings are "buckled." The most remarkable ring molecules have a "skeleton" consisting of as many as fifteen carbon atoms strung into a loop. These are found in the perfumes civet and musk, which are derived from animal glands, and which are extraordinarily permanent. The scent of vegetable oils leaves a garment in hours, that of musk only in months or years.

If the carbon atoms are linked into rings by single pairs of electrons, we get what are called polymethylenes; these are contained in petrol. If they have alternate double and single links, we get the very important hydrocarbons we call "aromatics." The chief of these are benzene with a ring of six carbon atoms, and toluene, which is the same with a CH_3 group hanging on.

Benzene and toluene are used (under the name of benzol) as a motor spirit and all sorts of important chemicals are made from them. Naphthalene (moth balls) has a pair of benzene rings fused together; it is made into all sorts of important dyes, as is anthracene, with 3 such rings and many other hydrocarbons with still more. All these are extracted by distilling coal-tar—a process we will talk about later.

The hydrocarbons we have mentioned are all colourless or white. Some are liquids, some are solids. They mostly burn very easily and well with an extremely smoky flame.

A group of hydrocarbons which deserve a mention are the terpenes from which a great number of perfumes are derived. They are all made up of the chain of atoms

```
          C—C—
             /
      C—C
             \
             C—
```

repeated twice, three times or more with slight variations. Turpentine, oil of lemon, eucalyptus, mint, camphor, the perfumes of orange blossom, roses, lilac, bergamot, are all variations on this theme. Pure oil of lemon (limonene) has the structure shown in Fig. 366 and can quite easily be seen to be made up of two of these five-carbon chains joined. If this five-carbon group is linked up a sufficient number of times, we get that extraordinary substance indiarubber, which apparently consists entirely of very long *tangled* chains of carbon and hydrogen atoms rather like a pile of spaghetti. When it is stretched, the chains are at least partly straightened, when released they go back to the old position again.

Another odd lot of hydrocarbons are the carotenes, the substances which make butter and flowers and carrots yellow and tomatoes and rose-hips and boiled lobsters red! They have long straight chains containing a great many double linkages like that in ethylene. The more of these there are in a molecule, the deeper as a rule is its colour. Like other hydrocarbons, carotenes do not dissolve in water. If you look at any dish containing tomatoes and oil or fat, you will notice that the orange red lycopene from the tomatoes dissolves in and colours the oil or fat, but not the watery part of the dish.

The hydrocarbons have only carbon and hydrogen in them. They are in a sense the fundamental substances of organic chemistry because the organic chemist can make a great many of his compounds by turning out one or more of the hydrogen atoms and putting in other atoms or groups in its place. Thus, we can take ethane and instead of one of its hydrogen atoms put a chlorine atom or an —OH (hydroxyl) group or, indeed, almost any group of atoms which can be linked by a single electron-pair. Thus, we can get from ethane the following (though in actual fact there are much better ways of making them).

$$
\begin{array}{ccc}
\mathrm{H}\ \ \mathrm{H} & \mathrm{H}\ \ \mathrm{H} & \mathrm{H}\ \ \mathrm{H} \\
|\ \ \ | & |\ \ \ | & |\ \ \ | \\
\mathrm{H\!-\!C\!-\!C\!-\!H} & \mathrm{H\!-\!C\!-\!C\!-\!Cl} & \mathrm{H\!-\!C\!-\!C\!-\!OH}\quad\text{etc.} \\
|\ \ \ | & |\ \ \ | & |\ \ \ | \\
\mathrm{H}\ \ \mathrm{H} & \mathrm{H}\ \ \mathrm{H} & \mathrm{H}\ \ \mathrm{H}
\end{array}
$$

Ethane	Chlorethane (Ethyl chloride, an anæsthetic)	Hydroxyethane (ordinary alcohol)

From benzene we can get:

$$
\begin{array}{cccc}
\mathrm{H} & \mathrm{Cl} & & \mathrm{H} \\
\mathrm{C} & \mathrm{C} & \mathrm{C\cdot OH} & \mathrm{C} \\
\diagup\ \diagdown & \diagup\ \diagdown & \diagup\ \diagdown & \diagup\ \diagdown \\
\mathrm{HC}\ \ \ \mathrm{CH} & \mathrm{HC}\ \ \ \mathrm{CH} & \mathrm{HC}\ \ \ \mathrm{CH} & \mathrm{HC}\ \ \ \mathrm{C\cdot NO_2} \\
\|\ \ \ \ | & \|\ \ \ \ | & \|\ \ \ \ | & \|\ \ \ \ |\quad\text{etc.} \\
\mathrm{HC}\ \ \ \mathrm{CH} & \mathrm{HC}\ \ \ \mathrm{CH} & \mathrm{HC}\ \ \ \mathrm{CH} & \mathrm{HC}\ \ \ \mathrm{CH} \\
\diagdown\ \diagup & \diagdown\ \diagup & \diagdown\ \diagup & \diagdown\ \diagup \\
\mathrm{C} & \mathrm{CH} & \mathrm{C} & \mathrm{C} \\
\mathrm{H} & & \mathrm{H} & \mathrm{H}
\end{array}
$$

Benzene	Chloro-benzene	Hydroxy-benzene (Carbolic acid)	Nitro-benzene

So every hydrocarbon (there are thousands known and millions possible) provides a host of "derivatives" with molecules having the same skeleton of carbon atoms but different groups of atoms attached to it.

One of the simplest classes of derivative are the chloro-compounds which are hydrocarbons with one, some or all of their hydrogen atoms replaced by chlorine atoms. You can make them by bubbling chlorine gas through the liquid hydrocarbon under the right conditions, but a better way is often to start from the hydroxyl compound.

Let us glance at a few of these chloro-compounds. They are mostly colourless liquids or solids like the hydrocarbons, but instead of smelling like petrol as do most hydrocarbons, they smell like chloroform or have sharp smells which irritate the nose. There are a few quite important things among them.

Chloroform, still used to-day as an anæsthetic in spite of the invention of scores of others, is the most important of them. It is methane in which three hydrogen atoms have been replaced by chlorine. Chlorine and methane when mixed produce it, together with some other similar compounds, but the best way to get it is cautiously to warm bleaching powder with water and alcohol or acetone.

$$
\begin{array}{ccc}
\text{H} & \text{Cl} & \text{Cl} \\
| & | & | \\
\text{H—C—H} & \text{H—C—Cl} & \text{Cl—C—Cl} \\
| & | & | \\
\text{H} & \text{Cl} & \text{Cl} \\
\text{Methane} & \text{Chloroform} & \text{Carbon tetrachloride}
\end{array}
$$

Nobody quite knows why the vapour of chloroform makes a man lose consciousness. It is thought that it may dissolve in the fatty sheath of the nerves. Ethyl chloride, the formula of which is on p. 605, is sometimes used as an anæsthetic, and a good many of these chloro-compounds act in the same way, but most of them are too poisonous to use for this purpose.

If all the hydrogen atoms in methane are replaced by chlorine we get another interesting compound—carbon tetrachloride CCl_4 which has a variety of uses. It is a clear liquid with a heavy smell like that of chloroform. It easily turns into vapour and it won't burn.

This makes it ideal for fire extinguishers. When it is thrown on a fire, it boils and turns into a heavy vapour which "blankets" the fire and prevents oxygen getting to it. It is very good for small petrol fires. Petrol floats on water, so it is useless to throw water on a petrol fire! Carbon tetrachloride mixes with the petrol and its vapour puts it out.

It is very good stuff for cleaning clothes. It dissolves grease or oil and unlike petrol it cannot be set alight. Many deaths have been caused by cleaning clothes with petrol in front of a fire. Carbon tetrachloride is rather poisonous, but for that very reason it has proved an enormous blessing to tropical races, for, as described on page 973, it has proved to be an almost perfect way of killing the hook-worm which lives in their intestines and ruins their health.

Many of these chloro-compounds are useful and familiar to chemists, but only one or two reach us in our daily lives. Mustard gas (which is not a gas but a liquid) unfortunately may be one of these; it contains both chlorine and sulphur. Its formula is:

$$
\begin{array}{ccccc}
& H & H & & H & H \\
& | & | & & | & | \\
Cl{-} & C{-} & C{-}S{-} & C{-} & C{-}Cl \\
& | & | & & | & | \\
& H & H & & H & H \\
\end{array}
$$

and its name is dichlorodiethyl sulphide. It is two molecules of ethyl chloride (p. 605) with an atom of sulphur taking the place of atoms of hydrogen from each. No one knows exactly why the vapour of this liquid will irritate the skin until it rises into blisters and sores. It causes great suffering and the sores are very slow to heal, but the proportion of recoveries to deaths is very much greater than with chlorine or phosgene.

Poison gas is not entirely warlike in its use. Much loss is caused by the roof-beams of old buildings being attacked by various wood-boring beetles. These remarkable creatures manage to live and increase on a diet of dry wood, and since they inhabit the tortuous tunnels they have driven in the beams, the only way to get at them is to poison them by some vapour, which is usually a mild form of poison-gas. The means used to eradicate

them from the ancient timbers of the roof of Westminster Hall
was a spray of a mixture of

$$
\begin{array}{c}
\text{H} \quad \text{H} \\
\text{C---C} \\
\end{array}
$$

paradichlorobenzene, Cl—C   C—Cl

$$
\begin{array}{c}
\text{C} = \text{C} \\
\text{H} \quad \text{H}
\end{array}
$$

Cl H
C—C

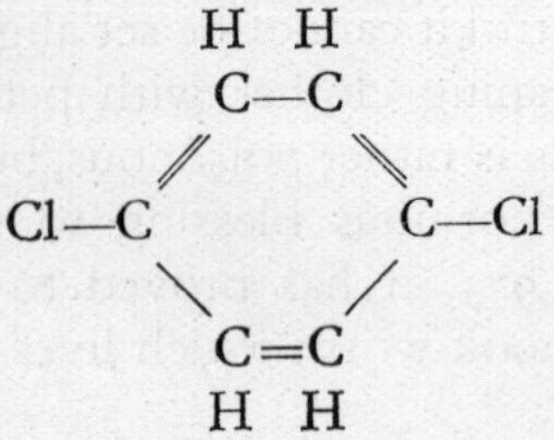

and orthodichlorobenzene Cl—C   CH

C=C
H H

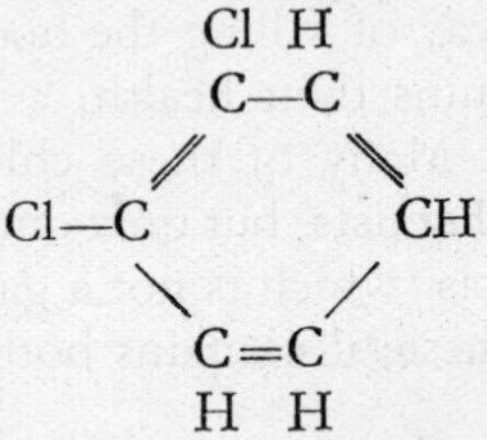

ALCOHOLS

The chloro-compounds are mostly death-dealers—for anæsthetics, though agents of mercy, in rather stronger doses are
poisons. The hydroxy-compounds, with one or more —OH
groups substituted for the hydrogens of hydrocarbons, are many
of them foodstuffs. The chemist calls these compounds alcohols,
though most of them have little resemblance to the alcohol we
know. They include such important substances as ordinary
alcohol, glycerine, starch, sugar, and cellulose. Some of them,
such as wood-alcohol (methanol) and hydroxy-benzene (carbolic
acid) are poisonous, however.

The organic compounds with the —OH group in them are
very unlike the hydrocarbons and chloro-compounds. They are
not oily or waxy substances like petrol or candle grease, but are
liquids or solids which mostly dissolve or mix easily in water,
which attracts their —OH group: alcohol, glycerine, sugar and
gum are examples of this.

The organic chemist gives the name alcohol to the compounds
which result when the group of atoms —OH is put in the place of

PLATE XXVII

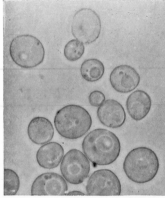

Yeast growing by budding-off new cells. (By courtesy of Professor R. H. Hopkins, The School of Brewing and Biochemistry, Birmingham.)

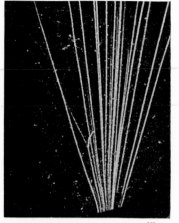

Transmutation of nitrogen into "heavy oxygen."

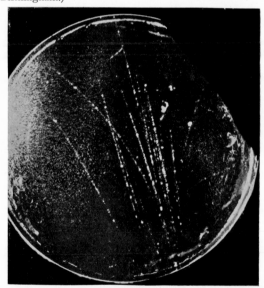

Cloud chamber photograph showing tracks of electrons (curve to left) and of positrons. (Both by courtesy of Professor P. M. S. Blackett and [above] Messrs. George Bell & Sons, Ltd. [below], The Royal Society.)

PLATE XXVIII

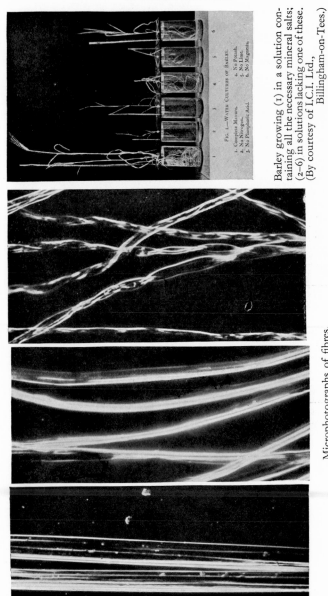

Fig. 1.—Water Cultures of Barley.

1. Complete Manure.
2. No Nitrogen.
3. No Phosphoric Acid.
4. No Potash.
5. No Lime.
6. No Magnesia.

Barley growing (1) in a solution containing all the necessary mineral salts; (2–6) in solutions lacking one of these. (By courtesy of I.C.I. Ltd., Billingham-on-Tees.)

C—Cotton × 150

Microphotographs of fibres.

B—Silk × 150

A—Rayon × 150

one or more of the hydrogen atoms in a hydrocarbon molecule. Thus the molecule of ordinary alcohol (ethyl alcohol) is that of ethane with an —OH group put instead of one H atom.

$$
\begin{array}{ccc}
\text{H} & \text{H} \\
| & | \\
\text{H—C—C—H} \\
| & | \\
\text{H} & \text{H} \\
\text{Ethane}
\end{array}
\qquad
\begin{array}{ccc}
\text{H} & \text{H} \\
| & | \\
\text{H—C—C—OH} \\
| & | \\
\text{H} & \text{H} \\
\text{Alcohol}
\end{array}
$$

The simplest alcohol is methyl alcohol (methanol, wood spirit) which is made in great quantities by passing water-gas—carbon monoxide and hydrogen—compressed to 1,500 to 3,000 lbs. per sq. inch over a catalyst of zinc chromite kept at 400° C. A mixture of alcohols—mainly methyl alcohol—results. As methyl alcohol is poisonous and undrinkable, it pays no duty, so in industry it is used for all sorts of purposes, varnish making, etc., where "spirit" was formerly employed.

Ethyl alcohol is the most famous of chemical substances. Every nation and tribe, civilised or otherwise, some of the strictest Mahommedans alone excepted, makes a weak and impure mixture of alcohol and water in the form of wine, beer, saké or the like, and most semi-civilised peoples distil these and get a stronger mixture of alcohol and water—spirits.

The way in which the weak mixture is made into pure alcohol has already been described (on pp. 557–559), but the process of fermentation by which sugary solutions are turned into alcohol is very interesting. All the various alcoholic drinks in the world start from sugar or starch. A fruit or sap contains sugar; a seed contains starch. Now yeast, a minute single-celled plant rather like a bacterium, has the gift of changing sugar into alcohol, but will not deal with starch, so if you want to make alcohol from a starchy material, you must turn the starch into sugar. This is not difficult. If a seed is allowed to sprout, it changes its own starch into sugar. When barley is turned into beer, it is soaked

20

and left to sprout. By the time it has just begun to put out its spike and roots, it has turned all its reserve starch into a kind of sugar, in readiness to feed the young plant. The brewer now kills it by drying it and it is called malt. If this malt is boiled with water, it gives a weak solution of malt-sugar, which when cool enough can be fermented. If the starch is not in the form of a seed, it must be turned into sugar otherwise. The Pacific islanders sit in a circle and chew their starchy cassava and spit it into a big bowl. Saliva contains a digestive "enzyme," amylase, which turns the starch into sugar which can then be fermented. The drink is very good, but Europeans feel a little doubtful about it! Our civilised method, used when spirit is made from potatoes, is to boil these with a little sulphuric acid which is later removed by adding chalk.

ALCOHOLIC LIQUORS

From Sugar

Liquor	Source	Process
Wine	Grapes	Pressing out juice and fermentation.
Cider	Apples	
Perry	Pears	
Mead	Honey	Diluting with water and fermentation.
"Wash" for making into rum	Molasses	
Koumiss	Mare's Milk	Adding old koumiss (containing the yeast) to fresh milk, warming and bottling.

From Starch

Beer	Barley (in some countries other seeds)	Sprouting, boiling with water and fermentation of the liquor.

From Starch—continued.

"Wash" for making Potatoes into methylated spirit		Boiling with acid, removing acid by chalk; fermentation.
Saké	Rice	Boiling. Treatment with a mould and a peculiar yeast. Product thinned with water & fermented.

The actual process of fermentation is done by the yeast plant. Yeast is a mass of tiny living cells—Plate XXVII shows what it looks like under the microscope. Fruit juices will keep for years if all yeasts (or bacteria or moulds) are kept out. Bottled fruit is a good example. The fruit and water are put in the bottles and heated to boiling. This kills all living things and the bottles are closed up while still boiling so that no living cell or spore can enter. If this has been properly done, they will keep for ever. Now if any sugary liquid is bottled up in this way, it remains as sugar; but if a cell of yeast enters—often from the air—it starts to grow. It buds off other cells and these bud off more, so that in a matter of days a single cell becomes a million. Men and animals get energy by making the sugar (glucose) in their blood and muscles combine with the oxygen of the air and make the carbon dioxide, which we breathe out, and water. But the yeast plant needs no oxygen and can flourish happily in a closed champagne bottle! It gets its energy by breaking glucose into alcohol and carbon dioxide, a process which the chemist cannot perform at all without the yeast plant's help. The process is rather complicated, at least four intermediate substances being produced.

Each molecule of glucose has six carbon atoms, twelve hydrogen atoms and six oxygen atoms: these are sorted out into two alcohol molecules (each with two carbon, one oxygen and six hydrogen atoms) and two molecules of carbon dioxide.

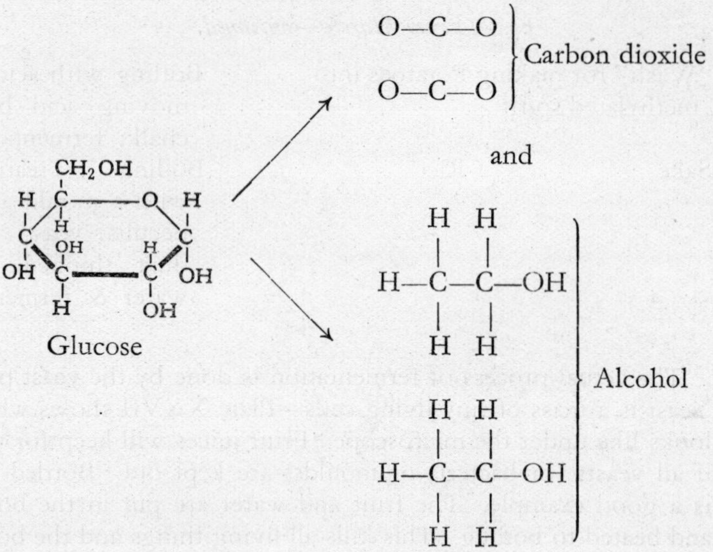

$$O—C—O$$
$$O—C—O$$
$\Big\}$ Carbon dioxide

and

Glucose

$$
\begin{array}{cc}
H & H \\
| & | \\
H—C—C—OH \\
| & | \\
H & H
\end{array}
$$

$$
\begin{array}{cc}
H & H \\
| & | \\
H—C—C—OH \\
| & | \\
H & H
\end{array}
$$

$\Big\}$ Alcohol

The most obvious thing to the eye about fermentation is the appearance of vast numbers of bubbles of carbon dioxide. The word "fermentation" means "boiling," and is taken from this. In some stages in the making of beer the froth of carbon dioxide bubbles can be very clearly seen.

Alcohol is chiefly used as a drink, and as people want it so much that they are willing to pay anything for it, the Government taxes it more heavily than any other substance. A pint of the purest alcohol costs 27s., the duty on it is no less than 16s. As a concession to the manufacturers who do not want to drink alcohol but want to use it industrially for various chemical jobs, it is sold duty free as methylated spirits, which is a mixture of about 85% alcohol with about 11% of water and 4% of methyl alcohol which renders it rather poisonous. The methylated spirit sold to the public is even more impure. It contains about 80% of alcohol with methyl alcohol, petroleum, bone oil and a blue dye which together make it poisonous and evil-tasting.

When an alcoholic beverage is drunk, the alcohol very quickly passes into the blood. It is definitely a food, for the body can oxidise it and use its energy; moreover, it is a food which needs no digestion. However, its consumers do not take it as a food. They drink it because of its effect on the nervous system. It gives a feeling of well-being; worries and cares are forgotten; one's conversation and that of one's friends becomes freer and appears to be brilliant; pain vanishes. As intoxication increases, the power to do anything accurately or to think clearly disappears. Next, the control of the muscles goes; the alcoholic may see double because he cannot direct his eyes. He staggers in his walk and finally collapses. There appear to be no permanent ill-effects unless considerable quantities of alcohol are drunk, but the chronic soaker usually dies young.

Alcohol seems to be much the least harmful drug used by the human race, which, overwhelmed by cares, is always seeking to forget them. Cocaine, opium, hashish, mescal—all have their devotees, but alcohol is humanity's dangerous but sovereign remedy for the malady of thought.

Alcohol dissolves a great many oily and fatty substances which water will not. It is therefore used to dissolve perfumes and drugs—for this, pure alcohol is needed—and also resins and gums to make quick-drying varnishes. It is also made into various chemicals of which chloroform and acetic acid are the most important.

Some alcohols have two or three or more hydroxyl groups. Glycerine is one of these.

Glycerine or glycerol as the organic chemist calls it has three hydroxyl groups:

$$
\begin{array}{c}
\text{H} \quad\quad \text{H} \\
\diagdown\;\;\diagup \\
\text{C} \\
\diagup\;\;\diagdown \\
\quad\quad \text{OH} \\
\text{HO—C—H} \\
\diagdown\quad\quad \text{OH} \\
\text{C} \\
\diagup\;\;\diagdown \\
\text{H} \quad\quad \text{H}
\end{array}
$$

A hydroxyl group has a certain amount of attraction for its neighbour in the next molecule: a consequence of which is that glycerine molecules hang together, and it has a rather high boiling point; since water has also —OH groups, it attracts the glycerine molecules and so glycerine mixes easily with water.

Glycerine is a by-product of the soap industry which we will talk of later. It has one or two interesting uses. A mixture of glycerine and water freezes at a lower temperature than is ever likely to be reached in an English winter; consequently, crude glycerine is often mixed with the water of the radiator of a car to prevent it freezing and so bursting the pipes. Many other substances could be used instead of glycerine, but they are all either poisonous or expensive or inflammable or corrosive to metal. Glycerine has such a high boiling point that it does not evaporate, so that anything which is to be kept damp and flexible may be treated with it. An interesting use of it is in the making of nitroglycerine, the explosive, of which we shall have something to say later.

CARBOHYDRATES

Sugars and starches are called carbohydrates. They have large molecules and many hydroxyl (OH) groups, and so can be called alcohols. They are very difficult and sometimes impossible to make by laboratory methods, but all plants make starch or sugar with consummate ease and we have no real idea how they do it. A green plant (white plants like mushrooms can't do it) takes in water by its root and carbon dioxide through its leaves. Certain tiny green bodies called "chloroplasts" contained in the cells of the leaf use the energy of the daylight to turn carbon dioxide and water into sugar and oxygen! The diagram shows that this is quite possible, but to a chemist the process seems amazingly unlikely. He has tried to imitate it in his laboratories, but so little sugar can be made in this way that a great many chemists

are doubtful whether those who claim to have made a few grains
of it from carbon dioxide and water are not mistaken.

$$6 CO_2 + 6 H_2O \xrightarrow[\text{energy}]{\text{light}} \text{One glucose molecule} + 6 O_2$$

One glucose molecule

Six carbon dioxide
molecules and six
water molecules

and six
oxygen
molecules

The green pigment "chlorophyll" can easily be dissolved out
of leaves by soaking them in alcohol. It is a mixture of two substances, chlorophyll-*a* and chlorophyll-*b*; we know how the
molecules of these are built up, but this disappointingly tells us
nothing about the way it makes sugar. It is generally believed
that chlorophyll outside the leaf won't make any sugar for us;
if so, the mysterious living proteins contained in the chloroplast have a finger in the pie. If we could once find out how the
leaf makes sugar and starch, we could make much of our food
without the trouble of growing it. But I am afraid the problem
is not likely to be solved till we know rather more about the
proteins.

There are dozens of different sweet substances with molecules
much like that of glucose; to these we give the general name
of sugars.

Glucose is easily made from starch by boiling it with acids. It
is the perfect energy-giving food, because it needs no digestion

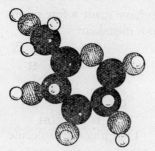

FIG. 367.—The molecule of glucose. (Courtesy of Messrs. Edward Arnold and Prof. Haworth, from the latter's *Constitution of the Sugars*.)

but passes straight into the blood where it is needed. It is much used as a cane-sugar substitute in jams, sweets, etc. Now that it can be made in a very pure condition, there is no reason at all against its use as a food. Honey is chiefly glucose.

Fructose is a sugar contained in fruits; it is even more easily digested than glucose. Dahlia tubers and Jerusalem artichokes contain a sort of starch called inulin which breaks down into fructose. This breaking down is not easily accomplished by the human digestive organs, so inulin is not easily utilised as food.

These are the two simplest sugars. Three rather important sugars have molecules rather like two glucose molecules hitched together. They are cane-sugar or sucrose, of which the world yearly eats 22,000,000 tons; maltose, the sugar in malt; and lactose, the sugar in milk. The last two need only just be mentioned as examples of sugars other than cane-sugar. The ordinary sugar we buy in blue packets at 2½d. a lb. has a complicated molecule.

It is so difficult to make it artificially that, though one Frenchman did it a few years ago, many expert chemists have been unable to repeat his experiments and feel in some doubt about the matter. Sugar is made chiefly from the juices of the sugar-cane and the sugar beet. Cane-sugar and beet-sugar are precisely the same stuff; if they taste at all different it is only because some impurities are left in them. There is not space in this book to describe more than one way of making sugar; as the sugar beet is the more familiar plant, we will describe the way it is made into sugar. Anyone can taste the sugar in an ordinary beetroot. By years of breeding and selection, a race of beetroot has been evolved which is white and contains up to 20% of sugar. Fields of sugar beet are now a common sight in England as are the piles of roots waiting to be taken to the factories. Fig. 369 shows a sugar-beet. Like all plant tissues it is made of tiny compartments or cells (Chapter XLI), each of which is distended with a sweet sap containing two

FIG. 369.—A sugar-beet.

pounds or so of sugar to the gallon. But those cells also contain slimy substances with big molecules, "pectins," which would make it difficult to crystallise the sugar from the juice.

The manufacturer's problem is to get the sugar out of the cell and leave the pectins behind. He does this by taking advantage of the fact that sugar molecules, though large, are small enough to pass through the pores of the membrane round the cell; the pectins cannot pass through. Accordingly, he cuts his beetroot into "cossettes" like so much vermicelli and lets them soak in many changes of water. The sugar diffuses out of the cells into the water and the manufacturer has now only to decolourise the solution with charcoal (p. 589) and evaporate off most of the water in order to get the sugar to appear as crystals.

Starch is one of the most important foods; indeed, it is the chief food of man. Wheat, potatoes, rice, sago, tapioca are mainly starch together with some nitrogen compounds which greatly increase their food value. Starch has a big molecule made up of some twenty glucose molecules all linked together in the same sort of way as the two halves of the sugar molecule on p. 616. When it is digested (or boiled with acids) these molecules come apart and first malt-sugar and finally glucose are produced. Starch

20*

is the substance which most plants store up for future consumption. The starch in wheat is put there to nourish the young wheat plant; in the tuber of the potato it is ready to push the next year's plant into rapid growth. Most large fleshy roots like carrots, parsnips, beet, artichokes, etc., are plant storehouses full of sugar, starch or inulin. The starch is stored as tiny granules which, greatly swollen, are easily visible in a boiled potato. If these granules are boiled a slimy solution results—called starch-paste—much used for pasting up wall-paper, stiffening linen, coating paper, etc. Gums are probably not unlike starch but derived from other and simpler kinds of sugar.

We have seen that twenty or so molecules of glucose can link together into a big molecule of starch. The plant can do better than this, for it makes its strong framework of fibre out of cellulose which has a huge threadlike molecule of about 200

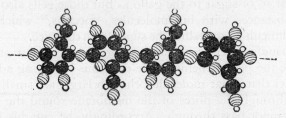

Fig. 370.—Four "units"—about a fiftieth—of a cellulose molecule, represented about 30,000,000 times natural size. The whole molecule represented on this scale would be ten feet long.

glucose molecules hitched end to end. Paper, linen, string, jute, coconut fibre, wood, all owe their strength to cellulose. Figure 370 gives some idea of about a fiftieth part of its long threadlike molecule, which may be about 2000 A.U. (one five-thousandth of a millimetre) long and only about 7.5 A.U. wide. The actual fibres you see with a microscope (Plate XXXVIII) are bundles of these tiny microscopic fibres held together by the attraction of their many —OH groups. This makes a cellulose fibre little less strong than a steel wire, for to pull its tiny fibres apart one must overcome the attraction of countless millions of molecules for each other.

The uses of cellulose fibres are countless. They are beaten and torn into little bits and felted together to make paper. They are twisted into cotton or linen yarn and spun into cloth, an industry the importance of which may be measured by the fact that Great Britain alone exports some £140,000,000 worth of cotton goods every year. But as chemistry is chiefly concerning us now, we must say something about the new way of using cellulose by turning it into artificial silk. There are at least four ways of doing this. All of them depend on dissolving the cellulose in something to make a sticky solution and drawing this out into very fine threads which are smooth and brilliant like silk threads. Real silk is entirely different chemically, for it is a compound of carbon, hydrogen, oxygen and nitrogen atoms. Cellulose contains no nitrogen and the likeness between real and artificial silk is simply that both are made of fine smooth transparent fibres like tiny threads of glass. Cotton and linen fibres are flat and twisted and so look entirely different when woven.

Most of the world's artificial silk is made by the Viscose process which has the merit of great cheapness, though other processes are considered to produce a finer product. The starting material is bleached wood-pulp. It is soaked in 17% caustic soda solution and after some hours treated with the evil-smelling volatile liquid bisulphide of carbon. The result is a orange-coloured gelatinous mass, which can be dissolved in caustic soda solution, so forming a thick viscous solution of cellulose. This is spun by forcing it through very fine jets into a solution of dilute acid. The acid neutralises the caustic soda and so turns the issuing viscous liquid back to solid cellulose. This is treated to remove traces of sulphur, bleached, washed, and spun into yarn.

The true carbon ring compounds (the sugar ring has an oxygen atom in it) include several important hydroxy-compounds.

Phenol (carbolic acid) is benzene with a hydrogen atom replaced by an OH group. The developer hydroquinone has two hydroxyl groups instead of one and pyrogallol ("pyro") has three. These developers work by taking oxygen from the water, leaving hydrogen which turns the silver bromide into hydrogen bromide and silver.

Coal-tar contains much of the hydroxy-compounds, phenol and cresol, which are very useful disinfectants, and this is perhaps a good place to say something about the way coal-tar is made into a number of useful things. Tar, you will remember, is the stuff which condenses out of coal gas. It is a black strongly smelling liquid containing a great number of different things. All large gasworks distil their tar and turn it into:

(1) *Benzene* and toluene, used as motor spirit and for making dyes and drugs.

(2) *Creosote* (containing cresols and phenol), used for preserving wood and for making disinfectants.

(3) *Naphthalene*, used as a soil disinfectant and as a source of dyes.

(4) *Anthracene*, used to make dyes.

(5) *Pitch*, used for making roads.

The table on p. 621 will give some notion of the kind of substances which can be made from it. If it is added that a recent list of dyes contains 11,000 items almost all made from coal-tar, the importance of the industry may be even more apparent.

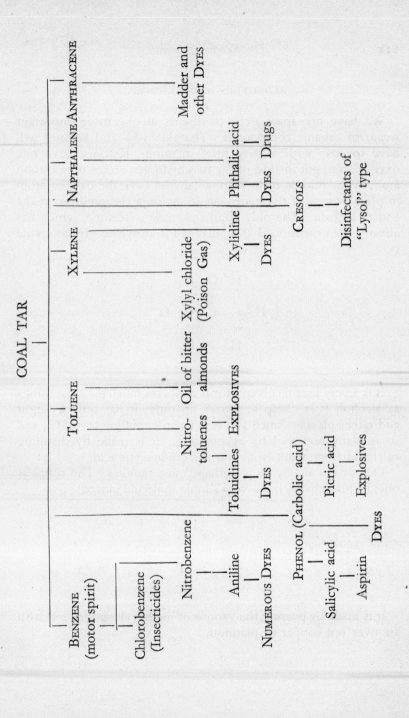

ALDEHYDES AND KETONES

We have not space even to discuss all the most important *groups* of organic compounds. The aldehydes and ketones will have to pass with a very brief mention. Ketones have one oxygen atom put instead of the two hydrogen atoms on a carbon atom in the middle of a chain; aldehydes have the oxygen atom in place of two of the hydrogen atoms on a carbon atom at the end of a chain. The only familiar ketone is acetone, which has already been mentioned as a solvent for acetylene. Its molecule is

$$
\begin{array}{ccccccc}
 & H & & O & & H & \\
 & | & & \| & & | & \\
H\!-\!\!\!&C&\!\!\!-\!\!\!&C&\!\!\!-\!\!\!&C&\!\!\!-\!H \\
 & | & & & & | & \\
 & H & & & & H &
\end{array}
$$

It is a very useful solvent, for it dissolves much the same things as alcohol; it is cheap and pays no duty, it has only a slight and rather pleasant smell and it is volatile, boiling at 56° C., and so is easily removed by evaporation. It is made by distilling calcium acetate, made from lime and crude acetic acid.

One of the aldehydes is perhaps more familiar. The simplest one, formaldehyde, has a very simple molecule indeed

$$
\begin{array}{ccc}
 & O & \\
 & \| & \\
H\!-\!\!&C&\!\!-\!H
\end{array}
$$

It is made by passing the vapour of methyl alcohol mixed with air over hot copper or platinum.

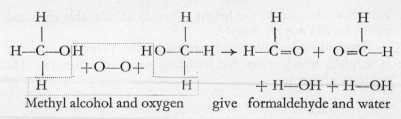

Methyl alcohol and oxygen   give   formaldehyde and water

It is a gas—probably because its molecule is so small—and it is sold as formalin, a 40% solution in water. It is a curious substance. First of all it has a hardening effect on proteins—animal tissues. No one quite knows how it works, but a piece of meat or gelatin soaked in it becomes tough and leathery and will not decay. Bodies for dissection are stored in formalin. It is a useful disinfectant probably for the same reason: it combines with the living protein of bacteria and renders it incapable of the reactions which must accompany life. But the most important use of formaldehyde is in making what are called "plastics"—strong and tough substances which can be moulded into any shape. The most familiar is bakelite—so much used for wireless-set cabinets, electric light fittings, etc. It is made from formaldehyde and phenol (carbolic acid), whose molecule is shown on p. 605. These link up when heated into meshworks of "phenol ring-molecules" joined by formaldehyde "link-molecules." After a certain amount of heating, a material rather like sealing-wax is obtained, the molecules of which are not too big to melt. This can be softened, moulded into electric light fittings, cigarette holders, fountain-pens and a thousand other articles. These are then heated in the moulds. The process of linking up continues in the mould, and a hard, strong object, quite unsoftened by heat, finally results. It is this power of being able to mould bakelite and then harden it, which makes it so useful. Sometimes a sandwich of alternate layers of bakelite and paper is used. The paper is invisible within the finished article, but its fibres make the bakelite very tough. Many substances can be used instead of phenol. Some of them yield transparent or translucent materials—familiar as the bright coloured unbreakable cups and plates we can buy so cheaply.

Many aldehydes have very powerful smells. Worth mentioning is acrolein which gives the irritating smell to burnt fat. Fat contains glycerine.

$$
\begin{array}{ccc}
\text{OH} & & \\
\text{H—C—H} & \text{H—C—H} & \\
| & \| & \text{HOH} \\
\text{H—C—OH} \longrightarrow & \text{CH} + & \\
| & | & \text{HOH} \\
\text{H—C—H} & \text{C—H} & \\
| & \| & \\
\text{OH} & \text{O} &
\end{array}
$$

and this turns into acrolein and water when heated. Pure acrolein has a really appalling smell!

Benzaldehyde is oil of bitter almonds, cinnamaldehyde is oil of cinnamon; they have rather similar molecules:—

$$
\begin{array}{cc}
\text{Benzaldehyde} & \text{Cinnamaldehyde}
\end{array}
$$

ORGANIC ACIDS

Organic acids are an important class: almost all of them contain the group of atoms

$$\overset{\displaystyle O}{\underset{\displaystyle \parallel}{}}$$
—C—OH

Almost the simplest is acetic acid, which is the acid in vinegar. It is made in great quantities—first, as vinegar: secondly, for making into acetone. Vinegar, in England, is made by "souring" a malt liquor like beer: abroad, by souring wine. This "souring" is simply changing alcohol and oxygen from the air into acetic acid and water. This is not difficult to do in the laboratory: but on the factory scale, we employ a fungus *mycoderma aceti* to do it for us.

This lowly creature gets its energy by turning oxygen and alcohol to acetic acid, much as yeast gets its energy by turning sugar into alcohol and carbon dioxide

```
    H  H                    H  O
    |  |                    |  ||
 H—C—C—OH              H—C—C
    |  |                    |  |
    H  H                    H  OH        H—O—H
          + O—O  ⟶                 +
    H  H                    H  O         H—O—H
    |  |                    |  ||
 H—C—C—OH              H—C—C
    |  |                    |  |
    H  H                    H  OH
```

Alcohol and oxygen give   acetic acid   and   water.

Vinegar made in this way is not only sour, but also has a pleasant aroma. Commercial acetic acid, used for making chemicals, is made in a much cheaper way—by distilling wood, much in the same way as coal is distilled to make gas.

Wood is chiefly cellulose. When cellulose (p. 618) is heated it changes into a variety of different molecules. The carbon, hydrogen and oxygen atoms re-sort themselves and a dense choking wood-smoke comes off. When this is cooled it gives a liquid which on standing separates into a brown watery liquid, chiefly a weak solution of acetic acid (5–10%), and a brown oily tar which sinks to the bottom. Much gas, chiefly methane, passes on and is sometimes used for heating. In the retort there remains charcoal. The acetic acid can be recovered by re-distilling the liquid, for it boils at a temperature about 20° C. higher than the boiling point of water. Acetic acid, when pure, freezes at 15° C., so that it is liquid in summer, but in winter freezes to a substance which looks like ice.

ESTERS

A combination of an alcohol and an acid is called an ester. Thus, if we boil ordinary alcohol with acetic acid (a little of any strong acid helps things on) and then distil the mixture we get a fruity-smelling liquid called ethyl acetate

$$
\begin{array}{ccc}
\underset{\text{Ethyl alcohol}}{H-\overset{\displaystyle H}{\underset{\displaystyle H}{C}}-\overset{\displaystyle H}{\underset{\displaystyle H}{C}}-OH} & \text{and} & \underset{\text{acetic acid}}{HO-\overset{\displaystyle O}{C}-\overset{\displaystyle H}{\underset{\displaystyle H}{C}}-H} \quad \Big\downarrow \text{ give}
\end{array}
$$

$$
\underset{\text{ethyl acetate}}{H-\overset{\displaystyle H}{\underset{\displaystyle H}{C}}-\overset{\displaystyle H}{\underset{\displaystyle H}{C}}-O-\overset{\displaystyle O}{C}-\overset{\displaystyle H}{\underset{\displaystyle H}{C}}-H} + \underset{\text{and water.}}{HOH}
$$

These esters made from alcohols and acids usually have fruity or flowery smells, and are used to make flavourings and perfumes that have never been near a plant. Thus a recipe for pear essence runs:

Amyl acetate	200 parts
Ethyl nitrite	100 „
Ethyl acetate	50 „
Alcohol	645 „

The first of the above, amyl acetate, is familiar nowadays. It has a most powerful odour of pear-drops—or, as some think, of bananas. Amyl alcohol differs from ordinary alcohol in having a 5-carbon atom chain instead of a 2-carbon chain. It is a cheap substance, for in making ordinary alcohol by fermentation, a little amyl alcohol is made, too, and is separated in the distillation. From this and acetic acid this powerfully smelling liquid is made. The flavouring of sweets is the least of its uses, for it dissolves celluloid, giving a sticky liquid used for patching films, and also dissolves cellulose acetate and gives the numerous cellulose paints which are so popular. The cellulose paint is hard and not at all easily damaged by heat or grease or petrol. It is very easy for the amateur to use because it leaves a smooth surface without brushmarks.

Other esters you may meet with are artificial jasmine and orange-blossom scents and the "pineapple" tear-gas, but the most important esters are the oils and fats.

OILS AND FATS

The acids with a —C—OH group tacked on to a long chain

$$\overset{\displaystyle \|}{O}$$

of —CH_2—groups are very important because they are the chief thing in animal and vegetable oils, fats and waxes. One has only to mention butter, lard, tallow, suet, olive oil, linseed oil, to remind oneself of the vast industry built up on these. Oils and fats are combinations of glycerol with a long-chain acid. All natural fats are mixtures of several molecules, but as a fair specimen we may take the fat "tristearin" found in beef suet. Glycerol is

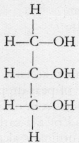

and stearic acid is

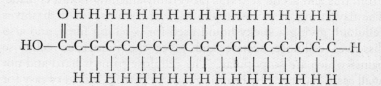

They combine by their two—OH groups giving out H_2O and linking up. So a typical fat molecule is a bunch of three long threads thus:

Fig. 371.—The molecule of the fat tristearin

This is obviously the sort of molecule that will not pack nicely into a crystal—so fats usually solidify to a confused muddle of small crystals, usually long and thread-like. Fats do not dissolve in water for the long chains have less attraction for water molecules than these have for each other (p. 81).

We should be hard put to it to make fats without the help of animals or plants—it could be done but the material would be impossibly expensive. Fat and oil are storage materials which both animals and plants put by for a rainy day. Plants, more often, link up their spare sugar molecules into starch molecules, but sometimes, by a truly remarkable piece of chemistry, they turn them into fats. Animals store almost all their reserves as fat. To obtain these fats and oils from animals and plants is simple. We squeeze oils out of things with a powerful hydraulic press (Fig. 110, p. 205). Seeds and nut kernels are our chief sources of oils. Fats can usually be got by mincing the crude fat and boiling it. The fat floats to the surface while the membranes and so on sink. Another way of obtaining fat is to dissolve it out with some solvent like petrol.

Oils and fats are used
(1) For food.
(2) For soap-making.
(3) For lubricating.

Most foods contain some fat. The foods which are nearly all fat are butter, margarine, and lard—to which, in many countries, should be added olive oil. Lard is pig-fat, best the fat which surrounds the kidneys. The less chemistry has to do with it, the better. Butter and margarine, however, raise some interesting problems.

Milk as we have seen is a watery solution of a protein, casein, and a sugar, lactose, and a little salt in which is suspended about 4% of fat in very small droplets. The fat droplets in milk are separated from each other by the watery liquid. In making milk into butter we agitate the milk so violently that a fine froth of air and milk is produced. Now, it is the casein in the milk—a sort of gluey material which gives the firm consistency to cheese—

which by forming a layer round the fat globules, keeps them separate. But this casein is attracted to the surface of an air-bubble more vigorously than to the surface of a fat globule. Churning therefore takes away the protecting casein layer and the fat globules meet and stick together. But however much they are squeezed, they still enclose some water globules, and so butter is an emulsion of water drops in fat, as milk is an emulsion of fat-drops in water. If you have ever fried anything in butter, you will realise how much water it contains.

We have bred cows to give incredible quantities of milk. A champion milker *has given its own weight of milk in* 10 *days*. None the less, milk contains only four or five per cent. of fat, so butter remains expensive. Naturally, there has been a great deal of money spent and made over margarine—a butter substitute.

Much of the taste of butter is due to its being an emulsion, so margarine is an emulsion of a watery liquid in some edible fat flavoured and coloured to look like butter.

Margarine is usually made from a mixture of fats and oils emulsified with milk. Coconut oil, palmkernel oil, beef fat, hydrogenated oil can all be used. The last is an interesting product. Many nutritious oils—such as fish oils—have a most unpleasant taste and cannot be used as food. If they are heated with a little finely divided nickel-powder and hydrogen gas is passed through them, they combine with the hydrogen and form odourless and tasteless fats. The nickel is removed by filtration. Whatever oils or fats are used must be most carefully refined and purified. The oil and fat are first churned with slightly soured skimmed milk to a thick emulsion of droplets of skim milk in melted fat. The emulsion is then run on to metal rollers kept freezing cold by brine circulating within them. The emulsion sets solid and is worked by kneading and rolling till it is of the correct buttery consistency. Margarine need be no less nutritious than butter, but it may well be less digestible and commonly contain a far smaller proportion of vitamins (p. 875).

The second great use for oils and fats is in making soap. Soap is the sodium salt of the long-chain acids, which in fats and oils are combined with glycerine. So, the fat is first split into glycerine and these acids, which, by the way, are such weak acids that you would not realise that they were acids at all. The splitting up of the fat-molecule can be performed in several ways; a usual method is to add a little lime and heat the fat with high-pressure steam in closed boilers. The fatty acids form an oily layer floating on the watery layer containing the glycerine. The melted acids are run into boiling caustic soda solution and form soap. This is mixed with perfume and colour (for toilet soaps) or soda (household soaps), cooled to set it, partly dried and stamped into bars or tablets. This is only one of half a dozen possible ways of making soap from fat or oil, and caustic soda. The peculiar behaviour of soap is partly due to the odd shape of its molecule, of which a diagram appears in Fig. 35, p. 93. The reason why it is so effective in cleaning things is because it lowers the surface tension of water. This makes it possible for water to wet greasy surfaces and so carry away the grease and dirt together. Thus, a soap solution is the only thing which will remove both greasy and sticky matter.

Waxes are esters like fats and usually have very long molecules. They are harder than fats and do not melt so easily: this makes them suitable for polishes. They are mostly produced by insects. Paraffin wax is not a true wax at all but a hydrocarbon.

The organic compounds we have discussed contain only carbon, hydrogen and oxygen, but many very important ones contain nitrogen as well.

ORGANIC NITROGEN COMPOUNDS

Nitrogen in an organic compound usually occurs as the group of atoms $-NH_2$ or $-NO_2$ or $-N=N-$, though of course plenty of other groupings are known. The $-NH_2$ compounds are called amines or amino-compounds. There are many of them, but we need perhaps only notice a few compounds which are vital to man and every living creature. These are the amino-acids. Suppose in acetic acid you put a —NH$_2$ group instead of one hydrogen atom, you would get the simplest amino-acid

$$
\begin{array}{c}
\text{H} \qquad \text{H} \quad \text{O} \\
\diagdown \qquad | \quad \parallel \\
\text{N—C—C—OH} \qquad \text{glycine by name.} \\
\diagup \qquad | \\
\text{H} \qquad \text{H}
\end{array}
$$

Now the compounds which we would, above all, like to understand are those of which our blood, body and brains are made, and without which no life at all can take place. These are the proteins. As examples, we may take albumen, of which white of egg is a solution, or keratin, which makes our hair and finger-nails, or hæmoglobin, the red pigment of our blood, or casein, the curd of milk. We should understand quite a bit more about life if we could make models of these molecules which are essential to life. Well, much work has been done on them. We have a fair idea as to their size. The smaller ones may be about two thousand times as heavy and bulky as a water molecule. They are very difficult to purify because they do not evaporate, and most of them will not crystallise. What we do know about them is that when we break them up into simpler substances we finally get little, if anything, else than a collection of amino-acids, which all have a molecule like this:

$$
\begin{array}{c}
\text{H} \qquad \text{H} \quad \text{O} \\
\diagdown \qquad | \quad \parallel \\
\text{N—C—C—OH} \\
\diagup \qquad | \\
\text{H} \qquad \boxed{\text{R}}
\end{array}
$$

in which R may be anything from a hydrogen atom to a big group like

$$
\begin{array}{c}
OH \\
| \\
C \\
HC \quad\quad CH \\
| \quad\quad\quad || \\
HC \quad\quad CH \\
C \\
| \\
-CH_2
\end{array}
$$

About twenty different amino-acids can be made from proteins. Now, amino acids link together in pairs like this:

$$
H_2N-C(R)(H)(NH_2) + HO-C(=O)(C.OH=O)(R)(H) \rightarrow H_2N-C(R)(H)(NH-C=O)(C.OH=O)(R)(H) + HOH
$$

and the molecule you get is *still* an amino-acid which can link up to another thing like itself. When a dozen or so amino-acids have been linked together like this, the stuff you make is very like the things you obtain when you partly split up proteins by very careful digestion.

A protein molecule then probably consists of long chains of

atoms linked thus: . . . CO—CH—NH—CO—CH—NH . . .

$$\underset{\boxed{R}}{|} \qquad\qquad \underset{\boxed{R}}{|}$$

etc. There are probably many of these chains linked together by a sort of loose attraction. The following

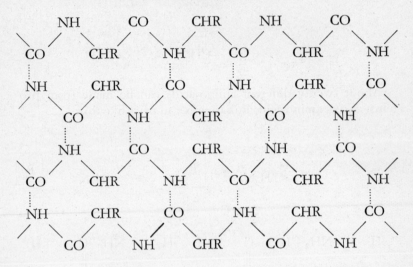

Magnified about thirty million times.

has been given as a reasonable arrangement for a protein molecule, the R's being various big groups of atoms which in the scheme are supposed to stand out above and below the network rather like the bristles of a hair brush!

Ordinary chemical methods are not very much use in dealing with molecules like proteins. We have only a hint or two about the way their molecules are arranged, and at present we have no technique by which we might follow these up.

The method of crystal analysis by X-rays has very recently been applied to a few of the proteins that crystallise, and has given us a few valuable pieces of information of the very type that chemistry is least able to supply. Chemistry can tell us what are the bits from which the huge protein molecules are built up: X-ray analysis can tell us the outline or general pattern on which they are put together: the detailed arrangement—exactly where each bit goes—is still unknown to us.

NITROCOMPOUNDS

The compounds containing the group $-NO_2$ are a very different lot. They are chiefly dyes and explosives. There are two kinds of $-NO_2$ groups. One is $-O-N=O$, the other $-N\begin{smallmatrix}O\\ \\O\end{smallmatrix}$.

In either case the things containing two or three of them are likely to be explosive. The reason is that these oxygen atoms are only loosely hung to the nitrogen atom, and when heated or violently shaken can get round the corner, when the carbon and hydrogen of the compound can burn in its own oxygen.

Look at the formula of the famous explosive "T.N.T." trinitrotoluene.

$$
\begin{array}{c}
H \\
| \\
H-C-H \\
O \quad | \quad O \\
\| \quad C \quad \| \\
N \quad\quad N \\
\diagup\,\diagdown\,\diagup\,\diagdown\,\diagup\,\diagdown \\
O \quad C \quad\quad C \quad O \\
\| \quad\quad | \\
HC \quad\quad CH \\
\diagdown\,\diagup \\
C \\
| \\
N \\
\diagup\,\diagdown \\
O \quad\quad O
\end{array}
$$

Give that molecule a violent shock and the oxygen atoms will switch round to the carbon atoms and become carbon monoxide, the nitrogen atoms will appear as nitrogen gas and the rest of the atoms perhaps as methane. At any rate, a pound and a half of T.N.T. turns almost instantaneously into a pound and a half of white hot gas!

Now, a pound and half of T.N.T. occupies, say, a pint. So the gas from the explosive for a moment occupies a pint also. But a pound and half of these gases when cold at atmospheric pressure occupies 3,600 pints, and at a white heat they would occupy about 18,000 pints. So if they are compressed into one pint, they exert a pressure of at least 18,000 atmospheres or nearly 200 tons to the square inch! No wonder the shell bursts and a devastatingly powerful compression wave of gas wrecks everything close by. Nearly all the best explosives are nitrogen compounds.

The chief merits of an explosive are power and safety. For blasting work, a rather slow acting explosive which rends the rock is preferred to a very rapid one which shatters it. Safety is ensured by having an explosive which will burn without exploding and which can be struck without exploding. The explosives which come best out of these tests are the military explosives like T.N.T. which have to stand the shock of being fired from a gun in a shell. A shell full of T.N.T., provided it has no detonator, can cheerfully be thrown out of a top window. In France, in the war of 1914–1918, it was a common sight to see an unexploded shell bedded in a road with lorries and tanks driving over it. The safest of all explosives is probably ammonal— ammonium nitrate and aluminium powder.

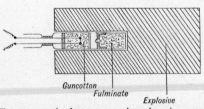

Guncotton
Fulminate
Explosive

FIG. 372.—A detonator. An electric current heats the wire bridge and fires the plug of gun-cotton. This ignites the fulminate, the small but very sudden explosion of which causes the main body of explosive to detonate.

If you can't explode these by hitting them or lighting them—how can you do it? The answer is: Give them a violent shock by exploding a detonator containing about a gram of a sensitive shattering explosive like mercury fulminate or lead azide.

Figure 372 shows the arrangements for exploding a blasting-charge.

Nitroglycerine is an oily liquid with the formula,

$$
\begin{array}{c}
\text{H} \\
| \\
\text{H—C—O—N} \diagram{O}{O} \\
| \\
\text{H—C—O—N} \diagram{O}{O} \\
| \\
\text{H—C—O—N} \diagram{O}{O} \\
| \\
\text{H}
\end{array}
$$

and so has a good supply of oxygen ready at a moment's notice to burn up the carbon and hydrogen into gases. It is rather danger-ously sensitive however. Dynamite is nitroglycerine soaked up in a sort of porous earth or better wood-pulp: it is safer than the pure liquid because it cannot be spilt.

DYES

One of the greatest feats of organic chemistry has been to provide the world with thousands of cheap, brilliant and beautiful dyes. Before, say, 1856, when Perkin discovered mauve, the first of the coal-tar colours, some of the shades we get to-day could not be dyed at all, and most of them could only be got by boiling the cloth in a very carefully adjusted mixture of dyes. For reds, they had cochineal and madder, for blue, indigo and a few dyes made from lichens. For yellows and greens there were a few good plant dyes. These colours were very good ones, but their variety was small and many of them faded badly. The organic chemist has now worked out pretty well the sort of combinations of atoms which give dyes, brightly coloured substances, which will stick firmly to the fibre of cotton, wool or silk or all of these.

He finds that the groups of atoms

$$-N{\overset{\displaystyle O}{\underset{\displaystyle O}{\diagup\diagdown}}} \quad, \quad -N=N-, \quad -\underset{\displaystyle O}{\overset{}{C}}{\underset{\displaystyle \parallel}{}}$$

—C=C— and some others, particularly when several times repeated in a molecule, make it *coloured*. A ring skeleton of carbon atoms also helps. If, in addition to these we have an —OH or —NH$_2$ group, it will probably be a dye. Here is one of the simplest dyes known as picric acid,

$$
\begin{array}{c}
\text{OH} \\
| \\
\text{C} \\
\diagup\diagdown \\
\text{O}_2\text{N.C} \qquad \text{C.NO}_2 \\
| \qquad\quad \parallel \\
\text{HC} \qquad\ \text{CH} \\
\diagdown\diagup \\
\text{C} \\
| \\
\text{NO}_2
\end{array}
$$

made from phenol and nitric acid. It dyes silk and wool a fine yellow. Its colour is chiefly due to the $-N{\overset{\displaystyle O}{\underset{\displaystyle O}{\diagup\diagdown}}}$ groups.

Here is another, malachite green, which owes its colour chiefly to its alternation of =C—C=C—C= groups.

CH₃ CH₃
\ /
N
|
C
/ \\
HC   CH
| ||
HC   CH
\\ / H H
C   C=C
| /   \
C—C   CH
|| \\ //
C   C—C
/ \\ H H
HC   CH
|| ||
HC   CH
\ /
C
||
N—Cl
/ \
CH₃ CH₃

Indigo (p. 595) has several of these groups. It is interesting to note by the way that the red colouring matter in a carrot (p. 602) is not a dye. It is brilliantly coloured but has no —OH or —NH₂ group to stick it to the fibre.

The process of dyeing is not merely soaking the fabric in a solution of the dye. If this is all that is done, most of the colour washes out again.

There are three chief ways of dyeing, direct dyeing, mordant dyeing and vat dyeing. The first is the one practised in the home with the dyes we buy in packets. The other two require a good deal of skill, and are chiefly done in the factory. The usual way of dyeing is to boil the dye with water, and often a little acid or alkali, and lower the damp material into it. It is boiled and stirred for half an hour or so and very often salt is put in which has the effect of driving the dye out of the solution on to the fibre. When fabric has been well dyed like this, no amount of washing will remove the colour, and the dye molecules are pretty certainly actually combined with the fibre molecules. Silk and wool are much more easily dyed than cotton.

Mordant dyeing is a very ancient practice which goes back certainly as far as the Greeks. If you try to dye a piece of wool with a solution of cochineal, it is coloured red or pink, but the colour all washes out again; but if the wool is first soaked with chloride of tin and oxalic acid and then dyed with cochineal it is dyed a beautiful fiery scarlet. The dye sticks to the tin compounds and these stick to the fibre, and no amount of washing will remove it.

The most ancient dyes known are on some of the mummy wrappings, etc. from Egypt. In the British Museum, you can see Egyptian cloth dyed with indigo and still unfaded after 4,000 years.

Indigo is a "vat-dye." It is quite insoluble in water, so it is hopeless to try and make a solution of it in which to boil the cloth. So the trick is to remove some of the oxygen from the indigo and so turn it into a colourless substance, indigo-white, which dissolves in water. The cloth is soaked in this and comes out white or yellowish. It is then hung up in the air. The oxygen of the air turns the indigo-white soaked up in the fibres back into indigo, and the cloth turns blue as you watch it! The ancient way of doing this was to cut down the indigo plant (woad was a sort of indigo plant), and let it ferment in tanks of water. The fermentation removed the oxygen, and the vat contained a crude solution of indigo-white! The modern way is to use various chemicals to remove the oxygen.

ALKALOIDS

There is a curious group of drugs and poisons mostly extracted from the plants, called the alkaloids. They all have rings of carbon atoms with a nitrogen atom interposed. They have very powerful effects upon the nerves and are mostly very poisonous. It is not very clear why they exist in the plant. Perhaps they prevent animals from eating them or perhaps they are just waste products. A short list shows how important they are.

Alkaloid	Plant Source	Used for
Nicotine	Tobacco	Poisoning plant pests.
Atropine	Deadly Nightshade	Dilating the pupil of the eye.
Hyoscine	Henbane	Causing unconsciousness or sleep.
Cocaine	Coca-plant	Numbing the nerves locally.
Quinine	Cinchona-bark	Destroying the malaria parasite.
Emetine	Ipecacuanha	Curing dysentery.

Alkaloid	Plant Source	Used for
Morphine	Opium-poppy	Dulling pain.
Codeine	,,	Preventing coughing, etc.
Strychnine	Strychnos bean	Stimulant and tonic. Also destroying vermin.
Aconitine	Monk's-hood	Local anæsthetic.

They are all very poisonous—except quinine. A medicinal dose of atropine is about a quarter of a milligram ($\frac{1}{275}$ of a grain), while one five-hundredth of a gram of aconitine has been known to kill a man. All of them have very complicated molecules. The formula of nicotine (left) is quite a simple example:

that of strychnine (right) about as complicated as any.

This glance over the organic compounds is very sketchy. A mere incomplete list of organic compounds, devoting only one or two lines to each, fills five volumes of 1,500 to 1,800 large pages. Every month, hundreds of new ones are discovered. This little account has hardly glanced at them. Let us end it by thanking the organic chemist for almost all the drugs the doctor uses. Most of them he has invented. Some, like opium, which has been known for centuries, he has converted from unreliable and variable mixtures to pure drugs of exactly known strength. But the majority of modern drugs he has created. After the doctor, the organic chemist has done more for human health than anyone else.

21

CHAPTER XXIV

Nitrogen the Food-giver

NITROGEN AS FERTILISER

WE live in a vast sea of gas of which four-fifths is nitrogen. For some not very obvious reason, nitrogen at ordinary temperatures is very inert and combines with almost nothing. The nitrogen of the air remains unchanged and inactive except when a lightning flash makes a stretch of air white-hot. Then, a little nitrogen and oxygen combine and with the water of rain make nitric acid. This soaks into the soil and all soils contain a little combined nitrogen in this form. The world, then, has in the air a vast supply of free nitrogen *molecules*. It has also a

FIG. 373.—The carbon circulation. Plants take carbon from the carbon dioxide in the air. Animals eat the plants and return the carbon dioxide to the air *via* their lungs. Water supplies the necessary hydrogen and oxygen for organic compounds and the sun supplies the energy to build them up.

vast demand for nitrogen *combined* with other elements; this it requires for two chief purposes first, to fertilise the soil, secondly, to make dyes, explosives and drugs.

First of all let us look at the fertiliser question. For centuries men farmed the ground. They grew crops—wheat, hay, cabbages, etc.—and they and their horses and cows and pigs ate them. The crops contained sugar and starch and proteins—or putting it more simply, carbon, hydrogen, oxygen, nitrogen and phosphorus atoms. The crops took carbon dioxide from the air, and water from the rain, and light from the sun, and built these into sugar and starch and cellulose. When men and animals ate the crops, they breathed out the carbon dioxide and water into the air once more. Carbon, hydrogen and oxygen circulated everlastingly through air and plant and animal by the motive force of the blessed sun. Nothing was lost except when plants or animals were buried, and even then the loss was small and in course of aeons would be restored. You may call a halt here and ask what happened to the plants that were not eaten. All plants are eaten! If they are not eaten by an animal, they die and rot, or, in other words, are eaten by bacteria and turned to carbon dioxide and water in just the same way.

Fig. 373a.—The circulation of nitrogen. Crops take nitrogen from the soil. Man and beast eat the crops: their nitrogen-rich excretions are returned to the soil once more.

The air contains a very large margin of carbon dioxide and man is always adding to it by burning coal and oil. It is not likely that food could fail for lack of carbon, but it is far otherwise with two of the essential food-elements, nitrogen and phosphorus. With a very few exceptions, plants cannot use the inert nitrogen in the air. When man is not disturbing the ancient equilibrium, thunderstorms and nitogen-fixing bacteria in the soil alone supply a minute pittance of nitrates to the ground. The rootlets of the plants, say grass, seek them out and cunningly combine their nitrogen into protein molecules. A rabbit eats the grass. He turns the plant proteins into rabbit proteins. All the nitrogen he does not assimilate he returns to the soil as urine or droppings. What he does assimilate goes back to soil when he dies and rots. The only way nitrogen is lost is by the work of some villainous bacteria which get their living by turning combined nitrogen into free nitrogen, but the loss by these is just compensated by the gain from the thunderstorms.

So the wood or field or heath for hundreds of centuries kept its little store of nitrogen ever built and rebuilt into stem and leaf, flower and fruit, insect, bird and beast.

Then man came to farm; and while he lived primitively, putting his refuse back into the soil, little harm was done. But as time grew on, great cities rose. To-day, thousands of tons of food representing perhaps 250 tons of combined nitrogen pour into London daily. That food is eaten. The nitrogen departs by only two routes—down the water-closet to the sea or in the hearse to be buried deep out of the plant's reach, or to be burned wastefully in the crematorium, setting nitrogen free in the air. An acre of ground may perhaps contain a couple of tons of combined nitrogen, so London's food is enough each day to rob a small farm of 125 acres of its fertility.

The problem has been solved in three ways. First, the world spends the capital accumulated in the past. In Chile, on the arid coast between the Pacific and the Andes, are vast deposits of sodium nitrate. No rain falls there, for the winds perpetually blow from east to west, and as they rise over the lofty mountains,

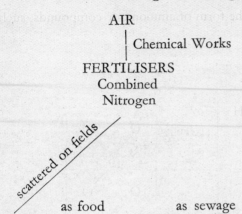

AIR

Chemical Works

FERTILISERS
Combined
Nitrogen

scattered on fields

                as food   as sewage
CROPS————————MAN————————RIVERS AND SEA

Fig. 374.—Modern man's supply of nitrogen.

they deposit all their moisture. For this reason, these deposits (which are about as soluble as sugar) have never been washed away. No one knows how they came there, but they are probably the remains of huge masses of decayed seaweed cast up from a primitive ocean. This sodium nitrate ($NaNO_3$) is somewhat purified and then shipped all over the world to restore the nitrogen the town dweller casts into the sea. There may be 200 years' supply of nitrogen in Chile; probably there is not so much.

While coal lasts, we have nitrogen on tap. Coal is the remnant of ancient plants and the nitrogen of their proteins remains. When coal is burned in a fire or furnace, the nitrogen is wasted, for it goes back to the air as free nitrogen. But when gas is made, the nitrogen appears as ammonia (pp. 250, 648) and is extracted and turned into ammonium sulphate and sold to the farmer. The plant requires nitrogen as nitrates such as sodium nitrate,

$$[Na]^+ \left[O\!-\!N\!\!\begin{array}{c} \nearrow O \\ \searrow O \end{array} \right]^-$$

and it cannot use it in the form of ammonium compounds, such
as ammonium sulphate,

$$\left[\begin{array}{c} H \\ | \\ H-N-H \\ | \\ H \end{array} \right]^{+} \qquad \left[\begin{array}{c} O \quad\quad O \\ \diagdown \quad \diagup \\ S \\ \diagup \quad \diagdown \\ O \quad\quad O \end{array} \right]^{=}$$

$$\left[\begin{array}{c} H \\ | \\ H-N-H \\ | \\ H \end{array} \right]^{+}$$

which contain the —NH_4 group of atoms. But in the soil are
bacteria (the chemists of the plant world) which have the power
of turning $[NH_4]^+$ ions and oxygen into water and $[NO_3]^-$ ions
which the plant can use. As coal may last 500–3000 years, its
nitrogen will not fail us for many a day.

Finally, the world is using its nitrogen capital by continually
breaking virgin unused soil, growing wheat on it, till its nitrogen
and its consequent fertility is decreased, and then either passing
on to new ground or importing nitrogen. The huge farms of
the U.S.A. and Canada are examples of this. The plant breeders
are continually evolving quicker-growing wheats which, being
able to ripen in the short Arctic summer, allow the wheat-fields
of Canada to be pushed north; they evolve, too, drought-resisting
wheats which can be grown in the virgin soil of the dry areas
where ordinary wheat cannot flourish.

There is one biological way of restoring the loss. Certain
"leguminous" plants—peas, beans, lupins, vetches, etc.—have a
remarkable habit of setting up a partnership with an able chemist

in the guise of a bacterium. These bacteria live in nodules on the roots of the lupins, etc. (dig up a lupin seedling or runner bean and look) and have the most remarkable power of turning the nitrogen of the air into combined nitrogen. So a good way of enriching a poor soil is to grow a crop of vetches and plough them, and the nitrogen they have made, into the soil.

The most recent and effective way of getting nitrogen for our food is to make it from the air. This is a difficult task for the chemist, but he has found four or five ways of solving it. We have only space to talk of one or two.

The Birkeland-Eyde process imitates the lightning. Air is blown through a huge electric arc at 2000° C. spread by magnetic forces into a flat disc of flame. The nitrogen and oxygen of the air partly combine and by the action of more air and water finally make nitric acid.

$$N \equiv N \quad N \equiv O \;\; O \qquad O = N = O \;\; O \qquad \begin{array}{c} H \\ | \\ O \\ | \\ H \end{array} \qquad \begin{array}{c} HNO_3 \\ \\ HNO_3 \end{array}$$

N≡N	N≡O O	O=N=O O	H | O | H HNO₃
O=O	N≡O O	O=N=O O	HNO₃
Air in arc flame	gives nitric oxide which on cooling combines with more air and makes	nitrogen dioxide which with more air and water finally gives	nitric acid.

The nitric acid is usually treated with limestone, giving calcium nitrate, which is a solid and can be charged into sacks and sold to farmers.

The cyanamide process uses calcium carbide (p. 601), heats it and passes over it nitrogen from the air. This makes calcium cyanamide, which in damp soils slowly changes to ammonium compounds, which bacteria change to nitrates.

The process chiefly in favour now is to make ammonia (NH_3) from nitrogen and hydrogen and turn this into ammonium sulphate, which soil-bacteria very easily change into nitrates. The process requires great feats of engineering because the gases have to be handled at fairly high temperatures and pressures of up to 200—300 atm. The first step is to make hydrogen, the manu-facture of which from water-gas has been described on p. 569. When two volumes hydrogen and one volume oxygen are ignited they explode and combine to form water; so if you mix five cubic feet of air (containing one cubic foot of oxygen and four cubic feet of nitrogen) with fourteen cubic feet of hydrogen, two of the latter will burn and turn all of the oxygen to steam; and a mixture of four cubic feet of nitrogen and twelve cubic feet of hydrogen will be left. This is the right proportion for making ammonia. Actually, a mixture of air and hydrogen would explode violently, so we mix the air and hydrogen together only as fast as they burn.

The nitrogen-hydrogen mixture is cooled and purified from traces of other gases and is then compressed to no less than 3000—5000 lbs. per sq. inch. It is then passed over a "catalyst" of metallic iron which in some not clearly understood manner makes them partially combine and make ammonia. Now, am-monia gas at the enormous pressure of 5000 lbs. per sq. inch boils at quite a high temperature. So it is only necessary to cool the gas to condense out the ammonia. The unused nitrogen and hydrogen are used again.

The liquid ammonia gas has now to be turned into a form which can be sold as a fertiliser. This is done by combining it with sulphuric acid to make solid ammonium sulphate.

AMMONIA

Ammonia, as we have seen, is a compound of nitrogen and hydrogen. Its formula is NH_3 and its molecule is arranged like this:

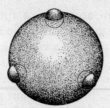

Diagram of Ammonia molecule.
The large sphere represents the
nitrogen atom: the three small
bulges hydrogen atoms.

Its smell is familiar to everyone because ammonia is often used
for cleaning. It turns grease into soap to some extent and it
softens water, but is not really a very efficient cleanser. The chief
use of it is, as we have seen, to make fertilisers. Liquefied
ammonia is used a good deal in refrigerators. The refrigerator
described on p. 118 employs liquid sulphur dioxide; ammonia
is used in a very similar way.

Ammonia's chief chemical characteristic is the way it combines
with acids. Acids combine with it and give it their loose hydrogen
atom and an electric charge. Thus, if you mix ammonia fumes
and hydrochloric acid fumes, you get a dense white smoke of
ammonium chloride or sal-ammoniac.

Ammonia and any acid will form a
solid ammonium salt of this kind.
Examples are *ammonium chloride*, sal-
ammoniac (above) used for Leclanché
batteries and in soldering and brazing.
Ammonium sulphate is used as a fertiliser. Ammonium chloride is not
used as a fertiliser because chlorides
are not very good for the soil, while
sulphates are enjoyed by plants like cabbages and onions which
contain a good deal of sulphur.

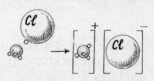

$NH_3 + HCl \rightarrow NH_4Cl$

FIG. 375. — Ammonia and
hydrochloric acid give
ammonium chloride.

Ammonium nitrate would be a very fine fertiliser but is rather
expensive. Its chief use is as an explosive. A molecule of the
solid $[NH_4]^+ [NO_3]^-$ when given a violent shock changes into

21*

two molecules of steam and one of nitrous oxide $O=N\equiv N$ (the gas that the dentist uses) and for the reasons given on p. 636 causes a violent explosion. It is a very safe explosive indeed.

The other great use of ammonia is for making nitric acid. Nitric acid can be made by the Birkeland-Eyde process (p. 647) or from sodium nitrate, but the easiest process to understand,

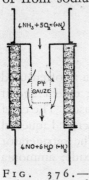

and probably the most important one, is its manufacture from ammonia. The principle is simple. Pass a current of mixed ammonia gas and air through a few thicknesses of hot platinum wire gauze. Ammonia and air have nothing to say to each other in the ordinary way and even at a white heat only turn into nitrogen and steam. But the surface of the platinum in some unexplained way makes the nitrogen of the ammonia and the oxygen of the air combine and make the gas nitric oxide NO. This combines with air and water, giving nitric acid just as in the Birkeland-Eyde process.

FIG. 376.— Ammonia and oxygen, when passed through platinum gauze, give nitric oxide which with air and water gives nitric acid.

NITRIC ACID

Nitric acid is a very useful chemical substance. It has a great deal of chemical energy. It is a strong acid—i.e., with water it produces a great deal of H_3O^+ hydroxonium ion; it has a great deal of oxygen to give away to anything which will accept it and, finally, has the power of putting $-N\diagdown\substack{O\\O}$ groups into organic compounds. Without nitric acid you cannot carry on a war, for all explosives are made from it. Unfortunately for the cause of peace, it is made, as we have seen, from the air, so no country need be without it.

Pure nitric acid is unpleasant to handle. It is a colourless liquid (if not quite pure, yellow or brown) which gives off a sharp-smelling fume. If you drop it on your skin, it will make a dangerous burn before you can wash it off, and will make holes in your clothes. Ordinary "strong" nitric acid as sold contains about a third of its weight of water and is not quite so destructive —though dangerous enough. Its chief use in the world's work is to make fertilisers and organic nitro-compounds. Thus T.N.T. is made by mixing liquid toluene C_7H_8 (a substance closely related to benzene) with several successive portions of strong sulphuric and nitric acids of increasing strength. Aniline, from which so many dyes can be made, is produced by treating benzene with nitric and sulphuric acid for a shorter time and at a lower temperature. The almond-smelling yellow oil nitrobenzene floats to the top. It is run off and washed, treated with scrap-iron borings and water and a little acid. The iron takes its two oxygen atoms and also one from the water so making the—NO_2 group into an —NH_2 group.

Nitric Acid
HO.NO$_2$

Benzene   Nitrobenzene   Iron   Water

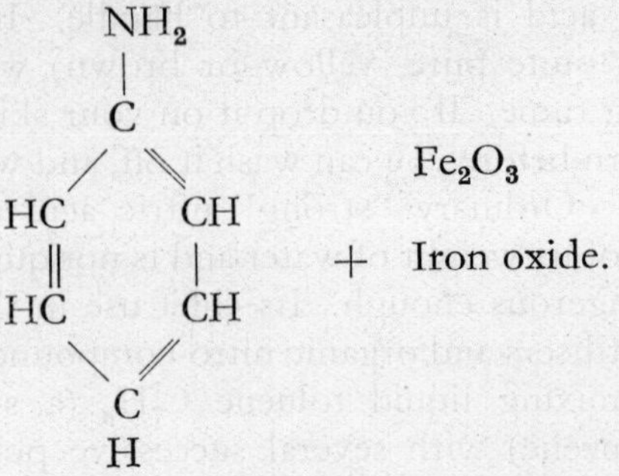

$$NH_2$$
$$|$$
$$C$$

HC CH Fe_2O_3

HC CH + Iron oxide.

$$C$$
$$H$$
Aniline

The aniline is distilled to purify it.

There are hundreds of other compounds of nitrogen, all interesting to the chemist. We can just mention its oxides, laughing-gas $O=N\equiv N$ which the dentist uses; the heavy brown gas, nitrogen peroxide $O=N=O$ which you see when you put a halfpenny in strong nitric acid: its remarkable explosive chloride whose special line is blowing eyes and fingers off eminent chemists. The cyanides with the group of atoms $-N\equiv C$ are interesting. They are very potent poisons indeed. Hydrocyanic or prussic acid HCN is the quickest poison known, and may kill within 30 seconds. Very few other poisons (except gases) will kill under several hours. Even this horribly dangerous substance—made worse by the fact that it is a liquid which evaporates far quicker than the lightest petrol to an intensely poisonous vapour —finds its uses. It is not poisonous to plants: consequently, it can be pumped into (or made in) a greenhouse, and will kill every living animal—aphis, spider or bug. In California, where fruit is grown in vast quantities for canning, they erect a tent over a tree, pump into it a dose of prussic acid, thus killing all pests. They then pass on to the next tree and clear their orchards very effectively.

CHAPTER XXV

PHOSPHORUS : SILICON

PHOSPHORUS AND PHOSPHATES

PHOSPHORUS is a very odd element—not of very great importance—but its compounds, the phosphates, are essentials of life, and it looks as if our descendants will have trouble in finding enough of them.

The element phosphorus can sort out its atoms into molecules in two different ways. Consequently, we can make two kinds of phosphorus, red and white, both made entirely of phosphorus atoms but as different in their way as diamonds from charcoal. Red phosphorus is contained in the paste which covers the outside of a safety-match box. It is a dark red powder. It has no smell. You can eat it and not be harmed. It is very inflammable, and at about 200° C.—the temperature of a hot oven—catches alight and burns brilliantly. Its use on the match-box is simply to start to burn as a result of the heat of friction and so to set fire to the less inflammable match-head.

White phosphorus is a very different material. It looks rather like white wax, though it can be made into brilliant little crystals. It has to be kept under water; for, in air, it either catches alight or smoulders away. If you pick up a stick of phosphorus with tongs (the warmth of your hand would set it alight and burn you badly) you can see it smoking, and if you take it into a dark room you can see it glowing with a faint greenish light. The glow is phosphorus vapour burning (combining with the oxygen of the air) in a peculiar way and giving out light with very little heat. Some heat is produced and the phosphorus usually warms up gradually, and when it gets to about the temperature of a warm bath, it catches alight. White phosphorus is very poisonous indeed—a tenth of a grain may be a fatal dose. White phosphorus used to be employed in match-heads, but its vapour made the teeth and even the jawbones of the workers decay, and every civilised country has now forbidden its use.

Plants and animals must have phosphorus because the most essential part of the cell, the nucleus, contains compounds called nucleo-proteins, which contain a little phosphorus. The fresh bones of animals contain as much as 9% of phosphorus, for the strong hard part of them consists largely of calcium phosphate.

$$[PO_4] \equiv \begin{matrix} [Ca]^{++} \\ [Ca]^{++} \\ [Ca]^{++} \end{matrix} \quad [PO_4] \equiv$$

Dry bones contain more still. This absolutely necessary phosphorus must ultimately be obtained from plants.

Now phosphorus is not a very common element: all soils contain a little, but very few contain much. In a state of nature, phosphorus circulates and is not lost. The plant takes it from the soil; the animal eats the plant and uses the phosphorus for its cell-nuclei and its bones; both plant and animal die and return to the soil.

But into London, every day, we are pouring tons of combined phosphorus in the form of food. Every year in the British Isles half a million people die and their bones are buried. We bury in them at least 200 tons of phosphorus, equivalent to 2,000 tons of the best phosphate rock. Needless to say, the soil will not stand the strain and we have to give it phosphates. In many parts of the world are phosphate-deposits. This phosphate rock is mined, ground up, treated with sulphuric acid which makes the phosphorus more quickly available, and sold as superphosphate to fertilise the soil. But we are spending capital. One day the phosphate rock will be finished, and unless our descendants find some new source of phosphorus, they will be unable to get enough food from the impoverished soil. Then, indeed, they will be glad to dig us up and use our bones to fertilise the fields: they will indeed "grind our bones to make their bread." Business-like people would insist on being cremated and scattered on the soil from which they sprung, so returning their phosphates. Cremation, it is true, would waste their nitrogen, but we can always get that back from the air.

SILICON

The element silicon is the chief one which binds the rocks together. We shall have more to say about rocks and the earth in Chapter XXXII, but, generally speaking, one may say that the crust of the earth is mainly made of silicon compounds and of calcium carbonate. All the volcanic rocks like granite, basalt, porphyry; all the clays and shales; all the sands and sandstones are silicon compounds. The only really common rocks that are not silicates are chalk and limestone.

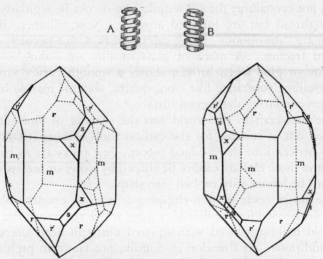

FIG. 377.—Right- and left-handed crystals of silica: above, right- and left-handed screws for comparison. (Lower portion by courtesy of Messrs. Macmillan & Co.; from Tutton's *Crystallography and Practical Crystal Measurement*.)

The element silicon itself is not of much practical use, but its oxide silica is one of the commonest substances in the world. Its formula is SiO_2.

Crystallised silica is rock crystal or quartz. In this crystal, the molecules are arranged spirally as if they lay on the thread of a very coarse-pitched screw. Now, we know a screw may either be right-handed or left-handed and, accordingly, we get right- and left-handed quartz crystals! If you look at a quartz crystal you can see little "hemihedral faces" (r', s, x, Fig. 377), and in a batch of crystals you will find some like each of the two crystals illustrated. These are like reflections of each other in a mirror, as are a right-handed and left-handed screw.

Quartz is found as small grains—ill-shaped crystals—in many rocks, and when these break up by the action of wind, water and weather, the very hard grains of quartz remain behind, in the form of sand. Ordinary sand is mainly waterworn particles of quartz or flint.

Flint is also silica (as are opal, chalcedony, agate and carnelian) but is not crystalline: the silica molecules do not lie regularly on a screw thread but are jumbled anyhow. Now, all these things which are "amorphous" as we call it, break with a peculiar shell-shaped fracture. A piece of glass or flint or sealing wax or bakelite or glue when broken shows a smooth curved surface. A crystalline substance like iron, quartz, soda or marble breaks and leaves an irregular jagged surface.

The first craft in the world was the shaping of flint. It was marked out as suitable for the earliest tools because it could be easily broken into sharp-edged pieces. Few rocks are as hard as flint, and those that are cannot be shaped by blows or pressure, but have to be laboriously rubbed into shape.

The hoary trade of flint-chipping is not yet extinct. Shaped flints are needed for the flint-lock guns which survive in the East, and old buildings faced with squared flint still need alterations and additions. At Brandon in Suffolk, not far from prehistoric flint mines, the tradition of "flint-knapping" continues. Plate XXX illustrates the knapping of flints, and the beautifully shaped gun-flints made thereby.

Almost all rocks, except chalk, marble and limestone, are made up of silica and silicates. A silicate is a compound of metal ions with silicate ions, which are electrically charged groups of silicon and oxygen atoms. A typical and rather simple one is talc, made of magnesium, silicon and oxygen atoms in the proportion shown by the formula $Mg_3(OH)_2Si_4O_{10}$. Most of the natural silicates have very complicated molecules, made up of long chains or wide networks of alternate silicon and oxygen atoms with ions (electrically charged atoms of metals) clustering in the interspaces.

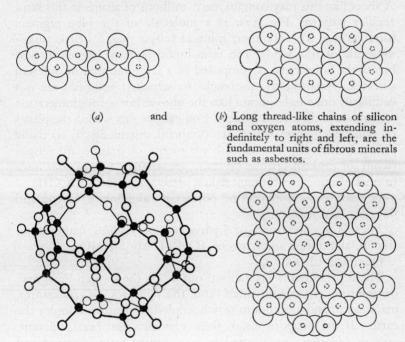

(*a*) and (*b*) Long thread-like chains of silicon and oxygen atoms, extending indefinitely to right and left, are the fundamental units of fibrous minerals such as asbestos.

(*c*) A closed basket-like network of silicon and oxygen atoms. These are found in ultramarine and in felspar.

(*d*) Plane networks of silicon and oxygen atoms extending indefinitely in every direction are the fundamental units of minerals, such as mica, which readily split into thin leaves.

Fig. 378.
(From Dr. R. C. Evans' translation of O. Hassel's *Kristallchemie*, published by Messrs. William Heinemann.)

Fig. 378 shows typical examples of these networks. The large white spheres are oxygen atoms: the little dotted spheres in Fig. 378*a*, *b*, *d*, and the black spheres in Fig. 378*c* are silicon atoms. The metal ions must be thought of as clustering round these frameworks. Those in Fig. 378*a*, *b*, are the sort of chains that one might find in asbestos or a mineral which has fine fibrous crystals. Such chains as these might, of course, continue for hundreds of atoms to right or left. Flat sheets of atoms (Fig. 378*d*) are found in minerals like talc and mica, which split into thin sheets. A sheet like this may contain many millions of atoms in this same regular pattern. Fig. 378*c* is a molecule of the blue pigment ultramarine. The common mineral felspar has a "basket-like" molecule of this kind. The semi-liquid layer of the earth next below the solid crust is composed of a large number of different silicates. Accordingly, the rocks to which it solidifies are not ordinarily one single silicate like the above, but a conglomeration of crystals of different silicates. You can see this well in the pieces of polished granite which are doubtful ornaments to so many public buildings. The chief constituents of granite are felspar (white or pinkish opaque crystals), transparent quartz, and mica in small shining and brilliant flakes, often black (Plate XXXIII).

Felspar is a compound of potassium, aluminium, silicon and oxygen, $KAlSi_3O_8$.

Mica is a compound of hydrogen, potassium, magnesium, silicon, aluminium and oxygen[1], $(OH)_2 K Mg_3Si_3 AlO_{10}$.

Quartz is silica SiO_2.

These presumably crystallised out when the molten "magma" or mixture containing silica and the silicates of potassium, magnesium and aluminium slowly cooled for centuries under the earth. If the proportions of these elements had been different, crystals of other complicated silicates might have appeared and we might have had basalt or olivine instead of granite.

If a molten mixture of silicates is suddenly cooled, instead of crystals there appears an amorphous glass. This often happens with volcanic lavas: the almost black glass so produced is called

[1] There are several different felspars and micas.

obsidian. It breaks like flint and so primitive peoples have chipped it like flint into razor-edged arrow-heads and knives. The Mexican priest sacrificing his victim, cut open his breast with an obsidian knife—a tradition dating probably to the days before metals were known.

Glass is a mixture of silicates. To make ordinary glass, it is not enough to melt rocks and cool the liquid, for since the rocks all contain a good deal of iron, the glass would be nearly black. Ordinary glass is the mixture of the silicates of sodium, potassium, calcium and lead or some of these.

Soft glass as used for windows is made from:

      Soda, 30 parts

      Chalk, 35 parts

      Sand, 100 parts

      Broken Glass, a variable quantity

A more brilliant-looking glass suitable for ornaments is made from:

      Potassium carbonate, 20 parts

      Red Lead, 60 parts

      Sand, 100 parts

      Broken Glass, a variable quantity

and numerous other mixtures can be used for special purposes, such as glass for lenses. Boron oxide may replace silicon to some extent. The strongest glasses for resisting heat and violence are those like pyrex which are used for oven-glass and for making chemical apparatus: these are "borosilicates" of the above type.

Glass is made by melting the above mixtures in a regenerative furnace of the type shown in Fig. 386. A rather sticky liquid is obtained when the materials first melt, and even at a white heat it is by no means as limpid as water. The glass is kept melted for a long time so as to allow all the air-bubbles to float out of it to the surface.

Now, given the molten glass, how are articles made from it? The traditional method is "blowing," a most skilled trade!

The glass worker gathers a lump of treacly semi-molten glass on the end of a long iron tube. By blowing into the tube the glass

is inflated into a bulb. This can be shaped by twirling the tube, by
swinging it so as to extend the soft bulb by the action of gravity,
by reheating it and blowing softly or vigorously. Very few and
simple tools are used, and great skill is required.

Sometimes the bulb is blown inside a hot iron mould: this
enables a large number of vessels of exactly the same dimensions
to be blown.

Blowing machines are extremely complex: they operate on the
above principle and produce almost all the cheaper bottles—e.g.,
beer-bottles—which are required.

Many articles such as the cheaper glass dishes are pressed. Hot
glass is poured into a mould and a shaped plunger comes down
on it and forces into every corner. The mould opens and the glass
article has by that time cooled to the solid state.

Window glass is usually drawn. The sheet of glass has one
end dipping in the molten glass and is continuously pulled up
by rollers. This has the effect of drawing out of the tank a
continuous sheet of glass
which solidifies as fast
as it leaves the furnace.
Glass which has cooled
quickly is in a state of
strain due to uneven con-
traction and is very easily
broken. All the glass ar-
ticles are therefore *annealed*
after they have been made.
They are heated to the
temperature when the
glass is just beginning
to soften and then cooled
very slowly for an hour
and a half or more.

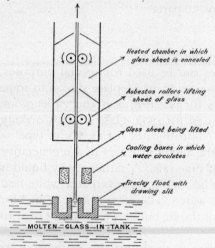

FIG. 378a.—Mechanical drawing of sheet glass.

Labels in figure:
Heated chamber in which glass sheet is annealed
Asbestos rollers lifting sheet of glass
Glass sheet being lifted
Cooling boxes in which water circulates
fireclay float with drawing slit
MOLTEN GLASS IN TANK

CHAPTER XXVI

CHLORINE

COMMON SALT

CHLORINE has an evil reputation, for it was the first of the poison-gases to be used in warfare. But in its compounds, it is not only useful but essential for the whole fluid contents of our bodies, blood, tears, milk, lymph, sweat, urine are a weak solution of common salt which is more than half chlorine. There seems to be no very obvious reason why sodium chloride rather than, say, potassium chloride should be the most abundant salt in our bodies. It is thought that all land creatures have been evolved from marine creatures: these, which naturally would contain the salt of the sea, have handed on to us the chemical inheritance of a cell contents which requires salt.

The most important compound of chlorine then is salt— sodium chloride—which as Fig. 16 p. 47 shows you, consists of sodium ions—sodium atoms with one electron removed—and chlorine ions—chlorine atoms with one electron added. The original source of it is not very certain; but all the deposits of salts found in the world have been produced by the drying up of inland seas.

Some of these deposits are tremendously thick. At Stassfurt, in Germany, there is at least half a mile thickness of salt. Now the sea contains only about 3% of salt and so (since salt is about $2\frac{1}{2}$ times as heavy as water) a mile depth of sea would only deposit about 20 yards of salt. So the Stassfurt deposits would have needed a sea about forty miles deep to produce them. This we can't believe in! So, the usual theory is that a salt deposit started as an inland sea, perhaps separated from the ocean by a bar over which waves broke freely in winter. Every winter the sea filled it up: every summer the sun dried up the shallow basin and deposited a layer of salt. Gradually the basin sank—land is always slowly rising and falling—and so a vast depth of salt was deposited and a salt bed formed. Most of our English salt-mines in Cheshire have been flooded by water breaking in from above. So salt in England is "mined" by pumping out the strong salt solution or "brine" from the flooded salt-beds and boiling this down till the salt crystallises. The most remarkable salt-mines are at Wieliczka in Hungary, where a whole town has been hollowed out of the gleaming crystalline salt. Plate XXIX shows the mining of the salt and also the chapel of St. Barbara, in which the walls, floors, carvings and even the chandeliers are made of salt.

Salt when purified is familiar enough to everybody. Actually, table-salt is often mixed with a little bone-ash (calcium phosphate) to stop it clogging in damp weather. Kitchen salt does not contain this but may contain traces of other salts. The world uses about twenty million tons of salt a year, say, 22 lbs. a person. About two-thirds of this is used for eating, cooking and preserving salt meat and fish: the rest is turned into soda, caustic soda, chlorine, hydrochloric acid, sodium sulphate, etc., and is also used up in the glazing of pottery, dyeing, etc.

CHLORINE

The element chlorine itself is largely used for making bleaching-powder, and for making many organic chemicals—drugs and dyes—and for making hydrochloric acid.

It is made by passing an electric current through ordinary salt solution. This is just positive sodium ions and negative chlorine ions and water. So an electric current attracts the sodium ions to the negative pole (cathode) and the chlorine ions to the positive pole (anode). The chlorine ions *give up* an electron each to the current supply at the anode and so become chlorine atoms which join up to chlorine molecules. These bubble off as chlorine gas. The sodium ions *receive* an electron from the cathode and so become sodium atoms. But a sodium atom and a water molecule combine and give a sodium ion again and a hydroxyl ion and a hydrogen atom. So, at the cathode we get sodium ions and hydroxyl ions in equal numbers (this we call sodium hydroxide or caustic soda) and hydrogen gas.

So the electric current splits salt water into chlorine, caustic soda and hydrogen. The manufacturer uses all these. The chlorine he sells to the chemical works or turns it into bleaching powder by combining it with lime; the caustic soda he sells to the soap makers and the hydrogen he probably uses to make inedible oils into useful fats.

Something has been said already about storing chlorine under pressure as a liquid in tanks. This is possible because dry chlorine does not affect iron. If moisture is present, it corrodes any metal away in a very short time.

Chlorine gas is a substance which forces itself on one's notice. It is greenish-yellow in colour: this means it absorbs the light of the other parts of the spectrum (red, etc.), and this light increases its energy. A remarkable result of this is that chlorine is much more chemically active in light than in the dark. If a chemist wants to make chloracetic acid from chlorine and acetic acid, he waits for a bright sunny day, knowing that the experiment will be complete in about half the time that would be needed on a dull day. Its smell is very noticeable too. Even the insensitive nose of a man will smell a great deal less than one part of chlorine in ten million of air. When very weak, it smells rather like sea-weed, but when strong, it has a scalding and choking odour. It is very poisonous indeed, for, as little as one part in 50,000 of air will cause serious injury to the lungs if breathed for some time. It was the obvious poison-gas to use in warfare, for it is not only poisonous but heavy and cheap. The results were terrible. The delicate membranes of the lungs irritated by the gas defended themselves by pouring out quantities of fluid designed to wash away the irritant: the effect was, the victim was drowned in the exudations of his own lung tissues. Many of those who survived were permanently weakened and succumbed to tuberculosis or other such infections. Mustard gas and the lacrymators or tear-gases were painful but comparatively humane, for most of their casualties recovered completely; but chlorine was a completely brutal method of causing death.

Gas-warfare is a competition between the chemist who synthesises new compounds and the chemist who devises masks. I am not sure whether any nation is sufficiently barbaric to bomb open towns with gas (written in 1935). But, if such a thing ever happens, it is as well to know what to do. As a makeshift, if you are out of doors and have no access to a room which can be securely closed, get on to the highest place you can and if possible obtain a rubber sponge, or a wet sock or cloth, and a basin of water with some washing soda. Dip the sponge in the water or solution of soda, wring it out and breathe through it. It is very unlikely that aeroplanes can put down enough gas to be dangerous at the level of the housetops. Your makeshift mask would be little good against big concentrations of gas,

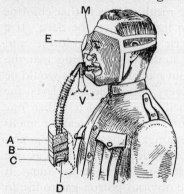

FIG. 379.—Gas-mask. A Charcoal
B Soda-lime
C Charcoal
D Air-entry
E Eye piece
M Mask
V Valve
(Courtesy of the McGraw Hill Publishing Co., Ltd.)

but might tide you over a mild attack. In your own house an upstairs room with the windows and doors sealed with wet cloths and the chimney blocked by towels would probably remain gas-proof till the wind blew the gas away. A military gas-mask is designed to deal with as many different gases as possible. It contains a filter to get rid of the poisonous smokes, charcoal which (p. 588) absorbs many organic gases, and granules of caustic soda and lime which absorb chlorine, phosgene and some others. Most chemists would be sceptical about the possibility of the discovery of any gas much worse than the present ones. All deadly gases have fairly simple molecules, and nearly all the possible simple molecules have already been put together by chemists.

Because chlorine is poisonous it is therefore an excellent disinfectant, for it kills all kinds of bacteria, but in the form of chlorine gas it is too dangerous to handle. Accordingly, it is made into "chloride of lime," or "bleaching-powder," which is even better for the purpose, for it is one of the few disinfectants which is not dangerously poisonous to human beings. To make it, chlorine is passed over slaked lime till no more of the gas is absorbed.

This chloride of lime has a smell very like that of chlorine. It is an excellent substance for disinfecting water, because it is not poisonous, and because a very small amount of it will kill all disease germs. In the war of 1914–1918 all the wells in the war areas of Belgium and France were treated by throwing into them chloride of lime. The troops disliked the taste of it in their water, and probably few chemical compounds have been better cursed, but men did not die of typhoid-fever in thousands as they had in every previous war. Chlorine or chloride of lime is often put into swimming-baths. An undisinfected and unfiltered public swimming-bath should never be entered by anyone; and no one who has read a medical officer's report on the contents of such a bath would ever wish to go near it. Everyone who goes in allows their saliva to enter the water, and children—particularly the less well trained ones—do things far more objectionable, filling the bath with every kind of contamination and disease germ. In rivers and the sea, it is not quite so bad, for the great volume of water dilutes the dirt till it is inappreciable.

The two ways of making a swimming-bath safe are, first, treating it with chlorine, chloride of lime or sodium hypochlorite (which is like bleaching powder, but has sodium in it instead of calcium), and secondly, continuously filtering it. Both ways are safe, but the last is the pleasanter because the disinfectants make the eyes smart.

Chlorine is a very active element indeed, and it combines particularly enthusiastically and violently with hydrogen. Hydrogen burns in chlorine just as it does in oxygen. A mixture of hydrogen and chlorine explodes violently if set fire to. It also explodes if exposed to sunlight! This is because the green chlorine absorbs the light and has the energy of its molecules raised till they begin to split into atoms. The atoms then start reacting with the hydrogen in ladies-chain fashion, much like the hydrogen and oxygen on p. 574, and make hydrochloric acid. This is used a good deal in industry. It is made by burning hydrogen and chlorine together, and dissolving the hydrogen chloride gas in water, or by pouring sulphuric acid on salt. Hydrochloric acid is a very common and important chemical. It used to be employed for cleaning lavatory pans, because it breaks down organic matter but does not affect earthenware. But it is not much used in the household, for it is a dangerous material, poisonous unless diluted with a great deal of water, and very destructive. It has been displaced by "Harpic," which is substantially sodium hydrogen sulphate, a strong acid in a solid form, and therefore as good as hydrochloric acid, but not liable to be drunk in mistake for medicine.

Chlorine will very often take hydrogen out of an organic compound. It may break it up altogether, or it may, if water is present, take the hydrogen from the water leaving an oxygen atom which enters the compound.

Chlorine + Water + Dye → Hydrochloric + Colourless compound
acid   or dye and oxygen

Suppose we let chlorine act on a substance coloured by some dye stuff. It will probably break the dye molecule up or put oxygen into it—thus changing it into a new molecule. Now for every coloured molecule there are a hundred colourless ones, so chlorine is very likely to change a coloured thing to a colour-less one and so bleach it.

Chlorine cannot be used to bleach the protein fibres of silk or wool, because it attacks the —NH— groups in a protein. But cellulose stands limited treatment with chlorine, so cotton and linen can be safely bleached by it. The usual way of bleaching cotton is to run the woven material first through bleaching powder solution and then through weak sulphuric acid. The bleaching powder solution and acid together produce chlorine *on the fibre* where it is wanted, and there is no risk of poisoning anyone by using chlorine gas.

If you want to see some chlorine for yourself, GO OUT OF DOORS, put a table-spoonful of bleaching powder in a jam jar. Stand to windward of it, add half a teacup full of accumulator acid and cover the jar with a saucer. You will see the green gas, and if you put a flower in the jar, it will be bleached at once. But treat the gas with respect!

CHAPTER XXVII

SULPHUR

THE Devil is popularly believed to disappear leaving a smell of sulphur. Sulphur is almost odourless, so the recounters of the tradition either believed he disappeared with a smell of sulphuretted hydrogen—like a rotten egg—or more likely with a smell of sulphur dioxide—the smell of burning sulphur, fireworks or French matches. Perhaps fraudulent magicians helped their diabolic displays with a few fireworks, so supporting the connection between deviltry and sulphur dioxide— or perhaps the notion that volcanoes (which often exhale sulphur dioxide) were the mouths of hell, led to the association. Be this as it may, sulphur is connected in the public mind with hell, smells and bad language. Milton was of the opinion that hell was paved with sulphur.

> "—down they light
> On the firm brimstone——"

Sulphur is, in real fact, sometimes associated with volcanoes. For many years all the world's sulphur was obtained from the volcanic region of Sicily: to-day, it nearly all comes from Louisiana and Texas. The winning of this sulphur was perhaps the most remarkable feat of mining engineering. The sulphur—almost pure—lies under a layer of quicksand saturated with water. It might have been possible to freeze this (p. 219) and sink a steel lined shaft into it: but the sulphur deposits were full of poisonous gases so that even if they had been reached, the miner could have only worked in a gas-mask, and you cannot do much work under such conditions. The brilliant idea of Hermann

668

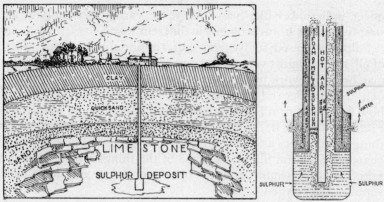

FIG. 380.—The Frasch system of mining sulphur.

Frasch was to melt the sulphur and pump it up. Sulphur melts at about 115° C., a little above the temperature at which water boils. But under a pressure of 140 lbs. per square inch water boils at 175° C. Frasch's plan was to pump super-heated water, at 170–180° and under great pressure, into the sulphur bed, and let it both melt the sulphur and force it up another tube to the surface.

Fig. 380 shows the "sulphur pump." The hot water goes down the outer pipe and issues into the sulphur bed. The melted sulphur is much heavier than water and flows down round the bottom of the pump. The pressure of the water drives the melted sulphur up the inner tube (marked FOAM OF MELTED SULPHUR AND AIR in Fig. 380). To lessen the weight of the column of melted sulphur, compressed air is blown down the central tube so that a froth of air and melted sulphur comes out at the top and is run into vast bins.

Sulphur as thus made is fairly pure. It is a yellow and brittle substance without any smell or taste. It does not dissolve in water. It can be made into beautiful octahedral crystals by dissolving it in some liquid like carbon bisulphide and letting it evaporate. Sulphur can also be made into needle-shaped crystals and (by boiling liquid sulphur and pouring it into water) into a queer indiarubber-like mass. All these varieties of sulphur are simply sulphur atoms arranged in different ways.

Sulphur is used for several quite important purposes. First of all, since it lights very easily, it is used in making fireworks and matches. Firework-making is a rather subtle business: the success of a firework depends not only on what you put in it, but also on how finely you grind it, how well you mix it and how solidly and evenly you pack it. A firework mixture always has in it something which burns and something which supplies oxygen. Sulphur, charcoal, fine iron filings are some of the things which burn and saltpetre (potassium nitrate) or some other nitrate usually supplies the oxygen.

Here is a recipe for red fire and an explanation of what each ingredient does:

Sulphur, 12 parts—Burns.

Potassium chloride, 6 parts—Colours flame.

Strontium nitrate, 36 parts—Supplies oxygen and colours flame red.

Antimony sulphide, 2 parts—Burns and makes flame brighter.

Lamp-black, 1.5 parts—Burns.

The materials are ground very finely and most thoroughly mixed.

The most interesting firework is the rocket, for it is used not only to delight the eye but to carry a line to a wrecked ship: and some adventurous souls have attempted to propel cars by them and send mails across an arm of the sea. The principle of the rocket is simple. When the firework mixture in it burns, it changes into gas which streams out at the base. There is, therefore, a pressure of gas on the inside of

FIG. 381.—How a rocket is impelled.

the rocket which drives it up. It goes up for just the same reason as a man on roller skates goes backward when he hurls a brick.

The fascinating thing about a rocket is that it is *self-contained*. The car pushes against the road, the ship against the sea, the aeroplane against the air, but the rocket requires nothing to help it on its travels, for it pushes against the gas it has itself made. Consequently, a big enough rocket could fly right out of the atmosphere through space to the moon; it therefore provides the most nearly possible way of making a journey to another planet. But there are very grave difficulties. A very big rocket is apt to explode with most remarkable violence; it is at present unsteerable, and can only be aimed like a gun, but very unreliably. None the less, if there was air to breathe and enormous riches to be gained on the surface of the moon, I would wager that someone would get there in a rocket-propelled vessel within a century. But big rockets are very expensive, and an attempt to reach the moon—an arid and airless desert—would entail almost certain death, consequently, no one is very keen to attempt it.

Mars is perhaps the most hopeful planet for colonisation, but as it would take some four years at a thousand miles an hour to get there, science may easily need a few thousand years' development before it finds the way.

The second great use of sulphur is to kill moulds. Sulphur seems perfectly harmless to the higher animals and to ordinary green plants. But certain moulds have the strongest objection to it, and about 100,000 tons every year are used to dust vines to keep off the oidium fungus, a sort of mould which causes great destruction to vines and hops.

Great quantities of sulphur are used to make sulphur dioxide— for bleaching wood-pulp, and for making sulphuric acid.

HYDROGEN SULPHIDE

Most people have heard of the compound of sulphur and hydrogen. It is commonly called "sulphuretted hydrogen," though chemists call it hydrogen sulphide. The smell is thought disgusting by most people, for they associate it with rotten eggs, decaying cabbages, sewage and other unsavoury things. But "there is nothing either good or bad, but thinking makes it so," and the chemist who works every day with the gas ceases to dislike it, and even rather enjoys it in time. It can be made in the Kipps apparatus of Figure 353, using iron sulphide as the solid and sulphuric or hydrochloric acid as the liquid.

$$FeS + \begin{array}{c}[H_3O]^+ \\ [H_3O]^+\end{array} = H_2S + \begin{array}{c}H_2O \\ + H_2O\end{array} + Fe^{++}$$

Iron sulphide	hydroxonium ion	hydrogen sulphide	water	iron ion.

Sulphuretted hydrogen is not much use except to the analytical chemist, who uses it to separate and detect the various metals. Thus, it gives a black insoluble substance (copper sulphide) with an acid solution containing, say, copper or lead, but does not affect an acid solution containing iron. So if the analyst wants to see if some iron chloride contains copper or lead, he can bubble sulphuretted hydrogen through it and see if any black solid is produced.

Sulphuretted hydrogen is poisonous. It is not by any means as poisonous as chlorine, but air containing 1% of it will soon kill a man. As one part in ten thousand makes a pretty foul smell, no one is likely to get poisoned unless he cannot get away.

This is just what may happen in sewer-gas poisoning. Sewers are not gardens of roses, of course, but they do not as a rule smell very bad, and have not a poisonous atmosphere. The danger arises when an unventilated place has been in contact with sewage and the gas has accumulated.

SULPHUR DIOXIDE

The gas sulphur dioxide is the gas which gives the smell to fireworks, etc. It has the formula SO_2, its molecule consisting

PLATE XXIX

The Wielicza salt-mines. (*Left*) Mining the salt. (*Right*) The Chapel of St. Barbara. Walls, decorations, chandeliers are all made of salt. (By courtesy of Photo-Plat, Warsaw.)

A smoky and a smokeless town. (*Above*) Hanley. (By courtesy of *The Times*.) (*Below*) Barcelona. (By courtesy of *Wide World Photos*.)

PLATE XXX

Gun flints made by flint-knapping at Brandon, Suffolk.

Making gun flints.

Squaring flints for building. (By courtesy of Messrs. Photopress, Ltd., and Messrs. Bird, Watton, Norfolk.)

of a sulphur atom linked between two oxygen atoms. Since burning is combining with oxygen, this gas is produced when sulphur burns or when anything containing sulphur burns. It is usually made in this way when required for bleaching or making sulphuric acid. It is very easily condensed to a liquid by cooling it and compressing it, and this liquid is sold in iron cylinders or glass syphons (Fig. 53A, p. 125). But sulphur dioxide is continually being produced whether we want it or not. Coal always contains a small proportion of sulphur and when coal burns, the gases produced contain sulphur dioxide. Anyone who travels through a long railway tunnel where, of necessity, the air contains much coal smoke, experiences that peculiar flat metallic sort of taste in the mouth which is a sure sign of sulphur dioxide. It is not a very poisonous gas, so its presence in tunnels is more unpleasant than dangerous. But the presence of sulphur in coal has a much more serious effect, for it causes the smoky air of London and other big towns to contain sulphur dioxide. Now this gas, air and water combine—rather slowly—giving sulphuric acid, a remarkably corrosive substance which costs the Londoner a lot of money. It corrodes his stonework—compare the surface of St. Paul's with that of a far older country cathedral of similar stone— say Winchester Cathedral. It makes ironwork corrode and rust more quickly. Zinc roofing and guttering is almost unusable in towns. It is doubtful how far the gas harms plant-life, for it is probably a film of tarry soot that kills all but a few dozen kinds of plants in Central London. The presence of sulphur dioxide in the air of towns is an evil which is not easy to cure. At the great new power-station at Battersea where 900 tons of coal are burned every day, the issuing smoke (or burned gases, for efficient furnaces do not let smoke escape) passes through a fine rain of water, which dissolves out the sulphur dioxide. If all London's coal was burned in power-stations and gas-works to produce gas and electricity, no gases but carbon dioxide and nitrogen would have to enter the air, and London houses could be as clean as those in a country village (Plate XXIX).

Certain industries produce great volumes of sulphur dioxide.

22

Copper ore is a combination of copper and sulphur, and the first stage in getting copper from it is to burn it so that the sulphur turns to sulphur dioxide gas. At the same time, arsenic (usually present in the ore) also passes out as vapour so that a copper smelting works produces a whitish and stinking fume. This can sometimes have its sulphur dioxide turned into useful sulphuric acid, but it is often allowed to escape, whereby the ground for a mile or more round the works is stripped of every green plant. Swansea used to be an example of this in England.

Sulphur dioxide is used a good deal for bleaching delicate materials like wool and silk which chlorine would destroy. The process is at least as old as the time of the Romans, who bleached their woollen garments by hanging them in closed rooms in which sulphur was burnt. It bleaches colours by putting hydrogen into them which usually destroys the colour-producing group. But it contains no hydrogen! It gets this from water and, accordingly, it will bleach only damp materials.

$$
\begin{array}{ccccccc}
H & & & & H & \\
\diagdown & & & & \diagup & + & \boxed{D} & \longrightarrow \\
& O + O = S = O + O & & \\
\diagup & & & & \diagdown & \\
H & & & & H & \\
\text{water} & \text{sulphur} & \text{water} & & \text{dye} & \longrightarrow \\
& \text{dioxide} & & \\
\end{array}
$$

$$
\begin{array}{ccc}
H^+ \begin{bmatrix} O & & O \\ & \diagdown \diagup & \\ & S & \\ & \diagup \diagdown & \\ O & & O \end{bmatrix}^= & & H \diagdown \\ \diagup D \\ H \diagup \\
H^+ & + & \\
\end{array}
$$

Sulphuric   +   colourless com-
acid   pound of dye
and hydrogen

A little sulphuric acid is produced in the process: this must be carefully washed out, as the fabric would be weakened by it.

SULPHURIC ACID

Sulphur dioxide is chiefly used to make sulphuric acid which is employed in such a large number of diverse trades that Disraeli is said to have stated that the degree of civilisation of a country could be estimated by the quantity of sulphuric acid it used.

If for "civilisation" you read "industrial civilisation" it is pretty well true. Sulphuric acid is used for making hydrochloric acid, sodium sulphate (for glass making), copper sulphate, ammonium sulphate, and "superphosphate" (fertiliser). It is used for making sugar from starch, soap and glycerine from fats, almost all explosives and dyes from coal-tar, ether from alcohol, thorium for gas-mantles from monazite sand, etc., etc. It is used for "pickling" castings (loosening the scale of iron oxide which adheres to them), for the acid in accumulators and, when much diluted, for sprinkling on wheat fields to kill the weeds without burning the corn. No other single chemical has so many uses—common salt perhaps comes next on the list.

Sulphuric acid is made by two processes. The first is the lead-chamber process which makes a cheap impure acid of about 60% strength from impure sulphur dioxide, which can be got very cheaply by burning iron pyrites. The second is the contact process which makes very pure 100% acid from pure sulphur dioxide. As industry demands both cheap impure acid and more expensive highly concentrated pure acid, both processes continue to flourish.

The contact process only will be described here—as it is the easier to understand. We will suppose that we start from sulphur and want to make pure 100% sulphuric acid. The principle is to burn the sulphur and make sulphur dioxide. This—mixed with air—is passed over a "catalyst"—metallic platinum—

which, at 400° C. or thereabouts, makes the sulphur dioxide combine with oxygen and turn into sulphur trioxide. This combines with water and gives sulphuric acid.

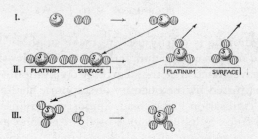

Fig. 382.—I. Sulphur burns in oxygen making sulphur dioxide
II. Sulphur dioxide and oxygen in presence of platinum make sulphur trioxide.
III. Sulphur trioxide and water make sulphuric acid. (Oxygen atoms shaded, sulphur marked S.)

Simple enough in principle, this process fairly bristled with difficulties when attempts were first made to work it on the large scale. The chief trouble was the platinum. No one really knows how the platinum makes the sulphur dioxide and oxygen combine. It is certain that it attracts a layer of the gases on to its surface and that they combine there, so the surface of the platinum must first of all be made very large, and secondly must be kept from covering itself with other things than sulphur dioxide and oxygen.

The first requisite is got by making the platinum into an exceedingly fine layer on the surface of another material (asbestos or magnesium sulphate). The magnesium sulphate can be moistened with platinum chloride solution and then be made red hot when the chlorine goes off and leaves a fine layer of platinum coating the grains of magnesium sulphate. Now suppose we have a centimetre cube of platinum. It has a surface of 6 square centimetres (six sides, each a square centimetre). Suppose you spread the platinum out into a coating only one atom thick. Well, a cubic centimetre of platinum contains about 6×10^{22} atoms. Each atom, if they were all touching each other chessboard fashion, would occupy about one square Angstrom unit, 10^{-16} square centimetres. So 1 gram of platinum spread out to 1 atom thick would occupy $6 \times 10^{22} \times 10^{-16} = 6,000,000$ square centimetres, about an eighth of an acre. So by spreading out the platinum cube to a layer only one atom thick, we make its effective surface a million times greater. Although, in practice, you cannot spread your platinum as thin as this, it is easy to see that by coating the platinum on to some inert base like asbestos we make it far more effective.

Economy in platinum is most necessary. A unit of contact plant often contains £5,000 to £10,000 worth; this money might well earn £600 to £1,200 a year if put into improvements or the setting up of new lines of business: so though the platinum is not used up, it represents a yearly sum to be knocked off the profits.

The greatest difficulty was found in keeping the platinum clean. If the sulphur dioxide contained arsenic—a very common impurity, this "poisoned" the platinum, i.e., occupied its surface and excluded the sulphur dioxide and oxygen. Many other things act like arsenic, and so if the process is to work it is very necessary that the sulphur dioxide should be made by burning sulphur (which is always very pure), or that, if some impure ore like iron pyrites is burnt, the gas should be purified. This disadvantage has really proved a boon, because everyone now knows that "contact acid" *must* be made from pure material and so is certain to be pure. In the manufacture of food-stuffs (e.g., glucose) or drugs, contact acid is always used, as chamber acid is under the suspicion—not always justified—of containing lead and arsenic.

The third difficulty was that the sulphur trioxide formed a kind of fog which took a long time to dissolve completely in water. This was got over by dissolving it in some of the sulphuric acid already made and adding the water to this acid.

Sulphuric acid, or *oil of vitriol* as it is called in the trade, owes its value, its interest and its danger to three things. First, its molecules will combine with any water molecule they can get hold of and make ions.

Sulphu- + water → Hydro- + hydrox-
ric acid   gen sul-   onium
           phate ion   ion

Secondly, it behaves like a strong acid if it is diluted or if any water is about. Thirdly, it can give away some oxygen to another molecule and change back to sulphur dioxide and water.

Most people have seen strong sulphuric acid, a heavy colourless liquid (brown if impure), which pours rather like thin oil. It has no smell and gives off no vapour. It does not boil until 337° C., not far off the temperature of melting lead. The thing about it which strikes the imagination is that when mixed with cold water it gets very hot. The reason is simply that its molecules and the water molecules are re-sorting their atoms and giving out energy in doing so: the result is that, if sulphuric acid and water are slopped into each other anyhow, they may boil up violently and injure someone: while hot sulphuric acid and hot water if mixed will cause a sort of explosion of steam and strong acid. This is one of the chief causes of the few laboratory accidents to beginners. There is one, and only one safe way of mixing sulphuric acid and water—that is pouring a thin stream of *cold* acid into *cold* water, stirring all the time.

The water-snatching habit of sulphuric acid molecules makes the strong acid very destructive to almost any kind of organic matter. Almost all organic matter has in it the constituent elements of water, hydrogen and oxygen. Sulphuric acid seems to be able to break up these molecules and combine with this water.

Drop a little cold sulphuric acid on cotton or paper. A brownish colour appears, then shortly after a blackened ragged hole. Drop it on woollen cloth and it will be destroyed in a few seconds. If the strong acid falls on your skin, you have from ten to thirty seconds to rinse it off, and you must *flood* it with water—put it under the tap—because the acid and a little water get hot and are worse than the acid alone. If not washed off it destroys the skin, and if there is much acid it destroys the cells which regenerate true skin, so that the healed wound is a great contorted scar. The vitriol-thrower is rightly treated as one of the worst of criminals.

The diluted acid used in accumulators has none of these savage properties. You could not drink it safely, but a spot on your hand would not give trouble for several minutes. It stains one's clothes red. If it is allowed to dry on clothing, the water evaporates and leaves much stronger sulphuric acid which will corrode a hole.

Sulphuric acid diluted with, say, two hundred parts of water is quite harmless and tastes very much like lemon juice. The danger of sulphuric acid resides largely in its thirst for water: slake this and it becomes no more harmful than vinegar.

The use of sulphuric acid as an acid has already been discussed on page 675. Enough to say that it is the cheapest and most convenient strong acid and is used wherever a strong acid is required.

CHAPTER XXVIII

THE METALS

THE various metals are sufficiently alike to be discussed together in a single chapter. For chemical purposes, we have a very practical way of grouping them. We may class them as:

(1) *The Reactive Metals.* These include sodium, potassium, calcium and magnesium and four or five rarer elements. These act vigorously upon water and produce hydrogen, and so are no use for any mechanical purposes. Their compounds like salt, saltpetre, chalk and so on are very important indeed.

(2) *The Heavy Metals.* These are of great practical value; they are corroded away by moisture only slowly or not at all. They are quickly or slowly changed into oxides when heated sufficiently in air, and most of them are corroded fairly easily by acids. The most important metals are in this class. Aluminium, tin, lead, antimony, copper, zinc, mercury, chromium, iron, nickel are among them.

(3) *The Noble Metals* include silver, gold, platinum and a few rare metals. These may be made white hot without tarnishing (or oxidising). They are not affected by water or most acids. Silver is the least "noble" because it is corroded by nitric acid or hot strong sulphuric acid.

THE REACTIVE METALS

These metals are made by electrolysis, but the methods are beyond our scope. Metallic sodium and potassium are only

680

met with in chemical laboratories or occasionally in photo-electric cells.

They are very strange materials indeed. They are quite clearly metals, for a clean surface shines like silver: moreover, they are very good conductors of electricity. But they are quite remarkably soft and fusible. You can cut a piece of sodium like cheese with a wire, you can mould it in your fingers (a dangerous trick) like putty. It melts at 97° C., and potassium melts at the even lower temperature of 62.5° C., a temperature less than that reached under a tropical sun! A very odd thing occurs when sodium and potassium are mixed. It is said that a member of a chemical firm once made some beautiful pure bright specimens of these metals to show at a foreign exhibition. He packed them, as is necessary, under water-free oil to prevent air and moisture from tarnishing them, but he packed them in the same bottle. On arrival he found the bottle apparently half full of mercury. On investigation he found that the "mercury" was an alloy of the two metals which is permanently liquid at ordinary temperatures.

But these oddities are nothing to the strangeness of their chemical behaviour. If a bit of sodium, the size of a pea, is thrown into water, it melts with the heat it produces, and swims about at a brisk pace, dwindling all the time and finally disappearing in about a minute. Sodium swims, because though a metal, it is lighter than water. It moves because the caustic soda it forms lowers the surface tension of water (p. 93). It dwindles because it changes into caustic soda which dissolves and hydrogen which escapes.

Sodium + water → Sodium ions, hydroxyl ions
and hydrogen gas

If the sodium is prevented from swimming about—by throwing it on to wet sand or blotting-paper, the hydrogen catches alight

22*

and burns with a flame coloured brilliantly yellow by sodium vapour (pp. 434–436).

If the lump of sodium is the size of the top joint of your finger, it explodes violently, and this experiment should not be done, as the performer has a good chance of losing an eye. The reason is said to be the explosion of the mixture of hydrogen and air, but it does not sound like a gas explosion. Moreover, little bits of sodium dropped into water sometimes explode quite unexpectedly and dangerously, and there is probably something still to be found out about it.

Potassium behaves much like sodium, but is more violent. Calcium is heavier than water and sinks to the bottom and produces a steady stream of hydrogen. Magnesium reacts only very slowly with water, but too fast to allow it to be used for machine parts, etc.

All these metals burn brilliantly if heated in the air. Sodium burns with a vivid yellow flame, potassium with a vivid violet one, calcium with a bright red one. Magnesium, everyone has seen burn. It gives a blinding white light which is very good for photographic purposes.

Flash powders are mixtures of magnesium powder with something containing a lot of oxygen, usually potassium permanganate. They have been a good deal superseded by the new flash lamps described on p. 584.

THE HEAVY METALS

There are about a dozen metals in common use. As was pointed out in Part I, metals are useful because they are strong, fairly hard and very tough, easily cast in moulds and worked on the lathe; to these valuable properties may be added their power of conducting electricity.

It is interesting to see why we use so many different metals, each one having their merits. Cheapness is a merit, so the cost per ton (July, 1935) is given.

Aluminium (£102 a ton) is very light and very strong for its weight and, therefore, is used for machine parts, car-bodies, aeroplane parts. It is not easily corroded and so is used for pots and pans.

Zinc (£14 a ton) is fairly cheap and stands corrosion pretty well. Roofing sheets and perforated metal are among its uses, but it is most used for coating, "galvanising" iron of which more hereafter.

Lead (£14 a ton) is valuable because it is not affected by water or weak acids: because it is very soft and easily bent into shape and very fusible—therefore easily cast. Lead pipes and lead roofing sheets are its chief uses.

Tin (£230 a ton) is too expensive for most jobs. It is used to coat iron and prevent it from rusting; also for alloying with other metals.

Antimony (£75 a ton) is very brittle. It expands on solidifying, and makes very sharp castings. This property it retains when alloyed. Its chief use is for making type-metal.

Chromium (£270 a ton) is intensely hard. It does not tarnish and is, therefore, very useful for coating iron. Its other use is for making stainless steel. Pure chromium could be made fairly cheaply, but is so hard as to be almost unworkable.

Iron (cast iron £3 10s. a ton: mild steel £8 10s. a ton). Iron is cheap and in the form of wrought-iron, cast iron and steels of various tempers can be made tough, brittle, hard or soft. The only strongly magnetic metal. Its greatest disadvantage is rusting.

Nickel (£205 a ton). Fairly hard, very tough, and very resistant to heat. Not readily tarnished. It is chiefly used to plate on iron and for making tough, strong non-corrodible alloys.

Copper (£32 a ton). Very tough indeed, fairly strong and an excellent conductor of electricity. Not easily corroded. It is chiefly used for electrical conductors and for making brass and bronze.

Silver (£4,626 a ton). Too expensive for much use except as an ornament. Its chief practical use is to coat mirrors.

Gold (£228,600 a ton). Since it is absolutely uncorrodible it is used for plates, crowns and fillings in dental work. For the rest, it is chiefly used for ornament and money.

Platinum (£228,600 a ton).[1] This metal is uncorrodible and is fairly tough and strong. It is used for scientific apparatus and in dentistry. It is also used as a catalyst (p. 675) and as jewellery.

When metals are melted together they usually dissolve in each other, and make a mixture called an alloy. It does not seem at all certain how far the different atoms in an alloy are chemically linked together; for most purposes they behave much like a simple mixture of the metals.

Many of these alloys are more important than the metals which make them. Hundreds are used but only half a dozen can claim our limited space.

Most of these alloys are simply made by melting the metals together, but stainless steel is made by taking the oxygen from mixed iron and chromium oxides which are found as the ore chromite.

Duralumin is extremely light and strong, and is used for aeroplane work. It contains 94% aluminium, 4% copper and 1% manganese with a trace of silicon. It can be tempered in much the same way as steel. It is more than twice as light as steel, and weight for weight, nearly twice as strong.

Solder contains lead and tin (p. 70). Plumber's solder contains 33% tin: tinman's solder 50%.

Stainless steel contains 86% iron, 13% chromium and 1% nickel. Very hard and does not rust.

Bronze contains about $87\frac{1}{2}\%$ copper and $12\frac{1}{2}\%$ tin. Many modern bronzes contain iron or nickel. It is extremely strong and tough.

Brass contains about two-thirds copper and one-third zinc. It has a beautiful colour, and is very easy to cast and to work on the lathe.

German Silver. A mix-up containing copper, nickel, zinc and tin. It is a sort of white brass, and is used as a base for silver-plating.

---

[1] Platinum is at present abnormally cheap and gold abnormally expensive. Platinum is usually about three times the price of gold.

HOW METALS ARE MADE

The making of metals is tremendously important to the world. The only metals commonly found as actual metal are platinum and gold, though native copper is abundant in some parts of the world, and iron is rarely found as meteorites.

The metals are chiefly found combined with oxygen or sulphur. Thus, lead is found as a hard bright metallic-looking substance, galena, the molecules of which are each made of a lead atom linked to a sulphur atom PbS. Iron is often found as rust-red hæmatite, which has a giant molecule of "sandwiches" of iron and oxygen atoms in the proportion of two to three. The metallurgist removes these oxygen or sulphur atoms and leaves the metal. Unfortunately, nearly all ores contain more than one metal, so that special tricks have to be used to get rid of the ones that are not wanted.

The simplest case is an oxide ore which has metal and oxygen in it. This case is well illustrated by tin. Tin is found as tin dioxide, tinstone, which has one tin atom to two oxygen atoms.

Tinstone is not found pure: usually one part of tinstone is mixed up with two hundred of rock. This ore is first roughly broken, then crushed to a fine mud by dropping on it heavy "stamps" weighing 3 cwt. or more. Water flows through the boxes in which the ore is crushed and carries the fragments off as fine mud. Tinstone is seven times as heavy as water (as heavy as iron): the rock is only about as heavy as ordinary stone. The result is that the tinstone settles out of the water far quicker than the rock and by running it over a "buddle"—a simple form of which is a trough with transverse slats nailed to the bottom—the rock mud can be made to flow on and the tinstone stays behind.

Now, if we have a fairly pure tinstone (some specimens have to be purified) we have only to turn it into tin. This is quite easily done, for carbon combines with oxygen much more vigorously

Carbon + tin dioxide   give   Carbon monoxide and tin

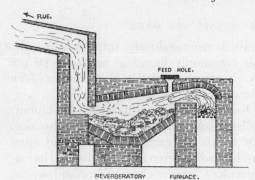

FIG. 383—Reverberatory furnace as used for smelting tin.

than tin does, and so will take it away. So the tinstone is mixed with powdered coal and heated in a reverberatory furnace, Fig. 383. The carbon takes the oxygen and makes carbon monoxide gas and the molten tin is tapped off. It often needs refining, and this is done by a queer process called "poling." The tin is melted and poles of green wood are thrust in. The poles give off steam and smoke which bubble through the tin and stir it up. The air then seems to combine with the impurities, and these rise to the top as a scum.

The manufacture of iron is one of the world's most important industries. Iron is found as three chief ores, hæmatite, magnetite and ironstone. Now, the first two are composed of iron and oxygen, the last when heated turns into a compound of iron and oxygen, so all three can be smelted in the same way in the blast furnace.

Iron ore, then, is iron oxide (iron linked to oxygen atoms) with usually a good many impurities in the forms of compounds of sulphur, phosphorus, manganese, arsenic, etc., and a good deal of clay or sand—silicates of various kinds. The blast furnace takes the oxygen away by means of coal which turns it into carbon monoxide and carbon dioxide; it takes the clay and sand and a good deal of the other impurities away by means of limestone, which makes them into a sort of opaque glass called slag. All that is left is iron mixed up with 5% or so of carbon, sulphur, phosphorus and manganese. This is called cast-iron.

Blast furnaces have been used for at least 300 years, and are now rather near perfection. Fig. 384 and Plate XXXI show how an ironworks is laid out. The blast furnace is a huge tower 90–120

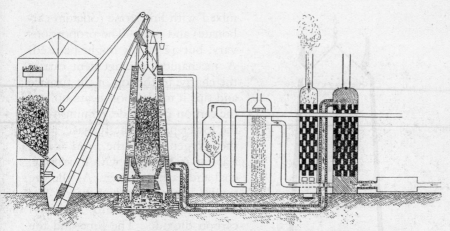

Fig. 384.—Diagram of a blast furnace, stoves, etc. The air is pumped in at the right-hand side, passed through the hot stove (shaded) and is blown into the base of the furnace. The gas evolved passes through dust removing apparatus and is in part used to heat up the cool stoves (unshaded), and in part to drive the blowing engines. The happenings in the furnace itself are set out in Fig. 385.

feet high. It is lined with special firebrick. It has a big lead-off pipe at the top for gas, and a balanced cone for letting the charge of ore enter at the top.

At the bottom are pipes, "tuyéres," through which a blast of hot air is forced into the glowing mass, and two tapping holes from which slag and iron are drawn off. The gas which comes out of a blast furnace contains some carbon monoxide and will burn. Accordingly, it is used to drive the gas-engines which pump the air for the blast. It is also burned in order to heat the kilns used to dry the ore. Its chief use, however, is to heat huge stoves seventy to a hundred feet high, packed with bricks in chequer-work. There are usually four of these.

The air which is to go to the furnace is pumped through one of these and so heated, which of course enables the blast-furnace to get far hotter than it would otherwise. When the stove has cooled down, the air is switched over to another and the cool one is heated up by burning more blast-furnace gas in it.

The ore as it comes from the mine is crushed and dried and

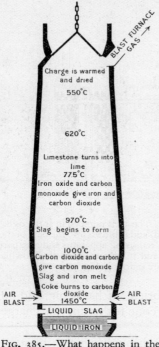

Charge is warmed
and dried
550°C

620°C

Limestone turns into
lime
775°C
Iron oxide and carbon
monoxide give iron and
carbon dioxide

970°C
Slag begins to form

1000°C
Carbon dioxide and carbon
give carbon monoxide
Slag and iron melt
Coke burns to carbon
dioxide
1450°C

AIR
BLAST

AIR
BLAST

LIQUID   SLAG

LIQUID IRON

BLAST FURNACE GAS

FIG. 385.—What happens in the different levels of the blast furnace.

mixed with limestone (calcium carbonate) and coal. The proportions vary, but 12 : 3 : 5 might be used. A mechanical arrangement carries the charge to the top of the furnace and tips it in. It soon heats up and the carbon monoxide, coming from the lower part of the furnace, takes the oxygen from the iron oxide, leaving iron mixed with limestone, coal and earthy matter. As the ore travels down it gets hotter. The limestone changes into lime and carbon dioxide. The lime and the earthy matter turn into the slag: the carbon dioxide and coal make carbon monoxide which travels up the furnace. Lower down still, the coal burns in the blast of air from the "tuyéres" and gives carbon monoxide just as it does in a producer (p. 254): the heat melts both the slag and the iron. Melted iron is heavier than melted slag, so a pool of molten iron settles at the bottom and a pool of slag above it. These are run off; the slag into trucks and the iron into moulds of sand. The slag is usually broken up for road-mending.

Cast iron is all very well for heavy castings which do not have to bear a bending or tensile strain, e.g., for pillars, low-pressure water-mains, lamp-posts, hot-water radiators, bed-plates of machinery, etc. But where both strength and toughness is needed, we want steel. Steel is iron with perhaps 1% of manganese, one-half to one and a half per cent of carbon, and very little sulphur or phosphorus.

Cast iron has much more impurity than this. To turn cast iron into steel we make the impurities combine with oxygen, which they do more easily than does iron. Once they are oxides, we can make them combine with lime or with silica (sand) and make a slag. There are several ways of doing this. The open-hearth is much the most important, the Bessemer probably the next.

In the open-hearth process cast iron is melted with iron oxide in the form of iron ore. The oxygen of the iron ore and the impurities in the iron combine and these with the lining of the furnace (either lime or sand) give a slag. A tremendous temperature (about 1500° C.) is wanted in a very big furnace for the successful operation of the process.

This temperature could not be reached except on the small scale until the principle of regenerative heating was invented. The furnace is heated with ordinary producer gas (carbon monoxide, etc.), but the gas and air are made red hot *before* they meet and

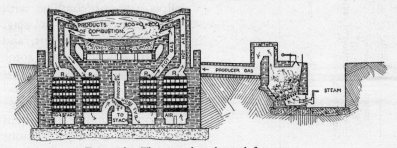

Fig. 386.—The open-hearth steel furnace.

burn. Consequently, instead of starting at say, 20° C., and reaching 1500° C. by burning, they start at, say, 500° C. and reach 2000° C.! This is achieved by using the burned gas from the furnace to heat brick stoves through which the incoming gas and air are then taken.

This way of making steel only requires cast iron, iron ore, a little sand or lime, and heat. It gives a very good uniform steel.

The Bessemer process uses nothing but air and "ganister," a sort of natural firebrick. The Bessemer converter provides the finest

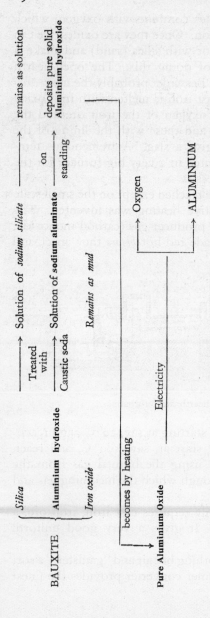

show of fireworks in industry. It is a big steel vessel which is swung on trunnions so that its contents can be poured out. Its bottom is perforated, and a powerful blast of air can be blown through the holes. The principle is to run a charge of molten cast iron (often straight from the blast furnace) into the converter and blow air through it. The carbon, the silicon, the sulphur, phosphorus and manganese all burn in the air blast and produce oxides. These go off as gases or combine with the lining to make a slag. Almost pure iron is left, and to turn this into steel some spiegeleisen, a sort of cast iron, rich in manganese and carbon, is added. This brings the composition of the liquid mass to the right proportions for mild steel, namely about 98.5% iron, 0.4% carbon, 0.9% manganese, 0.1% silicon, 0.1% phosphorus, 0.06% sulphur.

On pp. 240–243 some account was given of the way in which electricity is made for aluminium manufacture. The process of manufacture now demands our attention. Aluminium occurs in the form of bauxite—impure aluminium hydroxide. This commonly contains a fair proportion iron and it is most important that little iron should be present in the final product. The bauxite is heated with caustic soda under pressure which turns the aluminium into soluble sodium aluminate $Na_2Al_2O_4$ while iron oxide and other impurities are undissolved. The clear solution is run off and, as it cools, decomposes and deposits pure aluminium hydroxide $Al(OH)_3$ which is filtered off and heated leaving pure aluminium oxide Al_2O_3.

The furnace is, in principle, like the electroplating bath, illustrated in Fig. 168. It consists of a large open tank lined with carbon. Carbon resists high temperatures and as it conducts electricity can be made the cathode of the cell. The negative pole of the dynamo is connected to it. The bath contains melted "cryolite" (sodium aluminium fluoride). This is not used up

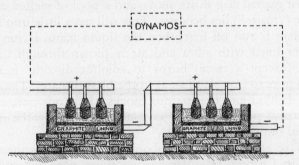

FIG. 387.—Manufacture of Aluminium.

appreciably; it is the solvent, like the water which dissolves the copper sulphate in our plating cell. The heat of the current keeps it melted. The anodes of the furnace, connected to the positive pole of the dynamo, are of carbon also. The pure aluminium oxide, made from the bauxite, is added from time to time and dissolves. The electric current decomposes it into aluminium which appears at the cathode—the furnace-walls—and collects in a molten condition on the floor of the furnace; and oxygen which combines with the carbon anodes and produces carbon monoxide, which burns at the surface.

As a final illustration of the way a metal is won from its ores, we may take the example of copper. Copper is found as copper pyrites, made up of compounds of sulphur with copper and iron. The problem is to get copper without any sulphur or iron. If the ore is not too poor, this can be done by the agency of the air alone! The ore is charged into a small blast furnace with some sand and just a little coke.

The ore has two things in it, cupric sulphide—one atom of copper to one of sulphur—and iron sulphide, one atom of iron to one of sulphur. The latter burns more easily, and produces sulphur dioxide (p. 672) and iron oxide: this, with the sand makes iron silicate which melts to a slag. The copper sulphide loses some sulphur and makes cuprous sulphide (two atoms of copper to one of sulphur). This melts too; so (just as in iron smelting) a layer of melted slag floats above and a pool of melted cuprous sulphide ("matte") lies beneath. This still has a little iron in it.

The slag is run off first: then the liquid matte is run into a converter lined with silica and air is blown through. All the sulphur (except a trace) burns to sulphur dioxide; nearly all the iron goes to iron slag just as in the blast furnace. The copper remains behind and is cast into blocks. It is not pure enough for electrical purposes, so it is usually refined by the method described on page 302.

We have said a good deal about the way metals themselves behave in Chapter IV. Perhaps no more need be said here. The metals, however, have a great many most important compounds, and some of these must be discussed. A few, such as salt and caustic soda have been mentioned already.

CHAPTER XXIX

A FEW COMPOUNDS OF METALS

CORROSION

ONE of the chief practical merits or demerits of a metal is its freedom from or liability to corrosion. By corrosion we mean the gradual eating away of a metal caused by its change into a compound of the metal and some other element, such as oxygen. Now, a metal in use will certainly be exposed to moist air, almost certainly to liquid water. It may even have to be heated to a red heat in air. So, a metal in use is exposed to oxygen, water and carbon dioxide. In towns, it also suffers from attack by sulphuretted hydrogen and very dilute sulphuric acid (p. 673) both derived from coal; near the sea, it also has to withstand salt.

No metal or alloy except chromium, stainless steel and gold and platinum will withstand these conditions in the cold: at a red heat, only gold and platinum remain untarnished. Indoors, metals corrode very slowly because they are kept dry. Out of doors, only chromium and stainless steel and, of course, gold and platinum seem to be permanent. Copper and lead have a very long life indeed, however. Some lead roofs are hundreds of years old and still keeping the weather out.

It is very unfortunate that iron, the most useful of metals, suffers so badly from corrosion and rusting. The iron and steel made yearly exceeds a hundred million tons; its value is nearly a thousand million pounds: the fate of nearly all of it is to be destroyed by rust. So, naturally, a great deal of scientific research has been centred on finding out why iron rusts and how it may be, at any rate partly, prevented from doing so.

Two very simple experiments show what rust is. If you knock a chunk or two of rust off an old tank and make it red hot in a strong test tube, you see a dew of moisture condensing on the cold glass. Chemical tests prove this to be water. If you heat the dry rust in a current of hydrogen gas and pass the issuing gases through a U-shaped glass tube cooled by an ice and salt mixture, you find that water condenses in the U-tube and a black powder is left in the heated tube. This powder is iron, as you can show by attracting it with a magnet. Now, you put hydrogen H_2 in and get water H_2O out, so the rust must contain iron, oxygen and (from the first experiment) water. It is actually a mixture of iron oxide and iron hydroxide which is what we should expect since it arises from iron, air and water.

Now, iron won't rust if it is dry (your pocket knife doesn't rust): it won't rust without air, for if water is boiled till all the dissolved air has been carried away with the steam, iron will not rust under it as long as air is kept out. So, air *and* water are needed for rusting. Iron rusts much more quickly in weak

Fe_2O_3 $Fe(OH)_3$

FIG. 388.—Rust is a mixture of these.

solutions of salts or acids. Everyone knows how soon iron is corroded in sea-water.

Finally, pure iron rusts far less than impure iron. This is a little difficult to illustrate, but it is often possible to see that blacksmiths' work (chains, hinges on gateposts, etc.) made of the purer wrought iron, lasts much better than the cast iron of rain-water pipes, door scrapers, etc.

It has now been fairly well worked out why rusting takes place. The villains of the piece are the currents of electrons caused by one part of the iron being different from another. Turn back to page 295; you will see that where two different metals (carbon acts like a metal in this respect) touch in presence of a liquid which conducts electricity, a current of electricity flows and one metal changes into ions and dissolves. In the Leclanché battery, the zinc changes to zinc ions and electrons flow through the wires from the zinc to the carbon. Now, suppose we have a chunk of cast iron with a speck of carbon— a very common impurity—embedded in it. And suppose this has a drop of water, impure enough to conduct electricity well, sitting on it. Suppose the impurity is a trace of salt—any other impurity of the kind will do. What happens? The iron atoms lose two electrons each and so change into "ferrous ions" which dissolve in the water. The electrons flow round, through the metal, to the carbon where they turn the sodium ions into

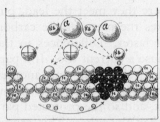

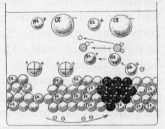

Stage I. Electrons (bottom) flow from iron atoms to the speck of carbon (black). The iron atoms turn into iron ions (marked with cross) which dissolve. The positive ions begin to migrate to the carbon and the negative ones to the rest of the metal.

Stage II. The electrons each turn a sodium ion into a sodium atom. This with water (p. 663) gives a sodium ion, a hydroxyl ion and a hydrogen atom.

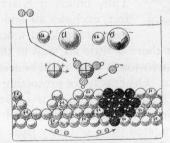

Stage III. The hydroxyl ions formed in State II, the iron ions, and oxygen from the air all meet and make ferric hydroxide—rust.

FIG. 389.—Rusting of iron.

sodium atoms. The sodium atoms and water give sodium ions
once more, hydroxyl ions, and hydrogen (p. 663). Now the
ferrous ions meet the hydroxyl ions and some oxygen from the air
and all three combine and make *rust*, iron hydroxide. Fig. 389
may make this clearer.

It is, perhaps, rather a complicated story, but it is not difficult
to remember that for rusting is needed air, not quite pure water,
and something to make an electric current in the iron. That
something may be a speck of carbon or of some metal less easily
corroded than iron. You have probably seen iron railings set in
lead corroded almost to nothing where they meet the lead, but
fairly intact up above. The lead takes the place of the carbon
in Fig. 389 and makes the iron rust faster. Differences in the
liquid in contact with the iron can cause a current too. If a part
of the iron is exposed to water and plenty of air and another
part to water without much air, a current of electrons goes from
the protected part to the exposed part, and so the protected part

rusts more than the other. This causes
a great deal of trouble, for it makes a
rust spot corrode worst at the deepest
part and so "pit" into a hole.

To protect iron from rusting we
cover it up. Sometimes paint is used.
This, unless it is scratched or imperfect, excludes air and water. Once rust
gets to work in a scratch, it spreads,

FIG. 390.—Iron rusts most
quickly at the deepest part
of the spot, where air is
scantiest. Hence rust *pits* it.

for under the paint there is little air, and in the scratch there is
much air—so the corrosion is most rapid beneath the paint at the
edges of the scratch. Other ways of protecting iron are galvanising it—coating with zinc—and tinning it—coating with tin.

To galvanise iron, it is cleaned and dipped into molten zinc.
Chicken wire, corrugated iron, ordinary pails are all galvanised.
This is a very good rust protection because zinc is only slowly
corroded if there is no acid about. And, best of all, electrons
flow from zinc to iron. So, if a scratch is made, it is the zinc
that corrodes and until the zinc has all gone, the iron does not

rust. The trouble with galvanised metal is that the acid air of towns rapidly corrodes it away. In the country, however, it has a long life.

Tinned iron stands weak acid well. Ordinary tins can be used for fruit: galvanised iron would be corroded through very soon. "Tins" also have a brilliant appearance, while galvanised iron is dull. But once a tin is scratched it rusts far quicker in a wet place than unprotected iron, for the electrons flow from the iron to the tin which acts like the carbon in Fig. 389.

Stainless steel, so to speak, provides its own paint. Air and water convert its surface into a combination of iron and chromium oxides. These make a very thin coating which is invisible, transparent, waterproof and very hard: if broken, it forms again and seals up the hole. If stainless steel were as cheap as ordinary steel, nothing else would be used, but it is many times as expensive.

An interesting half-hour can be spent looking at remains of Roman or earlier metal work.

The iron and steel is almost rusted away. Bronze and copper are thickly coated with a green compound containing copper, sulphur (or chlorine) and oxygen. Lead is not greatly altered. Silver is black with silver sulphide, but gold shines out as brilliantly as it shone when the artificer beat it into shape.

OXIDES

Metals, in general, form compounds with oxygen called oxides, and with oxygen and hydrogen called hydroxides. They also form "salts," which are associations of positive metal ions (atoms lacking one, two or three electrons) with negative ions (atoms or groups of atoms with from one to four extra electrons). These salts are usually made from acids and metals, or acids and oxides.

The oxides of the metals are quite important in their way. Most of them can be made by making the metal red-hot or white-hot in a good supply of air.

They are mostly earthy powders, absolutely unlike either a metal or oxygen! Some few are familiar to us. Zinc oxide is the solid part of zinc ointment; one of the oxides of lead—red lead—colours pillar-boxes red. Tin oxide gives white glass the milky appearance familiar in lampshades, etc. Arsenic oxide is the "arsenic" used as a poison and a weed-killer. Titanium oxide is used as a white pigment. Chromium oxide is the commonest

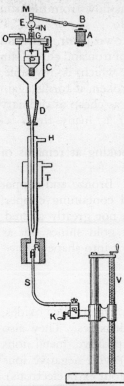

green pigment. There are two common iron oxides. The red oxide is the chief constituent of rust and also of the useful ore of iron, haematite. When ground with oil it makes the familiar red-brown paint used on bridges, gasometers and places where cheapness matters more than beauty. The other is the lodestone (p. 309), but is more familiar as the black scale seen on iron which has been made red-hot. Aluminium oxide is worth a few pounds a ton as "bauxite," used for making aluminium, but if crystallised and coloured with a little chromium oxide or iron and titanium oxides, it is worth thousands of pounds an ounce as ruby or sapphire. Naturally, as soon as chemists knew what these gems were made of, they tried to make them artificially.

Attempts were made to dissolve aluminium oxide in melted lead oxide and let it crystallise out on cooling: this method produced rubies: but these unfortunately appeared as very thin plates—useless for jewellery.

FIG. 391.—Verneuil's apparatus for making rubies. (Courtesy of Messrs. Masson & Cie., Paris; from *Les Annales de Chimie et de Physique* (1904).)

The problem was solved by Verneuil in 1904. He set up the apparatus shown in Fig. 391, by which aluminium oxide with a trace of chromium oxide is made to fall into an oxyhydrogen flame at over 2000° C. The powdered aluminium and chromium oxides are put in a little box P with a wire gauze bottom. The tapping magnet and hammer (A, B, M) (like an electric bell) gently shake a slow stream of powder from it. Oxygen from a cylinder enters at O and coal gas at H. Where these meet they burn with an intensely hot flame: the powder travels into the flame with the oxygen, melts, and sticks to a little rod of alumina R and forms a mass of ruby. By shifting the supports by means of the screws K and V a pear-shaped ruby can be built up. This is a true ruby crystal and can only be distinguished from the natural ruby by microscopic bubbles entangled in it.

The result of the process has been to decrease the popularity and value of rubies, since only experts can discover the imitation. Diamonds keep their price so well because any amateur can tell diamond from "paste."

But perhaps the most important of all oxides is lime, the oxide of calcium. Calcium is a very common element. Most of the calcium in the world is in the form of vast masses of calcium carbonate. Calcium carbonate, whatever its source, is a pattern of calcium ions and carbonate ions; its lay-out appears in Fig. 391*a*. There is always one carbonate ion to a calcium ion, and so we can call its formula $CaCO_3$. In the drawing there would appear to be 8 calcium ions to one carbonate ion. But the unit of pattern shown has its one carbonate ion to itself, whereas at each corner 8 "unit cells" meet and share a calcium ion, giving each a one-eighth share of 8 calcium ions, which is of course one such ion. It is interesting

FIG. 391*a*.—The unit cell of a calcium carbonate crystal. White circles are calcium atoms, shaded circles oxygen atoms, black circle carbon atom. The crystal is entirely made up of this pattern of atoms repeated in every direction.

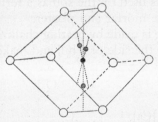

to note that the angles of the cleavage fragments of Plate II are the same as those of the tiny "unit cell" here figured. Pure calcium carbonate is pretty rare and rather valuable, for it occurs as beautiful water-white crystals of Iceland spar, which have certain optical properties which make them much sought after.

The vast mass of it is found as billions of tons of limestone and chalk which have been entirely made by shell-forming water-beasts. It is also found crystallised as marble and one or two other minerals. Marble clearly started like limestone, but it is not very certain how it became crystallised. It may have been subjected to heat and pressure in the depth of the earth.

You may object, however, that even if the improbable story about hills of chalk being made by sea-beasts is true, they must have got the calcium from somewhere. That is quite true. There is some calcium in volcanic rocks and "gypsum," calcium sulphate, is a common mineral: these probably supplied the calcium to the primæval seas. It is not difficult to see that chalk was actually made by tiny sea shells. Plate ooo is a microphotograph of some chalk and the tiny shells are there for you to see.

The first really important thing about calcium carbonate is its use as building stone: most houses which are not built of brick are built of limestone. Of our great cathedrals the great majority are of limestone: Winchester and Lincoln and Gloucester are good examples. Chalk is too soft for building, but the hard limestones are nearly perfect. They do not split like slate, they are hard enough to stand weather but soft enough to be easily cut and carved. They weather to beautiful and mellow colours.

The second important use of chalk or limestone is to make lime which is used on the soil as a fertiliser, and in the building trade to make mortar and plaster.

Lime is made by heating chalk. The simple old way was to dig a pit in the side of a hill and make a draught-hole at the bottom.

$$[Ca]^{++} \quad \begin{bmatrix} O & O \\ & \diagdown \diagup \\ & C \\ & | \\ & O \end{bmatrix}^{--} \longrightarrow [Ca]^{+} \ [O]^{-} \ + O = C = O$$

The pit was filled with lumps of chalk and fuel: this was lighted and left to burn out. The chalk at 1000° C. and higher gave up its carbon dioxide gas and left calcium oxide, quicklime, behind.

The lime often contained a little chalk and always some ash: but this did no harm. To-day, lime-kilns are towers rather like blast-furnaces. The chalk is fed in at the top. Producer gas and air are led into the tower about one-third of the way up and there burn among the lumps of chalk: the lime is raked out at the bottom.

Quicklime is a hard, stony white solid: when it is wetted it falls to a soft white powder called slaked lime, and this is the sort of lime we use. It is made of two hydroxyl ions to every calcium ion.

$$[Ca]^+ [O]^- + \underset{\displaystyle H}{\overset{\displaystyle H}{O}} \longrightarrow [Ca]^+ \begin{array}{l} [OH]^- \\ [OH]^- \end{array}$$

Quicklime   water   slaked lime

When this is ploughed or dug into the soil it does three things. It combines with the acids in a "sour" soil: most plants dislike an acid soil and thrive better if it is limed. However, some wood-land and garden plants, rhododendrons, azaleas, camellias, and many lilies thrive in an acid soil and perish where lime abounds. All English farm crops, however, prefer a non-acid soil. Lime also makes heavy soils lighter. Clay consists of minute grains of rock (usually sand) bound together by a sticky "clay-substance," probably aluminium silicate. If a lime is worked into such a soil, it combines with some of the "clay-substance" and makes the soil less sticky. It also helps to release some of the plant foods like potash by turning them out of insoluble compounds that the plant cannot use.

Builders nowadays use lime-mortar but little. The old rhyme that

> "Lime and sand and water
> Make a very good mortar"

is true enough, but mortar made with cement instead of lime is so much stronger than lime-mortar that a brick wall can be made much thinner if cement-mortar is used: this saves the builder money!

But plaster is still used for floors and ceilings, and this is very nearly the same thing as mortar. The builder makes plaster by slaking lime and mixing it with water, more or less sand and some cow-hair (to stop it cracking). This plaster of the consistency of mud, is used to line walls and ceilings.

Why does it harden? First of all, it dries and hardens just like mud does. Mud walls are common enough in many parts of the world. But the carbon dioxide in the air takes a hand too. It turns the wet lime into chalk and the chalk crystallises between the lime grains and so binds all together. Plaster is weak stuff and very slow to set : it keeps in favour, however, because the possible substitutes are more expensive or, like Portland cement, cold and not porous enough, so that in certain states of the weather, water condenses on them and trickles down—a depressing sight.

Plaster of paris is very useful for casts which need have little strength. It is made by gently heating gypsum or alabaster, which is a compound of calcium sulphate and water, till nearly all the water is given off. This gives a dry white powder. If this is mixed to a cream with water, it sets in five minutes to a hard mass of very fine interlacing needles of another compound of calcium sulphate and water.

Cement is the characteristic building material of the twentieth century, and its manufacture is a gigantic industry. The materials from which cement is made are clay and chalk. Sometimes these are found ready mixed as "marl," more often they are separately quarried. These materials are ground with water so as to make a thin mud or "slurry." This mud is fed into a rotary kiln, a huge cylinder as big as a factory chimney, 8–14 feet wide and from 150 to 350 feet long. It is gently sloped and slowly rotates so that the slurry works its way from the top to the bottom. Into the bottom end a huge flame 40 or 50 feet in length is driven by a pulverised coal burner. The hot end of the kiln may be at 1500° C. This roasts the chalk and clay to cement, which emerges as hard stony pebbles as big as marbles. It is now cooled and then ground,

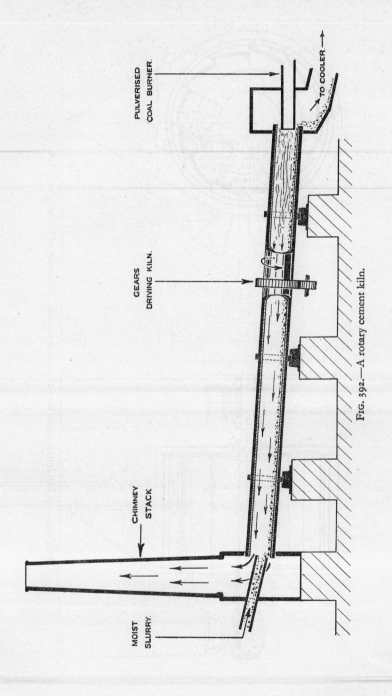

PULVERISED
COAL BURNER.

TO COOLER →

GEARS
DRIVING KILN.

CHIMNEY
STACK.

MOIST
SLURRY.

Fig. 392.—A rotary cement kiln.

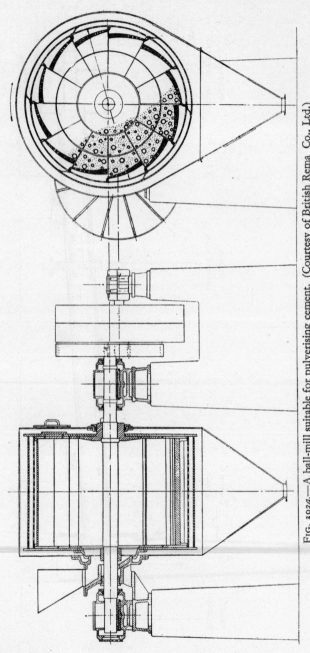

FIG. 392a.—A ball-mill suitable for pulverising cement. (Courtesy of British Rema Co., Ltd.)

PLATE XXXI

Blast-furnace plant. T, pipe supplying blast. C, conveyor for hoisting ore. B, blast-furnace. D, dust-catcher to remove most of dust. G, gas main from furnace to D. E, gas main from D to S, S, S, S, stoves. W, washer removing all dust from the part of the gas to be used to drive the blowing engines. (By courtesy of Messrs. Newton Chambers & Co., Sheffield.)

Pouring off slag from a ladle full of molten steel. (By courtesy of the Eisen-und-Hüttenwerke, Akt., Bochum, Germany.)

PLATE XXXII

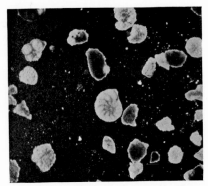

Minute shells—foraminifera, etc., in chalk ($\times$ 35).

Stalactites, stalagmites and other formations in a limestone cave. (By courtesy of Messrs. Cox's Cave, Ltd.,
Cheddar, and Messrs. Frith & Co., Ltd., Reigate.)

usually in a tube mill, a strong steel cylinder partly filled with steel balls which, falling one over the other, rapidly reduce the cement to the finest dust. It is essential that it should be very fine and accordingly Standard Portland cement is ground until 95% will go through a sieve with 28,900 holes to the square inch.

The reason why cement sets is not really understood. It seems to dissolve slowly in the water and combine with it, forming other compounds which crystallise out again as hard microscopic interlacing crystals.

Everyone has seen cement used. It is only necessary to point out its great strength to indicate why the modern world is building in steel and cement. If its appearance could be made a little better without increasing its cost, it would put the crown on its merits.

Lack of space forbids the discussion of literally hundreds of interesting compounds of the metals; soda, Epsom salts, alum, lead acetate, copper sulphate, arsenic are a few of these. But chemistry is a science which mainly consists of innumerable facts just as physics mainly consists of a few principles and a great deal of reasoning.

So, I must pass on to the study of the vast Earth beneath us, and the unimaginable immensities of space.

PART V

THE EARTH AND HEAVENS

CHAPTER XXX

THE EARTH AS A WHOLE

THE SCIENCE OF GEOLOGY

OUR survey of Science has now reached its first stage. We have studied all the fundamental factors; first, electrons, protons, neutrons, atoms, molecules, solids, liquids, gases and their heat-motions: secondly, energy in all its forms, especially in the form of radiation. In the earth, in the stars, in the body of man we have not discovered any other kind of matter or of energy: our material would, therefore, appear to be sufficient, if we apply it aright, to allow us to frame some working hypothesis as to the nature of the universe around us. There are, of course, many things on earth, in the heavens, and in ourselves which we do not understand; but so far science has not needed to suppose that any forms of matter and energy other than those we know of are to be found in them.

The study of Geology, our knowledge of the Earth, has an outstanding and, indeed, quite disproportionate effect on human thought. In the years preceding 1850 men had made many most important discoveries in physics, chemistry and biology. The public and the powers that were welcomed most of these discoveries as a token of Man's good use of his natural gifts: at worst the new discoveries aroused ridicule or mild reprobation.

But geology, in the nineteenth century, provoked a fierce, lengthy and wide-spread controversy. In short, the geologists adduced convincing evidence that the account of Creation set down in the Bible was historically untrue. To us, to-day, it seems incredible that the book of Genesis could ever have been held to be scientifically accurate, but the great majority of civilised people seem to have read it as being literally and word-for-word correct. In an earlier age, the geologists might have been burned or banished, but in the nineteenth century the scientific habit of thought and the freedom of discussion were not to be repressed. The bitter controversy that ensued ended in a tacit victory for the scientific view. Its final result has been that, to-day, the historical truth of all the facts in the Bible is maintained by only about as many people as believe in a flat earth. Of the educated population of the world a considerable proportion believe neither in a God nor a future life: while hardly any believe in the real existence of such a God as the man-like Jehovah of the Old Testament. Men of Science, with few exceptions, do not consider the question of the literal truth of the Biblical account of Creation to be worth discussing, since there is no evidence for, and much against, it. The existence of a God, they regard, from the point of view of facts, as unproven. The thinking religious man with a scientific training would agree: for his knowledge of God he would look into his own mind, not out into the world of matter and energy.

The thunders of religious controversy have died away; and the geologist to-day continues to extend his knowledge of the history of the Earth and its functions, undisturbed by the fulminations of bishops and the rejoinders of professors. Geology has, like most sciences, both a pure and an applied side: thus it is not only exceedingly interesting but is also of the greatest practical value for the study of the earth's past and present, and for the tracing of lodes of metallic ores, seams of coal, underground water and so forth.

SIZE AND SHAPE OF THE EARTH

In our study of the earth, our first task is to find its shape, its size and its weight. Men knew some 2,500 years ago that the earth was a sphere, though subsequently the knowledge was for a

long time lost. Aristotle gives many reasons for the belief, some
good, some bad. Everyone knows to-day that the "world is
round." I suggest to you that, before reading further, you ask
yourself why you believe it. The reasons usually given are the
following.

First of all, the earth can be circumnavigated. It is said that if
you sail due westward, you will finally get back to the place
from which you started. This is not so simple as it sounds. You
can't sail a ship due westward or in any direction continuously,
because the land interferes. Moreover, if the north magnetic pole
were in the centre of a flat circular earth (Fig. 393), and a ship was
sailed westward by the compass, it would come back to its starting
point! A better piece of evidence is that the curvature of the earth

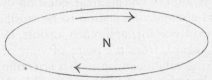

FIG. 393.—Circumnavigation on a flat earth.

is obvious from the way a
ship comes into sight over
the horizon, first masts, then
hull. This shows that the
earth is curved, but not that
it is a sphere. The fact that
the earth's surface is limited
and that you never come to the edge of it also shows that it is
some sort of rounded solid.

The fact that the force of gravitation is everywhere approximately the same and directed vertically downwards shows
the earth must be a sphere.
Thus, if it were cake-
shaped, as some of the
Greek philosophers
believed, a plumb bob
(which would always point
to the centre of gravity)

FIG. 394.—If the earth were a disc the plumb-
bob would hang vertically only at its centre.

would hang at different angles to the surface of the earth in
different parts.

A really good piece of evidence, however, is seen when there
is an eclipse of the moon. This means (Fig. 269) that the earth's
shadow is thrown on to the face of the moon. Now, the edge of

the shadow is always an arc of a circle, and there is only one solid, which, however you may twist and turn it, always gives a circular shadow: this solid is a sphere.

Lastly, we have the fact that for every 2,000 miles you travel to the south, the polestar appears 30 degrees lower in the sky till, south of the equator, it is invisible. This could only happen on a

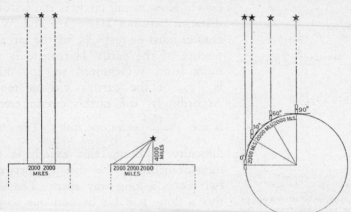

On a flat earth the Pole-star, if enormously distant (left), would not appear to shift as the observer travelled away from the pole. If it were not very distant (centre) it would shift but each successive journey of, say, 2,000 miles would cause a smaller shift than the previous one. The Pole-star would nowhere be invisible.

On a spherical earth (right) at the end of each successive journey of 2,000 miles southward from the pole, the Pole-star sinks by 30° and finally becomes invisible.

FIG. 395.—Evidence for a spherical earth.

spherical earth. If the earth were flat and the Pole-star an enormous way above it, the Pole-star would seem to be overhead wherever the watcher stood. If the Pole-star was fairly near, it would seem to drop in the sky as you travelled from the pole, but the first 2,000 miles would make a much greater difference than the next 2,000 and however far from the pole you were you could still see it.

The last piece of evidence shows us a way of measuring the size of the earth. Suppose we see a star exactly overhead at Harrogate, and at the same time a man at Winchester, 200 miles south of

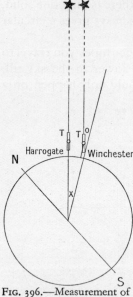

FIG. 396.—Measurement of
the circumference of the
earth.

Harrogate, has to point his telescope T
3° away from the vertical to see it. Then,
since the angle marked X is obviously
the same as the angle marked O, the
angle from Harrogate to the centre of
the earth and back to Winchester must
be 3°. Now, a full circle is 360°, so the
distance between Harrogate and Winchester must be just $\frac{3}{360}$ of the circumference of the earth. Harrogate is 200
miles from Winchester; so 200 miles
is $\frac{3}{360}$ of the earth's circumference.
Accordingly, the earth's circumference
is 200 × $\frac{360}{3}$ = 24,000 miles. The chief
difficulty in doing this exactly is the
measurement of the distance between
two places a long way apart. The way
this is done is a bit beyond our scope.
Error is also introduced by the fact that
the earth is not a perfect sphere, but
for this corrections can be made.

Measurements of this kind show that the earth has a radius of
6,378,388 metres (3,963 miles) measured from equator to centre.
From pole to centre it is less by $\frac{1}{297}$, so that its shape is that of a
sphere flattened a little at the poles. Of course, this radius is
measured to sea-level, and in all these calculations it is supposed
that the earth is perfectly smooth and of sea-level throughout,
which is not quite true. It is not far out though, for if the earth
were reduced to the size of a football, the highest mountains
would appear about as high as the thickness of three or four
sheets of paper on which this book is printed, and the deepest
gulfs of the sea would be a film of moisture a little thicker than this.

The highest parts of the earth are obviously the continents and
the lowest are the sea bottoms. These are arranged roughly like
the sides of a tetrahedron, so that the earth can be thought of as

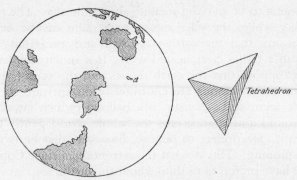

FIG. 397.—The earth as a tetrahedron.

very slightly flattened in the places where the sides of a tetrahedron would come, and very slightly raised where the corners would come. But the idea of a "tetrahedral" earth fades rather when you realise that the flattenings and raisings would be invisible on a scale model the size of a football.

The weight of the earth we have already discussed. It is approximately 6×10^{21} (six thousand million million million) tons. Now, this is very nearly 6×10^{27} grams. The volume of the earth can easily be calculated. It is $\frac{4}{3} . \pi . (637,838,800)^3$, that is 1.08×10^{27} cubic centimetres. So, a cubic centimetre of the earth-stuff on an average weighs $\frac{6 \times 10^{27}}{1.08 \times 10^{27}} = 5.5.$ grams. But oddly enough, a cubic centimetre of granite or any average rock taken from its surface weighs less than three grams. The conclusion is that the earth must have a very heavy centre since its outside crust is so much lighter than the average of the whole. We shall see that there is a good deal of evidence that this is true.

MOTION OF THE EARTH

That the earth is rotating and also revolving in an orbit round the sun appears from the observation that every heavenly object seems to be moving steadily across the sky. The position in the sky where the stars appear each night *can* be explained by supposing that the earth stays still and everything else is moving in a rather complicated way. It is much simpler, however, to suppose that the earth moves and the stars (which we know for other reasons are enormously distant) are so far off that they seem still. A man in a balloon (which always spins slowly round and round) sees the whole world gently turning below him. He prefers to believe, however, that he is the one who is spinning. This is what the astronomers since Copernicus (*c.* 1530) have preferred to think about the earth.

The most direct evidence that the earth is rotating is given by a large gyroscope which, as is explained on p. 169, keeps its axle pointing the same way however the earth which supports it may move.

The earth spins on its axis at a wonderfully steady rate. No clock is accurate enough to check it: it is used instead to check the clocks. At the most, it may vary as much as a minute in a hundred years—speeding up and then slowing down. Probably, on an average, it is slowing down, and some measurements appear to show that each day is about $\frac{1}{3000}$ second longer than the same day a year before. But this is probably an over-estimate. The earth is very probably 3,000,000,000 years old. There is evidence that the earth's time of rotation has decreased by some four hours during geological time. This corresponds to an average increase of $\frac{1}{200000}$ second, not $\frac{1}{3000}$ second as above.

The relation of the earth to its neighbours in space will be mentioned later, but we may take for granted that it revolves round the sun and see how this explains the seasons.

Granted then that the earth revolves in an orbit which is nearly a circle

FIG. 398.—How the inclination of the earth's axis causes summer and winter.

with the sun at its centre, it is easy to see why we have the alternation of summer and winter on which much of the world's weather depends. The axis of the earth, about which it turns, is *not* at right angles to the plane of its orbit, but is inclined at about 23½° to it. Consequently, at one period of the year, the sun at mid-day is overhead in certain places north of the equator. The northern hemisphere then gets most of the sun, and it is summer there and winter in the southern hemisphere. Six months later affairs are reversed. If the earth's axis were at right angles to the plane of its orbit, a perfectly equable climate without seasons would result.

It would seem reasonable to expect that the axis of the spinning earth, like the axle of a gyroscope, would remain pointing in the same direction while the earth itself revolved. This is nearly true, but not quite, for the earth is slightly flattened at the poles. The sun is always pulling the "bulge" of the equator towards the plane of the orbit. This makes the earth "precess" like a gyroscope (p. 170), and its axis shifts round and round like a wobbly top, a complete wobble taking 25,800 years.

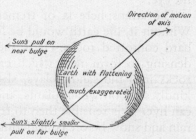

FIG. 399.—The earth as a gyroscope.

The axis of the earth now points only about 1° away from the north-star. In the time of the Greeks it was 12° from it, and 13,000 years ago it was 47° from it, and our neolithic ancestors must then have seen many of the stars which are now only visible from southern latitudes.

23*

CHAPTER XXXI

THE AIR

AIR AND WIND

THE earth is obviously made up of three layers, a layer of gas—the atmosphere: a layer of liquid—the sea: and a layer of solid—the crust. Within this are further "layers" not visible to the eye.

The atmosphere is of tremendous significance for geology. Without it, the earth would be like the lava fields of a volcano—hard contorted rocks. It is the air and its water vapour condensing to form rain which has worn away the hard volcanic rocks into the sands, clays, slates from which are derived the kindly soils on which plants, and the animals that feed on them, can live. It is sensible then to try to understand wind and cloud, rain and snow before considering the story of the rocks.

A huge sea of air envelopes the globe. It is made up of some 78% nitrogen and 21% of oxygen with 1% of argon, a variable amount (0-5%) of water vapour, and very small amounts of carbon dioxide and many other gases. It stretches above us for some five hundred miles, rapidly thinning out as we rise. When we are three and a half miles up, half the air is below us and half above. If all the air above us was compressed till it was as dense as the air at sea-level, it would be approximately five miles (nearly 8 kilometres) high. Now, the area of the earth is just about 500,000,000 square kilometres, so if the air were uniformly dense and eight kilometres deep, there would be 4,000,000,000 cubic kilometres of it. This is 4×10^{24} cubic centimetres.

Now, 1,000 cubic centimetres of air at normal pressure and

714

temperature weigh about a gram, so the world's air weighs 4×10^{21} grams or nearly $4 \times 10^{15} = 4,000,000,000,000,000$ tons. If this contained only 1% of water vapour, it would contain about forty billion tons of water—enough to cover the whole world about four inches deep (but not enough for Noah's flood!). It is not surprising then that the atmosphere can make all the water of the world everlastingly circulate between sea and mountain.

"The wind bloweth where it listeth, and thou hearest the sound thereof but canst not tell whence it cometh or whither it goeth."

It is only in the last hundred and fifty years that we have begun to understand the great winds of the world, much less the small eddies that bring the rain to our islands.

A very rough and idealised picture of the world's winds is given in Fig. 400. The poles and equators are calm. The winds blow west to east in the belt nearest the poles. Then comes a region of calms, the doldrums or horse-latitudes; then a region where the winds blow from east to west—the trade winds. At the equator again there is calm. This is of course a much simplified scheme, for eddies which we call cyclones or anti-cyclones are formed. The winds are much more regular at sea than over the land, where the hills and the patches of hot and cold ground disturb them greatly.

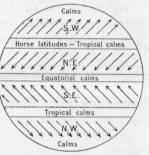

Fig. 400.—A much simplified representation of the world's winds.

The reason for this system of belts of air moving westward and toward the poles, and belts moving eastward toward the equator is fairly simple. Our enquiry splits into two questions. First, why does the air move? Secondly, why does it take these directions?

The reason why the air moves is that the poles are cold and the equator is hot. Hot air is therefore rising from the equator and its place is being supplied by air from north and south.

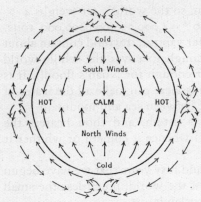

FIG. 401.—How the winds might blow if the earth were not rotating.

Air is being cooled at the poles and flows downward and outward, its place being taken by air from above. Accordingly, we might expect an air circulation as in Fig. 401, but in actual fact we do not get it because the earth is rotating.

However, the idea has a germ of truth in it. Let us see what the idea will do if we add to it the notion of a rotating earth. First, the earth's surface is moving fastest at the equator (a thousand miles an hour) and is not moving at all at the poles. Secondly, there is centrifugal force driving the air from the poles to the equator, the force getting greater as we get further from the pole. Now let us start at the equator and work out how the winds would be likely to blow. Look at Fig. 402.

At the equator it is hot and air rises straight off the sea. The centrifugal force does not tend to drive the air any way but upwards. So at the equator there is comparative calm. Air must flow in from the north and south to take the place of that which rises. Now suppose the inflowing air starts from a thousand miles north. This air, rotating with the earth will be travelling, say, at 900 miles an hour to the east: when the air has reached the equator it will still be travelling (neglecting friction) at 900 miles an hour. But the earth at the equator is travelling at 1,000 miles an hour, so that this air is being left behind by the earth and therefore appears to be moving the opposite way, that is, from east to west, just as the air appears to anyone in a train to be blowing violently in a direction opposite to that of the train's movement. So our air moves to the equator from the north to the south and west, and is, therefore, a north-east wind. For just the same reason, the air moving to the equator from the south is a south-east wind. Of course these winds do not move at anything like the pace which the earth's rotation would be expected to give them. Friction slows them.

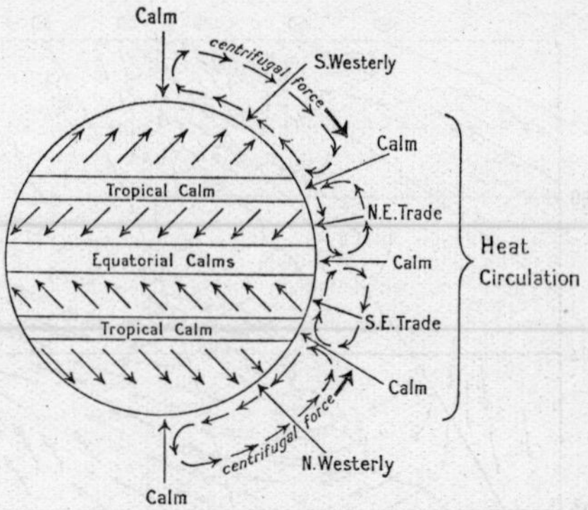

Hot air is all the while rising from the equator and flowing north and south: this air as it travels leaves the earth behind and, as it flows over the inflowing air, moves in an easterly direction as it goes both

FIG. 402.—How differences of temperature and the rotation of the earth cause the main air-currents.

north and south. The surface currents are the "trades" and the upper ones the "anti-trades."

Now, let us look at what happens at the poles. Consider the north pole first. The equator is lifting its hot air and pushing it in these upper currents towards the middle latitudes 30° to 35°. As this air comes north, it is opposed by the currents of upper air driven out from the poles by the centrifugal force of the spinning earth. So, we get a "heap of air" giving a high pressure in latitudes 30° to 35°. This air escapes along the earth's surface as a lower current travelling partly towards the equator and partly towards the pole. So air flows from latitudes 30–35° towards the poles. It starts with the velocity of the earth's surface in latitudes 30–35°, say 350 miles an hour. It is flowing to the polar regions where the earth moves slower so the north-moving air moves faster to the east than the earth does; consequently it catches up on the earth and blows from the south-west as it goes to the north pole and from the north-west as it goes to the south pole.

The map in Fig. 402 gives the course of the winds for a rotating earth which gets steadily hotter from poles to equator. The winds are a lot more complicated than this in actual fact, because, first, they form eddies and secondly, temperature does not fall

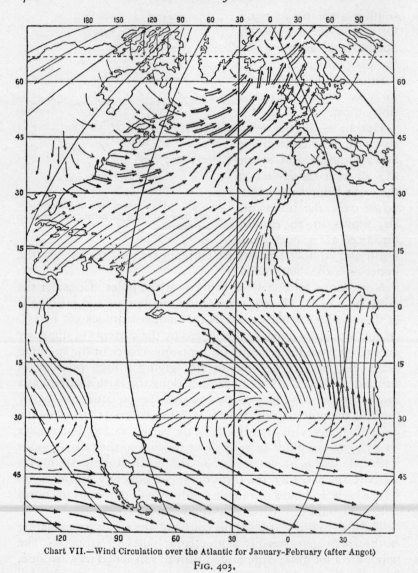

Chart VII.—Wind Circulation over the Atlantic for January-February (after Angot)

FIG. 403.

(By courtesy of Messrs. Blackie and

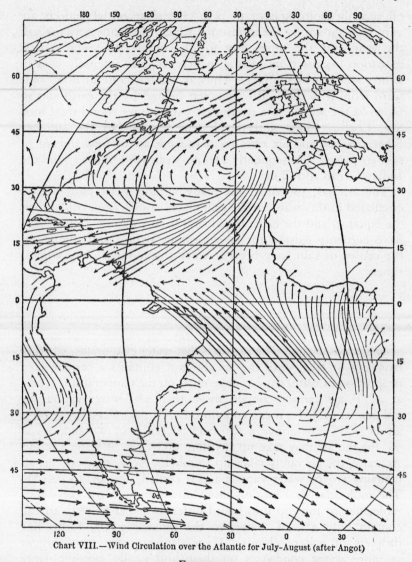

Chart VIII.—Wind Circulation over the Atlantic for July–August (after Angot)

FIG. 403*a*.

Professor Geddes, from the latter's *Meteorology*.)

off steadily from equator to pole. These secondary effects are very well shown by the monsoons which blow one way for half the year and the other way for the other half. The Asiatic monsoon is caused by Siberia, which becomes intensely cold in winter and hot in summer. Thus, in winter, cold air flows outward from it *to* the south. It is left behind by the earth and so blows *to* the west. So a north-east wind blows round the China Sea, Cochin China and the Indian Ocean. In the summer Siberia is hot and air rises off it causing air to flow inward to take its place. Consequently a south-west wind blows round the Indian Ocean and China.

The air has, probably, for many million years past, always circulated in this way, for the poles have always been colder than the equator, and the earth has always been rotating. The oceans have certainly existed for an enormous period and, therefore, the causes of rain have been at work throughout all geological time.

RAIN

Why does it rain? The reason is that water evaporates, whether from sea or lake, until the air above it contains a certain fixed proportion of water vapour depending on the temperature. Thus, at 45° F. air cannot contain more than 1% water vapour by volume; at 62.5° F., it can contain only 2%; at 76° F., 3%. So if air at 76° F. rests above a sub-tropical sea (also we suppose at 76° F.) the air may take up anything up to 3% of water vapour. Actually, the air rarely takes up so much. Now, suppose this air contains 3% of water vapour and is cooled, perhaps to 62.5° F. The molecular heat-motion slows down enough for the water-molecules to join up into liquid water-drops; at 62.5° F. air can contain only 2% of water, so the remaining 1% forms fine droplets of water—clouds. These droplets may grow bigger as more water condenses on them and finally become large enough to fall as rain.

Rain, then, falls when warm moist air is cooled. The simplest way in which this can happen is by warm moist air rising into the upper regions as it does at the equator. If we regard the globe as having the sort of air circulation shown in Fig. 402, the warm moist air from the equator will rise. It will expand and when air expands it becomes cooler (p. 136). Accordingly, the region near the equator has very heavy rainfall. The Congo, Brazil, and Assam are among the rainiest places in the world. In parts of Assam 400 inches of rain fall in the year. In the south-east of England 25 inches is an average figure.

North and south of rainy areas are the fairly calm regions of high pressure (lat. 30–35°). In these regions there will be little rain because the pressure is high and because no warm moist air is being brought to them. Actually, since the earth has its axis inclined to its orbit, the sun is not (as we assumed) overhead at the equator all the year round, and, in effect, the equatorial rain belt and the dry tropical calm belt shift north and south. Con-

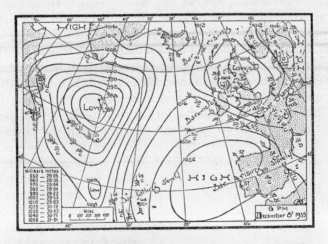

FIG. 404.—Diagram of atmospheric pressure 6 p.m. Dec. 8th, 1935. Note winds blowing clockwise round high-pressure areas, anticlockwise round low-pressure area. The arrows show direction of wind and, by the number of barbs, its intensity. (Courtesy of the Air Ministry and of *The Times*.)

sequently, many places somewhat north and south of the equator have alternate rainy seasons and dry seasons.

Finally, in the north and south, where the westerly winds are blowing, rain is nearly always associated with a "depression" or large vortex of air. Not much is known about the reason why these depressions are formed: it seems that they originate in the stratosphere, the calm region of the high upper air (pp. 723–726).

The weather of the British Isles is almost entirely the result of these regions of low pressure and high pressure travelling across the country.

A depression or cyclone is an area of air at low pressure, very roughly circular or elliptical as a rule. It may be 1,000 miles in diameter on the average.

If we measure the pressure with a barometer at different parts of it and draw a line ("isobar") through all the places where the pressure is at a particular figure, we get a picture like Fig. 404. The whole depression moves at from ten to forty miles an hour, and the wind blows, not, as one would expect, from the high pressure edge to the low pressure centre, but round it in a spiral, the opposite way from the hands of a clock in the northern hemisphere, but the same way in the southern. The reason for this is not too difficult to see. Suppose in the northern hemisphere the wind starts to blow from the south edge to the middle. It will catch up on the moving earth and so be a south-west wind. If the wind blows from the north-edge to the middle it will be left behind by the earth (p. 716) and so blow from the north-east.

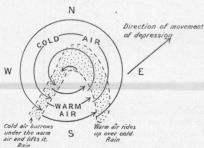

FIG. 405.—How a "depression" causes rain.

So, given a low-pressure area in the northern hemisphere the wind must blow round it the opposite way from a clock's hands. Now, as is seen in Fig. 405, the wind from the southern portion will be coming from a warmer and moister southerly area and will be

warm and full of water vapour. But at the north-east and
north-west sides, there will be colder air from the polar regions.
This cold air will be heavier than the warm air, which will therefore rise up over it. This will make the warm air expand and so
cool it, and the water vapour will condense to rain. Thus a
depression causes rain, first, in its front part where the warm air
rides up on the cold and, secondly, where the cold air comes
round to the south again and meets the warm air and burrows
underneath it, causing it to rise.

One more cause of rain must be mentioned—the mountain
range. Where a wind meets a mountain range it is forced to rise.
As it rises, it expands and therefore (p. 137) becomes cooled: its
water condenses and rain falls.
When it descends the other
side, it contracts and becomes
warm again. It has lost much
of its moisture and is dry and
warm. Good examples of this are found as near home as
Scotland. The wind is usually westerly, so the west side of
the hills is very wet indeed. Thus, Fort William on the west
coast of Scotland has a yearly rainfall of 80 inches, while
Aberdeen, on the east coast, receives but 29. Fort William is
far from being the wettest place in these islands, for in parts of
the Snowdon district the yearly rainfall reaches 200 inches.

FIG. 406.—How mountains affect climate.

THE UPPER AIR

All these currents take place in what are comparatively the
lower reaches of the air. The air is quite definitely divided into
two layers, the troposphere, the region of winds and of all but the
highest clouds; and the stratosphere, the lofty region of calm air.

Let us take an imaginary journey upward from the earth's
surface. The upper air and a part of the stratosphere has been
explored by the use of vast balloons supporting closed metal
spheres with glass windows. The sphere used by Professor

Piccard in his pioneer ascent to the stratosphere is illustrated on Plate XXV. Such an ascent might take us up some 14 miles: above this our journey must be an imaginary one.

At a mile height we pass the region of the heavy rain clouds; at two or three miles up, we have left most of the big clouds beneath us and only the little clouds of "mackerel-sky" and the threads and wisps of the fine lofty "cirrus" clouds are left. At seven miles height, all clouds are left behind except in very exceptional weather.

We are now well above the highest mountain in the world. All this time the temperature has been falling. At the ground, it was 65° F., we suppose. At about two miles up, it was freezing, and the thermometer drops steadily as we rise, till we are some eight miles up, when the temperature has reached the truly Arctic figure of − 50° F. We are now in the calm stratosphere, and though we continue to rise, it gets no colder. No one has risen higher than some 14 miles so our journey must continue in the imagination. Observations have been taken by sending "sounding balloons," equipped with thermometers, as high as twenty-five miles, and the temperature stays steady. Curiously, the stratosphere is coldest (−110° F.) over the equator and warmest (about −40° F.) over the poles!

All the while we have been rising, the sky has been becoming a deeper blue shading into a rich indigo. As we go higher, fewer and smaller particles remain above us to scatter the sun's light back to our eyes (p. 472). Nothing sent up by man—except sounding balloons and Big Bertha's shells—has been higher than 14 miles, and they have brought back no reports of what they saw in the upper air. In airless space, the sky would probably be dead black and sown with blazing stars. At about 20 miles up we should reach a layer of air, where the ultra-violet light from the sun turns a good deal of the scanty oxygen into ozone. Oxygen consists of pairs of oxygen atoms, ozone of triplets of these; and to turn oxygen into ozone needs much energy. Ozone absorbs a good deal of light (it is perceptibly blue): and the energy of the light warms it up: thus we have reason to believe the air here (above the

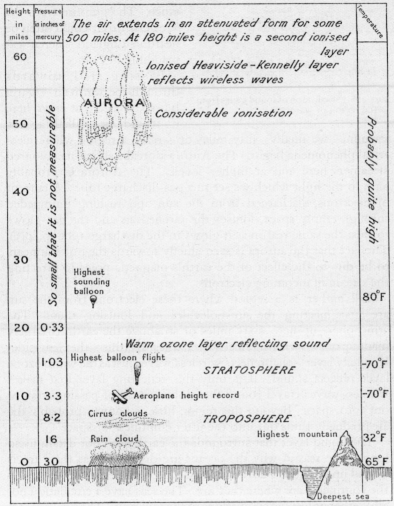

Height in miles	Pressure in inches of mercury		Temperature
		The air extends in an attenuated form for some 500 miles. At 180 miles height is a second ionised layer	
60		Ionised Heaviside-Kennelly layer reflects wireless waves	
50		AURORA Considerable ionisation	Probably quite high
40	So small that it is not measurable		
30		Highest sounding balloon	
			80°F
20	0·33		
		Warm ozone layer reflecting sound	
	1·03	Highest balloon flight STRATOSPHERE	-70°F
10	3·3	Aeroplane height record	-70°F
	8·2	Cirrus clouds TROPOSPHERE	
	16	Rain cloud Highest mountain	32°F
0	30	Deepest sea	65°F

FIG. 407.—Illustrating the successive layers of the atmosphere.

stratosphere) is quite warm. This layer of warm air reflects sounds and affords the reason why loud sounds, like gun-fire, are often heard a hundred miles away, but not heard at twenty miles' dis-

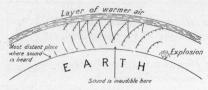

FIG. 408.—Reflection of soundwaves from the region of warm air.

tance. The gun-fire from the Western Front could often be heard in England when it was inaudible in France.

Passing still upwards through the warm air—warm but so rarefied that down here it would be called a low vacuum—we finally—fifty miles up—reach a region where electrical phenomena begin. The Aurora Borealis shows its coloured streamers here and at higher levels. The Aurora is probably akin to the light which we see in a gas-discharge tube. A current of electrons, discharged from the sun and rushing unimpeded through empty space, ionises the rarefied air and the gas glows for just the same reason as it glows in the discharge-tube (p. 443). The fact that the aurora is seen chiefly towards the poles appears to be due to the effect of the earth's magnetic poles in directing the stream of incoming electrons.

Still higher is a region where these electrons from the sun are first meeting the air-molecules and ionising them. The atmosphere up here, sixty miles or so above the earth, is largely made up of ions with big electrical charges. It is this—the Heaviside-Kennelly layer—that reflects wireless waves just as the warm ozone layer reflects sound. It is only this reflecting layer that makes wireless waves travel round the globe instead of passing straight out into space. Beyond this region little is known: probably the air gradually thins out into the utter emptiness of space.

The liquid layer that surrounds the earth need not detain us so long. The reason why the oceans are distributed as they are is bound up with the question discussed in Chapter XXXIII, of why the continents are where they are. The seas have a circulation not altogether unlike the circulations of the lower air. The rise of warm water and the fall of cold, the earth's rotation and centrifugal force, have their part in guiding them as has also the tidal pull of the gravitational force of the sun and moon. The sea is salt: this too must be discussed later under the heading of the age of the earth.

CHAPTER XXXII

The Interior of the Earth

STRATA

THE solid earth itself—what is it made of? Let us imagine ourselves taking a boring or sinking a mine shaft. We find that as we dig down we pass through many different kinds of rock. Chalk, clay, gravel, limestone, etc., are encountered. We notice, however, that these are not scattered about as irregular masses, but that as a general rule they lie in layers like a pile of sandwiches, so that a number of borings made in the same district encounter them in the same order. These layers we call *strata*. Let us suppose our shaft is to be sunk in London, say somewhere near Euston. We find a few feet of "soil" first, consisting of grains of sand and rock, a little clay-substance, some dark vegetable decayed matter or humus, probably some chalk. Beneath this is loam, a sandy clay, and some 20 feet down a layer of gravel, rounded pieces of flint. Only one thing smooths the rough flints we dig out of chalk into neat round pebbles, and that is the action of water. To anyone who has observed a river-bed, gravel is quite obviously stones worn by water. A few years ago in Endsleigh Street near Euston, vast bones were dug out of this loam and gravel layer. They were those of a mammoth, a primitive elephant-like creature which has been extinct for a vast period of time, to be measured at least in hundreds of thousands of years. The gravel and loam, then, are water deposits, they are clearly very old and they were once at the surface, for not even a mammoth can die twenty feet underground!

Below this, we find London clay—equally obviously deposited by water—for we can find water laying down deposits of clay

all over the world to-day. Examination of London clay by a
real expert—you and I would make nothing of it—reveals
fruits and seeds converted into mineral matter. These are
obviously the remains of ancient plants and trees, but, most
astonishingly, of plants and trees something like those which
grow in the Malay States to-day. When its clay was deposited by
water London must have had a warm climate, perhaps even
tropical. London was then the bottom of an estuary on whose
banks flourished magnolias, redwoods, breadfruit trees, ferns,
etc. We find, too, in the clay the remains of crocodiles, of queer
toothed sea birds and of primitive mammals not very like any
creature alive to-day but perhaps as much like the hippopotamus
as any. As we shall see (pp. 741–744), it is possible to ascertain
the date of most strata, and the London clay is probably some
fifty million years old. We continue to dig and find that the
London clay continues for some four hundred feet. Think for
a moment of the vast lapse of time needed for a river to deposit
400 feet of sediment. Continuing, we pass through 50 or 60 feet
of sands and clays, which were evidently (from the shells they
contain) laid down on an ancient sea bottom. Next, our boring
enters the chalk and for 650 feet or so we penetrate the solid mass
of tiny shells which we call chalk. We find in it remains of fish,
sea urchins and extinct coiled shells—ammonites. These creatures
lived perhaps 100,000,000 years ago. Under the chalk, we find
some 300 feet of dark grey sandy clay, deposited from some
ancient sea and below this very ancient rock indeed, perhaps
500,000,000 years old, with ancient sea shells and crustaceans
embedded in it. No one has bored deeper than this in London,
for the borings are made by well-sinkers and at this stage an
abundant supply of water is reached. But, we have every reason
to believe that if borings were continued for a few thousand feet
more, we should find ourselves drilling through granite or some
such rock which shows no sign of having been deposited from
water, which contains no remains of living things, and which
looks to the man of science as if it was the result of cooling some
molten mass of silicates (p. 658).

Over large areas of the earth it is the same story. Dig down and you will pass through feet, yards or miles of "sedimentary" rock which bears obvious signs of having been deposited from water in some way. Beneath these is always rock which equally obviously has been made by the cooling of some molten mass. Sometimes this latter "igneous" rock can be seen to have thrust its way up through the sedimentary rocks: sometimes the layers of rocks have been twisted, crumpled and overturned: but the general rule is that you will find layers of rocks deposited from water overlaying layers of rock formed by cooling a molten mass consisting of silicates of the metals.

These sedimentary rocks are of two chief types. The first includes water-borne débris of igneous or of older sedimentary rocks: these are gravels, clays, slates and sandstones. The second consists of the remains of creatures once living. Thus chalk, limestone and marble are made up of incredible numbers of skeletons or casts of minute water-creatures.

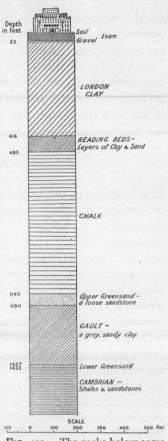

FIG. 409.—The rocks below some parts of London.

The igneous rocks include granite, syenite, diorite, andesite, diabase, basalt and gabbro. These rocks vary considerably, but are alike in being more or less crystalline masses of silicates and silica which have solidified from a molten condition. Rocks that have cooled slowly at a great depth have large crystals (granite is a good example); those ejected to the surface by volcanoes have cooled quickly and have either very fine crystals or none. They are also roughly to be divided into the acid type containing much quartz silica) and typified by granite, and the basic type containing little or no free silica. These are typified by basalt and olivine.

So by digging deep enough you will usually come to a granite-like rock. It is not possible to dig deep enough to find what underlies this, but fortunately volcanoes supply us with specimens of the contents of the earth's hot interior.

VOLCANOES

Volcanoes, in the widest sense, are the openings of "pipes" or channels which carry, or in the past have carried molten rock to the surface. A volcano is sometimes a great rift or crack in the level ground from which lava wells, but it is more usually a hill, small or great, with a crater or opening at the top through which lava, steam, dust and showers of stones issue when it is erupting. The hill itself is usually built of the materials which have issued from the crater; and these flowing or sliding down build up the beautiful cone shape so well seen in Mount Fuji, the subject of so many Japanese prints (Plate XXXIII).

We have reason to believe that volcanoes are tubes communicating with a layer of melted rock some twenty miles or so beneath the surface, because the lava which issues is usually of just about the same composition as certain of the igneous rocks. Moreover, the "pipes" of old extinct volcanoes can be followed deep into the earth by mining. The Kimberley diamond mines are in the pipe of a long extinct volcano; this pipe has been followed down for several thousand feet, and shows no sign of ceasing. Also chains of volcanoes often follow the straight lines of cracks in the earth's crust, and several cases have been studied where these lines are not far from twenty miles apart. Now, a solid, when bent, will not, as a rule, crack into bits smaller than its thickness (try it with toffee): so it is likely that the crust is somewhere about 20 miles thick in some volcanic regions, though probably far thicker in other parts. A further piece of evidence is that a deep mine often gets about 1° C. hotter for each 100 feet, though the figure varies a good deal. Thus, a temperature of 1,000° C. at which lava is soft, if not liquid, should be reached at a depth of 100,000 feet—about 20 miles.

Volcanoes commonly remain quiescent for long periods. Vesuvius did not erupt for several hundred years before the famous eruption which destroyed Pompeii and Herculaneum: so inactive was it, in fact, that the crater contained a lake and a wood in which wild animals abounded. The cause of an eruption is some sort of pressure from below, forcing the lava up the pipe. It does not seem very certain what brings this about. It is often thought that the sediment of rivers accumulating in the shallow seas which border the continents weighs down the overlying crust and so forces the lava up. It is notable that inland volcanoes are quite uncommon: almost all cluster along the coasts and islands, and many are under water! At any rate, there is a great pressure capable of forcing up the pipe a column of dense lava thousands of feet high. Now lava is not just molten rock: it is molten rock with quantities of gas—hydrogen, carbon dioxide, sulphur dioxide, steam, etc., dissolved in it under huge pressures. This gas exerts an enormous force for just the same reason that the gas from soda-water exerts a pressure in the syphon. At the beginning of an eruption the escape of both lava and gas may be impeded by a solid plug of frozen lava fitting the top of the volcanic pipe like a cork, and then—something has to go! Accordingly, a volcanic eruption often starts with a vast explosion. That of Krakatoa in 1883 was one of the most tremendous that has been recorded. The island before the eruption was some 18 square miles in area, and rose to a height of 1,400 feet. Terrific explosions occurred and the island was torn asunder, and within two days nothing remained but a deep hole in the sea-bottom.

The vast rush of escaping gas produced a detonation heard at Batavia, 100 miles away, and so intense a wave was created in the air that it travelled several times round the world before it died away. So much dust from the shattered rock was hurled into the air that the sky was black at midday 150 miles away, and the finest particles filled the whole of the earth's atmosphere. They rose to heights of fifty miles or more, and by reflecting and scattering the sun's rays produced magnificent sunsets all over the world, incidentally giving us a fine chance to track the winds in the upper air.

In the terrible disaster at Martinique, the compressed gas and steam, at a temperature little less than a white-heat, escaped by forcing a passage through a fissure which pointed down the side of the volcano of Mont Pelée. The scorching blast of gas, steam and dust in a few seconds destroyed every single one of the 26,000 people in the town of St. Pierre at its base. At Mont Pelée, later in the same year, the gigantic pressure of the lava and gas forced out of the crater a huge vertical column of rock a thousand feet high, three hundred and fifty feet in diameter, and weighing about eight million tons. Needless to say, these major feats are only performed when the lava and gas cannot get away otherwise. Often the side of the volcano is broken through. Fortunately, however, most volcanoes have their weak spots and after a few moderately violent explosions allow lava and gas to escape pretty freely.

The material thrown from a volcano varies in composition, and may be acidic like melted granite, or basic like melted basalt; but instead of being in fair-sized crystals like these rocks which have cooled slowly beneath the earth, it resembles a slag or may even take the form of obsidian (or volcanic glass).

The volcano almost always emits great quantities of gas which carries with it rock as small particles (ash, sand, pebbles, or chunks) forming the volcanic ash or tuff which covers large areas in volcanic regions. Showers of such ashes often cover the country for miles. The steam and ash make a vast eruption-cloud from which often falls a rain mixed with mud. When the lava or molten rock itself issues, it may be thick like pitch, and may solidify almost at once. It may, however, be almost as thin as water. By day, it usually looks black and dead, but by night it glows and forms a magnificent and terrible sight.

A few volcanoes show a continuous but less violent activity:

the crater of Kilauea in Hawaii affords the best example. The old crater of Kilauea is some four square miles in extent. The floor of this crater consists of black basalt, which glistens like polished steel in the sunlight, and has solidified into a roughly flat mass, showing all sorts of strange, rope-like, twisted, and contorted forms in places. This four square miles of the crater-floor has not a blade of grass or the tiniest plant growing on it. It looks as desolate as some landscape in the moon.

In the floor of this crater is a lake of melted lava some 180 acres or so in extent. The vivid description of an eye-witness[1] may help the reader to visualise these phenomena (Plate XXXIV).

"The great cauldron, over ½ a mile in diameter, is ringed with vertical cliffs of black basalt. Some hundred feet or so below me the molten basalt churned and boiled. At one time I counted over twenty "fire-fountains"—caused by the explosive force of the issuing gases—which hurled up pillars of molten rock to a height of a hundred feet or more. The dull-red, surface scale of cooling lava was rent by innumerable cracks, through which the brilliant yellow-red, molten rock could be seen swirling and bubbling. These cracks kept merging and coalescing, while new ones constantly broke out, often accompanying the genesis of a new fire-fountain. While I watched (three hours) the whole vast surface of the molten lake steadily fell—being some forty to fifty feet lower at the end of my vigil than it had been at the beginning. This was my own estimate, and I should hesitate to record it had I not had it confirmed by the super-intendent of the Hawaiian National Park, who stood by me as I watched the descent of the burning lake. And all the time the seething movements of its surface, and the leaping of its fire-fountains, were

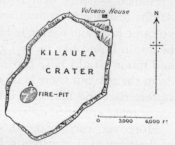

FIG. 410.—The crater and fire-pit of Kilauea.

[1] The author is indebted to Mr. H. Wynne Finch for this description, and for Fig. 410.

accompanied by an indescribable, dull, droning roar, which I can liken to nothing else that I have ever heard. The heat, when one stood at the edge of this great volcanic pipe, was so intense that one had to use a mask of cardboard perforated with eye-holes; and my spectacles protected my eyes in some measure. Another sign of the strength of the heat radiation from the vast surface of molten rock I also recall: the varnished woodwork of my camera emitted an odour which reminded me of that produced by a chair left too near a hot fire."

The gas dissolved in the lava often expands while the hot lava is of the consistency of dough, and so blows it out just as the carbon dioxide from yeast inflates the dough in bread-making. When such a rock is cold, it forms pumice stone, which is simply lava solidified to a sort of glass and inflated with a number of small air bubbles. The edges of these are sharp, consequently pumice is useful for rubbing away soft materials like wood or paint. Powdered pumice is much used in the coarser metal polishes.

The volcanoes, then, present us with samples of the matter in the earth below its solid crust; and it appears that the interior of the earth contains hot melted rock, liquid enough to flow, and saturated with gases. The lava is apparently not very hot, not much hotter, as a rule, than a coal-fire, and usually not as hot. Presumably—since heat is always leaking outward—at greater depths than the bottom of volcanic pipes the earth is hotter than volcanic lava, and the melted rock, or "magma" as we call it, should be a thin liquid like melted glass. Now, if this were so, the sun and moon would raise enormous tides in the liquid just as they do in the sea: but there is no evidence of these tides. The earth's surface rises and falls very little if at all, nor does the state of the moon make any great difference to the action of volcanoes.

Moreover, earthquake shocks are transmitted by the interior of the earth as if it were a solid. An earthquake is a fairly superficial affair: the trouble that causes the shock is something in the crust of the earth, often not twenty miles below the surface. Sometimes the cause is a "fault," by which we mean that the strata break and slip over each other: sometimes it seems to be a volcanic explosion. At any rate, it sets the earth shaking.

Now a liquid can vibrate only in one way: it can transmit compression waves—sound waves in fact.

A solid can transmit these too, but it can also waggle and vibrate sideways as does a tuning-fork. In this sort of vibration the solid *bends* and springs back the other way: a liquid offers no resistance at all to bending and so it cannot spring back. Now an earthquake-shock, say in New Zealand, sends waves of vibration through the whole earth. It has recently been shown that no matter how these travel through the earth-centre or crust, they come both as longitudinal waves—"compressions"—and as transverse waves—"waggles." So the earth, though it casts up liquid lava and must be far above the melting point of any kind of stuff that is likely to be within it, none the less behaves like a very rigid solid.

The reason may be that, in all probability, liquids under vast pressures no longer move freely. Even a hundred miles down the pressure is 750,000 lbs. to the square inch, and the highest pressures we have experimented with on earth are less than a fifth of this. The atoms of the "magma" must be forced so close to each other that their outer electrons are very likely to interact in quite new ways.

Our earth, then, has at the surface a mile or two of sedimentary rocks: below this, on land at least, is granite rock. The solid crust probably extends down for some 20 to 40 miles. Below this is very hot "magma": this comes to the surface as a liquid lava which solidifies to a black basic rock resembling basalt or olivine. This is, roughly speaking, a silicate of magnesium and iron. While the liquid is still beneath the earth the vast pressure seems to keep the hot mass fairly rigid.

Does this basic type of rock continue to the centre of the earth? Probably not. First, the earth is so dense (5.5 times as heavy as water) that it is unlikely that any pressure could compress igneous rock enough to give it this density. Secondly, we have good reason to believe that the earth is of much the same stuff as the other planets and that all of this stuff came from the sun. Now some of the meteorites or shooting stars which burn in our upper air and sometimes reach the ground are supposed to be fragments of an exploded planet. Whatever they are, they must be samples of star-stuff. Now meteorites are of three types. First, they may be stony, much resembling a sample of igneous rock; secondly, and most commonly, they may be made of metallic iron with a proportion of nickel, while a few are composed of both rock and iron. Now, if meteorites are fair samples of the stuff the earth is made of there must be a lot of iron in it. Iron has a density of 7.8. Accordingly, if there is much iron in the earth, it is likely to be in the centre of it: this iron would account for the density of the earth being as high as 5.5.

We suppose then that there is, below the basic layer of magma, a stretch of basic silicates mixed with iron, and at the centre a sphere composed chiefly of nickel and iron. No one has any idea how iron and nickel would behave under a pressure of a hundred and fifty million pounds to the square inch, and an enormously high temperature. They would probably be utterly unlike anything known to man. This theory is not the only one held. It is believed by many that below the basic magma there is a layer of heavy liquid sulphides of metals.

Why is the interior of the earth hot? It was at one time believed that the earth, originating from a mass of glowing matter ejected from the sun, had simply cooled ever since, and that the heat of its interior was solely the residue of its original patrimony. Since the discovery of the radioactive elements (p. 545) it has become clear that these are continually giving out energy in the earth's interior. The interior is so vast and the means of escape for the heat through

FIG. 411.—A section of the earth. The narrow black line represents the sedimentary rocks, the dotted layer the granitic rocks beneath. The nature of the deeper layers is by no means certainly known.

PLATE XXXIII

Microphotograph of granite showing its component crystals.

Mt. Fuji from Lake Kawaguchi—Springtime. (By courtesy of the N.Y.K. Line [Japan Mail], London.)

PLATE XXXIV

A glacier descending a valley: stream flowing from lower
end. (By courtesy of Messrs. E. Birkeland.)

The fire-pit of Kilauea. (*Above*) Photograph taken at
night showing cracks and glowing lava: (*Below*) general
view. (By courtesy of Mr. H. Wynne-Finch.)

miles of poorly conducting crust is so inadequate, that it is believed by many that the earth's interior is hardly cooling at all and will not do so until the radioelements have largely decayed. As these are formed from uranium and thorium which will not be seriously diminished in quantity even after 2,000,000,000 years, the earth's internal heat is likely to last for a period at least as long as its past life. We may think of the radioelements in the depths of the earth as equivalent in heating power to a vast furnace burning some 80,000 tons of coal a second.

THE CRUST

The part of the earth which most concerns us is the top two miles of the crust, which are chiefly composed of sedimentary rocks. Such rocks as shales, sandstones, slates, clays, and so on, have all been made directly out of fragments of the igneous rocks. Limestones, chalk, etc., are composed of calcium carbonate which marine organisms have obtained from sea-water. This calcium, however, must ultimately have come from primitive igneous rocks. In sandstones, you can recognise the grains of quartz which probably were once a part of granite or other siliceous rocks, and in slates magnified by the microscope, we can recognise flakes of mica which come from the same source. For these and other reasons we believe that the sedimentary rocks have mainly been made from the igneous ones, by the powers of wind, water and ice.

We suppose then that many million years ago the earth was a globe of igneous rock which had just become cool enough for water to exist on it in the liquid state. How long ago was this? Some of the oldest sedimentary rocks can be shown by their uranium–lead ratio (pp. 741, 742) to have been deposited about 1,800,000,000 years ago. Perhaps, then, it was some two thousand million years ago that geological history really began with the first condensation of water. Naturally, the date is not at all certain, but it is unlikely to have been as much as 500 million years earlier or later.

24

Nobody knows where the continents and oceans were in those distant times: there is much reason to suppose they were very differently placed from the present positions. Volcanoes often have a good deal of salt and iron chloride and other materials incrusted in their craters: so very probably the earth, before rain first fell, had much soluble material on it. The first torrential rains must have washed this away, and so formed salt oceans in the lowest parts of the earth's crust. With the formation of seas the circulation of winds and the seasonal rains must have begun. The water flowing off the higher ground formed rivers in the valleys. The torrents carried with them volcanic dust and loose stones, which wore both themselves and the river beds to mud and sand which the water carried out to sea.

Water soaked into porous rocks. When frosts first occurred the water changed to ice and, in doing so, expanded, splitting the stones. Expansion in the hot sun and contraction in the cool of the night gradually cracked and split the rocks; and rain and rivers carried the fragments to the sea. Winds carrying dust and sand rasped and polished and wore away the hills. The sea, no less tempestuous then than now, battered the coasts and broke away boulders, smashed these into pebbles and wore them to sand.

The speed with which rocks are worn away might be guessed at from the fact that some of the external ornaments of St. Paul's cathedral have weathered half an inch or more in three hundred years.[1] The forces which will eat away half an inch of rock in three hundred years will, as a matter of arithmetic, eat through more than a hundred miles of the same rock in the time since water started to act on the earth.

Wind and water then are the agents that have shaped the surface of the earth: to them we may add ice. A glacier is a mass of ice, usually filling a valley. Ice flows very sluggishly, as if it were a very viscous liquid, and consequently a glacier moves very

[1] The air of London is, it is true, exceptionally corrosive. On the other hand, the stone of St. Paul's is a fairly resistant one.

slowly down its valley—perhaps a few inches in a day. Its weight is enormous, and it grinds the loose rocks beneath it against the valley floor and most effectively wears away the rocks to stones, sand and mud which is carried away by the streams of ice-water which flow from under it (Plate XXXIV).

The fragments are carried down by the rivers into the sea. The coarser grains sink very soon as sand. Further out, very much finer material deposits as mud, but very little of the material brought down by the rivers gets far out to sea. Most of it deposits quite near the land. Far out at sea the bottom is made of a fine red or grey clayey material and the deep sea oozes, consisting of the casts of minute organisms. These sands, muds and oozes ultimately were hardened by the pressure of other rocks forming above them, and by warmth and drying, and finally became slates, shales, limestones, and siliceous rocks like "diatomaceous earth."

Perhaps in the earliest and primitive sea there was no life, and in the deepest and most ancient rocks no remains of living things are found. So, in the ancient ocean which laid down these earliest rocks there was no living thing with a shell or a bone or any part hard enough to leave an impress on the mud. There may have been soft microscopic creatures like modern bacteria: we cannot tell. . . .

It stands to reason that if the sedimentary rocks were deposited from the sea the oldest should be at the bottom. One might think that it was only necessary to dig down and record what one found in order to get a complete record of rocks from the mud deposited in the Thames yesterday to the Archæan rocks two thousand million years old.

But this is unfortunately very far from true. First of all, the earth has always been rising and falling throughout geological times. Sometimes the rise or fall is sudden, as when a huge tract of land near Bombay, the Rann of Cutch, sank several feet in the earthquake of 1819, and was consequently converted into a shallow salt morass or lake, which has, however, since been largely filled up by wind-borne sand and dust. Sometimes

the rise and fall is gradual. If the change is but a millimetre a
year it will amount to some three thousand feet in a million
years—no great time as geologists reckon it.

Suppose now that the ocean bed rises and carries up with it a
few thousand feet of water-deposited shale or sandstone. No
sooner is this in the air than the forces of wind and rain begin to
destroy it once more, and send it back as mud to the ocean. So
most of the sedimentary rocks have not survived at all. They
have been lifted from the ocean beds and denuded away. None
the less, the geologist can piece together the story. In one
part of the world the most ancient rocks are preserved: in
another are rocks of another period, and by comparing the
different strata of different areas of the world he can say with
tolerable certainty that the chief sedimentary rocks were
originally formed in a certain order, however much they may
have been since disturbed.

THE AGE OF THE ROCKS

For a long time, the geologist knew only the order in which
the rocks were deposited. Thus, he knew the Silurian slates were
laid down before the Devonian and the Carboniferous strata, and
these latter before the chalk. Only recently have we got a pretty
close idea of the age of these strata. Astronomy does not help us
much. It makes it clear that something between 1,000,000,000 and
10,000,000,000 years is a reasonable age for the earth: the basis of
this notion is rather too complicated for this book. A rough
estimate is afforded by the time it would have taken for the
retarding effect of the tides to slow up the moon from the speed
it must have had when it was cast off from the earth to its present
value: these calculations indicate an age of roughly 4,000,000,000
years. Again, in order to make a rough guess at the time when
water first appeared and sedimentation began, we may say (1) all
the salt in the sea came into it via the rivers. (2) There are 32×10^{14}
tons of salt in the sea. (3) The rivers bring down 39×10^6 tons

of salt a year. Consequently, they have been doing it for $\dfrac{320 \times 10^{14}}{397 \times 10^{6}}$

= about 80,000,000 years.

But, unfortunately, we have really no idea whether the rivers brought down more or less or the same amount of salt in the past, and we do not know how much salt finds and has found its way into the sediments the ocean deposited. So we only get a rough guess, indicating from fifty to several hundred million years, for the age of the ocean.

In the rocks, however, there is hidden an accurate clock if we can read it aright. If you turn back to the table on p. 548 you will see that the atoms of the radioactive element uranium break down and that by a series of changes each uranium atom ultimately becomes eight atoms of helium and one atom of lead. An atom of uranium weighs 238 units and an atom of the isotope of lead we get from uranium weighs 206 units.

Now the "half-life period" of uranium is 4,500,000,000 years, so out of any quantity of uranium you take, one half will change into lead and helium in 4.5×10^{9} years.

Now suppose a kilogram of a mineral when formed contains 10 grams of uranium and no lead. After 4.5×10^{9} years it would contain only 5 grams of uranium and $\dfrac{5 \times 206}{238} = 4\frac{1}{3}$ grams of lead. After another 4.5×10^{9} years, half of this uranium will have disappeared, so 2.5 grams of uranium will be left and $6\frac{1}{2}$ grams of lead will remain. Thus, the *proportion* of uranium to lead will depend on the *age of the mineral*, by which we mean the time which has elapsed since it started with pure uranium and no lead.

The trouble of the method is that there are very few minerals which do not contain some ordinary lead which has not been manufactured by uranium. However, the lead which uranium makes has atoms weighing 206 units each and ordinary lead has 12 atoms weighing 206 units to every 8 atoms weighing 208 units. So the process is this. Extract all the uranium from, say, a kilogram of the mineral and find its weight. (W grams.)

Extract all the lead from the mineral and find out what proportion of its atoms are 206 units in weight[1] and what proportion of them are of 208 (and other weights). Knowing the proportion of 208's and others to 206's in ordinary lead, deduct from the total 206's enough to go with all the 208's to make ordinary lead. These atoms came from the lead originally in the mineral. The rest of the 206's (P grams in weight) were made from the uranium. From the ratio W/P we can calculate the age of the mineral, as shown on p. 741 above.

Another way is to find the ratio of uranium to helium. 238 grams of uranium by decomposing make 32 grams of helium, and there is not likely to be any helium in the mineral to start with. So by weighing the uranium and the helium a ratio can be got which tells how far the uranium has got with its decomposing, which ratio tell us how old the mineral is. The trouble is that helium is a gas, and we do not know how much is trapped in the mineral and how much in the enormous periods of geological time finds its way out. The result of studying the order in which the strata were laid down and measuring their age by the uranium methods gives an extraordinary picture of the vast antiquity of the earth. *The oldest strata are nearly two thousand million years old.* No one can picture this, but a few comparisons might help. Imagine yourself with the faculties of a god, able to picture a man's whole life in the space of a second. Then you would sit for a year, night and day, before you had pictured the story of the earth. The life of a man bears the same proportion to the age of the earth as a blink-of-an-eye to a month! Suppose a super-sluggish snail, travelling as slowly as the hour-hand of a watch, had set out on his travels then. He would have crawled a hundred million miles by now, four thousand times round the earth.

Now these waterborne strata, of the age of which we now know something, contain fossils: shells and bones and imprints of living creatures. These must have lived at the time of the deposition of the strata in which they occur. Naturally, the remains are scanty.

---

[1] There are at least two good ways of doing this which I have not space to explain.

Dig about in an ordinary field and see how many bones of birds and rabbits you can find! Only a very few of earth's past inhabitants have been preserved in the rocks, but the work of the last hundred and fifty years has pieced together, from their remains, a very fair notion of the creatures that lived in the remote youth of the world.

The table which follows gives a notion of the rocks of the chief geological periods, showing the order in which, if undisturbed, they are found: their age and the kind of creatures that are found preserved in them. In each of these periods several different kinds of rocks may be formed. Column 3 mentions one or two of the most typical.

Period.	Age in millions of years.	Some rocks of each period.	Inhabitants.
ARCHÆAN	1800	Sands and slates and clays, baked or melted by the hot magma below.	None.
PROTEROZOIC	1000	Limestones and sandstones.	The presence of some carbon and much-altered limestones makes it likely that living creatures existed.
CAMBRIAN	500	Slates of North Wales. Some sandstones.	Crustaceans rather like large woodlice, a few shells, sponges and worms and water-plants in the sea. No evidence of land creatures. No fish.
ORDOVICIAN	450	Shales and a few limestones.	The chief fossils are graptolites, a sort of colonised animalcule allied to the sea-firs and jellyfish. Abundant life in the sea but no fish as yet.
SILURIAN	400	Shales, rich in fossils; limestones. (Wenlock Edge is silurian limestone.)	The sea was full of corals and sea-lilies related to them. For the first time fish appear. The first back-boned creatures. First remains of plants on land.

Period.	Age in millions of years.	Some rocks of each period.	Inhabitants.
DEVONIAN	350	Most typical are the Old Red Sandstone (a land deposit, probably hardened blown sand) and some limestones.	The Old Red Sandstone shows remains of quite large tree-like plants—giant mosses and horse-tails. The limestones show abundance of true fish.
CARBONIFEROUS	300	The chief coalfields of the world. The limestone of many English hills (the Pennines and Mendips).	The first land animals, spiders and other insects and amphibious reptiles of no great size. Huge forests of mosses and horse-tails which form our modern coal.
PERMO-TRIASSIC	220	Sandstone laid down on land.	Bigger reptiles are found on land and later the first mammals appear on land.
JURASSIC	130	Slates and limestones.	The age of giant reptiles up to a hundred feet and more in length. Birds first appear and flying lizards. Mammals are still small. In the sea, the spiral-shelled ammonites lived; corals were abundant.
CRETACEOUS	100	Chalk is the most characteristic.	The giant reptiles are fewer. Mammals and birds become more numerous. Flowering plants appear.
TERTIARY	60	London clay. "Crag" beds.	Mammals and birds become bigger and more numerous. The familiar animals like horses and elephants and monkeys become recognisable.
QUATERNARY	20	Gravels, boulder clays and other surface deposits.	Many of the biggest mammals disappear. Man appears in the last ten million years; and in the last ten thousand years of the period dominates and transforms the world.

Here is the material of the idea of Evolution. The ancient rocks have few, simple and almost mindless species. As time goes on, more complicated, more adaptable and larger-brained creatures appear—culminating in Man, that strange beast which has discarded the weapons of teeth and claws and speed and armour, and by adapting himself to the world and adapting the world to himself, has enslaved or subdued almost every creature.

Evolution must be considered from the point of view of biology rather than geology. But it must never be forgotten that the idea of Evolution is not based on someone's arguments. It is based on the succession of creatures in the rocks, dated by the uranium clock!

THE CRUMPLING OF ROCKS

The strata are not always found in the order in which they were laid down. Picture a large flat jam-tart made with a layer of pastry, then with a layer of red jam, then another layer of pastry, then a layer of yellow jam and so on. This might represent the strata as first laid down. Now, suppose it lay on the kitchen table waiting to be cooked and someone gave one end a steady slow push. The soft pastry would first go into hummocks, then folds, and finally would be bundled into layers in which the jam and pastry would take quite a different order.

This is just what has happened to the Earth's surface. Huge forces have raised it up, lowered it and, above all, thrust it sideways and in places utterly confused the pattern of strata. Not only is the pattern of strata altered but even the structure of the rocks. A slate has often been crushed under the vast weight of overlying rock until the lines of cleavage along which it splits are no longer parallel with the ocean bed on which it was laid down. Such a rock is said to be *altered*. A further stage is found when pressure and heat have altered even the texture of the rock. Limestone may be transformed into hard crystalline marble which may bear little, if any, sign of its watery origin.

24*

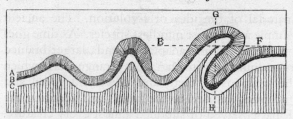

FIG. 412.—How the order of the strata is altered by **folding**.

It is easy to see then that if the crust of the earth were slowly and powerfully pushed in one direction, the strata would be bent into hummocks and finally into folds. The strata in Figure 412 were laid down in the order C, B, A. Now, suppose the rocks were folded as in the picture and then denuded by wind and weather down to the dotted line EF. If we then sink a boring

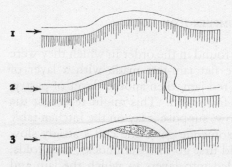

FIG. 413.—The effect of a sideways thrust (1) Fold; (2) Overfold; (3) Overthrust.

GH we find the strata in the order (going downward) C, B, A, B, C instead of ABC as we should expect. Even folding of this kind does not exhaust the possibilities of a thrusting force. One stratum may be slid over the top of another. The stages are first a fold (1) then an overfold (2) then an overthrust (3).

This process of thrusting has made most of the big mountain chains of the world. Mountains like the Alps (the best studied of all mountains) have not been pushed up from below. They are not even, as some people would think, the effects of or remains of volcanoes.[1] They are a huge pile of sheets of rock which have been forced on top of each other by tremendous pressure maintained for several million years. Naturally, they have been

[1] Some great mountain chains, like the Andes, may be topped with volcanic rocks, for the strain of lifting and crumpling may crack the crust and cause volcanic action.

intensely eroded—cut away—by ice and water, and to this much
of their shape is due. But the rocks that are to-day the peaks of
the Alps were for the most part laid down originally in the sea
and have been forced one over the top of the other till they look
down on the world from ten thousand feet or more. It has been
reckoned that this amount of folding means that the crust must
have been pushed through a distance amounting to perhaps
fifty or even a hundred miles. The question of where these fifty
or more miles of crust came from and what force raised them is
interesting and still doubtful. To account for the raising of the
world's mountains an area as big as Mexico must have been
used up.

The oldest theory, which is still quite widely held, was that the
earth was cooling internally, and as its centre contracted, its fairly
rigid skin became too small for its centre and so became folded
and creased like the skin of a shrivelled apple. There is no
evidence that the crust of earth is cooling appreciably. If
2,000,000,000 years ago, it was solid and cool enough to allow
water to rest on it, it can hardly have been so greatly hotter than
it is now. The internal heat of the earth slowly leaks away to the
exterior and the earth's hot interior therefore slowly contracts,
so withdrawing its support from the crust. The latter being
strong and rigid remains still and rigid until the stress becomes
too vast. It then begins to crack and crumple, so raising vast
mountain ranges. This weakens it, and in a period short compared with geological time, it settles down upon the hot core.
The cracks melt up and become soldered together and the crust
becomes once more rigid. Thus there are, as the rocks show us,
alternate rapid periods of mountain-building, times of vast
earthquakes, landslides and catastrophes, followed by long
quiescent periods in one of which the earth is now. Some
geologists, however, believe that this theory is not enough to
account for the raising of the Alps, let alone the Himalaya. Some
altogether new cause has to be found for these huge thrusts and
crumplings: we shall see that Wegener's theory of floating
continents (p. 754 ff.) helps to supply this.

Folding is not the only reason why strata do not lie in the positions in which they were found. *Faults* in the rocks are very common: in fact, few strata are free from them. A glance at Fig. 413*a* shows what is meant by a fault. The rocks have been forced up or slipped down along a sharp face. Faults are a great nuisance to miners. They may be following a seam of coal when they reach a fault: the seam disappears and a considerable search may be needed before its continuation is found.

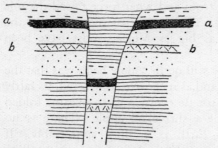

FIG. 413*a*.—A trough fault. Part of the strata has slipped downwards. (Courtesy of Messrs. Charles Griffin & Co., Ltd., from Park's *Geology*.

Faulting, the sudden breaking of strata and falling of countless thousands of tons of rock, is the chief cause of earthquakes. It used to be thought that earthquakes were caused by volcanic eruptions: however, the worst earthquakes frequently occur in non-volcanic districts. A really serious earthquake usually involves a large tract of land being suddenly raised, lowered or thrust sideways for a distance of some ten to thirty feet. The shock of the sudden movement sets the earth vibrating. An earthquake is one of the most terrific of human experiences. Everyone testifies to a peculiar terror felt when the solid ground rocks beneath them. The description by an eye-witness of such an earthquake is more valuable than anything which can be written by one who has never experienced an earthquake. The following account[1] was written by an observer of the Indian earthquake of June 12th, 1897—an earthquake so violent and widespread as to level almost every brick or stone building in an area little smaller than England.

"At 5.15 a deep rumbling sound, like near thunder commenced, apparently coming from the south or south-west. . . . The

[1] From *A Study of Recent Earthquakes*, Davison. (Walter Scott Pub. Co., 1905.)

rumbling preceded the shock by about two seconds . . . and the shock reached its maximum violence almost at once, in the course of the first two or three seconds. The ground began to rock violently, and in a few seconds it was impossible to stand upright, and I had to sit down suddenly on the road. The shock was of considerable duration. . . . It produced a very distinct sensation of sea-sickness. . . . The feeling was as if the ground was being violently jerked backwards and forwards very rapidly, every third or fourth jerk being of greater scope than the intermediate ones. The surface of the ground vibrated visibly as if it was made of soft jelly; and long cracks appeared at once along the road. . . ."

Another observer writes of the same earthquake that it presented "the aspect of a storm-tossed sea with the difference that the undulations were infinitely more rapid than any seen at sea." These waves in the earth's surface frequently crack at their tops—for the ground has no toughness or elasticity—and fissures open. It is these fissures which so often and horribly swallow up the victims of such catastrophes. Near the sea earthquakes are often made more destructive by tidal waves and by the sinking of tracts of land beneath the water. A witness of the destructive earthquake at Port Royal, Jamaica, in 1692, writes:

"The morning of this dreadful day was very fair and clear, affording no suspicion of the least evil, but in the space of three minutes about half an hour after eleven in the morning, *Port-Royal*, the fairest town of all the English Plantations, the best Emporium and Mart of that part of the world, exceeding in its riches, plentiful of all good things, was shaken and shattered to pieces and sunk into and covered for the greatest part by the sea. Few of the Houses that stood were left whole. So that by them falling, the opening of the Earth and the inundation of the waters, it is reckoned there were lost fifteen hundred Persons. The Sunday after, the Minister preached to them in a Tent, not daring to venture among the shattered Houses, the People were overjoyed to see him among them and wept bitterly when he Preached to them. It was a sad sight to see all that Harbour, one of the fairest and goodliest in all *America*, covered with the dead bodies of People of all conditions, floating up and down without burial, for the great and famous Burial-place called the Pallisadoes, was destroyed by the Earthquake, and the Sea washed the Carcases of those that were buried out of their Graves, their Tombs being dashed to piece by the Earthquake, of which there were hundreds in that place. Multitudes of Rich men were utterly ruined, whilst many that were poor, by watching opportunities and searching the wrack'd and sunk Houses, even almost while the Earthquake lasted, and terror and amazement was upon all the considerable People, have gotten great riches. From *St. Anns* there was news that above a thousand acres of Wood-land were turned into the sea and carried with it whole Plantations, but no place suffered like *Port-Royal,* where whole streets were swallowed up by the opening of the Earth, and the Houses and Inhabitants went down together. Some of them were driven up again by the Sea which arose in those breaches and wonderfully escaped. Some were swallowed up to the neck, and then the Earth shut upon them and squeezed them to death, and in that manner several were left buried, with their heads above ground, only Some Heads the Dogs had eaten. Others were covered with dust and Earth by the remaining people to avoid the stench. Great bellowing and noises were heard sometime after in the Mountains, which made them apprehensive of an eruption of Fire; but thanks be to God, no ill Event hath yet succeeded."

If these displacements of the earth's surface by a few feet at a time reduce us to such straits, how will mankind fare when the next great period of mountain building raises a range like the Alps or Himalaya?

MINERALS

We have talked so far as if all the crust consisted of sedimentary rocks as an upper layer and igneous rocks below. It is, however, very common for molten igneous rock to be forced up into the sedimentary rocks and there to solidify. It may penetrate along a fault, in which case it forms a flat, more or less vertical sheet called a "dyke." When the surrounding rocks are softer they are weathered more easily than the dyke, which then sticks up like a wall. The molten material may also penetrate between the strata making flat horizontal sheets called "sills" or sometimes irregular lens-shaped masses (Plate XXXV). These sills and dykes, etc., are sometimes accompanied by valuable minerals.

So far we have talked as if the common igneous rocks like granite and basalt, and the sedimentary rocks made by their decay, were the only important rocks. The mineral ores which are valuable as the source of our metals are of the utmost importance to us but are really quite rare. Estimates have been made of the quantities of the various elements in the earth's crust. The table which follows shows the amounts of the different elements in parts per million. We start with the remarkable fact that the earth's crust is about half made out of the gas oxygen and about a quarter made of silicon. The other 88 elements only make up a quarter between them.

AVERAGE COMPOSITION OF THE EARTH'S CRUST[1]

ONE MILLION PARTS CONTAIN

1	Oxygen	492,000	15	Sulphur	600
2	Silicon	256,700	16	Barium	400
3	Aluminium	75,000	17	Chromium	330
4	Iron	47,100	18	Fluorine	300
5	Calcium	33,900	19	Nitrogen	300
6	Sodium	26,300	20	Strontium	200
7	Potassium	24,000	21	Nickel	200
8	Magnesium	19,300	22	Vanadium	160
9	Hydrogen	8,700	23	Copper	104
10	Titanium	5,800	24	Zinc	39
11	Chlorine	1,900	25	Lead	20
12	Phosphorus	1,100	26	Arsenic	3
13	Manganese	900		The other 64 elements[2]	3,844
14	Carbon	800			
					1,000,000

[1] After Dr. Henry Louis following F. W. Clarke.
[2] These are not included in the list because they are unimportant or difficult to analyse or negligible in quantity.

Consider such an element as copper. Less than one part in ten thousand of the "magma" from which rocks are formed is made of copper; but great masses of copper ore containing from 5 to 50% of copper are found in various parts of the world. How did this ore sort itself out of the magma?

These ores of metals usually fill up cracks in the rocks—"faults"—or else they form masses which appear to have pushed their way among the shattered rocks. Often a "vein" or "lode" of ore runs up a fissure and pushes branches in between the layers of sedimentary rocks showing that it was injected into the crack as a liquid. The commonest ores of metals are sulphides—

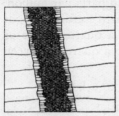

combinations of the metal with sulphur. Iron, lead, zinc, copper, nickel, antimony, mercury and a good many other metals are very commonly found as veins or masses of mixed sulphides. The very

Fig. 414.—Mineral (black) filling a fissure in the surrounding rocks.

difficult and not wholly settled question of how these ores separated out from the magma can hardly be put in a few sentences. The best way to think of the matter is to consider the original hot melted magma as containing all the elements in the table on p. 751. Now a mixture like this contains a great variety of molecules: all sorts of compounds of these elements can be formed. We can think of the magma, then, as a hot solution of all manner of oxides, sulphides, silicates, etc. As it cools, chemical compounds—minerals—will crystallise out as soon as the gradually cooling "solution" becomes saturated (p. 85) with them. First, there separate the minerals of the common elements—silicon, oxygen, aluminium, iron, magnesium, sodium, potassium, calcium, etc. Thus, on cooling the magma, crystals of quartz (i.e., silicon oxide), of mica (potassium aluminium silicate, often with iron and magnesium), of felspar (potassium or sodium aluminium silicate) come out and constitute granite. These crystals leave behind a liquid rock containing *all the less common elements*, and as it cools, further compounds of these may separate as solid crystals or as molten liquids (as oil separates from water).

Probably these sulphides like iron pyrites and zinc blende are the remains of huge masses of liquid magma from which all the common elements have already separated as granite or some other common rock.

Some ores have been deposited from water. Very hot water—under great pressure and far above its normal boiling point—certainly occurs in the depths of the earth. Such water has a vastly increased solvent power and is believed to dissolve certain materials out of igneous rocks and deposit them in the veins along which it flows. Many important ores must have deposited in this way, for they are decomposed at any temperature which could occur in the molten magma.

CHAPTER XXXIII

FLOATING CONTINENTS

TWO great problems have been left unsolved. First, what force crumples the earth's crust and raises the mountains? Secondly, why is the land and water of the globe distributed in huge masses—oceans and continents—instead of being dotted about anyhow?

The answer which has attracted much attention and controversy in recent years is Wegener's theory of Drifting Continents. There are several grave objections to it, but it links together so many facts so suggestively that it deserves discussion, though not an unreserved acceptance.

In the first place, we have seen that it is pretty clear that the continents are normally made of sedimentary rocks on a granite foundation. This granite foundation may be from ten to thirty miles thick. The deep oceans, on the other hand, under their negligibly thin sedimentary layers have a basaltic floor. Of course it is impossible to take samples of the rocks beneath the oceans, but we have some indirect evidence. Small oceanic islands usually have a basalt foundation. Moreover, the pull of gravity is a little more at sea than on land, which would be accounted for if the heavier basalt (roughly three times as heavy as water) were beneath the sea, and the lighter granite (two and two-third times as heavy as water) were beneath the land. Now land-volcanoes frequently and island volcanoes almost invariably produce lava of the basaltic kind; so it appears that there is basalt underneath the granite. We thus get a picture of continents of granite resting *on*, and partly submerged *in*, a layer of basalt. It is believed, then, that the lighter granite continents are actually *floating* in the heavier basalt magma just as a cork floats in water!

FIG. 415.—Floating block of wood, showing relation of emergent portion to submerged portion.

Now anything which floats displaces its own weight of fluid: that is to say it rises to such a height that *the amount of the liquid which it has pushed out of the way is equal in weight to the whole of the thing which floats*. Fig. 415 is a picture of a wood block of an area nine square feet and depth of one foot floating in water. The water weighs 62.5 lbs. per cubic foot, the wood weighs 50 lbs. per cubic foot.

The block is clearly 9 cubic feet and weighs $9 \times 50 = 450$ lbs. So it pushes 450 lbs. of water out of the way. 450 lbs. of water is $450 \div 62.5$ cubic feet. The water pushed out of the way by the wood, forms a block 3 feet $\times$ 3 feet in area and say d feet deep. Then, $3 \times 3 \times d$ (nine times d) is its volume and this must be $450 \div 62.5$ c. ft. The depth d then must be a ninth of this, i.e., $450 \div 62.5 \div 9$ feet $= \frac{4}{5}$ of a foot. So our wood block would float with $\frac{1}{5}$ out of the water and $\frac{4}{5}$ in it.

Now we have seen that there is some reason to believe continents are blocks mainly of granite, and with a mean thickness of twenty miles.

Granite weighs 2.65×62.5 lbs. per cubic foot. Basalt weighs 3.0×62.5 lbs. per cubic foot. The sea averages about $2\frac{1}{2}$ miles in depth and weighs about 65 lbs. per cubic foot. It is not difficult to see from this that it can be calculated how high a granite continent 20 miles thick should float above sea-level. It works out somewhere about 2,000 feet, which is nearly right for some continents. We are, of course, uncertain about the thickness of the granite under a continent, so our calculation is bound

FIG. 416.—How a granite continent (d. 2.65) might float in basalt magma (d. 3.0).

to be uncertain: but it is significant that the answer is not far from the truth.

This theory would account for several things. First, it makes it easy to account for the rise and fall of land which is always going on. If sediment was being rapidly deposited in the shallow edge of the sea, the weight would sink that part of the continental shelf and allow room for more sediment to deposit, and so allow for the laying down of very thick layers of rock which, we find, are formed without filling up the seas. Secondly, if the continents are floating on the basaltic magma as icebergs float in the sea, they may drift! This notion of drifting continents is the theory of Wegener.

Of course such drifting would be very slow, for the continental masses would be floating not in thin water but in thick pitchy magma. We cannot find any force adequate to cause this drifting: this is a serious objection to the theory, but not a fatal one, for we are very ignorant about all that goes on more than a couple of miles below the surface. Let us rather see if there is evidence that such drifting has really occurred or is occurring.

The first piece of evidence is very easily appreciated. The east coast of the Americas if slid across the globe would fit really quite simply into the contour of Europe and Asia. Labrador and Baffin Land would fit snugly on to Greenland. So North America and Greenland could be pushed across to fit against the coast of Europe. Now if this were done, not only would the coasts fit well (allowing for millions of years of raising, lowering and erosion) but the rocks would fit. Strata which are found in Norway and Scotland would join up with similar strata in Labrador. Just the same is true of the rocks of England, France and the U.S.A., and also of South America and South Africa.

All these facts then fall into place if we believe that at one time Europe, Africa and the Americas were joined, probably in the tertiary period, 60 million years ago, and have since drifted to their present positions. A motion of two or three inches a year is all that is needed to do it. If we believe in this drifting it gives us a very possible explanation of the force which has raised the great mountains. The great mass of Africa has drifted northward from its original position by the south pole and met the vast mass of Europe. It has driven the whole crust of the earth northwards for fifty miles or more and so raised the huge mountain masses of the Alps and Caucasus. India has drifted north against the mass of Asia and raised its southern edge into the vast but not very ancient range of the Himalayas.

Wegener supposes that a continent as it drifts will raise its forward edge, which feels the strain most, into the folds of mountain ranges. He believes that the Americas drifting rapidly west from Europe and

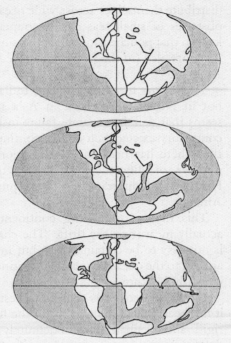

FIG. 417.—The continents as they may have been on Wegener's theory (top) 250,000,000 (middle) 50,000,000 (bottom) 15,000,000 years ago. (After Wegener.)

Africa have raised the Rockies and the Andes by this onward thrust.

Not only does this theory explain the shapes of the continents and the position of their great mountains, but it goes far to explain the animals which inhabit them.

First of all, a number of the less active species which would be barred by great mountain ranges or seas inhabit the southern continents and not the northern, while other species inhabit the northern and not the southern. If we believe that the continents have not been separated in a fairly recent geological period, we are forced to believe that these creatures have been able to distribute themselves across wide ocean but not across the smaller obstacles of small seas or of mountain ranges. Thus it is well known that pouched animals, "marsupials," are usual in Australia. They are also (in the form of pouched opossums) found in South America.

The lemurs too are in Africa, India and the Malay region, but not in North America or in Asia north of the Himalaya. It seems that definite separate fauna in the northern and southern continents existed before the continents were separated. Since then there has been much migration: but there still remains a number of differences following the line drawn along the Himalaya, Mediterranean and the junction of North and South America.

This theory of drifting continents may soon be tested by actually measuring the drift. The change of a few inches a year is not easy to be certain about: but in fifty years' time or less the answer to the question whether continents are now drifting should certainly be known.

Until the theory has thus been tested we must remember that it has been seriously attacked. In the first place the earth's crust is rigid and a small force indefinitely applied will not serve to deform it; we know of no large force which would supply the tremendous effort needed to shift continents and raise mountain ranges.

Other difficulties, too, have been raised. The regions of cold and heat at certain geological periods do not in all cases correspond to the parts of the world which, according to Wegener's theory, must have been near the poles and the equator respectively. It has been claimed by some that the thermal contraction theory of mountain building is enough to explain the raising of the great mountain ranges.

The notion of drifting continents is still, then, a centre of active work and discussion, and decisive evidence is still awaited.

CHAPTER XXXIV

THE SUN

BEYOND THE EARTH

WE have looked into the earth as deeply as we can; let us now look outward from it. Beyond the region of the atmosphere we see the sun, the moon, the bright points of light we call stars and planets, and occasionally the strange tailed bodies we call comets. Our information about these is largely limited to what we can learn from the light that comes from them. We can map out where they are and how they appear to move. We can see the surface of a few of them—sun, moon and the larger planets—and can therefore get some idea of what they look like. We can measure their size if they are big enough to appear as more than a point of light. We can find the mass of the sun, moon and planets by seeing how strongly they attract the earth (whose mass is known) or each other. Lastly, by examining the spectra of the stars, we can tell what elements they contain, how they move and how hot they are. These are the chief things astronomers can learn about the universe, but from them he can make a great number of calculations and probable estimates.

MAPPING THE SKY

First of all, how is the astronomer to measure the position of a star or planet? Till he can do this, he has no way of finding out how it appears to move. He defines the place where a star is by laying down the angle at which a telescope would have to be pointed at a given moment to show the star in the exact centre

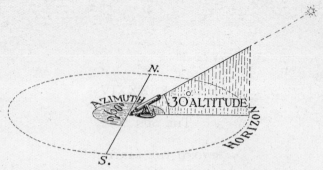

FIG. 418.—The position of the star may be defined as 260° of azimuth and 30° altitude.

of its field of view (usually marked by fine cross wires). This angle is most simply expressed by saying the star has so many degrees of altitude and so many degrees of azimuth. Its altitude is the vertical angle between the star, the eye and the horizon. The azimuth is the horizontal angle between the meridian the true north and south line (Fig. 418, NS), the observer and the point on the horizon which appears to be immediately under the star, the angle being reckoned from the south point westward (Fig. 418).

There are several other ways of reckoning the position of the stars, but they all come to the measuring of two angles.

The angles are measured by telescopes which have circles marked in degrees, minutes and seconds (Fig. 311) to show the angle they are making with the horizon or with the meridian. It is easy to see that if observations of the various heavenly bodies are made night after night for years, it will soon be very clear how they appear to move.

Now the result of these measurements is to show that the apparent motions of the sun, moon, stars and planets, their risings and settings, are completely explained if we believe that—

(1) The earth and the planets all rotate on their axes and at the same time revolve round the sun in orbits which are very nearly circles (but are actually ellipses).

(2) Smaller bodies, their satellites or moons, revolve round most of the planets.

(3) The stars are so distant that although actually moving very rapidly they cannot be *perceived* to move relatively to each other at all.

The solar system is the name given to the sun and the planets which revolve round it with their attendant moons. It covers an enormous tract of space compared with the earth and a very insignificant one compared with the whole universe.

Think, first, how vast the whole earth is compared with ourselves. Then realise that our earth in proportion to the solar system is like a single sand grain in a London square. Then realise that the solar system bears the same relation to the size of the universe, as judged by the distance of the furthest star-cluster yet measured, as a single sand grain bears to the whole of Africa.

THE SUN

It will be easiest to have a look at the solar system first, and later see how it may have come into being. The sun, the centre of our solar system, is a small star. It will be a good illustration of the way these things are done if we consider how the astronomers have measured its size, its weight and distance. The first of these to be measured is its distance. The distance of the earth from the sun varies a little from one time of the year to the other, but the method of measurement remains the same. The distance is a very important one, for once it is known, all the distances of all the planets can be worked out from it and from the times they take to complete their orbits. There are several ways of measuring it. Most of them involve much mathematics. One can see how long it takes the planet Venus to cross the disc of the sun when viewed from different parts of the earth. But Venus only crosses the sun's disc about twice a century, so this method is not exactly of everyday application.

One can measure the distance of the earth from some near planet like Mars on much the same principle as that upon which the distance of a near star is measured (p. 793). It is possible, knowing the distance of any two planets and the times they take to complete an orbit, to calculate all the others. But there is one way which is fairly easy to understand, though it is not so accurate.

If you have forgotten about the Doppler principle, read pages 385, 386 again, for it crops up continually in astronomy.

Suppose we select a star in the part of the heavens which the earth is directly approaching at the moment (Fig. 419). Suppose also that this star is stationary relative to the sun.[1] We focus a spectroscope on the star and observe the position in the spectrum of some line—say the yellow D line of sodium.

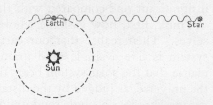

FIG. 419.—The earth, in the part of its orbit illustrated, will receive more light waves per second from the star, than it would 6 months later.

A sodium atom is, as far as we know, quite unalterable and gives out the same light on a star as on the earth. The light of the D line from a stationary sodium atom is known to give 5.0901×10^{14} waves per second, each wave being 0.00005893 centimetres long. Now when the earth is approaching the star we find that the sodium line in the spectrum is shifted a little towards the blue end of the spectrum, from which we can calculate that we receive from the star 5.0906×10^{14} vibrations per second of sodium light, that is $.0005 \times 10^{14}$ or 5×10^{10} vibrations *more* than we should from a stationary sodium flame. Clearly, then, the earth is *catching up* 5×10^{10} waves of sodium light every second. Each wave is 5893×10^{-8} centimetres long, so the waves which the earth is catching up cover a distance of $5 \times 10^{10} \times 5893 \times 10^{-8}$ cm., which is 29.46 kilometres or 18 miles. So the earth must be going towards the star at 18 miles a second. But the earth gets round

[1] Only for the purpose of our calculations. Any star can be selected and its motion allowed for in a very simple way.

its orbit in a year, which is about 31,560,000 seconds, so its orbit must be 18 × 31,560,000 miles long. If the orbit is a circle its radius, the distance from the earth's centre to the sun's centre, is the circumference (18 × 31,560,000 miles) divided by 2π, $6\frac{2}{7}$ nearly. This gives a radius of 90,000,000 miles. The actual distance is 92,800,000 miles: the above calculation is based on approximate figures.

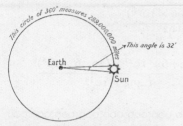

From this result it is not difficult to get the size of the sun. If a telescope is focused first on one "edge" of the sun, then on the other, the telescope has to be moved through 32 minutes, about half a degree. There are 360 degrees in a circle and 360 × 60 minutes, so the sun occupies $\dfrac{32}{360 \times 60}$ of a circle

FIG. 420.—Knowing the length of the earth's orbit, we can calculate the sun's diameter.

drawn with the earth as centre and with a radius of 92,800,000 miles. The circumference of this is 92,800,000 × 2 × $3\frac{1}{7}$ miles, and so the sun's diameter is $\dfrac{32 \times 92,800,000 \times 2 \times 3\frac{1}{7}}{360 \times 60}$, that is, 864,000 miles. This distance of 864,000 miles is about 109 times the diameter of the earth.

The distance and difference of size between the earth and the sun is easily visualised if we think of the earth as a mustard seed ($\frac{1}{20}$ inch diameter) and the sun as a water-melon ($5\frac{1}{2}$ inches diameter) at a distance of fifty feet.

We can weigh the sun by calculating that its pull on the earth is exactly balanced by the so-called "centrifugal force." The force required to keep the earth moving in a circular orbit with a steady speed is given by multiplying its mass (6×10^{27} grams as calculated on p. 160) by the square of its velocity (29.76 km. sec. or 29.76 × 10^5 cm. sec.), and dividing by the radius of the orbit (1.494×10^{13} cm.). This force must equal the gravitational attraction between the masses of the earth and sun.

The "centrifugal force" will be:

$$\frac{6 \times 10^{27} \times (29.76 \times 10^5)^2}{1.494 \times 10^{13}}$$

and the sun's attraction for the earth will be equal to the earth's mass multiplied by the sun's mass multiplied by the gravitational constant (p. 162) divided by the square of their distance. Call the sun's mass S, then the "attraction" will be:

$$\frac{S \times (6 \times 10^{27}) \times (6.66 \times 10^{-8})}{(1.494 \times 10^{13})^2}$$

So:

$$\frac{S \times (6 \times 10^{27}) \times (6.66 \times 10^{-8})}{(1.494 \times 10^{13})^2} = \frac{6 \times 10^{27} \times (29.76 \times 10^5)^2}{1.494 \times 10^{13}}$$

and by solving this little equation:
$S = 2 \times 10^{33}$ gms. nearly or 2,000,000,000,000,000,000,000,000,000,000 metric tons. The earth weighs 6×10^{27} gms. so the sun is $\frac{2 \times 10^{33}}{6 \times 10^{27}}$ or 330,000 times heavier.

Exact calculations show that the sun is 332,000 times as heavy as the earth, and as it is about 1,300,000 times as bulky, it must be made of much lighter material than the earth. The spectroscope, however, shows that the sun is made of very much the same stuff as the earth. The conclusion must be that a good deal of the sun is in the form of gas.

The sun rotates just as the earth does. We can tell this because spots are often seen on its surface. It appears to rotate in a period of about a month. An odd point is that the sun at its equator completes a revolution in 24 days 16 hours, but near the poles it takes about 34 days. The sun is probably so hot that it is all liquid or gas, so it is quite possible for some parts to move quicker than others.

We have no direct information about the inside of the sun. The outside is revealed to us as a sea of scorching flame, far hotter than any furnace, shaken and tossed by storms for which we have no comparison on earth.

The naked eye can tell very little about the sun, even when it is viewed through a dark glass. But photographs taken through a telescope give much more information. Plate XXXVI shows the curious mottlings which are noticed. They move considerably faster than a rifle bullet (15–20 miles a second) and are ever changing like clouds or waves.

They are very probably clouds of glowing gas. Each of these mottlings is about the size of France, so they are more easily visualised as clouds than waves! The sun's surface is continually swept by these racing hurricanes of white hot gas.

The surface of the sun, when photographed, very commonly shows sunspots. These are patches—well shown in Plate XXXVI —which appear to have a darker centre and a lighter band of shadow round them.

The centre is dark only in comparison with the rest of the sun. Actually it is blindingly brilliant. The sunspots are probably gigantic storms, like a cyclone on earth but of vastly greater proportions. The darker centre of a large sunspot would comfortably contain two or three earths. The spot seems to be a huge irregular vortex or whirlwind. The centrifugal force drives the gas outward and so lowers the pressure at the centre. When a gas has its pressure lowered, it becomes cooler—this accounts for the darker centre. At the same time, a vast hole opens into the sun's interior (for just the same reason as a "hole" opens in your tea when you stir it), and thence stream forth vast quantities of electrons—presumably liberated by the breaking up of atoms at the huge temperatures which prevail within the sun. These, circulating in the spot, make a rotating electric current and a magnetic field is developed as powerful as that between the poles of a big electromagnet. The effect of the stream of electrons is felt on earth. Big sunspots often cause a brilliant aurora (p. 726), and also "magnetic storms," in which compasses behave in an erratic manner.

That a sunspot really is a titanic whirlwind is clearly shown by picking out with a spectroscope the light given by the hydrogen atoms in the sun only and photographing the sun by this. The clouds of glowing hydrogen are seen to be streaming in great vortices as big as the whole earth. That the sun's surface should be the site of colossal storms is, after all, not surprising; the conditions on earth which bring about storms are differences of temperature, rarely as great as 50° C., and differences of pressure of up to a pound per square inch. The temperature differences in a sunspot may be 1000° C. and the pressure of the sun's atmosphere is at least 50 times that of ours.

Very remarkable features of the sun's surface are the prominences. These can be seen at any time with special instruments (Plate XXXVI): but in a total eclipse, when the moon just blots out the actual surface of the sun, they stand out as fiery red tongues of flame sometimes as much as half a million miles high and streaming up at three hundred miles a second. They seem to be a sort of eruption of gas, mainly hydrogen, arising often, but not always, from a sunspot. The gas is very rarefied and at a very low pressure and can hardly be compared to an earthly flame.

These prominences arise from a layer called the chromosphere, which is a sort of upper atmosphere of the sun. Though this layer is seven or eight thousand miles deep, it bears about the same proportion to the body of the sun as the earth's atmosphere does to the earth. Outside this glowing upper atmosphere of the sun is a bright "aureole," called the corona, extending some 250,000 miles from its surface (Plate XXXVII). It is very difficult to observe except at a total eclipse. It is an extremely beautiful object. It seems to be the result of the scattering of sunlight by molecules shot out of

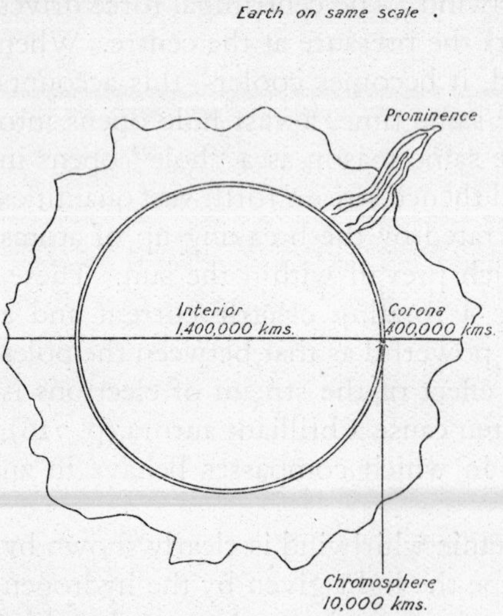

Earth on same scale .

Prominence

Interior 1,400,000 kms.

Corona 400,000 kms.

Chromosphere 10,000 kms.

FIG. 421.—Diagram of the structure of the sun.

the sun. The curious streamers which recall the lines of force round a magnet are not understood.

The interior of the sun is of course quite unobservable. We know that it must be largely of the nature of gas, because it is so light. We know also that it must be far hotter than the sun's surface, because heat energy is always being radiated from the surface. Its place must be taken by heat from within the sun, and this can only flow outward to the surface if the sun is much hotter at the centre than at the surface. A temperature of 20,000,000° C. has been calculated for the sun's centre: our highest earthly temperatures have reached 4000° C. Temperature is the kinetic energy of moving molecules. The lighter molecules on earth go about as fast as a slow rifle bullet: at the temperature of the sun they would be moving at a pace of about a hundred and twenty-five miles a second.

The energy radiated by the sun is enormous. Every square inch emits enough energy to run a fifty horse-power engine continuously. The whole sun throws off into space energy at the rate of 50,000,000,000,000,000,000,000 h.p., of which our earth succeeds in capturing 250,000,000,000,000. If we could utilise the sunshine which falls on the Sahara alone, the world would need no other source of power. The temperature of the surface of the sun can be estimated from this. If we assume the surface of the sun to be the best sort of radiator—the kind of material which gives out most heat at a given temperature—its temperature would be about 6000° C. It is probably, however, quite a poor radiator and therefore much hotter. A temperature of 6000° C. has never been attained on earth. Possibly 4000° C. may have been reached by sending big electric discharges through small wires.

Where does this lavish flood of energy come from? If the sun were simply a hot substance cooling, its temperature would be dropping more than 1° C. a year. Now 500,000,000 years ago, when the first living creatures swam in its seas, the earth was not 50° hotter. If the sun has simply been cooling at one degree a year, like a red-hot poker, it must then have been at least

500,000,000° hotter. Such an unheard of temperature would be enough to melt the earth: probably it would cause the sun itself to expand into a great glowing mass of gas reaching out as far as the earth's present orbit.

So clearly the sun must have been getting its radiation from other sources than its own capital of heat. A number of theories have been suggested to account for the sun radiating heat and light for some 2,000,000,000 years and getting very little hotter or colder. Only one of the suggestions is reasonable: that in the sun energy is being released from atoms. This can happen in two ways. Hydrogen atoms consisting of an electron and a proton could be forced together to make the nucleus of a larger atom. A sodium atom is made up of 23 protons and 23 electrons.

Now an atom of sodium is lighter than 23 hydrogen atoms, although it is made of the same numbers of protons and electrons.[1]

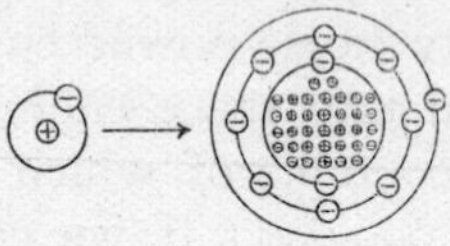

Twenty-three hydrogen atoms each like this weigh 23.179 units.

One sodium atom composed of the *same* units weighs 22.997 units.

FIG. 422.—A possible source of the sun's energy. If hydrogen becomes sodium in the sun, 0.78% of its mass is lost. One gram of mass becomes 9×10^{20} ergs of energy,

So if twenty-three grams of sodium were made in this way, 0.182 (nearly $\frac{1}{5}$) of a gram would disappear!

Now it has been convincingly shown that one gram of matter can be converted into 900,000,000,000,000,000,000 ergs of energy. So if hydrogen in the sun's interior was being built up into heavier elements at the rate of about 2,500,000,000 tons a second, the energy that the sun radiates could be accounted for. This is a bit difficult to believe, but the sun is so enormous that this quantity bears the same relation to it as a teaspoonful of water has to the North Sea.

Since the radioactive elements like uranium are always breaking up and forming a particular kind of lead, and since there is not such an enormous amount of that kind of lead in the earth,

[1] If the protons and electrons on being combined into the sodium atom produce some neutrons, the argument still holds.

PLATE XXXV

(*Above*) A horizontal "sill" of igneous rock overlying a sedimentary rock.
(*Below*) A vertical dyke of igneous rock forced upward as a liquid lava
through a crack in the overlying strata.
(Crown copyright: By courtesy of the Controller of H.M. Stationery Office.)

PLATE XXXVI

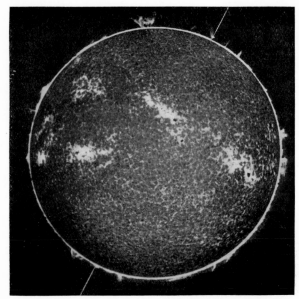

Photograph of the sun taken by calcium light, showing flocculi and prominences. (By courtesy of J. Evershed, Esq., Surrey.)

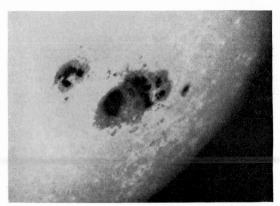

A sun-spot: a storm on the sun's surface. (By courtesy of The Royal Observatory, Greenwich.)

uranium must have been *made* some time, probably much less than a million million years ago. It is reasonable, then, to suppose that uranium must have been built up in the sun when the earth was still a part of it. Other elements too may very well have been built up in the same way. There seems, too, to be a great deal of hydrogen, the simplest building material, in the largest and presumably youngest stars.

Another way of providing the energy is for a positive proton and negative electron to meet and make—nothing but energy! The sun could, in this way, provide its energy by annihilating only about 4,000,000 tons of matter a second. It is so large that in a million million years—three times the probable life of the earth—it would not have lost one-tenth of its weight.

An objection to this latter theory is that a proton and an electron, by amalgamating, would probably produce a neutron with almost the same mass, so that no great amount of energy would be liberated. A positron (p. 528) and an electron (p. 528) would neutralise each other and give nothing but energy, but positrons are too infrequent for this to be effective. At present opinion is inclined to favour the view that the building up of hydrogen is a more probable source of energy than the mutual annihilation of protons and electrons. It is possible that both explanations are sometimes true. When a star is "young" it probably builds up elements from hydrogen: later in its existence it may annihilate protons and electrons.

CHAPTER XXXV

The Planets

THE SOLAR SYSTEM

WE now know something about the centre of the solar
system. Revolving in orbits round the sun are a number
of planets, with attendant satellites. There are ten large planets
and a collection of some hundreds of asteroids, small planets
from 500 miles to a few thousand yards in diameter.

The orbits are roughly in a single plane, which is the plane of
rotation of the sun. This would be very unlikely if the arrangement were a matter of chance, but if, as we have reason to think,
the planets were thrown off from the sun as a single elongated
mass, it is not surprising. If, on the other hand, the planets
were chance travellers through space, gathered into a system
by the sun's attraction, the plane of the orbit of one planet might
well be at right angles to that of another.

The best way to visualise the solar system is to make a scale
model of it. We will take as our scale one foot to a hundred
thousand miles. We shall need a good big space for it! Well, in the
middle we have the sun, a fiery globe eight foot six in diameter,

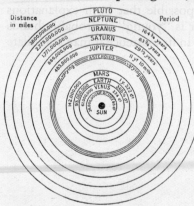

Fig. 424.—The planets, their distances and
periods of revolution. The diagram is
not to scale.

770

about as high as a rather tall doorway. We now take a walk and a hundred and twenty yards away we find the planet Mercury, like a small marble a third of an inch in diameter. We set off again, and when we are two hundred and twenty yards from the sun, we find Venus, like a ping-pong ball, about an inch in diameter. Another walk and three hundred and ten yards from the Sun is the Earth, about the same size as Venus, with the Moon, like a large pea, $\frac{1}{4}$ inch in diameter and two feet six inches from it. Continuing our walk, we reach Mars four hundred and seventy yards from the Sun. It is represented by a fair-sized marble, half an inch in diameter. With it are two moons, one of which is just visible as a dust speck $\frac{1}{200}$ inch in diameter; the other being invisible ($\frac{1}{1000}$ inch). On again, passing a swarm of asteroids. The largest, in our model, are the size of small shot, the smaller ones mere specks. We meet these all the way through our journey to Jupiter, which we find just under a mile (1610 yards) from our central sun-globe. Jupiter appears about the size of a football (between ten and eleven inches in diameter). It has nine moons round it. The biggest is not much smaller than Mars. They appear, then, successively as two small marbles and several tiny specks at intervals of one foot to fifty yards from it. Leaving Jupiter, we find our model of Saturn about a mile and three-quarters from the Sun. It appears as a globe eight inches in diameter with the well known rings which will be mentioned later, and nine moons, the largest of which appears as a fair-sized marble, the rest being very small. Somewhat exhausted, we plod on to Uranus, a globe about the size of a large grape-fruit and over three miles and a half from the model of the Sun. Its four moons appear like large shot and are from one to four feet from it. Off again for Neptune, just a little larger than Uranus and about five and a half miles from the Sun. Our journey only ends when we reach Pluto. This is probably very small and we shall therefore end our journey over seven miles from the central globe and there find a body like a small shot representing the outermost planet.

The remarkable thing about this solar system is its remarkable emptiness. If our model were set out on an open plain, you would have a very good chance of walking through it and noticing nothing but the model of the Sun! But its emptiness is nothing to that of space. If outer space were included, we should walk *sixty thousand miles* in our model after we left Pluto before we met the model of the nearest star *a*-Centauri, which would appear as a fiery globe, much like the model of the Sun.

All the planets revolve in orbits round the Sun. It is rather necessary to understand why the Earth (and the other planets) go round the Sun instead of falling into it. Imagine a globe a hundred million miles from the Sun and *at rest* relatively to it. The Sun and it would attract each other. It would rush inward at an ever increasing pace and within a few days bury itself in the Sun.

Now consider the Earth. It is revolving round the Sun at the rate of one revolution a year. The Earth therefore tends to move on in a straight line and it is kept in a circular path by the attraction of the Sun. The Sun's gravitational pull exactly balances the tendency of the Earth to fly off in a straight line, the tendency usually described as centrifugal force. The calculation has already been set out in a simple form on p. 764. It is not exact because the Earth's orbit is not an exact circle and because the other planets, the Moon, etc., all affect its path. But the result emerges that the Earth remains in its orbit because the Sun's attraction exactly balances this tendency to fly off in a straight line. A "balance" sounds rather precarious, but it is not so. For, suppose the Earth were forced by some imaginary giant to go a million miles nearer to the sun. Then its potential energy (the work it could do by dropping into the Sun) would obviously become less, because it could not then fall so far or so fast. This energy cannot be lost, so it would appear as kinetic energy and the earth would move *faster* in its new orbit. This would increase the "centrifugal force" which would force it outwards and back to where it was before. Thus the earth's orbit is stable: if it departs a little from its path, forces will drive it back again to it.

The time a planet takes to get round its orbit does not depend on its mass, because this must affect both the attraction inward and the centrifugal force outward in an equal ratio. It depends only on its distance from the sun. The rule is that the time in years to complete its orbit is one nine-hundred-thousand-millionth $\left(\dfrac{1}{9 \times 10^{11}}\right)$ of the square root of the cube of its distance (in miles) from the sun. Try it for Mercury. It is 36,000,000 (36×10^6) miles from the sun. The cube of this is $36 \times 36 \times 36 \times 10^{18}$, the square root of this is $6 \times 6 \times 6 \times 10^9$. This divided by 9×10^{11} gives $\dfrac{6 \times 6 \times 6 \times 10^9}{9 \times 10^{11}} = \dfrac{24}{100}$ or .24 of a year or 87.6 days. The actual period is 87.97 days.

We have assumed that the orbit is a circle; this is not quite true. The orbit is actually an ellipse. An ellipse is a curve, every point of which has the same total distance from two points called

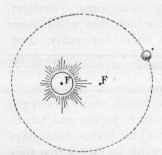

FIG. 425a.—The elliptical orbit of a planet. F, F are the foci of the ellipse.

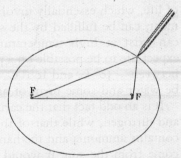

FIG. 425b.—Drawing an ellipse. The sum of the distances of the pencil point from the two pins F, F is always the same.

the foci. Fig. 425 shows how an ellipse can be drawn with two pins (the points) and a loop of thread, the length of which, less the bit between the pins, is the "distance which is always the same." The sun is always at one focus of the ellipse. Now the nearer together the foci are, the more nearly the ellipse approaches a circle, and most planetary orbits are nearly circles. A few of the asteroids have much "longer" or more eccentric ellipses while comets often move in elliptic paths which at their nearest come within a few million miles of the sun and yet pass right outside the whole solar system.

The conditions on the other planets are always exceedingly interesting, because we feel that there might be living creatures on some of them. No living creature of the kind we find on earth could live at a permanent average temperature of about 75° C. nor probably at an average temperature of below –50° C. The upper limit is the point at which protein molecules are altered: possibly creatures might be evolved with protein molecules resistant to higher temperatures, but it seems impossible to visualise life above the boiling point of water. It is sometimes suggested that "animals" with entirely different kinds of bodies— not made of carbon compounds—could exist, say, in the sun. This is not the sort of speculation with which science concerns itself, but it seems very unlikely, because none of the conditions of life, which essentially involves change in response to environment, can be fulfilled by the small stable molecules which alone can exist at high temperatures. We might reasonably, then, expect life to be possible on a planet with an average temperature between –50° C. and 100° C. An almost certain necessity would be water and some form of atmosphere.

It is an odd fact that the earth's atmosphere is nearly all oxygen and nitrogen, while that of the great planets Jupiter and Saturn contains ammonia and methane. Since all the planets must have come from the sun, it would be reasonable to expect that they all started with the same atmosphere. A possible theory is that all the planets had an atmosphere containing carbon dioxide, nitrogen and hydrogen. The light hydrogen atoms would escape from the earth's atmosphere into space: plants subsequently may have converted the carbon dioxide into oxygen and the carbon now present as coal, oil and living creatures. Jupiter and Saturn are so large that they would be able to retain their hydrogen. Their powerful gravity and (probably) very deep atmospheres may make their atmospheric pressure huge. In these circumstances hydrogen and nitrogen would combine and form ammonia

(p. 648), while hydrogen and carbon dioxide would produce methane ($CO_2 + 4H_2 = CH_4 + 2H_2O$). The theory is tempting, but rests on a good many uncertain assumptions.

MERCURY

The innermost planet, Mercury, revolves in an intense glare of sunlight about nine times as powerful as that on earth. Since it is so near the sun—36,000,000 miles—it can only be seen near the sun, i.e., at sunset and sunrise. It travels round the sun in 88 days. It is not easy to tell in what period it rotates, because no clear markings can be seen on its surface. Some believe it rotates about once a day, others that it rotates once in 88 days— always keeping the same face to the sun. Mercury reflects only about a fourteenth of the light that falls on it. It cannot then have many clouds and is probably dark desert rock, which we know reflects about this proportion of light. There appears to be no air on it. Its "edge" is perfectly sharp. It is so light that even if it ever had an atmosphere it could not keep it. Its weight is only a twenty-third of the earth's and so gravity at its surface would be only about a quarter[1] of what it is on earth.

A man who could jump six feet on earth could jump 24 feet on Mercury. The result of this is that anything shot upwards from the surface of Mercury at two and a fifth miles a second would never return, while, on earth, a speed of nearly 7 miles a second would be needed (air resistance neglected). Mercury is so hot that if it ever had an atmosphere the most rapidly moving molecules would be travelling fast enough to escape into space. Mars with a smaller gravitation pull can retain its atmosphere because its molecules are cooler and move comparatively slowly.

The temperature of Mercury's surface at midday is about 440° C., so Mercury is a blazing, airless, rocky desert, hot enough

[1] Not a twenty-third, because gravity depends both on the mass of the planet and the square of the distance from the centre. Mercury is only 1600 miles in radius while the earth is 4000. The gravity is then

$$\frac{1}{23} \times \left(\frac{4000}{1600}\right)^2 = \frac{6.25}{23} = \text{about a quarter.}$$

to melt zinc and to boil mercury; illuminated by a huge sun three times the size of ours and beating down from a black sky.

VENUS

Venus is the nearest planet to us. At the closest it is only about 25 million miles away. But at its closest, it lies between us and the sun and so obviously turns its dark side to us or only shows a thin crescent like a new moon.

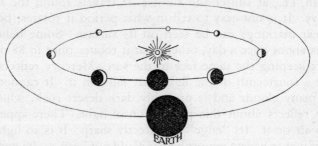

FIG. 426.—The phases of Venus. Note that the planet is invisible when at its nearest.

Fig. 426 shows why we see Venus in phases like those of the moon, also why the crescent always appears when Venus is on the near side of its orbit and therefore looks much longer than the diameter of the full Venus. Venus is a very mysterious planet. Only vague and hardly visible markings can be seen on it with a telescope and consequently it is very difficult to tell how rapidly it rotates. The only method is to observe the light coming from one side and then from the other. One side must be receding and so the wavelength is very slightly lengthened (pp. 385, 386); the other side is approaching the earth, so the wavelength of the light received is shortened. But the effect is a very small one and all that can be said is that it probably rotates in two or three weeks. The "day" on Venus is therefore from a week to ten earthly days long. Venus reflects nearly two-thirds of the light that falls on it. Only snow or cloud would be likely to reflect as much, and as Venus must receive more heat than the earth, it is probably cloud. No one can tell what is below the clouds. Venus has an atmosphere above its clouds, for this can sometimes be seen lit up by the sun, but there is at present no evidence of oxygen or water-vapour in it. Venus must remain a puzzle to us. We might guess at hot and steamy lands, densely shadowed by never-parting clouds, and possibly inhabited by living creatures; but at present there seems no prospect of penetrating the layer of cloud. A rocket-propelled sealed vessel could reach Venus if propelled from the earth at some ten miles a second. At this pace it could reach the planet at its nearest in about a month.

Rocket-propelled machines are highly unreliable and ten miles a second is about a hundred times faster than a human being has yet travelled. None the less, a journey to Venus is not to be thought of as wholly impossible within the next thousand years. Venus at its nearest is ten million miles nearer than Mars at its nearest.

THE MOON

The earth we have already discussed pretty fully, but this is perhaps a good opportunity to talk about its satellite the moon. Neither Mercury nor Venus have moons, though all the other major planets have.

The moon is by far the nearest of the heavenly bodies. It revolves round the earth in an almost exact circle about 240,000 miles in radius. Of course the moon travels with the earth, so its path *relative to the sun* is not a circle but a wavy line alternately inside and outside the earth's orbit.

The light of the moon, like that of the planets, is reflected sunlight. Only half of the moon is illuminated at once. At "new moon" only the dark half is presented to the eye of an observer, at full moon the light half is seen and at intermediate phases part of each half. Fig. 427 shows clearly why the moon shows "phases." The moon rotates on its axis, but does so once a

25*

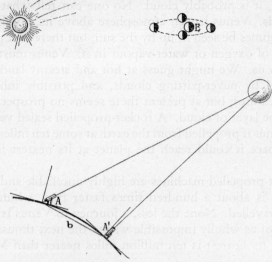

FIG. 427.—Illustrating (above) the phases of the moon. When the earth lies between the sun and the moon the latter appears full. In the reverse position the moon will be invisible (new moon). Below. Measurement of the distance of the moon.

month, thus keeping the same face always to the earth. We shall probably never know what the back of the moon is like, but no doubt it is very much like the front!

The distance of the moon is measured by determining at the same moment the altitude of a marking on it as seen from two different observatories, preferably several thousand miles apart. Knowing these two angles (A, A^1) and the distance between the observatories (b), it would be possible to draw a scale diagram and so show where the moon is. Actually, the distance of the moon is not plotted in a diagram, but is calculated by trigonometry from the angles (A, A^1) and the distance between the observatories.

The weight of the moon is calculated from its orbit. It is only $\frac{1}{82}$ of that of the earth, whereas its bulk is about $\frac{1}{50}$. Consequently the moon must be lighter than the earth, and it is probably chiefly made of the olivine-basalt layer of rocks with little or no nickel-iron core.

The moon is a dead world. There may have been life on it in the past; though this is unlikely, since it is too light a body to have been able to keep an atmosphere. The moon, as we see it to-day, is a desert of fantastic rocks and mountains as high as all but the highest of earthly mountains. The oddest features of the lunar landscape are the craters (Plate XXXVII). A circular range of mountains which may be twenty thousand feet high surrounds a level plain up to a hundred miles across, in the centre of which is often a smaller peak. These craters are very puzzling. They were at one time believed to be volcanoes, but they are unlike any earthly volcanic craters in size, though the walls and central peak rather recall them. But there seem to be no lava masses round them such as would be expected near a huge volcano. The level character of the middle of the crater is also an odd feature.

Some believe the craters to be the scars where huge meteors have struck the moon's surface. But if so, why is there only one such crater on earth (in Arizona), and why have all the meteors struck the moon head-on and made neat round craters instead of elliptical ones, which would be expected from the more usual glancing hit? A third theory supposes that when the moon was just cooling from the liquid state, the gas in the molten magma blew up huge domes or bubbles, which later collapsed again. The edge of these remained as mountains; the centres were melted down again into a level plain. Since the force of gravity on the moon is but a sixth of that on the earth, it is quite reasonable to suppose that far greater masses of magma could be lifted by gas-pressure than would be possible on earth.

Besides the craters, there are large darker patches called *maria*, "seas." They are not water but are possibly plains of solidified lava. Other features of the moon are long cracks extending for hundreds of miles, and "rays" of queer light surface markings, possibly volcanic ash. The moon is without air and without water. Consequently nothing tends to change it: there is no denudation and it is probably very much the same now as when it first solidified, probably 3,000,000,000 years ago. Nothing changes on the moon. We can see it so clearly and magnified so much that the Houses of Parliament would be visible as a speck, and if there were any woods or lakes or large rivers, they could be easily recognised. Descartes (1596–1650) believed that astronomers of the future would possess telescopes capable of displaying animals or human beings on the moon, if any existed. Our best telescopes can only show points 200 yards apart as separate and for the same sort of reasons which show us that there is a limit to the magnification of microscopes (p. 487), it is thought unlikely that telescopes will be greatly improved in this respect. There is no real certainty that any change takes place on the moon, although some astronomers think they have seen slight colour changes. The moon is intensely hot by day and cold by night. Water would boil in full sunlight on the moon: and carbon dioxide would freeze at the moon's midnight.

The moon is slowing down. Every day it drags the masses of water we call the tides round the earth, and it takes something like 1,500,000,000 h.p. to do it. This energy comes from the moon's rotation round the earth. It is, therefore, slowing up. The tides, too, are acting as a brake on the earth, and, if the oceans do not disappear in the course of æons, will ultimately bring it to the state when the same face of the earth always faces the same face of the moon. The earthly day will then be six weeks long: it will, however, be thousands of millions of years before it happens. The sun's tides will, however, then continue and the earth will be further slowed. These tides will act on the moon and speed it up once more. The moon's period will therefore shorten: its orbit will become smaller. Finally it will approach the earth so nearly that the earth's pull on its surface will be stronger than its own. It will then break into fragments, which will partly fall as vast mountain ranges on the earth's equator and partly form a ring like those surrounding Saturn.

The moon is rightly a melancholy sight as well as a beautiful one. It is a sphere of death—a picture of the state of the planet which air and water have left: it revolves, the skeleton of a world.

MARS

Mars has been the subject of a vast amount of conjecture. There is something to see on it: there are changes and they are indistinct enough to have given rise to most elaborate theories. The Man from Mars is established in the public mind as a possibility. Really, however, all that is *known* about conditions on Mars can be put in quite a few words. First of all, Mars is, after Venus, our nearest planet: it approaches at the nearest to within 35 million miles of the earth. It is decidedly smaller than the earth, being about half the earth's diameter and about a ninth of its weight. Its gravitational pull is only about a third of that on the earth. If the "Martian" of so many tales came to earth he would be much embarrassed by his own weight, which would be three times as much as on his native planet. It seems that the gravitational pull is enough to hold an atmosphere. It seems pretty clear that its atmosphere is rather rarefied, but it certainly contains water and oxygen and no doubt, plants and animals could be evolved capable of living in a very rarefied atmosphere. It rotates in just about a day, but its temperature varies very much because there is little air to blanket it. The average day temperature in the warmest regions is probably near that of an English winter (50° F.), while at night, temperatures as low as – 112° F., like Siberia in winter, may be reached.

No earthly creatures except mosses and lichens would withstand this, but it is very possible that if the earth had had this temperature for millions of years, forms of life would have evolved capable of resisting it.

Plate XXXVIII gives an idea of what Mars looks like through a telescope. Actually, however, it is a coloured object. The pole-caps show brilliantly white. These pole-caps shrink in the Martian summer and increase in its winter. The southern cap sometimes disappears altogether. These caps must almost certainly be ice or snow, the only other—and not at all probable—substance being solid carbon-dioxide.

The rest of Mars shows bluish-grey or greenish patches and also brownish and orange areas.

These last are very probably desert regions like our Sahara. The blue-grey regions are not seas, for if they were we should see the sun reflected in them. They may be regions covered with vegetation, but there is no direct evidence of this.

The canals on Mars have been the subject of much argument. Several observers, Schiaparelli, and Lowell in particular, have observed a network of lines crossing the surface of Mars. On the other hand, no one has ever been able to photograph these, and they are generally thought to be an optical illusion. Lowell suggested they were artificial canals made by intelligent beings with the object of carrying water from the polar caps (which melt in summer) to irrigate the arid regions of Mars, as the Nile carries water from the snows of the Mountains of the Moon to irrigate Egypt. This is a fascinating notion; but we are very uncertain whether the canals are there at all, and even if they are, they are at the limit of visibility; so it seems unscientific to build up so much speculation on such slender foundation. Mars has at least the necessary conditions for a rather difficult life.

The Martian night sky shows two moons. The larger is only 5,800 miles from it and 40 miles in diameter. It would look much like our moon though less bright. It revolves round Mars in seven hours and a half. This is a shorter time than the planet itself takes to revolve on its axis, a case without parallel in the solar system. The second moon would be a very small object, only a fifteenth the size of the other.

THE ASTEROIDS

Not much is known of the asteroids. There are at least 1,200 of them circulating in orbits between Mars and Jupiter. The largest, by name "Ceres," is about 500 miles in diameter, but most of them are less than fifty miles in diameter with an area of about that of England! They can have no atmosphere nor water, for their gravity is too feeble to retain any gas.

Many of the asteroids have remarkably eccentric orbits. Eros approaches within 14,000,000 miles of the earth and Amor, a mass of rock, perhaps a couple of miles in diameter, comes within ten million miles. It is a credit to our telescopes that it can be seen, a feat equivalent to discovering a halfpenny eighty miles away! Another asteroid (only known by a letter and number) comes inside the orbit of Venus!

It is certainly odd that this group of little planets should lie between Mars and Jupiter. Some think that there was once a planet there which burst into a cloud of asteroids: but the orbits do not seem to be of the type that would be expected from such an origin.

JUPITER

Beyond the asteroids lies the huge planet Jupiter. It is about ten times the diameter of the earth and 1,300 times its volume, but only about 317 times its weight.

Jupiter must, therefore, be made of some very light material. Either it has a very large atmosphere and we see clouds much above its surface, or it must have a great amount of water or ice on it. Plate XXXVIII gives a picture of Jupiter. The belts surrounding it are probably dense clouds blown into belts by tradewinds. There are some obscure changes of colour, and one rather conspicuous object, the Red Spot—a large oval marking which lasted some forty years but has now disappeared. It may have been the dust and gases from an eruption below the clouds. The spectrum of Jupiter seems to indicate the existence of ammonia and methane—a very odd sort of atmosphere. The clouds which we see as the surface are very cold and apparently at about $-130°$ C. The low density of Jupiter makes it probable that the clouds we see are the top of an enormously deep atmo-

sphere—perhaps thousands of miles thick. Under this may be
great glaciers, for the surface of the planet is probably very cold,
for it receives very little heat from the sun. Certainly Jupiter
must be utterly unlike the earth.

Jupiter has no less than nine moons: four are large, the largest
being very little smaller than Mars; five are very small objects
indeed. The largest can be seen by a person with exceedingly
keen sight.

SATURN

The planet Saturn is, like Jupiter, cloud-covered. It has 760
times the bulk of the earth and 95 times the weight. It is, therefore, very light and has only about ⅔ of the density of water. It
must be mainly gaseous. It rotates in ten hours and a quarter. It
would seem that what we see as Saturn must be largely cloud and
atmosphere, and the probable conditions on the planet are much
like those of Jupiter.

The really interesting things about Saturn are the extraordinary
rings which surround it. Three flat rings, all in the same plane
and level with the equator, encircle the planet. They are very
large: it would take five earths set end to end to reach across the
belt. They are also very thin, for when viewed edgeways they
simply disappear and so cannot be more than 60–70 miles
thick (Plate XXXVIII).

One of the rings—the innermost—is called the Crêpe ring.
This is semi-transparent and all the rings are transparent enough
for a star to be seen through them, thus showing that they cannot
be solid. It has been proved that a solid ring of this kind would
break to pieces, and it is believed that the rings are a swarm of
minute satellites!

Their velocity has been determined by the Doppler method,
and it has been shown that the edges travel slower than the
middles, whereas, if they were solid, the edges would travel
faster. The accepted theory of the birth of these rings is that a
satellite approached so near to Saturn that the attraction of the

planet tore the satellite into the pieces which now form the rings. Saturn has nine moons, one larger than the Moon, the rest a good deal smaller.

URANUS, NEPTUNE AND PLUTO

The planets Uranus and Neptune are so distant that very little is to be discovered about conditions on their surfaces.

Uranus is just visible to the naked eye. It is, like Jupiter and Saturn, large (31,000 miles in diameter) and very light, with a density of about the same as Jupiter. It rotates quickly in about $10\frac{3}{4}$ hours. From its brightness and its faint markings it must be heavily clouded. It seems to be intensely cold—at a temperature near that of liquid air in fact. The intensity of the sunlight that falls on it is only about a four-hundredth of that which falls on the earth and the sun would appear only a twentieth of the size it does on earth. Uranus has four smallish moons.

Neptune is so distant that nothing can be observed on its surface. It is a large planet (33,000 miles in diameter), of low density and probably clouded and intensely cold. It has a single moon. Neptune is on the average 2,800,000,000 miles from the earth: the last planet known, Pluto, is at the vast distance of 3,600,000,000 miles. It was only discovered in 1930. Its discovery came about in the same way as that of the planet Neptune, eighty-four years before. The motion of Uranus could not be explained by the combined attractions of the sun and known planets, and consequently its calculated positions failed to correspond with the position in which it was actually observed. An unknown planet was, therefore, suspected to be perturbing the orbit of Uranus. After laborious calculations Adams, at Cambridge, determined the position which the supposed planet should occupy, and a little later Leverrier in France did the same. Leverrier sent his results to Dr. Galle of Berlin and within a few hours the latter found the planet within about 52' of its expected position.

However, Neptune's attraction did not entirely account for Uranus' behaviour, and Lowell in 1915 calculated that there must be another planet beyond Neptune. The irregularities in Uranus' behaviour were very small indeed; the calculations were therefore not capable of great accuracy and the planet was not found as easily as was Neptune. But fifteen years later Tombaugh, at Flagstaff Observatory, who had photographed a portion of the sky at three days' interval, found a "star" that had moved and showed that this was the missing planet Pluto. It is probably a good deal smaller than the earth, and is far beyond the reach of the naked eye.

COMETS AND METEORS

Besides the planets, our solar system is inhabited by comets and by meteors. A large comet is a most conspicuous object. The photograph (Plate XXXIX) gives a good notion of their appearance.

They show a luminous cloud with a brighter centre or nucleus from which streams away a less bright tail.

Comets visible to the naked eye occur more often than would be thought. On the average, there is one a year. Most of these require looking for, but occasionally they are very conspicuous objects, even being visible in full daylight.

They have always been considered as alarming phenomena, prognosticating disasters, deaths, wars, pestilences and famines. Some comets certainly revolve round the sun in an elliptical orbit. Halley's comet returns every seventy-five years: it was here in 1910 and will be back in 1985, and many other comets which return in this way are known.

It is quite probable that all comets are members of the solar system and return after a long enough interval.

A comet behaves in a most odd manner. It is invisible when distant from the sun. As it approaches, it appears first as a faint luminous cloud: as it gets nearer, it *develops* the usual apparatus of a head with a bright nucleus and a tail. As it passes round the

sun the tail generally points away from the
sun, so that a comet receding from the sun
travels tail first! The tail cannot then be a
sort of streamer hanging out behind but
must be something *repelled* from the head of
the comet by the sun.

A comet may be enormous or may be extremely small. Its head may be much larger
than a planet, and the tail may be from a
million or so to a hundred million miles
long. Though so vast, they are very empty.
Stars can be seen shining through the
densest part of a comet, its head, almost as
brightly as if nothing were there. They are
very light: their mass is not enough to
perturb the orbit of a satellite, let alone a
planet. The head of a comet seems to consist of a cloud of small meteors quite a long
way from each other and a certain amount of
gas, carbon monoxide and cyanogen chiefly.
These gases are poisonous, but since the
density of gas in a comet is not much more
than in an exhausted electric light bulb, it is
unlikely that if a comet collided with the
earth we should even notice it!

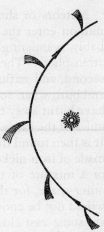

Fig. 428.—Illustrating
the way in which
the tail of a comet
keeps turned from
the sun. Note that
the tail is longest at
the comet's nearest
approach. (Courtesy
of the Oxford Uni-
versity Press and
Professor Chambers,
from the latter's
Story of the Comets).

The glow of the comet is partly reflected from the sun, but the
greater part seems to be a glow like that which we see in a neon-
sign. The torrents of electrons from the sun probably ionise the
low-pressure gas in the head and make it glow.

The tail of a comet is a very odd affair. It seems to be a very
tenuous cloud of dust particles repelled by the actual pressure of
the light from the sun, and it can be shown that a small enough
particle will be repelled by the light more strongly than it is
gravitationally attracted to the sun. Comets, we may say, are
more showy than important. They may be the most brilliant objects
in the sky and yet have less matter in them than a small asteroid!

Meteors or shooting stars are very common objects. Several million enter the earth's atmosphere every day. They are probably wandering stones from space which meet the earth's atmosphere. They very commonly travel at 50 miles or so per second, and naturally quickly heat up by friction, catch alight and burn when 80 miles or so above the earth. The great majority have burnt away to nothing by the time they have come within 50 miles of the earth. A few reach the ground and can be examined. It is then found that, as explained on page 736, they are commonly made of iron-nickel alloy, but sometimes of a sort of igneous rock or a mixture of this and iron. Most meteors must come from outer space, for they are moving so fast that the sun's attraction would not be enough to keep them in the solar system; but there are some vast clouds of meteors which move in a loose body or swarm round the sun. Thus, the earth's orbit crosses the tracks of meteor swarms on April 20–21, and August 10–11 every year. There is then a shower of meteors which varies a good deal in intensity. All the meteors seem to radiate from the same point in the sky, which is the point from which the swarm is approaching. These meteor swarms are believed to be the remains of disrupted comets. In one case at least a comet has disappeared and a meteor swarm occupies its old track.

THE CREATION OF THE PLANETS

The solar system is obviously a whole, not a fortuitous collection of objects. It is vast enough (a fast rifle bullet would take sixty years or so to get from the sun to Pluto) but it is positively a cosy-corner compared with the spaces surrounding it. If you think of the solar system as a 14 ft. bell-tent pitched in a desolate plain, the nearest star is another tent twenty miles away.

It is believed, for a number of good reasons, that the whole solar system originated from the sun. First of all, by no means all the uranium in the earth has yet turned into lead and helium. The crust of the earth can hardly be 2,000,000,000 years old. The earth must have been cooling fairly rapidly before the crust formed (for the hotter a thing is the quicker is its rate of cooling), so evidently the earth must have been molten at a time when, it would seem, the sun was not very different from what it is now. The reasonable conclusion is that the earth is much younger than the sun. If the earth did not come from the sun, it must have come from outer space: it seems quite incredible that the sun picked up ten bodies like the earth in such a way that their orbits all were within a few degrees of being in a plane.

Unless one accepts the idea of a Creation of the solar system as we see it to-day, it is reasonable to look for its source in the sun. The sun is a star. We may search the heavens and we find nothing at all like the solar system. True, the planets of a star might well be invisible, but we have no warrant for supposing from our observations that any other stars have planets. So, it is reasonable to suppose that planet-formation is not a normal incident in a star's life. The first probable theory of how the earth was formed was that the sun started as a vast rotating cloud of glowing gas. As it cooled, it contracted, converting its potential energy into kinetic energy, and therefore rotating ever faster. A time came when the rotation was so speedy that the centrifugal force, on the outside of the sun, exceeded gravity, and part of the outside was flung off as planets. This theory is useless, however, because the sun can be proved never to have rotated fast enough to split up in this way.[1] Moreover, if the sun were to throw off planets in this way, it would first have to assume a flattened shape like a lens and if it had once had this shape there seems to be no reason why it should not have it still.

No one has been able to suggest a way in which the sun could, *by itself*, cast off the planets; so, naturally, we must look at the possibilities of some other body intervening. Sir James Jeans has over the last twenty years built up an explanation of how the solar system could be formed by a star passing close to the sun and

---

[1] Because a body which is rotating can only slow itself down by setting something else rotating: the rotation of all the bodies in the solar system if concentrated in the sun would not speed it up enough to make it burst.

raising tides in it so huge, that a mass of matter could be drawn from it which would break up into planets.

The near approach of two independent stars must be very rare. A reasonable diameter for a star is a million miles: the sun and the nearest star are twenty-five million million miles apart. Consequently they stand in the same relation to each other as two fair-sized snails, one in Vienna, the other in Cologne (about 410 miles away). Suppose these snails crawl off in any direction they choose. What chance have they of meeting? Well, if the experiment is done enough times, the snails will one day happen to take the right direction to meet. Jeans calculates that if there are 100,000,000 stars in the "galactic system" to which the sun belongs, one would expect a pair of stars to come near enough to form planets about every five thousand million years. Consequently there is no reason to think any "solar systems" have been formed since ours.

Jeans pictures a star approaching the rotating sun rather slowly. The gaseous sun would first be flattened and a huge tide raised on it: this would finally eject a long cigar-shaped "filament" of gas. This would be narrow at first when the star was still fairly distant, would be thickest when the star was at the closest and thinner again when the star was receding. The filament would cool and liquefy, and would then be unstable and break up into separate portions. The small bodies would soon solidify, but the large ones, Jupiter and Saturn, would not, and tides raised on the larger bodies by the *sun's* attraction would again cause

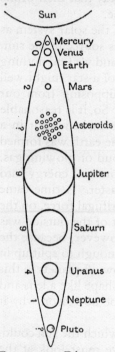

FIG. 429.—Diagram showing how a cigar-shaped filament of gas might have condensed to a planetary system. (Courtesy of the Cambridge University Press and Sir James Jeans, from the latter's *The Universe Around Us*.

filaments of matter which would solidify into satellites to be drawn out.

This theory explains quite a number of odd facts about the solar system.

First, it explains that the orbits of the planets are all in a plane: secondly, that all the planets and their satellites (with three exceptions, all small satellites) rotate and revolve in the *same* direction. It explains the biggest planets having the middle positions and also having the most satellites. It explains the fact that planets are so much smaller than the sun, and the satellites so much smaller than the planets. The chief difficulties are the smallness of Mars and Uranus, which should, on this theory, be larger than the Earth and Neptune respectively, but are not. But if the Earth and Neptune broke off from the filament as liquid, and the planets from Mars to Uranus as gas, the gaseous planets may have lost a great deal of their outer layers before they liquefied. It should not be thought that a theory like this is undisputed. No one has found a better explanation of how the solar system could have come into being, and there is no argument by which it can be shown to be unreasonably improbable.

A sun acquires a system of planets, then, as the result of an almost incredible bit of luck. Any named star can be expected to be sufficiently nearly approached by another to cause planets to be formed once in every 5×10^{17} years. It seems that the life of a star is only 5×10^{12} years: so one star in 100,000 might have planets round it. These calculations are only the roughest estimates, but they make it clear that a star with planets is a freak. Only a small proportion of planets have air, water and a temperature at which complicated molecules can both exist and execute the elaborate changes characteristic of living matter. We may expect, then, very few homes of life in the Universe besides our own.

The sun, then, was a star long before there was an earth. Let us try in our next chapter to trace the history of a star from its beginning to its end—if stars have either beginnings or ends.

Here you may well say—why should not the Universe have always been as it is now? The reason is simple. The stars are pouring out light and heat rays. This store of energy must come from their heat or their matter (p 210). If this emission has been going on for ever, the stars must have once been infinitely hot or infinitely large; unless, perhaps, the light is somehow transformed back into stars. If this emission of light and heat has not been going on for ever, there must have been a beginning. It is then impossible that the Universe can have been the same in the distant past. The astronomers have done something to lift the curtain which conceals the origin of the universe, but they have not solved the problem which may be crudely stated thus. "Hot things are cooling—why, if infinite time lies behind us, have they not all cooled to a dead level?"

CHAPTER XXXVI

STARS AND THE UNIVERSE

OUR KNOWLEDGE OF STARS

WHEN we look out into the clear night sky we see, in addition to the inhabitants of the solar system, only stars and cloudy diffuse matter—nebulæ. The naked eye, on a clear night, can distinguish about 3,000 stars. The ancients divided the sky into constellations which are quite arbitrary arrangements. Thus the stars in Orion are actually in parts of the Universe very distant from one another, but happen, as seen from the earth, to form a pattern. The brightest stars have names, the fainter stars are catalogued and known by numbers. The faintest stars remain unnamed and uncatalogued.

The constellations, then, do not *mean* anything. The interesting things about the stars are the different kinds, their distances and the way they are really grouped in space. It is a very familiar fact, that when you move, the nearer objects of the landscape seem to shift their position relatively to the further ones. A tree which from one point seems opposite a distant church tower, is no longer opposite it when you have walked a few yards on. The further an object is from the observer, the less it seems to shift as he moves. This shift is used for the measurement of the distances of stars.

It is reasonable to expect that some stars are near and some are distant; and so, as the earth rotates round the

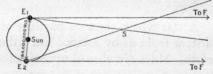

FIG. 430.—Measurement of the distance of a star.

793

sun the near stars should appear to shift relatively to the distant ones. Suppose (Fig. 430) we make observations from the earth when at opposite sides of its orbit, i.e., at intervals of six months. Suppose S is a star of which we want to know the distance and F is a faint star[1] so far off that it does not seem to shift at all, relative to other very faint (and probably therefore very distant stars). Suppose we measure the angle between S and F. Then, it is easy to see that from these angles $S E_1 F$ and $S E_2 F$ and from the diameter of the earth's orbit we could make a scale diagram and measure $S E_1$, or SE_2, the distance of the star. Actually, a scale drawing would not be made, for it would have to be impossibly large, but trigonometry would be used to calculate the lengths. This method has a serious disadvantage in that it can only be used to measure the distance of something (*e.g.*, S) which has something vastly more distant (*e.g.*, F) behind it. So it will not avail for the distant stars. The angles $SE_1 F$ and $SE_2 F$ are actually measured. From these we can get the angle $E_1 SE_2$ which is the angle at the vertex of the triangle formed by the star and the diameter of the earth's orbit. This angle is called the "parallax" of the star. Actually, the stars are so distant that this parallax is at most $\frac{3}{4}$ of a second of arc. Well, a second is $\frac{1}{3600}$ of a degree. If you were to put a halfpenny three miles and a quarter away it would be invisible: the angle from one edge of that halfpenny to your eye and back to the other edge is a second of arc. The astronomer measures this fairly easily. He can detect a parallax of a hundredth of a second of arc, though he cannot measure it with any accuracy. This angle is the angle made by the opposite sides of a human hair over a mile and a half away! The usual method employed is to photograph the sky and measure the relative shift of the star images.

A star which shows a parallax of one second of arc would be distant from us by 200,000 times the distance of the sun from the earth. Miles are absurd units for these distances. There are two

[1] F is put in two positions because the diagram is so small. Actually F is so far away that the angles $E_1 E_2 F$ and $E_2 E_1 F$ are both the same.

chief units in use for star-measurements, the *parsec* and the *light-year*. A parsec is the distance at which a star shows a parallax of a second of arc. A light-year is the distance which light (in a vacuum) travels in a year, at the rate of 186,000 miles a second.

Here is our astronomical table of units:

Astronomical unit = 92,870,000 miles = 149,450,000 kilometres. (Earth's distance from Sun)

One light-year = 0. 3069 parsec = 5,880,000,000,000 miles
= 9,461,000,000,000 kilometres.

One parsec = 3.26 light-years = 206,265 ast. units
= 19,150,000,000,000 miles = 30,830,000,000,000 kilometres

If the earth's orbit were scaled down to the size of a half-penny, a parsec would reduce to one mile, eleven hundred yards nearly. On this scale the earth itself could just be seen by the aid of a good microscope.

The parsec or the light-year then is our yardstick for measuring star distances. The nearest star—too faint to be seen by the eye— is about one parsec and a third away. The nearest well-known star is Sirius, the famous Dog-Star, which is 2⅓ parsecs or 8.6 light-years away.

The parallactic way of measuring the distances of stars is really only satisfactory within some ten or twenty light-years of the sun. Within five parsecs (16.3 light-years) of the sun there are only 26 stars. As a reasonable deduction of the number of stars suggests that there may be about thirty thousand million, it is clear that, though the parallactic measurements survey a part of the universe in which the earth is as a speck of dust in a great city, they leave untouched the rest of the visible universe which is vastly greater.

There are two other ways of assessing distances in the universe, and both depend on the fact that stars of the same *type* have about the same brightness. The first method is based on the fact that if the spectra of the two stars are precisely the same the two stars must be precisely alike, not only in material and temperature but in size and luminosity. Thus, suppose we find a star which gives exactly the same spectrum as Sirius but from which the earth receives only one millionth of the light it receives from Sirius. The star must really be emitting the same quantity of light as Sirius. The amount of light we receive varies as the square of the distance, so the star must be $\sqrt{1,000,000}$, i.e., 1,000 times as distant as Sirius. Sirius is 8.6 light-years away, so this star must be 8,600 light-years off. The method can be used for any star distinct enough to have its spectra measured. Of course, a suitable near star with the right spectrum cannot always be found. However, ways have been found of comparing stars with very slightly different spectra. The disadvantage of the method is that only moderately bright stars give distinct spectra.

The finest weapon for attacking the problem of the distance of far-off stars is the Cepheid Variable star. These stars give a light which fluctuates in a perfectly regular way. Thus, a certain Cepheid may brighten to a maximum every 12 hours with perfect regularity. Now, there are Cepheids of all sorts of periods from hours to weeks, and the brightness of a Cepheid depends on its period. The slower it pulses the brighter it is. This has been proved by observing a set of Cepheids which are in the same star cluster and therefore at nearly the same distance from us. Now the distances of a few Cepheids have been measured by the parallactic method, so we know just how bright, say a five-day Cepheid should appear at, say, twelve light-years distance. Now suppose we see a distant star cluster and spot a five-day Cepheid in it. If it appears to have only a hundred-millionth of the brightness of the one twelve light-years away, it must be $\sqrt{100,000,000}$, i.e., 10,000 times as distant and be 120,000 light-years away. The distances of very many of the stars can be measured in one of the three ways I have described. As we can measure the angles they make with each other and with the earth, we can tell how they lie in space and, in fact, map out the Universe.

One more thing at least is necessary to get a real picture of the stars and that is to know how they move. Of course, the stars appear to move across the sky in a regular way and to shift through "parallax," but these are only the effects of our own motion—the rotation and revolution of the earth. The real motions of the stars relative to the whole solar system are called their proper motions. Stars may move through an angle of ten seconds of arc or less in a year, but the vast majority move less than a second of arc a year. Now, when a star moves across the sky, you only see its *sideways* motion: for if it was coming directly towards us, it would not appear to move at all. But our old friend the Doppler principle comes in to help us (p. 762). The lines of the spectrum are shifted towards the blue when a star travels towards us, and towards the red when it recedes. So we can measure the sideways motion by seeing how far the star moves across the sky, and the head-on motion by examining the spectra; by combining both we can see how fast a star is travelling (relative to the Sun) and in what direction.

THE PLAN OF THE UNIVERSE

Using these observations of distance and speed we can form a stupendous and terrible picture of the Universe.

The Sun and its little flock of planets lie in a cloud of stars a couple of parsecs or so apart. One may think of these stars as being as isolated as peas a hundred and fifty miles apart. If you look at the sky on a clear dark night you see a band of light, the "Milky Way" (Plate XXXIX), entirely composed of faint stars. If you could see underfoot as well as overhead it would seem to form a great circle. The conclusion has been reached that we are in the midst of a lens-shaped crowd of stars, of which our sun is one, situated near the middle. Naturally we see fewer stars if we look towards the middle of the vast lens than if we look towards the edges, which we see as the Milky Way. This gigantic collection of stars is probably about 75,000 parsecs in diameter. Within this mass are many minor but still enormous clusters of stars and also a number of nebulæ, hazy masses of gas. The stars appear on the whole to be streaming round the centre of the galaxy. The whole mass of the galaxy, 75,000 parsecs in diameter, is rotating on itself once in every 250,000,000 years. Even this slow rotation means a very great speed for the outer stars, as much as 150 miles per second.

The edges then of the galaxy are some 30 or 40 thousand parsecs from us: the top and bottom of it are far nearer, probably about six or eight thousand parsecs.

There are a number of nebulæ in the sky, of which the great nebula of Andromeda is an example, which under great magnification are seen not to be hazy clouds but to consist of myriads of stars. The distance of these clouds of stars can be measured, for they contain Cepheid variables. The Andromeda nebula is no less than 270,000 parsecs, nearly a million light-years away. It is a gigantic object. It occupies nearly three degrees of the sky, and is, therefore, about 15,000 parsecs in diameter. Its enormous size makes it clear that it is a galaxy like our own, though smaller. The Andromeda nebula is then a vast island universe cut off by a huge tract of space from ours. It is by no means the only one of this kind. Hundreds are known with distances up to forty million parsecs. The light-waves from these which we focus into an image in our telescopes started on their journey to us before there was a man, before there was even a monkey: in fact, when the giant reptiles were wallowing in the earth's swamps, that light set out for the earth, travelling at such a pace that it would encircle the earth in a seventh of a second. There are probably two million or so of these island universes scattered about. Sir James Jeans makes a vivid comparison.

"We can construct an imaginary model of the system of the great nebulæ by taking about 50 tons of biscuits and spreading them so as to fill a sphere of a mile radius, thus spacing them about 25 yards apart. The sphere represents the range of vision of the 100-inch telescope: each biscuit represents a great nebula of some 4,000 parsecs diameter."

Our galaxy and some others would have to be represented by a large sponge-sandwich instead of a biscuit. Now turn back to pp. 27–32 and try to picture how small an electron is. Our earth in this model would be about the size of an electron. What size would you be? Do you feel now that the stars were created to afford you illumination? Man and his works are of utterly insignificant size. If he has any merit in this universe, it is because he, an insignificant speck, can make in his brain an image of the totality of things.

Is the boundary of the Universe within our vision? There is no reason why a 100-inch telescope should show all that can be seen, and at first sight the giant nebulæ, galaxies of stars, might be thought to extend *infinitely* in every direction. We cannot at present tell, though it is at least thought to be unlikely.

A most remarkable result is reached when we examine the spectra of these different galaxies. The spectral lines of all are shifted toward the red and consequently each (except the one in Andromeda) is retreating rapidly, and the further off they are the more rapidly they are moving. The distant ones are racing away at a speed of nearly 25,000 miles a second. The Universe appears to be expanding. If we trace this motion back, it seems that the whole universe must have been concentrated at a centre no more than 150,000 million years ago; a figure which is difficult to reconcile with the usual estimates of the age of the stars! Perhaps the Universe pulsates, alternately contracting and expanding. The theory of relativity seems to indicate that the universe must either pulsate like this, or must expand for ever, or must contract first from a great size to a minimum value and then expand. We *know* that the light from these nebulæ is of the type which would come from rapidly receding objects and so far as we know from no others: the explanations are by no means so certain.

The picture of vast, widely scattered galaxies of stars rushing away from each other, gives a notion of the universe as it is now. The picture in Time—birth, rise and decline of stars and systems —is at least as interesting as the picture in Space.

If you had to study the development of Man from cradle to grave and your own life was only that of a butterfly, you could not follow any single man from birth to old age. Instead, you would look at the crowds and see man at every stage in his life. Our first task, then, in tracing the history of the stars is to look at all the different types of star, expecting to see among them the young, the middle-aged and the senile.

The only objects (other than the island universes visible as great nebulæ) which we can see in the sky are luminous stars which appear as bright points, and nebulæ which appear as more or less hazy clouds which may be either light or dark. It is almost certain that there are many dark stars, which perhaps much outnumber the bright ones.

Now the only thing we perceive from a star is its light. By splitting up this light with a spectroscope we get a series of lines, each of a single wavelength. Each of these lines (pp. 436, 464) represents an electron in an atom moving from some position in the atom to some other. From these lines we can tell not only what kind of atoms make up the surface of a star but also under what sort of conditions they are vibrating. Thus, carbon vapour at 3,000° C. gives a rather different spectrum from carbon vapour at 6,000° C. The spectra of a quarter of a million stars have been classified and all of them fit into a *series*. This, of course, suggests that stars have a common origin. Thus, you can put all mixtures of milk and water into a place in a *series* starting with milk and ending with water, but you could not find a place for a glass of beer in the milk and water series. The stars then grade steadily from the O type to the S type, and every new star that is examined can be fitted in. The table gives an idea of what these types are like. The spectra of the O, B, A, F, G, K and M types are shown in Plate XL.

PLATE XXXVII

Total eclipse of sun, showing corona. (By courtesy of The
Yerkes Observatory, Wisconsin.)

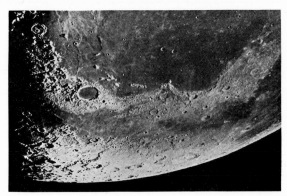

A part of the moon's surface. Note craters, in some cases with
central cone. (By courtesy of The Mount Wilson Observatory,
California.)

PLATE XXXVIII

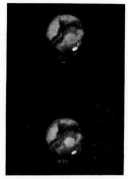

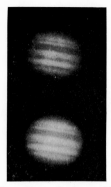

Mars. Note polar cap
—probably snow. (By
courtesy of The Yerkes
Observatory, Wisconsin.)

The planet Jupiter. (By
courtesy of The Lowell
Observatory, Arizona.)

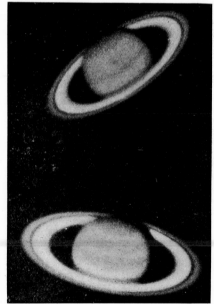

The planet Saturn. (By courtesy of
J. H. Reynolds, Esq., Birmingham.)

Type	Colour	Chief Spectral lines
O	Blue	Faint continuous background, lines of hydrogen, ionised helium, ionised oxygen and nitrogen.
B	Blue-white	Continuous background with dark[1] lines of hydrogen, helium, ionised oxygen and nitrogen.
A	White	Hydrogen lines, calcium and magnesium.
F	Yellowish White	Less hydrogen, more lines of metals.
G	Yellow	Hydrogen and many metallic lines.
K	Orange	Low temperature metal lines; bands due to titanium oxide and compounds of hydrogen and carbon.
M R N S	Red	Absorption bands or lines largely due to gases such as cyanogen and carbon monoxide.

New stars (or "novæ") in a gaseous nebulæ have a different kind of spectrum—discussed on p. 806.

The natural belief is that stars progress through the stages represented above. We might take it as reasonable that young stars are very hot, and contain simple atoms like those of hydrogen, helium, oxygen and nitrogen, and that, as they cool, the large metal atoms are gradually formed; then, at the lowest temperatures the vapour of the metals condenses and only gases like carbon monoxide and cyanogen give a spectrum.

The colour of a star is a guide to its temperature. Just as a piece of iron as it cools passes through white heat, yellow heat and red heat, so does a star. But it must not be taken that a yellow-

[1] Bright spectra llines come from glowing gas: dark spectral lines from a light shining *through* glowing gas.

hot star is at the same temperature as yellow-hot iron. Stars are made of gases which are very bad radiators of heat and light. A gas must be made far hotter than a solid in order that it shall glow. The surface temperature of the surfaces of various types of star are roughly:

Type	Temperature
B	23,000—15,000° C.
A	11,000—8,500° C.
F	7,500—6,500° C.
G	6,500—5,500° C.
K	5,000—4,500° C.
M	3,500° C. downward.

Some recent determinations would make the temperatures higher. As stars may reasonably be supposed to be getting cooler, this is another reason to suppose that they travel down the scale as they age.

We have seen already that we can find the brightness of a star and its distance. A good deal of information has been gained by studying the *real* brightnesses of the stars, not only their apparent brightness.

The sun is 92,800,000 miles from us. We know how much light from it falls on each square foot of the earth. We can thus calculate that the total light emitted by the sun is 3×10^{27} candles. Now Sirius is 500,000 times further away than the sun, so if it were as bright as the sun it should appear only $\dfrac{1}{500,000^2}$, that is $\dfrac{1}{25 \times 10^{10}}$ as bright. Actually, it appears twenty-six times as bright as this, and must be giving twenty-six times as much light as the sun. We can say that the real brightness of Sirius is twenty-six times that of the sun. This real brightness is commonly expressed as the *absolute magnitude* of the star which is the magnitude it would appear to have if it were 10 parsecs away.

This figure, the absolute magnitude tells us how bright a star really is. If we make a graph, showing the brightness of the stars

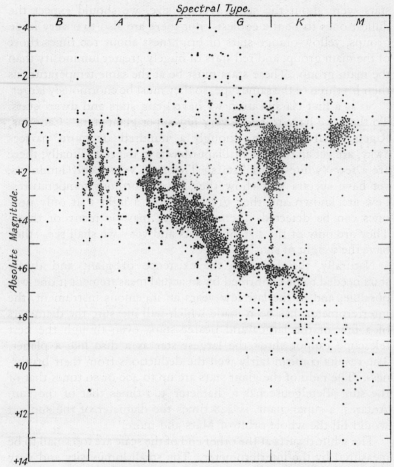

Fig. 431.—How the brightness of a star varies with its spectral type. (Courtesy of
Messrs. Edward Arnold & Co., and Professor Spencer Jones, from the latter's
General Astronomy (new edition.)

along one line and the type (B, A, F, G, etc.) along the other, we
can see that the brightness depends on the spectral type in a
peculiar way. The general trend is that the brightness falls off as
we pass from B stars to M stars. This is reasonable, for if the

stars were about the same average size, we should expect the dullest ones to be the coolest. But there are also two very large groups, yellow-orange stars of brightness about 100 times those of the main group, and red stars of hugely greater luminosity than the main group. These stars must be at the same temperature as their brethren of the same type, so they must be enormously larger.

So as a first classification we have giant stars and dwarf stars. To these we have to add a very few super-giant stars—Canopus, Rigel, Antares—which, though a hundred or more parsecs away, are yet among the brilliant objects in the sky. Finally, there are a few "white-dwarf" stars. These are very feebly luminous, yet have spectra that show they have enormous temperatures. Few are known and they give so feeble a light that only near ones can be detected. Actually, there may be many of them. They are only of the size of planets and yet—we shall see—they have the weight of suns!

Naturally, this belief in the existence of giant and dwarf stars needed to be confirmed by an actual measurement if one was possible, and in the last few years an ingenious instrument, the interferometer, has been made which will measure the diameters of a few of the larger and nearer stars, even though the best telescope cannot show the largest star as a disc like a planet. The results confirm fairly well the deductions from their brightness. The radii of the giant stars are up to 400 or so times that of the sun. Betelgeuse has a diameter 300 times that of the sun. Antares, a super-giant, is 428 times the diameter of the sun. It would fill the whole orbit of Mars and more!

The white dwarfs at the other end of the scale are too small to be measured by the interferometer. The small luminosity and very high temperature, though, proves that they are from a twelfth to a hundredth of the size of the sun. Almost the most extraordinary discovery of modern times was that these stars have the most gigantic densities. The brilliant star Sirius, and a white dwarf-star Sirius B form a double star, a sort of planetary system of two stars rotating round each other. Now, we have a pretty fair notion of the mass of Sirius from its brightness, spectrum and distance, so we can calculate the mass of its companion from its orbit and time of rotation. It weighs almost the same as the sun but has only about a thirtieth of the radius. Now, if it has $\frac{1}{30}$ of the radius, it has $\frac{1}{30} \times \frac{1}{30} \times \frac{1}{30} = \frac{1}{27000}$ of the bulk. So a cubic foot of Sirius B must weigh 27,000 times as much as a cubic foot of the Sun. The Sun is about 1.4 times as heavy as an equal bulk of water, so Sirius B must have a density of about 39,000!

The densest thing on earth is platinum, with a density of 24. Suppose you could get a bit of Sirius B, the size of a brick. It would weigh sixty-eight tons: a bit the size of a decent lump of sugar would weigh as much as a heavy man. Now, there is only one thing we know that is as dense as this—the nucleus of an atom. The nucleus of a radium atom is about 10^{-11} cm. in diameter and (supposing it spherical) about 10^{-33} cm. in volume,[1] it weighs 4×10^{-22} gms., and so its density must be about 4×10^{11}, vastly greater than that of the densest dwarf star. The conclusion we are driven to is that white-dwarfs are largely made of atoms from which the outer electrons have been torn, leaving a tightly jammed mass of nuclei with few or no electrons attached to them. This could hardly be believed without further confirmation, which has, however, been found. If the white-dwarf has this small size and huge weight the gravitational force at its surface will be gigantic. According to the theory of relativity spectral lines must shift towards the red in an intense gravitational field. This is found to be true for the light from Sirius B. The cause cannot be the Doppler effect caused by the star retreating from us, because Sirius, its constant companion, does not show the shift!

We want then some explanation of the existence of giants, dwarfs and white-dwarfs among the stars. If the explanation can also show how the flaring up of a faint star into a bright star or "nova" can occur and can also throw some light on the gaseous nebulæ, it will be worth hearing.

[1] It is obviously not correct to calculate volumes and densities as if the nucleus were a billiard ball: none the less, it is certain that the nucleus is enormously dense.

NOVÆ

Every now and again a small faint star increases in brightness by ten thousand- or a million-fold. The whole process may be over in a couple of days, though it may take two or three weeks. The brilliance then falls off again in the course of a few months, though not to its previous degree of faintness. The most brilliant nova on record blazed up till it was brighter than Venus. This happened 350 years ago, and the star is now so faint that it cannot be distinguished from other faint stars in the neighbourhood.

What is this extraordinary phenomenon? At one time it was thought that a nova was the result of a collision of two stars, or perhaps of a dark star becoming ignited, like a meteor in air, when it rushed into a dark nebula. But these theories are unlikely. First, novæ are much commoner than collisions are at all likely to be: secondly, they do not seem to occur only or especially in regions where dark nebulous matter is known. The spectrum of a nova shows by no means the changes one would expect if cooler stars were heating up as a result of the collision. In a recent nova (Nova Pictoris 1925) the spectrum altered very little in type. The only cause then for the brightening was a vast expansion. If a star is expanding its surface will be approaching the earth and the spectral lines will shift slightly towards the blue. This actually happens, and it is clear that a star, when it becomes a nova, practically explodes. Nova Pictoris swelled at the rate of 12,000,000 miles a day, till it became as huge as the super-giant Antares. After this expansion it seems that a thin layer of gas shoots on outward like a sort of surrounding shell, while the star itself gradually shrinks.

It is a disturbing thought that these outbursts of novæ are common enough to happen to each star once in 10,000 million years and, according to one theory, it is quite likely to happen to the sun, resulting of course in the utter annihilation of the earth, which would probably melt like a piece of sealing-wax in a blast furnace. Still, as far as the astronomer knows, it is by no means certain to happen, and in any event no more likely to happen in our lives than at any other time in the next hundred million years or so: so the chance of being burnt up by a nova is less than that of being killed by a lightning flash, which is not worth bothering about.

NEBULÆ

The gaseous nebulæ are of three kinds, dark nebulæ, diffuse nebulæ and what are misleadingly called planetary nebulæ. The dark nebulæ appear simply as patches of sky without stars. It is clearly a black cloud and not merely a place which lacks stars. It is believed that these are tracts of space containing fine dust, very thinly scattered. The diffuse or bright nebulæ are clouds of hazy light which cannot, however magnified, be resolved into separate stars. The most probable theory is that they are clouds of fine dust lit up by starlight. A bright nebula is then a dark one lit up by neighbouring suns. The "planetary" nebulæ appear to the telescope as little round discs. They are, of course, enormously larger than the stars, which never show any disc at all. Their spectra are rather like those of the hottest (type O) stars and indicate an enormous temperature, greatest towards the centre.

The centre of a planetary nebula is a star and seems to be a white dwarf. It seems likely that a nova—perhaps a very large one—would separate into a nebulous envelope and an extremely hot white-dwarf centre.

THE LIFE OF A STAR

No one has produced an entirely satisfactory theory of the way in which a star is born and dies. The account given here is based on the theories of Russell, Eddington and Jeans, and it is certainly probable that something like it is true. The factors which take part in the shaping of a star are the following.

Gravitation will tend to make a star contract. As the star

contracts, its potential energy is turned into kinetic energy: this kinetic energy can appear as rotational energy and as heat energy. The effect of its own gravitation on a star will be to make it *smaller, faster in rotation and hotter*. A star can only lose heat from the outside, consequently the inside must be vastly hotter than the outside, which itself may be at a temperature of 5,000 to 50,000° C. The centres of the stars then have temperatures probably about ten to twenty millions of degrees.

The effect of gravitation in decreasing the size of the stars is obviously opposed by other forces—otherwise the stars would shrink to nothing. The forces which tend to make a star expand are, first, the repulsion of the atoms (or ions, for atoms do not remain intact at these huge temperatures) for each other; secondly, the *radiation pressure*. We have seen that the light from the sun can push a comet's tail away from the earth. The interior of a star at a temperature of millions of degrees radiates so intensely that the blaze of heat, light, ultra-violet and X-rays drives the atoms and ions outward with a pressure up to several million tons per square inch.

These factors enable us to make up a story of an evolving star which agrees first with the sequence of spectral types (p. 108) and with the sizes and masses of the stars of different kinds. No one would maintain that this story must be true: at best we can say that there is no other story we can invent which fits the facts better.

The beginning of our history is a cloud of gas as big as our "local" universe or galaxy of stars. This gas was incredibly attenuated, far rarer than the gas in a good vacuum on earth. Probably some parts of it were gently moving. The effect of its own gravitation would be to make it contract, warm up and begin to rotate. The gas would also condense locally to form dense parts and rarer parts, the first beginnings of stars. As gravitational contraction continued and the rotation quickened the great mass would become flattened and disc-like, and the great spiral nebulæ (Plate XLI) are supposed to represent such a stage in the evolution of a universe of stars.

Turn now to the individual stars. Each is a vast hazy mass of gas steadily contracting, steadily rotating quicker and ever becoming hotter. A giant star of the M type is thus formed. As the temperature rises conditions in the centre of the star become such that hydrogen atoms (whose nuclei are single protons) build up into the more complicated atoms, releasing great amounts of energy. The star thus gets ever smaller and hotter, and successively goes through the types M, K, G, F, A, B, by which time the central temperature becomes so enormous that the hydrogen atoms of the stars begin to unite, forming atoms of heavier elements and producing great amounts of energy. The star then steadily radiates away its mass and so becomes smaller. The star becomes more opaque as it contracts and so the surface gets cooler and so the star steadily passes back from the B type, through A, F, G, K, M back to darkness and the state of a cold dead world. But there is another fate for a star. The temperature and pressure of the interior may be such that not only are the outer rings of electrons knocked off the atoms by the heat-jostling and radiation, but the innermost rings, too, leaving the bare nuclei. If the temperature suddenly reaches the point where this is possible, the effect will be as if the atoms had all been vastly decreased in size.

The result then of breaking up this final "K-ring" of electrons is to allow the star to contract enormously (for the nuclei are enormously smaller than the K-rings); this process of contraction also liberates energy, so the star probably explodes. There is an enormous rise of temperature: a nova is produced, a shell of gas being driven out and a white-dwarf being left. The white-dwarf is intensely hot—i.e., its particles are moving very fast—but it cannot radiate much because there are not many nuclei with electrons left on them to leap from orbit to orbit and cause radiation (p. 436). They, none the less, slowly cool and finally become yellow dwarfs and black dwarfs.

It is not known whether this outburst is an incident in every star's life, but it is at least probable. The rareness of the final product—white dwarfs—would be explained by their feeble

26*

light, which would render them visible only at short distances.

DOUBLE AND VARIABLE STARS

In our sketch of a star's career we have omitted a common occurrence—its splitting in two. Double stars are common objects in the sky. Many are accidental doubles—stars, dozens of parsecs apart, but happening to be nearly in the same line of sight. But these doublets are much too common to be merely chance neighbours, and a great many systems of two stars rotating round each other are known. In a few cases, where the stars are a good distance apart, they may have been neighbours always, but in most cases they are believed to have been formed by a star rotating so quickly that it broke in two. A star rotating slowly will be nearly a sphere; quicker rotation flattens it at the poles. If moving quicker still it will then form an ellipsoid rather like a Rugby football: this, if spun still quicker, will develop a waist and separate into two stars not very different in size. These will continue to rotate round each other or more accurately about their common centre of gravity in a period which may be months or hundreds of years. Sometimes we can see both stars of a pair— twenty thousand or so pairs are known—but, in many cases, we only notice the odd behaviour of the spectral lines.

When one star is at its nearest to us and the other at its furthest, neither will be approaching us or going away from us, but both will be travelling sideways. Consequently their spectra will be normal. But a quarter revolution later one will be coming and the other going, so the light from one will have its spectrum shifted towards the red, and the other will have its spectrum shifted to the blue. So, at this point, the lines of the light from the two will split or, if one star is much brighter than the other, as is usually the case, will shift to one side. So if we find a star has a spectrum of which the lines are *alternately* normal and shifted to one side or the other, we know it is a double. If the plane of rotation of a pair is in the line of sight there may be an eclipse once each revolution. The famous star Algol becomes fainter for five hours, then brighter for five hours. It becomes slightly brighter for twenty-five hours, then slightly duller, then brighter again for twenty-five hours. The cycle then repeats itself. Here we have a very bright star and a rather dull star revolving round each other. The light is brightest when both can be seen, a little less bright when the bright star eclipses the dull one, and much less bright when the dull one eclipses the bright one! Several other queer alternations in light are known, their character depending on the size, speed and relative brightness and plane of orbit of the pair.

The Cepheid variables, the light of which rises and falls regularly in periods of ten hours to a month, and whose brilliance and period are connected, have been mentioned in connection with the measurement of stellar distances. They do not seem to be double stars, for the light does not vary in any way which could be deduced from a pair of stars of the right size and brilliance. These stars are believed to be pulsating, swelling and shrinking alternately in periods of a few days. This is possible. Suppose a star was in any way forced to shrink. It would turn gravitational energy into heat energy. The heat would then make it expand out again. The enormous mass of the outer part of the star could not be stopped and would overshoot the mark somewhat until gravitational force pulled it back once more and the whole process started again.

THE AGE OF A STAR

The life of a star must be enormously long: for liquid water has existed on the earth for two thousand million years: consequently the sun can then have been giving out little, if any, more heat than now.

2,000,000,000 years is then only a short chapter of a star's life. We know, roughly, the mass of the giant stars and the mass of the sun. We also know about how much energy a star radiates. If the sun had started as a giant star and produced its energy by turning electrons and protons into radiation, it would have required some seven million million years to bring it to its present mass. At this rate the life of the earth since its crust has been formed is about $\frac{1}{3500}$th of the sun's life. If, on the other hand, as seems more likely, the sun has produced its energy by turning hydrogen into heavier elements, the quantity of these in the sun indicates that it can only have been radiating for the far shorter period, 150,000,000,000 years, only 15 times the earth's probable life. It is not at present possible to decide between these very different ages. The expansion of the universe can be calculated to have started about 150,000,000,000 years ago, and it is difficult to picture the sun and stars as having existed as such before this expansion. Other evidence points to the greater age as the more probable. The stars are always pulling on each other gravitationally. This will speed slow stars up, and slow speedy stars down, till finally a state is reached when all stars have the same energy of motion. This state has been nearly reached. A calculation shows that 5-10 million million years would be needed to bring this about. There are two other sound arguments for an age of some millions of million of years. Adopting the greater age for the sun, we might say,

Age of stars (and sun)	5,000,000,000,000 years.
Age of earth since its formation	3,000,000,000 years.
Age of oldest sedimentary rocks	1,750,000,000 years.
Age of life	1,000,000,000 years.
Age of Man	10,000,000 years.
Age of civilisation	10,000 years.

In comparison, we might say that if the sun has reached a late prime at sixty, the earth is but a fortnight old—life only four days. Man is an hour old or less, and civilisation but three seconds

But if we are to believe that time has flowed for ever, and will flow for ever, we are almost as far from a knowledge of the life of the Universe as were our forefathers. Our lives are as nothing in the history of a star: a star's life is as nothing beside Infinite Time. Whether in truth, Time and Space are infinite we cannot tell: perhaps it is impossible to know.

PART VI

LIFE

CHAPTER XXXVII

THE LIVING CELL

WHAT WE MEAN BY LIFE

WE are alive, and to solve the problem of life and its working would be the crown of scientific achievement.

Think of the things which we say are alive, men, beasts, birds, fish, insects, shell-fish, trees, grasses, mosses, seaweeds and the myriad microscopic creatures which inhabit every place where life can take a hold.

What have they in common that we call them living? To us, as men, the chief characters of Life appear to be motion and sensation, but these are not common to all living things. Thus plants do not move except to grow: nor have we any reason to suppose that they have anything akin to consciousness.

The true characters of life are the powers of growth and assimilation, reproduction and response to environment.

A living creature starts as a small object, takes in material, different from its own material, and changes this into its own substance, so growing larger, at least for a time. At intervals it generates new living creatures which ultimately become close copies of their parents. It responds to small changes in the outside world. That this is true of a man or a dog or a beetle is obvious. But consider some extremely simple creature such as the tiny green organisms (Fig. 515.1.) which often colour a pond green in a few days. This creature can turn carbon dioxide and water and the few metallic salts present in the pond water into a set of most complicated molecules—too complicated mostly for the chemist to unravel. It thus grows larger and after a few hours it develops a waist and splits into two smaller organisms like itself. It responds very sensitively to the conditions of the outer world. A minute increase or decrease of acidity in the water will cause it to die out. A proportion of copper sulphate of two or three parts per million of water will have the same effect. It will move to situations which are favourable to its growth and move away from unfavourable spots.

It is obvious, of course, that a brick or a tumbler of water is not living. Sometimes a crystal is said to approach living matter. A crystal of copper sulphate in a saturated solution of copper sulphate will grow certainly, but only by taking on its own material as an outer layer. It will not convert other substances into itself. It does not reproduce in any true sense. A piece might fall off and grow into a new crystal, but this would be an accidental occurrence, not a normal one in the existence of a crystal.

In what kind of material does life reside? It seems that life is invariably associated with the same type of chemical compounds. The only kind of matter which can live is a solution or suspension in water of proteins (p. 632), together with sugars, with curious fatty phosphorus-containing materials called lipoids, and with various inorganic salts. The secret of life is probably hidden in the intricate and tiny network of atoms which makes up the protein molecule.

It may be possible for life to reside in compounds of other elements than carbon, but on earth every living creature is made up of the same *kind* of material. Man, grass and bacteria must all contain proteins. The proteins in all three are different, but they are only different arrangements of the same couple of dozen of amino-acids (p. 632).

THE CELL

Living matter is never structureless—like a solution of sugar. As far as we know, life can exist only in a cell[1]—a minute compact

[1] Some of the viruses (p. 1016) which cause disease consist of particles so minute that we have been unable to study their structure. They *may* not be cells, but every other living thing from a cholera germ to a man is one cell or many.

assemblage of the materials of life. Every living thing is a cell or a collection of cells. The cell is the unit of life, as the molecule is the unit of matter.

The photographs of Plates XLIII, XLVII give some idea of the way in which living tissues of animals and plants are composed of cells. There is a very considerable likeness among cells. Whether the cell is a free-swimming animalcule in a pond or a part of a rose petal or of a philosopher's brain, it has certain necessary parts, though we understand very little about the way these work.

The cell is the unit of life: if we cut it to pieces, the pieces either cease to live or grow once more into complete cells. The cell is, moreover, an independent unit, for a single cell from the skin or muscle of a man, if supplied with the right medium to live in and the right conditions, can live and flourish and multiply apart from the creature of which it was once a part.

In Fig. 432 is drawn the idealised or pattern-cell. Individual cells may look very unlike it, because some parts are enlarged or diminished or of different shape, but every living thing is made of cells of this pattern.

Now let us look at the pattern-cell. Cells vary a great deal in size. It is not difficult to see the cells in a daffodil petal with the naked eye, while the smallest bacteria tax the resources of the microscope. We might consider our pattern to be about $\frac{1}{100}$ millimetre in diameter. This seems a contracted space, but it means that there may be in a single cell a hundred million most intricate protein molecules besides water, salts, sugars, etc. There is plenty of space here for the most complex of molecular machinery.

Every cell has two main subdivisions, the central nucleus and the surrounding "cytoplasm." Some bacteria, etc., appear to have no nuclei, but even in these there seems to be nuclear substance (recognisable by the way some dyes stain it) broken up and distributed through the cell.

Starting from the outside, there is often—but not always—a cell-wall. The tough woody substance of plants is the cell-wall made of cellulose. and the horny part of animal cells (e.g. of the skin cells) is also this outer cell-wall, which may be regarded as a non-living deposit or shell laid down by the living cell within. Inside this wall is the boundary of the living cell-substance, the plasma-membrane. This is a fairly firm or tough skin. It is probably not made of a different material from the cell-substance but may be more like the surface-tension "skin" (p. 90, Fig. 34) of a soap-bubble—a layer of molecules of different kinds, probably arranged in a regular way, e.g., with one particular group of atoms at the boundary. This cell membrane can evidently be altered in consistency from within: it allows certain kinds of molecules to enter the cell and keeps others out. All the cell's food must pass inwards through it, and all its waste products must pass out through it. It is sensitive: often a tiny alteration in the solution it rests in will make it swell or contract or alter in shape.

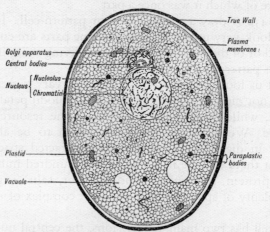

Golgi apparatus
Central bodies
Nucleus { Nucleolus
Nucleus { Chromatin
Plastid
Vacuole
True Wall
Plasma membrane
Paraplastic bodies

Fig. 432.—Diagrammatic section of a typical cell.
(Modified from Professor E. B. Wilson's *The Cell in Development and heredity.* (Macmillan, New York.))

Within the membrane is the cytoplasm, a clear viscid liquid, rather like very thin jelly, in which are suspended a vast number of very minute objects. The clear jelly-like solution always contains proteins, substances with extremely large molecules (egg-white and gelatin are simple examples), carbohydrates like glucose or cane sugar; semi-fatty substances like lecithin; all dissolved in a weak, salty solution much like diluted sea-water. This solution does not seem to be continuous like water, but to be divided up into a honeycomb of compartments, very much as the air in soap-suds is divided into a foam. The walls of the compartments are probably made of the "lipoid" fat-like material. All this is on a very small scale and to make it out taxes the resources of the microscope.

In this foam are suspended myriads of tiny objects, the smallest of which can only just be seen by the best microscopes: doubtless there are smaller objects which are invisible. The former are most easily seen by soaking the cell in solutions of certain dyes: these particles are then more strongly dyed than the rest of the cell. They are termed paraplastic bodies.

Very little is known about these tiny objects. Some are solid, some are oily droplets. Some of them are substances manufactured by the cell and kept ready for use. Thus a cell whose job it is to produce digestive ferments will store up tiny grains of a substance which, when the ferment is needed, disappears again. The granules are here probably a store of something which could be turned into "digestive juice."

Plant cells usually contain comparatively large bodies called plastids, which are little chemical factories in which sugar or starch or some such substance is made. The green pigment chlorophyll is contained in some of these.

Hollow spaces, "vacuoles," filled with liquid, are common in plants and single-celled animals. They may store up water, or act as "stomachs" for digestion, or as "bladders" for waste products. They are not in evidence in most animal cells.

Fibres are often visible and are probably the means by which a cell alters its shape: when a cell reproduces itself by splitting in two, these fibres are very evident. The cell also has a complicated arrangement of fine fibres, the Golgi apparatus, the object of which is not very certain but which may be concerned with the production of various chemical substances which the cell requires.

There is also a tiny granule called the centriole or central body from which may radiate a few fine fibres. These are called the aster, and will be mentioned again when we discuss the way in which a cell divides. A cell may contain small or relatively huge quantities of material it has made. A fat cell may appear as an oily drop which occupies almost the whole cell, crowding into a corner the living cytoplasm and nucleus which made it!

The nucleus is apparently the essential part of the cell in the sense that a cell without its nucleus cannot grow or assimilate or reproduce and very soon dies. The nucleus is a tiny hollow space surrounded by a firm skin, and filled with material more liquid than the rest of the cell. In it are skeins, knots and lumps of chromatin, a material which is recognisable because it takes up certain dyes very strongly. This chromatin mysteriously provides the *pattern* from which the whole animal or plant can be built up. It is the material which we receive from our parents and which makes up our heredity. Very little is known about what it is made of, but a great deal has been found about the way it behaves when a cell divides.

CELL COMMUNITIES

The single cell can perform all the functions of life. It can move, eat, digest, grow, multiply, perceive and move. But it is so small a creature as to be necessarily very helpless and almost wholly unintelligent. It cannot grow to any considerable size because it must breathe, eat and excrete through its surface. Suppose a cell were magnified a hundred times (from $\frac{1}{100}$ mms. to 1 mm. diameter), it would increase its surface $100^2 = 10,000$ times, but it would increase its bulk and weight $100^3 = 1,000,000$ times. So each bit of its interior would only get $\frac{1}{100}$th of the food and air it had before and so the cell would be very sluggish and ill-nourished. Consequently a single-celled creature as it grows becomes progressively less able to perform its functions; and therefore, at a certain stage, it must divide and make two smaller cells, each with a reasonable proportion of surface to interior.

A large single-celled creature is, therefore, impossible, and all animals large enough to be easily seen consist of many cells.

Animals and plants as we know them are a community of cells. It is possible to compare the State as a community of men with Man as a community of cells.

A man can perform for himself, rather inefficiently, the functions of feeding himself, clothing himself, housing himself and protecting himself. All this is much more efficiently done by allowing one man to grow food, another to make clothes, another to build houses: but in perfecting themselves in these trades men lose the faculty of performing their other functions. The single independent cell can grow a protective membrane, can gather food, can make ferments to digest it, can move, can respond to stimuli, can make another organism. But when many cells are combined into a single animal or plant, each perfects one aspect of its powers and to some extent loses the others. The skin cells become efficient in building a horny outer wall. The cells of the intestinal wall are expert in taking in food: the cells of the glands specialise in chemistry and make various compounds. The muscle cell specialises in movement and the nerve cell in sensitivity. All of them keep the power of division because the animal must grow. Some keep it always: others, like the nerve cells, are so specialised that when they become adult they lose their power of division. If a man of twenty destroys a nerve cell he can never grow another to take its place, though he may get another nerve cell to do its work.[1]

The logical way of studying living things would be to start with the simplest and work up to the complex ones. But simple creatures are often not easy to come by or examine. There is one creature with which we are very familiar indeed—man. We all have one specimen we can examine and mildly experiment on. So our first task shall be to study Man as a living creature and see how, from some thousands of billions of cells, all variants of

---

[1] A cut nerve may regenerate, for a nerve does not contain the essential part of the nerve-cell—the nucleus. The nuclei of the nerve-cells are in the brain and spinal cord: the nerve itself consists of long fibres spun out of their cytoplasm only.

the pattern we have studied, this body of ours is built. There are very many different kinds of cells in the human body: but they all fall into five great classes, which we may call skin cells, supporting cells (bone and cartilage), gland cells, nerve cells and germ cells.

HOW CELLS REPRODUCE

A single cell grows only to a certain size. When this is reached growth may stop or, alternatively, the cell may divide into two.

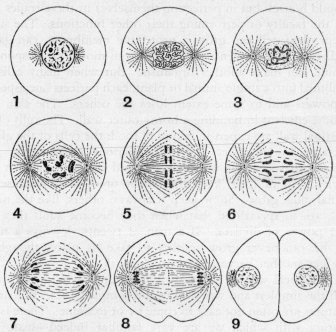

Fig. 433.—How a cell divides. (1) The chromatin in the nucleus organises itself into knots and clumps. (2) The chromatin forms long threads: the asters develop. (3) The threads becomes split longitudinally. (4) The chromatin splits into short stout lengths—chromosomes. (5, 6, 7) The threads of the asters draw half of each chromosome to opposite sides of the cell. (8) The new nuclei organise themselves: the cytoplasm develops a "waist." (9) The cytoplasm splits in two: the chromosomes disintegrate to rods and specks of chromatins. The two new cells will grow into replicas of (1). (After Wilson and others.)

As we shall see, each of us and every animal and plant started life as a single cell, and the many billions of cells in us have all been formed from this one. It split into two; these two then split into four, and this division and growth continued until we were full grown: and in some parts of our bodies continues till we die. This splitting and growing of cells is almost the most important thing in the working of a living creature, and it takes place in very much the same way in all living things, animals or plants. The process seems to be designed so that each of the two new cells shall have a nucleus exactly like the old one.

Fig. 433 shows rather diagrammatically the process of cell division. In Plate XLIII are microphotographs showing cell-division in the root of a plant and the testicle of a newt—two utterly different organisms. The process is evidently the same in each, and it is not difficult to pick out several of the stages of Fig. 433. We do not understand at all well what forces *cause* this division, but all our ideas about heredity depend on an understanding of the way it takes place.

The first thing that happens when a cell is going to divide is that the stuff in the nucleus we have called chromatin, instead of lying in fine scattered knots and threads and specks, begins to organise itself into larger masses. At the same time, the central body divides into two central bodies which move to the opposite sides of the nucleus and remain connected by a number of "rays" or fibres. Meanwhile, the chromatin has arranged itself into a long double spiral thread—the spireme—and this then rearranges itself into a number of short lengths called chromosomes. These are numerous in some animals and plants, and few in others. In man there are 48: in the cockroach there are 34, in the lily 24, in the fruit fly 8. These string themselves on to the rays which diverge from the two central bodies. Next comes the essential feature. Each chromosome splits along its *length*; then one half of each chromosome migrates to each aster. The half-chromosomes are evidently exact duplicates of the old chromosome from which they split. Consequently each aster receives *as many chromosomes as the original cell had*. The new sets of chromosomes combine again to a thread round which a new nucleus forms. The cytoplasm splits and two cells remain, just like the original but smaller! These then grow to full size, and then in turn divide.

CHROMOSOMES AND GENES

Now what are these chromosomes? Why is it that they are accurately divided between the daughter cells? Some creatures have very large chromosomes which we can see to be a string of rings or beads of chromatin, and we believe that all chromosomes have such a structure (Plate XLII). We can observe that in many cases if a particular "ring" or "bead" is missing, the animal is abnormal in some fixed respect. Each ring or bead[1]—we call them *genes*—gives the animal or plant a particular characteristic. A man is brown-eyed or red-haired or colour-blind because he has or has not a particular *gene* on one of his chromosomes. The set of genes are in fact a complete "specification" for an individual. It follows from the way cells divide that every cell in the body has the same outfit of chromosomes: and that, given a good microscope to display the genes—they are usually too small to be seen by any microscope—and the necessary knowledge to recognise them, we could tell from a single skin cell in his toe or muscle fibre in his arm whether a man was blue-eyed or red-haired or colour-blind! A male differs from a female in having (or in some species not having) a particular chromosome. Consequently a man or woman is male or female in every cell of his or her body.

A man or animal or plant carries his heredity in every single cell. A tiny piece of a begonia leaf will grow into a plant identical with the one the leaf was taken from. The leaf-cells had their sets of chromosomes, each a string of genes: the plant grown from it had an identical set in every one of its cells. The story of the ingenious arrangement by which sexual reproduction *com-*

---

[1] This is not quite accurate: for a characteristic hereditary factor may be due to the presence or absence of two or three of these rings. The chromosomes of a man may have fifty to a hundred thousand hereditary factors.

bines the mother's and father's chromosomes will be told in Chapter XXXIX. It is enough to remember that every cell of your body bears in it the exact copy of the set of chromosomes you received from your two parents: excepted only your germ cells—sperms or ova—which contain only half your set of chromosomes. The sperm or ovum which will make your son or your daughter *may* contain the genes which give you your large nose and your blue eyes, and omit the genes which give you your colour-blindness and bad temper. But it may equally well be the other way round. The supreme lottery of our lives lay in the manner of the selection, at our conception, of the half of our father's genes and of our mother's genes, which combined to make up the cell which developed into our adult selves.

CHAPTER XXXVIII

How a Man Works

THE HUMAN MACHINE

LET us now look into the working of the human machine; for the body may be regarded as a machine, even though we believe it to be more. The heart is a pump, the bones are hinged levers, and their working obeys the same principles as lifeless pumps and levers. Chemical reactions occur in the body and obey the same laws as they would in the test tube. If a pound of glucose combines with oxygen to give carbon dioxide and water in my muscles, glands and nerves, it produces just as much energy as it would if it were burnt in the kitchen stove. It has been found, then, that the changes which occur in the body can be explained in terms of physics and chemistry, if they can be explained at all; and accordingly science applies to the study of living matter the principles it has found to apply to dead matter.

It may not be possible to express life itself in terms of physics and chemistry—that is, ultimately, of moving electrons and atoms. Men of science, who have seen so many mysteries expressed in these terms, will press on in their investigation of life, and it is not for us to prophesy whether in time they will explain it or even create it.

BONES

A reasonably large animal cannot well support its own weight unless it has some stiffening tissues. A caterpillar gets on very well, in spite of being soft, because he is small. Considering a creature of some given shape, the stiffness or resistance to bending depends on the cross-section of the creature's body, which depends on the *square* of its length; but the bending force depends on its weight, which varies as the *cube* of the length. Consequently the bigger the creature is the 'floppier' it will be. Animals and plants, except some of the smallest, are provided with stiffening material. Vertebrates—mammals, birds, reptiles, amphibians and fish—have bones inside them. Arthropods—insects and crustaceans and the like—have a hard shell outside them. The only large and powerful creatures which have not either of these are the octopuses and squids, which (although they have an internal shell) depend for their strength and stiffness on a tough rubbery consistency of their bodies.

Man, then, has bones linked together by tough ligaments into a framework. These bones are the essential tools with which he performs his everyday actions, and they are the pegs on which he hangs his various specialised organs. To the bones are attached most of the engines of his body, the muscles, for the task of most of these is to move the bones.

Bone is a remarkable material. If an engineer were designing a man, he would use something a great deal stronger than bone to support him, probably stainless steel tubes; but a man must *grow* from a single cell and must deposit his bones from substances in his mother's blood stream or his own. So he must make them of some hard material which can be formed from food. Bone is laid down first as cartilage or "gristle." A rod of cartilage cells first appears where the bone is to be. Then, in the thick wall of cartilage, the hard strong material calcium phosphate appears. The new bone is also surrounded by a membrane (the periosteum) which lays bone over the outside. The cartilage is gradually transformed into bone, but the process is not completed in man before the age of 28. A large bone like a femur (thigh-bone) is hard like ivory outside, but inside has a sort of spongy network of bone. The spaces in this "sponge" are filled with bone-marrow, which is of two kinds—yellow marrow (largely fat) and red marrow, which is a most important kind of tissue, for it makes the red corpuscles of the blood. A bone is, then, a very efficient support, considering it is made of the rather unpromising materials calcium phosphate, which like most stony materials is rather brittle, and collagen, the tough material of gristle. Large bones are built both for lightness and strength, for they are tubes of hard heavy bone, supported by the light spongy bone within, which is disposed girder-fashion to take the strain.

A bone is a living material. It has tiny blood vessels running through it in every direction, as well as the bigger ones, leading to the marrow, which you can easily find in a beef bone. Under the microscope (Plate XLII), a bone shows myriads of tiny "canals," which carry nourishing fluids from the blood and a vast number of tiny cavities each containing a living cell: these communicate with each other and the canals by still tinier tubes.

Bone illustrates the remarkable power of repair, which some tissues possess and some—unfortunately—do not. A broken bone is the commonest of accidents. It is extremely instructive to see how the body sets about mending it.

When a bone breaks the blood-vessels are torn and a clot is formed round the ends of the broken bones. Within a few days cells begin to grow into the clot from all sides and gradually replace it by a gristly mass of cartilage. Then, just as in the growing child, bone is laid down in the cartilage, with the effect that the two broken ends are gripped by a lump of rather open-structured bone (callus), in the same sort of way as two ends of lead pipe are held together by a wiped joint of plumbers' solder. But now a new phenomenon appears. True dense bone begins to grow from under the membrane (periosteum) of the fragments: the growing ends meet and so truly unite the fragments into a single bone under the lump of callus. Next the callus is attacked by special bone-destroying cells and totally removed, leaving a perfect union. The body makes a temporary scaffold of bony callus while it is permanently repairing the broken bone.

Fig. 434 shows the bone-framework of the body. It is interesting to see how far each part is fitted for the work it has to do.

Start at the feet. The geological evidence shows that man has been much as he is for some ten million years. If, as we believe, his fore-runners were apelike, they did not habitually walk in this way. It is surprising that man in some ten million years has not become so well adapted to the erect position as the other mammals to the four-legged position which they and their ancestors seem to have held for some hundred million years. Man is not comfortable in the erect position for more than a few hours. His feet become tired: he wants to sit. Look at his feet (Fig. 434a). His weight rests chiefly on the heads of his metatarsal bones and his heel bone. His whole foot forms an arch held up by ligaments. It is not surprising that his whole weight, directed to flattening out that arch, sometimes succeeds in giving him flat feet. His foot, then, is rather an imperfect member. The ankle is

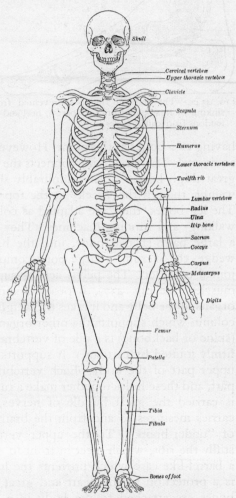

Skull
Cervical vertebræ
Upper thoracic vertebræ
Clavicle
Scapula
Sternum
Humerus
Lower thoracic vertebræ
Twelfth rib
Lumbar vertebræ
Radius
Ulna
Hip bone
Sacrum
Coccyx
Carpus
Metacarpus
Digits
Femur
Patella
Tibia
Fibula
Bones of foot

Fig. 434.—The human skeleton.
(Courtesy of Messrs. Longmans, Green, Ltd., from *Gray's Textbook of Anatomy*.)

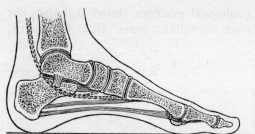

FIG. 434a.—The arch of the foot prevented from sinking by ligaments from fore-part to heel and by tendons from calf-muscles.

made up of 7 bones. It is a very complicated joint and allows movement in every direction. The ankle supports the two shin bones; the front one is the tibia, the back and smaller one the fibula. There seems no obvious advantage in having two bones at this point. However, all beasts have them and so do we! The knee joint connects the tibia with the femur, the great thigh bone. This is admirably shaped to take the body's weight, though the "neck" at the top is a source of weakness. The leg bones, then, are adapted as columns for support and as walking- and running-machines. They are jointed to the pelvis, a large basin-shaped bone, into the back of which fits, like a wedge, the sacrum, a large bone composed of several vertebræ joined together. The pelvis acts as support for many powerful muscles (see Fig. 437), it protects and supports the important organs of the belly and it takes the weight of the spine or vertebral column which supports the other organs. The vertebral column (spine or backbone) is a pile of vertebræ, short columns of bone, firmly jointed by cartilage. It supports the whole weight of the upper part of the body. Each vertebra has a hole in the hind part, and these holes together make a tube, in the cavity of which is carried the great bundle of nerves, the spinal cord, which carries messages to and from the brain and acts itself as a sort of "under-brain." To the upper vertebræ are jointed, rather stiffly the ribs, which meet in front in the breast-bone and make a barrel-like case which prevents the lungs from collapsing and is a protection to the heart and great blood vessels. The arm bones are attached to the body in a rather complicated way. The collar-bone is joined to the breast-bone at one end and the shoulder-blade (scapula) at the other. The arm-bones joint on to the shoulder-blade. This is why a fall on the arm often breaks the collar-bone, the weakest link between the arm and the body.

The arm is nearly a repetition of the leg. The humerus is rather like the femur in shape. The elbow, however, is not so much like the knee. There are two joints in the elbow, a hinge like the knee joint and a pivot which lets the two bones of the forearm (radius and ulna) slide over each other. This pivot enables you to turn your forearm. You cannot turn your shin at the knee because the tibia and fibula are tightly joined together. The wrist is not unlike the ankle, but while the hand has the same set of bones as the foot, they are jointed to allow of the freest motion instead of being bound by ligaments to give the greatest support. The key to the differences between an arm and a leg is that a common pattern has been modified to give the greatest freedom and range of motion to the arm and the greatest strength and stability to the leg.

The top vertebra is connected by a joint to the skull. The lower jaw-bone is hinged to the skull. For the rest, it is made up of no less than 21 bones rigidly joined together. These include the mouth (upper jaw) and nose bones and the cranium or brain box made up of thin bony plates. The skull is perhaps a rather vulnerable container for the most essential tissue of the body, the brain. Here is a respect in which man shows his character as a new-comer to the world. He has evolved a huge and very vulnerable brain, but he has not contrived to get a brain-box which will survive a moderate fall or a fairly vigorous blow.

The other animals with their smaller brains and large protruding jaws escape this danger.

JOINTS

The bony framework is bound together by ligaments. A joint is a very remarkable structure. An engineer might criticise it as lacking strength—no one dislocates his axles and pivots! None the less, the human joints are surprisingly strong: it is easier to break the femur than to dislocate the thigh. A joint,

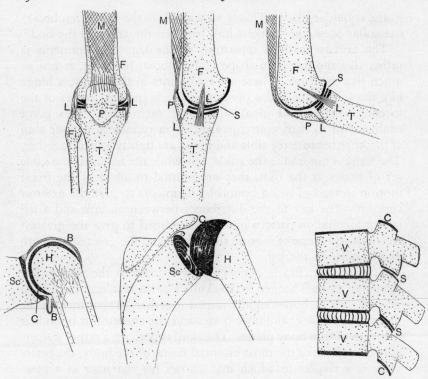

FIG. 435.—Typical joints. Bone is represented as dotted, the lining of cartilage as black. (Top) The knee; M, muscle; P, patella (kneecap); F, femur (thigh bone); T, Fi, tibia and fibula (shinbones); L, ligaments holding the joint together; S, lining cartilage. (Bottom left and centre) shoulder joint. Sc, scapula (shoulder blade); H, humerus (upper arm bone); C, cartilage. (Bottom right) spinal column. V, bodies of vertebræ joined by a non-sliding joint; C, cartilage; S, sliding joints, which also act as stops.

moreover, keeps itself well oiled and in repair for sixty or seventy years, which is a pretty considerable feat. A joint is made thus. The two bones have ends shaped to fit each other, and the surface of these is lined with cartilage. The joint is enclosed in a strong bag or capsule in which the ends of the bones move. This is clearly shown in the lower drawing of the shoulder joint (Fig. 435). This bag with other strong bands of cartilage (not

shown) keep the bones from coming apart. The walls of the
bag produce a lubricating fluid. The chief kinds of joint are,
first, ball-and-socket joints as in the shoulder and hip. These
can be moved in any direction. Hinge joints which can be moved
only in one direction are the commonest. The elbow, knee and
finger are good examples. The bones are moved by muscles
pulling on them. Muscles can only pull and cannot push, so
every motion involves at least two muscles, one to make the
motion and one to restore it. All bodily motions are adaptations
of the lever. The muscles give a very powerful pull for a very
short distance. The bones and joints are so arranged that the

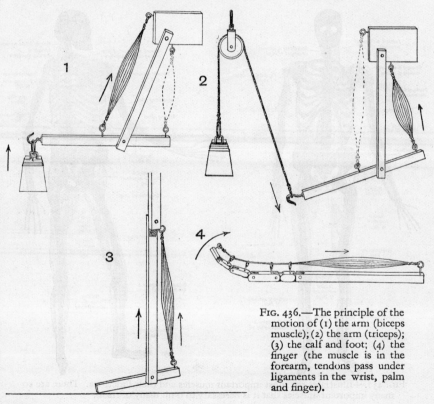

Fig. 436.—The principle of the
motion of (1) the arm (biceps
muscle); (2) the arm (triceps);
(3) the calf and foot; (4) the
finger (the muscle is in the
forearm, tendons pass under
ligaments in the wrist, palm
and finger).

short powerful pull of the muscle is converted into a much longer and much weaker motion. One of the simplest examples is to be found in the biceps muscle which flexes the elbow joint. A muscle has the power of contracting, i.e., becoming shorter and thicker. The biceps is attached to a part of the shoulder-blade above and to the forearm bone (the radius) below. When it shortens, it pulls the forearm and hand upward. Fig. 436 gives a few simple examples of how muscles and bones work as simple levers.

Our muscles are not only used for motion, but also to enable us to keep still! A dead man whose muscles are relaxed cannot be made to stand or sit. We keep our usual position by pulling

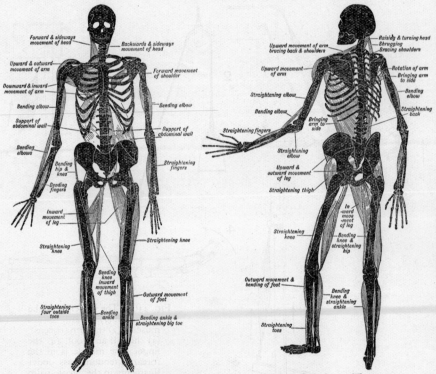

FIG. 437.—Illustrates the most important muscles and their functions. There are so many important muscles that it is necessary to omit many of them.

PLATE XXXIX

Halley's comet, 7th May, 1910. (By
courtesy of The Lowell Observatory,
Arizona.)

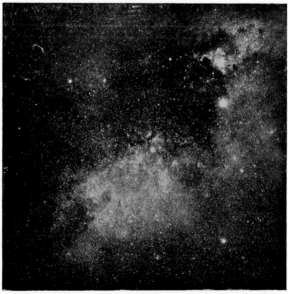

Part of the Milky Way. (By courtesy of The Yerkes Observatory, Wisconsin.)

PLATE XL

Dark Nebula south of Orion. (By courtesy of the Mount Wilson Observatory of the Carnegie Institution of Washington, Pasadena, California).

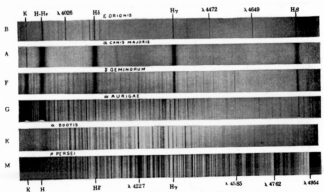

The spectra of stars of the B, A, F, G, K and M Types. (By courtesy of the Royal Astronomical Society.)

ourselves two ways at once. A tent pole can be kept upright by three or more stretched ropes pulling on it. This is how we support ourselves. Consider, for example, your head. If you fainted or even went to sleep, your head would fall sideways or forwards. It is kept up by several groups of muscles. Some stretch from the spine to the back of the head, so pulling it backwards, others from the lower vertebræ to the front of the skull pull it forward. Several large muscles also pull the skull sideways. At "rest" these muscles are gently pulling against each other and against the weight of the head. The head of man and of all animals is so balanced that it tends to fall forwards as, indeed, does the whole skeleton above the knees: consequently the muscles pulling it backward are very much stronger than those pulling it forward. Fig. 437 maps out the way in which the groups of muscles hold the body upright.

Look at the knee joint. If you fainted it would flex at once. A strong muscle, the quadriceps femoris (Fig. 437) attached to the top of the thigh-bone and the top of the shin-bone *pulls* the knee cap against the knee-joint and so prevents it moving forward. It cannot move backward on account of the way the joint is made.

Now look at the back-bone. A big muscle (sacrospinalis)—the bit we eat as the "eye" of a chop—is attached to the pelvis and pulls the spine backwards while the belly-muscles and, still more effectively, the weight of the body pull it forwards. A study of Fig. 437 will give a fair idea of the way the pulls of the groups of muscles balance and so hold the bones in the positions we demand.

There are, of course, many muscles which do other things than move bones. The action of swallowing, the churning of the stomach and intestine, the pumping of the heart—in fact almost every movement that takes place in the body, is the result of the contraction of a muscle-fibre.

There is nothing at all mysterious about the way muscles are *used*: in fact, it seems surprising that such simple devices are enough for the delicate manipulations of the human body. The wheel and the screw are not used anywhere in nature: the only

27

mechanical device employed is the lever. A very good reason for this is the difficulty of getting a supply of blood to a rotating wheel or screw; but in any case the way of nature is to work out the possibilities of one type of process in all its elaborate variations and leave the òthers alone. All the marvellous adaptations in animals and plants seem to have been brought about by an accumulation of little alterations: there has probably never been a sudden production of a wholly new type of creature or mode of working.

MUSCLE

But all simplicity disappears again when we turn to the muscle itself. This—the sole motive power of animals—is still a mystery, though much more is known about it than in former years. We know about as much of muscle—the human engine—as the worst type of car-driver knows about his engine. We know it needs fuel and air. We know what the fuel is and we know what the waste-products or exhaust are. We know what starts it moving and we know what it looks like. But as to how the machine works, we are still only hazarding guesses.

A muscle is a familiar enough object: a leg of mutton is a mass of muscle. You can see easily enough that it is composed of fibres all running in the same direction. When a muscle exerts its force, its volume does not alter much but its shape does, for it contracts, becoming thicker and shorter. You can see this easily enough on your own biceps or the muscles of your calf. The microscope shows that a muscle is made up of myriads of spindle-shaped muscle cells each too narrow to be seen. These may be about an inch long and $\frac{1}{500}$th inch wide. Each one has a nerve fibre attached to it, and if this nerve is stimulated by touching it or by electricity, the muscle cell shortens and thickens. Since all the cells in the muscle point the same way, the whole muscle shortens and thickens when the nerve-trunk leading to it (which has a nerve-thread for every cell) is stimulated. Leaving aside the question of how the nerve makes the muscle-cell move, let us examine more closely the muscle-cell itself. As example, we may take a voluntary muscle—moved at will—as distinguished from a muscle like those of the heart or the intestine, which do not obey our commands. All muscle easily divides into fibres: its fibrous nature is obvious in a tough steak. But it can further be divided up into much finer fibrillæ, which may be only $\frac{1}{100}$ mm. in diameter. These are the real units of muscle. Each fibre is equipped with a nerve thread which has the power to start it contracting, and the whole muscle is honeycombed with blood vessels running among the fibres to bring them their needed fuel and air. The muscle fibre has a number of nuclei dotted about it and can be looked on as a number of cells with their cytoplasm in common. This cytoplasm is the part which does the contracting. In a voluntary muscle, it appears to consist of alternate dark and light portions, which show up well in Plate XLIV. These are usually thought to be transverse bands, but some photographs indicate a spiral structure. The middle (dark) portion, when the muscle contracts, enlarges at the expense of the clear part; some liquid from the latter evidently flows into the former. The result, at any rate, is that each muscle fibre becomes thicker and shorter.

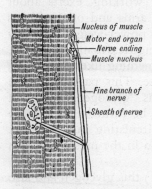

Nucleus of muscle
Motor end organ
Nerve ending
Muscle nucleus

Fine branch of nerve
Sheath of nerve

Fig. 438.—Muscle fibres much enlarged (see Plate XLIV).

No theory which will hold water has been produced to explain why the chemical changes which go on in muscle should cause this shortening. Nearly all the fundamental problems of the working of the body come down to the question, "What is going on in this cell?" and our answer is usually a declaration of ignorance. The cell is on so minute a scale that the chemist cannot apply his tests to different parts of it to find out the way the different chemical substances are distributed in it. In any event, he has no sensitive tests for small portions of individual proteins. The explanation of cell chemistry and with it of muscular contraction must await a new laboratory technique.

The muscle does work, and like every engine it must obtain its energy from somewhere. Its energy is supplied *ultimately* by turning sugar and oxygen into carbon dioxide and water; in fact, by burning sugar just as a steam engine burns coal. But the burning is done in a curiously roundabout way. It would not do for the muscle to liberate heat and turn this into work as a steam-engine does, for heat can only be turned efficiently into work if there is a fairly large temperature difference (p. 262) in the engine, and this would be impossible, for biological processes only work over a very small range of temperature. The muscle evidently turns chemical energy directly into work. Its efficiency is quite high, from 25% to 40%, always better than the best reciprocating steam-engine and sometimes as good as the best Diesel. Its power-weight ratio is poor. A man of 140 lbs. weight, rushing upstairs at his highest rate of working, exerts about 2 h.p.; deducting some 50 lbs. for his arms and other organs which do not contribute to the effort, his power-weight ratio may be 45 lbs. per h.p. A petrol engine may weigh less than 1 lb. per h.p.

The story of the muscle-engine is something like this. Food, when digested, gives the sugar, glucose. This passes into the blood and is partly stored in the liver as "glycogen," a sort of starch which at a moment's notice can be turned into glucose again. A small proportion is always circulating in the blood. Glucose is also partly stored as glycogen in the muscles (which may contain up to 1% of it).

The muscles, when resting, contain (1) this glycogen and also (2) a substance called phosphagen, creatine phosphate, which supplies "phosphate ions" when required and stores them when not in use. The muscle is now made to contract by a nerve-impulse. It gets the necessary energy by turning a molecule of glycogen, first into several molecules of another substance called hexose-phosphate, each of which then turns into two molecules of lactic acid and the phosphate ion.

This rearrangement of molecules liberates energy partly as work, partly as heat. This process, you will notice, uses up no

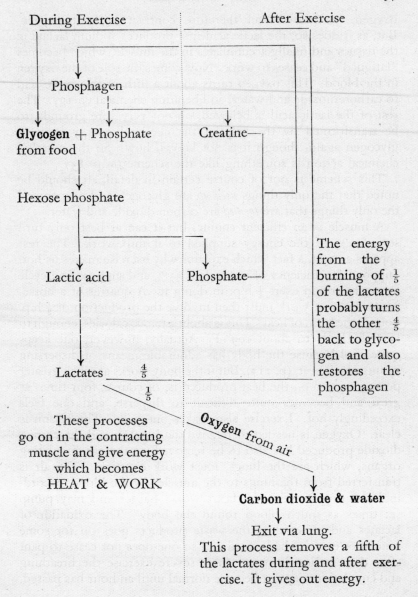

During Exercise | After Exercise

Phosphagen

Glycogen + Phosphate   Creatine—
from food

Hexose phosphate

Lactic acid   Phosphate—

Lactates $\frac{4}{5}$
$\frac{1}{5}$

The energy from the burning of $\frac{1}{5}$ of the lactates probably turns the other $\frac{4}{5}$ back to glycogen and also restores the phosphagen

These processes go on in the contracting muscle and give energy which becomes HEAT & WORK

Oxygen from air

Carbon dioxide & water
Exit via lung.
This process removes a fifth of the lactates during and after exercise. It gives out energy.

oxygen. A muscle can therefore contract without oxygen. But, as it does so, the lactic acid first produces sodium lactate in the tissues and finally accumulates in the muscle, which becomes "fatigued" and ceases to work. Now comes the rôle of the oxygen in the blood. This oxygen turns about a fifth of this lactic acid to carbon dioxide and water, so liberating chemical energy. The rest of the lactic acid is believed, on not very sure grounds, to be transformed by the help of the chemical energy back to glycogen again, though it is not known how. So the muscle's chemical action is something like the scheme on p. 837.

This scheme is not of course certain in detail. It should be noted that the only things *used up* are glycogen and oxygen and the only things that are *formed* are carbon dioxide and water.

A muscle is an efficient engine, but it can at best only turn some 40% of the energy supplied to it into work. The rest appears as heat, a fact which explains why exercise makes us hot. Suppose the efficiency of a muscle is 33% and suppose you cycle for an hour and exert $\frac{1}{4}$ h.p. in doing it. A quarter of a horse-power hour of work must then involve the production of $\frac{1}{2}$ h.p. hour in the form of heat. This is about 330,000 calories, enough to heat the body to about 109° F. Actually, however, one keeps quite cool because the body has admirable means of dispersing its unwanted heat. (p. 117). But if the body works at much greater power, say 1 h.p., the heat produced is, of course, four times as great and becomes quite difficult to disperse, and one feels exceedingly hot. Exercise also makes one pant. The reason is clear. Oxygen is needed to remove the lactates; and the carbon dioxide produced has also to be removed, so the gas-circulating organs, which are the lungs, must work overtime. The air is transferred from the lungs to the muscles by the blood; accordingly, during exercise the heart works harder and may pump six times as much blood round the body. The oxidation of lactates and removal of the waste products goes on for some time after exercise has ceased and so one does not cease to pant after the exertion is over. After severe exercise the breathing and circulation may not become normal until an hour has passed.

The oxidation too does not begin until a certain amount of lactate has accumulated; consequently, in a hundred yards sprint race, the runner often does not begin to pant till he has reached the tape.

THE BLOOD

The muscles, in order that they may work, need glucose to replenish their glycogen fuel, and oxygen to oxidise their lactates. These are supplied by the blood. Every single cell in the body needs a supply of oxygen, a supply of food material and a service for removal of waste products. A small single-celled animal has so small a bulk compared to its surface that it can take in dissolved food and oxygen and excrete its waste products all through its skin. Consider a small spherical bacterium about $\frac{1}{1000}$ mm. in diameter. Its bulk is given by $\frac{4}{3} \times \frac{22}{7} \times \left(\frac{1}{20,000}\right)^3$ cubic centimetres, approximately 0.5×10^{-12} cc. Its surface is $4 \times \frac{22}{7} \times \left(\frac{1}{20,000}\right)^2$ sq. cm. $= 3 \times 10^{-8}$ sq. cm. So it has about 1700 square centimetres of surface for every cubic centimetre of bulk. Now consider a man. His bulk may be about 70,000 ccs. and his surface about 12,000 square centimetres. Consequently he has only about one-sixth of a square centimetre of surface to every cubic centimetre of bulk. This shows clearly that a large assembly of cells must find a way of supplying air and food to each of its members. The animal's answer to the problem is to dissolve air and suitably prepared food in a liquid and pump this through a set of pipes to every cell in the body.

This liquid which brings air and food to the cells is the blood. The blood of many lower creatures is colourless. This means that it does not contain the substance hæmoglobin which is the chief carrier of air. Consequently, the only creatures with colourless blood are small—their relatively big surface allowing them to take in air mainly through their exterior. The insects have a system of air-pipes ramifying through their bodies, to bring oxygen to their muscles. They can therefore exist with a colourless blood which carries little oxygen.

The human body contains about a gallon and a half of blood—say 15 lbs. Everyone knows its appearance—an opaque red liquid, brilliant red when taken from an artery, purplish red when taken from a vein. The microscope shows that it is a clear yellowish liquid (plasma) in which float a great number of very minute bodies. Most of these are round flat discs—red corpuscles. These are the air carriers. In addition, there is a much smaller number of colourless cells of several kinds (Plate XLIII).

If blood is centrifuged (p. 166) the heavier red corpuscles settle out and leave the clear yellowish liquid in which they were floating. This liquid is a watery solution of many substances, but chiefly of certain proteins. One is fibrinogen, which makes blood clot after it has been shed; the others, serum-globulin and serum-albumin, are rather like white of egg. The blood plasma contains about 8% of these.

The fibrinogen is made in the liver—no one knows what parts of the body make the rest. Why should the clear part of blood need to contain these proteins? First of all, the big molecules of proteins contain groups of atoms which behave as acids and other groups which behave as alkalis—consequently they combine with and neutralise (p. 579) any acid or alkali which might enter the blood and would seriously derange the body's working. Secondly, fibrinogen clots when blood is shed and so makes the blood stanch the wound from which it is escaping. There are a few families in which is handed down the defect of having blood which clots very slowly or not at all. The unfortunate hæmophiliac or "bleeder" may lose his life from the smallest cut, which continues to ooze for hours. Some of the royal families of Europe have this unfortunate heredity, which will be mentioned again in connection with inheritance. Clotting must not of course occur within the normal body and so a rather complicated chemical mechanism prevents this. If blood is drawn from a wound, it seems that minute bodies in it called platelets break up and liberate an enzyme (p. 863) *prothrombin*. This with calcium ions gives another enzyme *thrombin* which turns the soluble protein fibrinogen into fibrin, which does not dissolve in water and consequently appears first as a dark-red jelly and finally as a tough clot. The red colour is only due to entangled corpuscles: pure fibrin is yellowish. The difficult problem is why the blood clots when shed but does not clot in the body. It seems that the "platelets" from the blood are the deciding factor: some workers believe that the liver produces a substance which prevents clotting: others, that something which emerges from tissues when they are wounded starts it. Clotting can take place in the body if it has been internally injured or bruised.

The plasma of the blood, besides these proteins, contains always a little glucose, some 0.6% of salts—mostly common salt, a trace of calcium compounds and a certain small proportion of waste products like urea. It always contains some dissolved carbon dioxide produced by the activity of the cells, and it is the plasma which carries this carbon dioxide to the lungs. The blood, too, carries food material from the digestive tissues to the rest of the body, so during the digestion of a meal it may contain other substances, such as fat globules.

The red corpuscles of the blood are not true cells, for they have no nuclei. They are made in the red marrow of the bones. They bud off from the walls of the veins in the marrow and start with large nuclei like ordinary cells. They lose these nuclei as they grow older and become tiny slightly hollowed discs about $\frac{1}{130}$ mm. in diameter. Every cubic millimetre of normal blood contains about 5,000,000 of these discs, so a man's whole body contains about thirty billion corpuscles. A corpuscle lasts only about a month and then disintegrates. Every day a billion corpuscles are made and destroyed in your body. Each corpuscle carries a little of the red substance hæmoglobin. It is a very complicated substance containing a little iron. Its importance is that if supplied with plenty of oxygen—as in the lungs—it combines with it and becomes bright-red oxyhæmoglobin. This travels round

27*

in the blood via the arteries to the tissues—glands, muscles, nerves, etc. A tissue is always using up oxygen, consequently there is never much free oxygen in a living tissue. The oxy-hæmoglobin then gives up its load of oxygen in the tissues and turns back to the purplish hæmoglobin. The blood returns through the veins and takes this back to the lungs to receive another dose of oxygen.

The spleen is an organ as big as a fist (p. 878) and receives an artery from the aorta and sends a vein to meet the portal vein. It acts as a reservoir of red corpuscles. If the body receives a serious demand for more oxygen the spleen contracts and sends these corpuscles out into the circulation. Thus the spleen contracts when violent exercise is taken or in cases of carbon monoxide poisoning when blood corpuscles are put out of action (p. 590), or in anæmia, when they are too few. It also seems to be able to break up old corpuscles and set the iron in them free so that new ones can be made.

Extensive bleeding is of course a very serious condition: its ill effect is largely due to the reduction of oxygen supply to the heart and brain. The most effective treatment for loss of much blood is blood transfusion—taking blood from a healthy person and transferring it to the patient who needs it. When this was first practised, it was noticed that sometimes it was a spectacular success and sometimes a complete failure—often killing the patient. It was discovered that some specimens of blood when introduced into a foreign bloodstream *agglutinated*; that is to say, the red cells joined together into masses which blocked the smallest blood vessels and set up a disastrous set of symptoms. It was finally worked out that there were four groups of people with different kinds of blood. They are called Group AB, Group A, Group B, Group O.

Group AB's blood is agglutinated by the blood of every group but its own. Group A's blood is agglutinated by the blood of Groups AB and B. Group B's blood is agglutinated by the blood of groups AB and A. Group O's blood is not agglutinated by any blood. Accordingly, Group O people are the only ones who can give blood to anyone without danger of causing agglutination.

Everyone belongs to one of these groups. They are hereditary and the way they are inherited has been worked out. Thus, the children of two Group O people *must* belong to Group O; the children of two AB's *cannot* be Group O's . . . etc. On the Continent the blood-group of a child is accepted as evidence of his parentage. Thus, if Emma, who is of Group O, has a baby which is of Group AB, Charlie, who is also of Group O, cannot be the father! For some reason, the British courts have only very recently begun to accept this evidence. It cannot prove that anyone *is* the father of a child, but it can prove that certain people are not. A very interesting development is the study of the relative numbers of the Groups in different races. The table which follows shows how this varies in certain races:

Race.	Percentage of			
	Group O.	Group A.	Group B.	Group AB.
Western Europeans	46	43	7	3
Eastern Europeans (Hungarians)	33	37	19	12
American Indians	91	7	1	0
Indian natives	32	18	42	8

From evidence of language, it has long been believed that the gypsies came from India. Here is the percentage of Hungarian gypsies in the Groups:

Group O	Group A	Group B	Group AB
33	21	39	8

The great number in Group B shows that they are closely connected with the Indians and not with the Hungarians.

The white blood corpuscles are very different from the red. They are much fewer, averaging about one to every eight or nine hundred red. They originate in the tissues outside the blood-vessels and migrate through the walls of the tiny capillaries. They behave like independent living creatures, and indeed look and behave very much like a very small amœba (Plates XLII, XLIII). They can migrate about the body and their chief function is to engulf any foreign particles and digest them. They destroy bacteria or dead tissue cells and, in fact, are the defenders and scavengers of the body. Suppose you prick yourself with a dirty pin. The skin, when injured, produces something which makes the little blood-vessels widen—the region round is engorged with blood and a red spot is seen. The bacteria contained in the dirt on the pin-point begin to multiply. The white cells, attracted apparently by the chemical substances exuded by the injured tissue, migrate to the scene of action, devour the bacteria and the dead cells. The spot is cleaned up and returns to normal. If much dead tissue and bacteria are present, great numbers of white cells are brought up. They die, after digesting some of the dead tissue and bacteria, and a yellow liquid—pus—consisting of dead white cells, dead and living bacteria, etc., forms in the wound and constitutes an abscess, which, as it is a stronghold of bacteria, requires to be emptied by opening it up freely.

One more constituent of blood requires mention—the platelets, which are very small bodies about a third of the size of a red corpuscle. There should be about one platelet per twelve red corpuscles. Not much is known of them; but they are believed to help the blood to clot.

THE CIRCULATION

The blood is forced through every organ of the body. Even when we are at rest, the whole of our blood passes through the heart every minute. When violent exercise is being taken, as much as eight gallons a minute may pass through the heart. An ordinary kitchen tap turned full on gives only four gallons a minute, a fact which gives a picture of the rush of blood which swirls through our arteries. The object of the blood is to take food and air to the cells of muscle and bone and every other tissue. The blood cannot do this, unless it is brought very close to the cells. This is accomplished by means of a meshwork of minute tubes called capillaries which permeate every tissue in the body. These, invisible to the eye, are the place where the work of the blood is done. The great blood-vessels, arteries and veins are only pipes to lead the blood where it is wanted. These capillaries are often finer than a hair and the blood works its way along them but slowly; there are, however, such an enormous number of them that the blood passes quite quickly through such an organ as a big muscle. Fig. 439 gives some idea of the circulation through the hand. The blood from the heart travels *via* various arteries (lighter shading) to the wrist. These break up

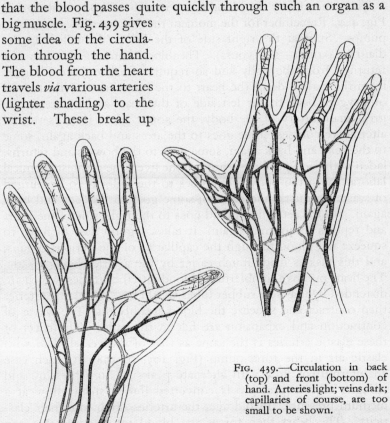

FIG. 439.—Circulation in back (top) and front (bottom) of hand. Arteries light; veins dark; capillaries of course, are too small to be shown.

into smaller arteries: these branch into smaller arteries still, till the blood is lost to sight in a maze of tiny tubes far too small to be drawn. Here it does its work of imparting air and food. The tiny capillaries converge and join to form larger tubes which again converge to form the veins (darker shading) which carry the blood back to the heart. This story is true of all the organs in the body; each has an artery which branches out into capillaries which rejoin to form a vein.

The general way the blood flows round the body is shown in Fig. 440. Remember for the moment that the heart is *two* separate pumps. Start at the right side of the heart (the fellow in the diagram's right—not yours). The blood entering this has just returned from the body and so requires fresh oxygen. It goes from the right side of the heart to the lungs, and, with its load of oxygen, back to the left side of the heart and thence to the great main artery of the body, the aorta. Here it takes several alternative courses: some goes to the arms and back again, some to the head and back again, some goes to the bowels and returns, laden with food products, through the liver, the greatest chemical laboratory in the body; some goes to the kidneys to be purged of waste products, and returns; some goes to the legs and back again. All the returning blood goes to the right side of the heart and repeats its journey again. It takes a good deal of force to squeeze the blood through the capillaries of the various organs; and this task is made much easier by the arteries being elastic. The heart pumps a tumblerful of blood into the arteries, which are distended by it as soft rubber tubes would be. The elastic arteries then contract and squeeze the blood steadily on. The waves of contraction and expansion are felt in the pulse. The effect of these elastic arteries is the same as that of the vessel filled with elastic air in the force-pump (Fig. 103, p. 198); in each case an intermittent flow with alternate peaks of high pressure and troughs of low pressure is converted into a steady flow at a medium pressure. In old age, the arteries often lose their elasticity. The heart then forces the blood into a tube that can stretch but little; consequently, a big pressure of blood is produced and a little blood-vessel may burst. If this occurs in the brain a "stroke" is the result. An artery, then, is a very strong elastic tube made up of several coatings. The biggest artery in the body is the aorta: it may be about as large as a table-napkin ring. The femoral artery which supplies the leg may be of about a centimetre bore.

Veins are very different from arteries. They are not having blood forcibly driven into them, for the effort of driving the blood through the capillaries exhausts all the force the heart originally gave it. Consequently thick, strong tubes are not needed for veins and thin and weak ones suffice. The blood

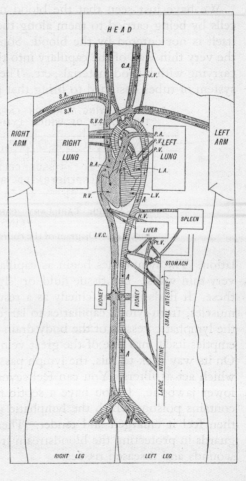

FIG. 440.—General circulation of blood as set out on p. 846.
R.A. right auricle (atrium);

R.V. right ventricle
P.A. pulmonary artery
P.V. pulmonary vein
L.A. left auricle
L.V. left ventricle
A. aorta
C.A. carotid arteries
S.A. subclavian artery
I.V.C. inferior vena cava
S.V.C. superior vena cava
S.V. subclavian vein
J.V. jugular vein
Pt.V. portal vein

In addition to these are shown the blood supplies to liver, spleen, intestinal tract, kidneys, legs.

returns through them, partly because the heart sucks it out like a pump, but more because they are furnished with valves which will let blood run towards the heart but not away from it. When you move, your muscles contract and squeeze the veins that lie near them; this pushes the blood towards the heart, for it cannot go the other way. Exercise is therefore directly helpful to the blood-circulation.

We have just seen that the blood nourishes and aerates the cells by being carried to them along the capillaries. But the cell itself is not entered by the blood. Some plasma filters through the very thin wall of the capillary into the tissue cells and spaces, carrying with it food materials, etc. The lymphatics are a separate system of tubes designed to bring that plasma back to the circu-

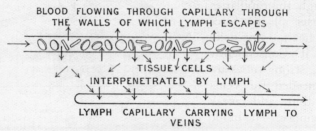

FIG. 441.—Diagram of the course of lymph.

lation. The lymphatics begin as capillaries with blind ends and very thin walls. The tissue fluid or "lymph" can pass through these. It finds its way, chiefly as a result of the pressure of the muscles, from lymph capillaries to larger and larger vessels. All the lymphatic vessels of the body drain into one large one which empties itself into one of the great veins at the root of the neck. On its way back to this, the lymph passes through lymph glands which act as filters. You can feel several as lumps under your lower jawbone. If you have a septic tooth, the lymph from it contains poisons which the lymphatic gland filters out: you can then feel it enlarged and tender. These glands are great safeguards in protecting the bloodstream from infective matter from wounds and diseased tissues.

THE HEART

The heart, mechanically speaking, is a pair of very simple pumps. In principle it is simply two bags which contract and

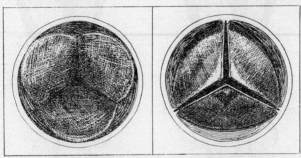

FIG. 442.—One of the valves of the heart (diagrammatic). Blood can flow only in the direction of the points of the flaps.

expand and which have an inlet and outlet valve, made of flaps of tissue so arranged (Fig. 442) that the pressure of blood in one direction forces them apart and in the other direction forces them together. Fig. 443 shows how it works. At stage one, the heart is expanding; the inlet valves are open. Blood is pouring into the muscular ventricles on the right side from the veins; on the left side from the lungs. At stage two the heart has begun to contract from the top downwards. The top portions, the auricles, are contracting and forcing the blood they contain into the ventricles below which have not yet begun to contract. At stage three the ventricles of the heart contract: the blood is forced through the outlet valves. From the right side, it goes to the lungs; from the left side to the whole of the rest of the body. While this is happening, the auricles are expanding again and receiving a fresh charge of blood from the veins. So the *action* of the heart is a wave of contraction starting (stage two) at the auricles and passing down (stage three) to the ventricles, followed by expansion (stage one). Before we consider how this

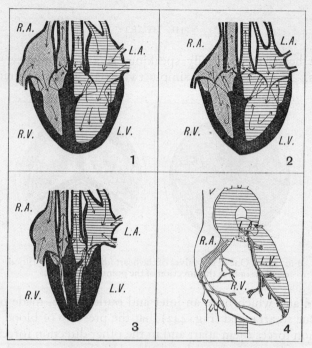

Fig. 443.—The heart. (1) Before contraction has begun (diastole): heart filled with blood. (2) Contraction beginning. Inlet valves just closing (presystole). (3) The heart fully contracted: blood driven out through the outlet valves (systole). (4) External view showing the coronary arteries which supply the heart itself with blood. R.A. Right auricle (atrium). L.A. Left auricle. R.V. Right ventricle. L.V. Left ventricle.

movement is controlled, we may reflect that the heart muscle itself must have a blood supply! Little side arteries, the coronaries, take a supply of blood from the aorta; this blood permeates the heart muscle and is returned to the right side of the heart.

The heart's most remarkable feature is that it may work apparently continuously for a hundred years. There is a little space of rest between each wave of contraction. This seems to be rest enough for it. The incredible reliability and lastingness of a pump made of such apparently unsuitable material must always be a source of wonder to the engineer.

The rate of supply of blood has to be adjusted to a very variable demand. The oxygen which is consumed by the body may vary from half a pint a minute at rest to nearly a gallon a minute when violent exercise is being taken. The only way to get this oxygen to the tissues is to increase the blood-flow. Accordingly, the body has to regulate the speed of the heart-beat very delicately. Two nerves, the vagus and the sympathetic, control the heart. The former slows the heart, the latter accelerates it. Both nerves arise from centres in the lower part of the brain, which is the centre of control. Everyone who has been in love or frightened knows the effect of the brain on the heart; but control is automatically going on even when we do not realise it. The pressure in certain of the arteries and veins affects nerves which can control the heart. Thus, if the blood pressure becomes low in the carotid sinus, a little pocket in the big artery of the neck, a nerve automatically transmits an impulse to the heart which speeds it up and so makes the blood pressure higher again. This process keeps the heart going at a steady rate. Now suppose you begin to take violent exercise. Your muscles, as they contract, squeeze the blood back through the veins far more rapidly than before. The pressure in the great returning veins increases. This operates a nerve mechanism which stimulates the heart to beat faster and circulate the blood more rapidly. A great deal is known about the way the wave of contraction spreads down the heart, but it is perhaps more important to doctors than to ordinary readers.

AIR SUPPLY

The supply of oxygen to the muscles and other tissues is, then, regulated to some extent by the rate of working of the heart, but the control of breathing by the acidity of the blood is a still more delicate adjustment. The apparatus for supplying air to the body is the lung. Blood supplied to the lung by the right side of the heart has its purplish hæmoglobin changed in the lung into bright red oxyhæmoglobin. The left side of the heart pumps this to the body. In the tissues where there is very little oxygen, the oxyhæmoglobin breaks up and gives oxygen. This dissolves in the plasma of the blood and diffuses through the capillary walls to the cells that need it. These make the oxygen combine with various chemical compounds and so get the energy they need. The final products of the cells' action are water and carbon dioxide. This latter dissolves in the tissue fluids, diffuses back through the capillary walls to the blood stream and is carried back with it to the right side of the heart and thus to the lungs again. Here the blood gives up some of its carbon dioxide and takes up more oxygen.

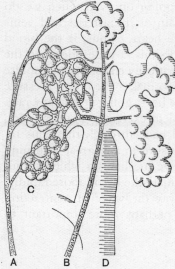

A   B   D

Fig. 444.—Diagram of the structure of the lung magnified 125 times. A. blood vessel carrying oxygenated blood to the left side of the heart. B. blood vessel bringing de-oxygenated blood from the right side of the heart. C. air cells and capillaries. D. bronchiole or tube bringing air.

The lung, then, is designed to bring the blood into close connection with a supply of air which must of course be continually changed as the blood removes oxygen from it and puts carbon dioxide into it. Air can enter the body by mouth or nose. The nose is the organ designed as an air-entry: the mouth is for use only when large air supplies are needed. The nose opens into a large narrow irregular chamber lined with warm, moist membrane. Consequently the air passing through it is warmed and moistened and to some extent freed from dust. It then passes down a wide tube—the trachea or wind-pipe—through the voice-box. This tube divides into two bronchi leading to each lung. The lungs are like an inverted tree whose trunk is the windpipe, whose branches are the smaller air tubes and whose leaves are little air-cells or alveoli. The branching structure is well seen in the X-ray photo of Plate XXVI. The walls of these air-cells are honeycombed with blood-vessels, with very thin walls of living cells through which oxygen and carbon dioxide can pass. All that separates the blood from the air is the very thin wall of the capillary and the membrane over it. Fig. 444 shows single grape-like bunches of air-cells magnified about 125 times: the piece shown would be $\frac{1}{50}$ in. long, just big enough to be seen. The whole lung is made up of these branching air-tubes and air-cells and the network of blood-vessels leading to them and lining them.

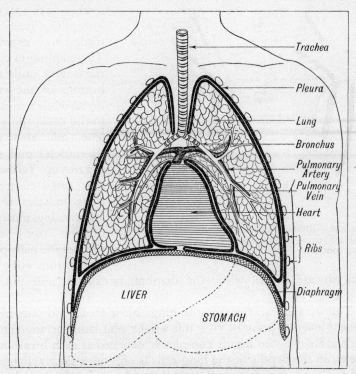

FIG. 445.—The lungs in position in the body.

Fig. 445 shows how the lungs lie in the body. They are completely enclosed in a case with a movable wall. The top of the case is the ribs and the bottom is the diaphragm—a big sheet of muscle which divides the body in two. This case is lined with a membrane called the pleura. This passes round the heart, which lies between the two lungs; the membrane in this part is called the pericardium. The lungs lie in this case and fill it completely. Now this case can expand and contract. When it expands, the lungs must expand too and so take in air; if they did not, a vacuum would be left between them and the lining of the case, and the air pressure in the lungs would instantly expand them. When the case contracts, air is forced out of the lungs.

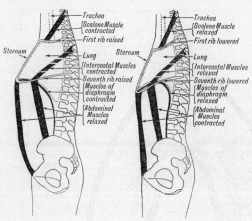

Fig. 446 shows how the "case" is made to expand. The diaphragm contracts and pulls the bottom of the case down while a muscle in the neck, the scalene, and also the rib-muscles pull the top ribs up. To make the case contract, these muscles relax and the big muscles of the front and sides of the belly pull the bottom edge of

FIG. 446.—Illustrating the manner in which the muscles (black) cause the lungs (left) to expand and (right) to contract.

the rib-case down, while the diaphragm expands and pushes the lungs up.

This arrangement makes the lungs blow air in and out; from the engineering point of view it is a poor ventilating arrangement, for the air is by no means completely expelled at each breath and the air in the depths of the lung cells is only quite slowly changed. None the less, it answers very well, for the very moderate design is made up for by the marvellously delicate adjustment of the speed of breathing. In the lower part of the brain is a "centre" or regulator, which in some way which is not understood responds to the acidity of the blood. If the blood is more acid than usual, the brain centre sends a message *via* a nerve to the diaphragm muscle, which is thereby made to contract more strongly and work the lungs more efficiently. If the blood is less acid (more alkaline) than usual, the centre sends an order to the diaphragm to make the lungs work more gently.

The differences of acidity it responds to are extremely minute, and even the most delicate electrical apparatus would not always detect them. Now, when cells of any kind in the body work extra hard, they produce more of the acid gas carbon dioxide. This dissolves in the blood and *makes it slightly more acid*. This makes the respiratory centre in the brain send its order that the lungs shall be speeded up. Consequently the air gets changed oftener in the lungs and so is fresher and contains more oxygen. The blood therefore gets more fully charged with oxygen. This is carried round to the hard-working tissues which need it! The extra ventilation in the lungs also gets rid of the extra carbon dioxide. This mechanism is quite easy to test.

I am now going to make myself breathe violently in and out as hard as I can for a quarter of a minute. This will ventilate my lungs and fill them with fresh air. The carbon dioxide of the blood will be rapidly carried away instead of accumulating in the air-cells and partly redissolving in the blood. My blood acidity will therefore be lowered and I shall breathe less.

I find that after this bout of forced panting I breathe so feebly and shallowly that very little air enters and leaves my lungs at all for the next minute or so. The opposite effect is used in artificial respiration. If you make a feebly-breathing man breathe a mixture of, say, 95% oxygen and 5% carbon dioxide, his blood becomes full of carbon dioxide and more acid than usual. The brain centre makes his lungs speed up and breathe deeply, and so he gets a good supply of the oxygen he needs: the extra carbon dioxide is quite harmless.

The defect of this regulator is that a lack of oxygen does very little to stimulate breathing. If you are at the top of a mountain where the air-pressure is only, say, ten inches of mercury, your lungs contain only a third of the oxygen they would at ground-level. But your blood contains no more carbon dioxide and is therefore no more acid, so breathing is very little faster.[1] The result is that the blood lacks oxygen. A moderate height, say 14,000 feet, where the air is about $\frac{1}{2}$ of the ordinary pressure, will make many people become blue (the colour of the hæmoglobin in deoxygenated blood) and often faint. A stay of several days causes a number of unpleasant symptoms—mountain sickness—occasioned by lack of oxygen. Now the city of Quito in Ecuador is at an altitude of 11,000 feet. Its citizens are quite happy in the rarefied air, though the casual visitor becomes exhausted after walking a few yards. They have adapted themselves to the lack of oxygen by growing many more red-corpuscles in their blood. They make up for the poor supply of oxygen which each corpuscle can carry away from the thin air, by using more corpuscles. They also produce more alkaline urine. The effect of this is to make their blood a little more acid, so that the carbon dioxide produced by quite a small amount of exercise will make their blood acid enough to cause their brain centre to increase their rate of breathing.

This compensation is only possible to a limited extent. The top of Everest, where the air pressure is less than one-third of the value of sea-level, certainly represents a region to which no one could become acclimatised. On Everest, at 28,000 feet, it was found that from seven to ten breaths had to be taken for every step forward and upward. Probably the most lofty village in the world is Aullagas, in Bolivia, 15,700 feet above sea-level.

High pressure of air is another thing which is not reckoned with by the body. The dangers of high pressure air are chiefly felt by divers. Divers at considerable depths can be enclosed in a pressure-proof-jointed metal case, in which air at the ordinary

[1] There is a compensation which increases breathing slightly and temporarily.

pressure can be supplied to them and they can work at great depths. Unfortunately a man in such a casing can do but little work. Plate XLV shows a man in such a diving dress.

The ordinary diving dress is flexible and a diver enclosed in it can do a fair amount of work. But he has got to breathe compressed air. What would happen if a diver, receiving air at ordinary pressure of 15 lbs., were lowered to a hundred feet depth, where the pressure is 60 lbs. per square inch? The pressure of the water would force the dress against his body, for there would be a pressure of 15 lbs. per square inch in his lungs and 60 lbs. per square inch outside, giving the same effect as a 5-ton lorry balanced on his chest. Consequently his chest would collapse; the blood too would be forced up into his head. This chapter of troubles is prevented by pumping air into the dress till it escapes through a valve. It does this, of course, as soon as its pressure is higher than that of the water. The diver is now reasonably comfortable. He has a pressure of 60 lbs. per square inch inside him and outside him. But the more a gas is compressed, the more soluble it is in a liquid. Consequently the diver's blood becomes charged with oxygen and nitrogen from the air. If he is then suddenly hauled to the surface, he is taken with agonising pains and is in serious danger of death. The reason is that when the pressure is lowered the dissolved gases appear in the blood and tissues as tiny bubbles, just as bubbles appear in soda-water when the bottle is opened and the pressure released. These bubbles may block blood-vessels and even prevent the heart from working. A diver therefore has to be slowly raised up from the bottom so that the pressure may fall very slowly, and his lungs may discharge all this dissolved gas. If he has been working at great depths, say, 200 feet, it may be necessary to take from two to four hours to raise him. This long wait in the cold and heavy dress makes diving very trying indeed. The best remedy found is the Davis decompression chamber. Fig. 446a shows this. The diver can come up and climb into it fairly soon. He can then take off his things and close the chamber, which remains full of compressed air. The chamber is hauled on deck and the

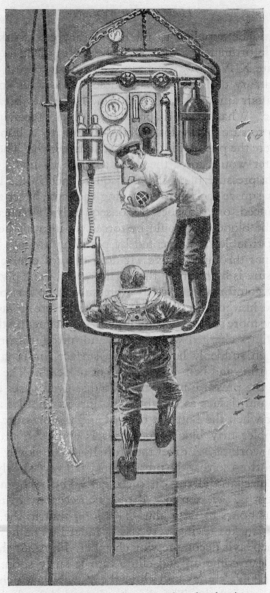

FIG. 446a.—The Davis decompression chamber in use.
(Courtesy of Messrs. Siebe, Gorman & Co., Ltd.)

diver can remain there fairly comfortably while the pressure is steadily and gently lowered.

We have seen how the blood acts as a carrier of air. Next in importance, perhaps, is the way it acts as a scavenger and a carrier of water and of foodstuffs.

THE SCAVENGING SERVICE

The kidneys have the task of removing from the blood all waste substances and of keeping the amount of water and salts in the blood always the same by removing any excess. They are absolutely essential organs: if both are completely put out of action, life cannot continue for more than a few hours.

Fig. 447 and Fig. 454 show how they are situated. The great main artery of the trunk sends off branches to carry blood to each kidney: the purified blood returns to the great main vein. The kidney removes waste matter in the form of a weak solution—urine. This passes down two tubes—ureters—to the bladder, a tough muscular bag which collects the urine to be discharged at our convenience. The problem of the kidney is to remove dissolved waste products from the blood without removing the useful proteins and sugar and without removing too much salt. The task of "pinching the sugar

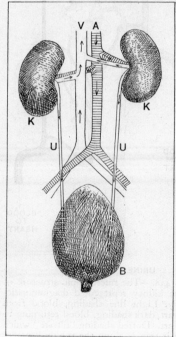

FIG. 447.—The apparatus for keeping the composition of the blood constant. A. aorta bringing blood from the heart. K. kidney. V. vena cava returning blood to heart. U. ureters carrying urine to B bladder.

out of a Scotchman's tea" is proverbial. His kidneys have to
pinch the waste products out of his blood!

The method of the kidney is this. First, it runs a supply of
blood through capillaries enclosed in a membrane which will let
all molecules and ions through *except* the big protein molecules.
Thus, it gets from the blood a solution containing water, glucose,
salt, waste products, etc. Then it takes the valuable glucose,
most of the water and some of the salt back and puts it once
more into the blood. Look
at Fig. 448. The blood comes
in from the artery, which
splits into thousands of tiny
branches. Each of these ends
has a tiny tuft of capillaries
enclosed in a bag made of
"filtering-membrane." Here
a certain amount of water
and of everything else in the
blood except protein oozes
through into the "uriniferous
tubule" (Fig. 448). This
solution is just the same as
blood without the corpuscles
or the proteins. We call it
"filtrate." This filtrate travels
along the minute uriniferous
tubule. This is lined with
cells which take out of the
filtrate most of the water, all
the glucose and some of the
salts. These cells hand their
water, sugar and salt back
to the blood in the capillary,

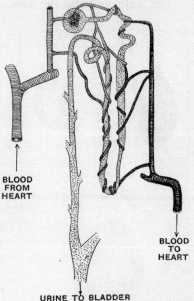

BLOOD
FROM
HEART

BLOOD
TO
HEART

URINE TO BLADDER

Fig. 448.—The microscopic structure of
the kidney represented diagrammatically. Light line shading, blood from
heart, dark shading, blood returning to
heart. Dotted shading "filtrate" which
as it travels along the tubule becomes
urine.

which after leaving the filtering chamber meanders around
and among the tubules till it finally joins with its fellows and
reaches a vein. The liquid which leaves the tubule is called urine.

The tubes' powers of gathering sugar from the filtrate are limited: if the blood contains a great deal of sugar, some will get out in the urine. This happens in diabetes, a disease in which the body cannot use up sugar.

The waste products which pass off in the urine are chiefly the remains of protein molecules which have been destroyed. These are chiefly turned into carbon dioxide which passes out by the lungs, water and urea which has the structure $H_2N - CO - NH_2$.

It is essential for the working of the body that the blood should always contain nearly *the same proportion of water molecules to "solid" molecules or ions.* If you drink half a gallon of fresh water, you will get rid of it all again as urine in two or three hours. But if you drink half a gallon of weak salt water, you will retain most of it, for both water molecules and salt ions are being taken in together.

The sweat glands filter from the blood a watery solution but, unlike the kidneys, they have no mechanism for putting any of the substances dissolved in this fluid back into the blood. Their function is simply to keep the body cool (p. 117) and not to keep the blood's composition always the same. If a man, such as a miner, does hard and heating work in a damp, poorly ventilated atmosphere, where evaporation is slow, he loses huge quantities of sweat in which is dissolved a great deal of salt. Loss of water makes him thirsty, so he drinks water. The net result is that he is putting in fresh water and taking out salt water; so he steadily loses salt. His blood becomes much more watery than usual and the result is apt to be very painful cramps. The discovery that this can be entirely prevented by drinking slightly salted water instead of fresh has abolished this painful and dangerous ailment.

DIGESTION

Air, food and water are the three things the body requires from outside. The first we have discussed. It is our next task to see how the body takes the miscellaneous collection of goods from the grocer and butcher and pastry-cook and turns them into flesh, bone, blood and fuel.

What can we eat? Only animals and plants in some form or another. We shall see that all useful foods are converted by digestion into sugars, fats, and amino-acids, in which form they enter the blood stream. Our foods, then, fall into three classes, though most of the things we eat are mixtures of all three.

First are *carbohydrates* (p. 614). These are changed into simple kinds of sugar (chiefly glucose) by digestion. Sugar and starch are the important carbohydrates. They include all sweet and starchy foods; bread, cakes, potatoes, rice, honey, sugar are all carbohydrate foods, though all except pure sugar contain a little protein.

Fats are familiar enough. Butter, oil, and the fat of meat are obviously fatty foods, and most cakes and almost every cooked dish contain fat.

Proteins are chiefly contained in the "lean" of meat, in fish and eggs. Seeds like wheat, peas and beans contain a fair proportion.

The body uses carbohydrates chiefly to produce glucose which is the energy-producer of the body. Fats are also energy producers. Proteins are necessary to make the amino-acids which we build into other proteins, which are the chief substances from which our bodies are built.

Surveying the problem, the chemist does not so much wonder at the complexity of the digestive organs, as at the fact that the task of turning foods into flesh can be done so rapidly and without the use of high temperatures or powerful reagents. The chemist can break down food into simple molecules in much the same way as the body does. He cannot, however, build the simple molecules up into complex proteins.

All the breaking down of food in the body is done *by combining it with water*. Thus, starch is a long string of twenty-five or more glucose molecules, each lacking two hydrogen atoms and an oxygen atom. By combination with water it breaks into smaller and smaller lengths. It first of all forms the fairly large molecules of the gummy substances called dextrins, then pairs of linked glucose molecules which are the sugar "maltose," and finally single molecules of glucose.

All sugars are broken down by the action of water into simple sugars of formula $C_6H_{12}O_6$ not, however, always identical with glucose.

Fats are broken down in much the same way. If we write the formula of a fat and that of three water molecules, we can see that water will split it into glycerine and a fatty acid (p. 333).

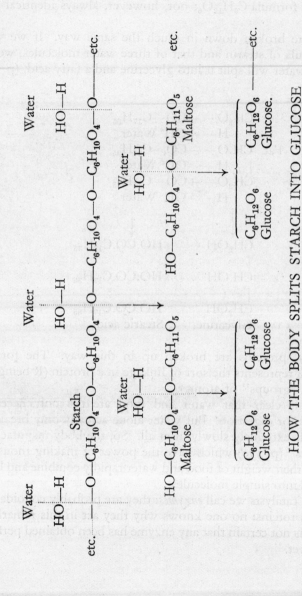

HOW THE BODY SPLITS STARCH INTO GLUCOSE

All sugars are broken down by the action of water into simple sugars of formula $C_6H_{12}O_6$; not, however, always identical with glucose.

Fats are broken down in much the same way. If we write the formula of stearin and that of three water molecules, we can see that water will split it into glycerine and a fatty acid. (p. 628)

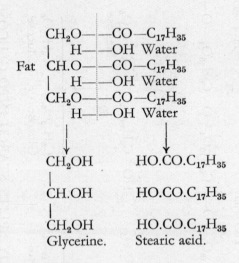

Finally, proteins are broken up in this way. The formula on p. 634 represents the sort of linkage in a protein (R being one of many "groups" of atoms).

So it is clear that water and food are the only necessary materials for digestion. But water alone actually only breaks up foodstuffs extremely slowly, if at all. So, the body manufactures "catalysts" (p. 570) which have the power of making thousands of times their weight of food and water rapidly combine and break up again into simple molecules.

These catalysts we call *enzymes*: they are probably colloidal and may be proteins: no one knows why they act in this remarkable way. It is not certain that any enzyme has been obtained perfectly pure as yet.

PLATE XLI

The Great Nebula in Andromeda. An island universe.
(By courtesy of The Yerkes Observatory, Wisconsin.)

Spiral Nebula. (By courtesy of
The Mount Wilson Observatory,
California.)

PLATE XLII

A portion of one of the giant chromosomes of the salivary glands
of *Drosophila*. One or more of the bands probably correspond to
each hereditary factor. (By courtesy of Messrs. Julius Springer,
Berlin, and Herr Klaus Patau.) (Greatly magnified.)

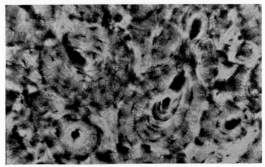

Microphotograph of a section of bone.

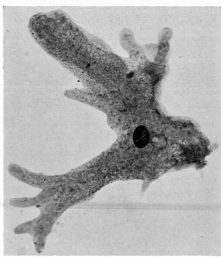

The amœba, a protozoon ($\times$ 135).

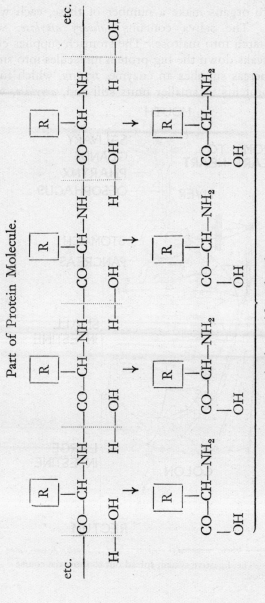

Part of Protein Molecule.

Amino-acid molecules

HOW PROTEINS AND WATER ARE SPLIT INTO AMINO-ACIDS
(The process actually proceeds by several stages)

28

The digestive organs make a number of these, each with a particular job. The saliva contains *salivary amylase*, which starts to turn starch into maltose. The stomach supplies chiefly *pepsin* which breaks down the big protein molecules into smaller units. The pancreas supplies an enzyme, *trypsin*, which further breaks down proteins to smaller units still and, *amylase*, which

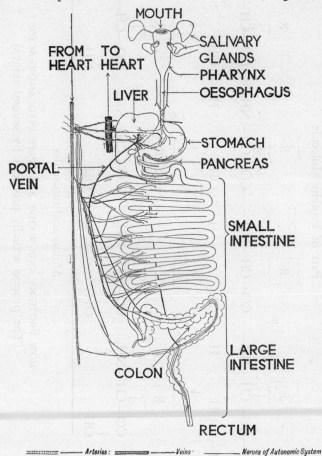

FIG. 449.—The digestive system spread out to show the course of the food.

turns starch into malt-sugar, and *lipase*, which splits fats into glycerine and fatty acids. The intestine secretes an enzyme, *erepsin*, which finishes the smashing up of the protein molecules and also three ferments, *invertase*, *maltase* and *lactase*, which break up cane sugar, malt sugar, and milk sugar into their simplest forms. It also supplies some *lipase* for fat-splitting.

Water and these nine enzymes are the tools used by the body to tear its large foodstuff molecules into units which it can build up into its own substance.

Bull's muscle (beef) differs from man's muscle chiefly in the way the small amino-acid units are arranged to make its vast protein molecules. When we digest beef, we split up its protein molecules and rebuild the fragments to make ours, in the same way that we might pull down a factory and build a cinema with the bricks. Enzymes are fussy about the conditions under which they work. The digestive apparatus of the body is designed first to provide the enzymes, then to give the right conditions of time, warmth, acidity, stirring etc. to make the enzymes work: then finally to absorb the products of digestion and send them to the parts of the body which can deal with them.

Look at Fig. 449, which shows the whole digestive system very much spread out. Fig. 450 gives a better notion of how it is fitted into the body. It is a tube with one opening at the mouth and the other at the anus. Nothing can get into the blood stream from the tube except through its walls. Its contents are really outside the body and an internal wound which lets the contents escape into the body is a very serious matter. Let us now follow a meal of roast beef and cabbage and potatoes through the body. The meal contains protein (muscle fibres etc.), fat, carbohydrate (potato-starch) and some cellulose (in the cabbage and potato-cell walls): so it is really representative of food in general.

The food is taken into the mouth and chewed. The fact of taking anything savoury into the mouth sends a nerve message *via* the brain, causing the salivary glands to pour out a liquid which is nearly all water with a little salt and a little of a starch-digesting enzyme. Chewing breaks food up into little fragments:

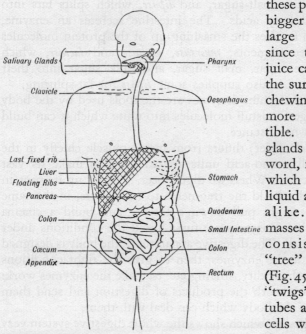

Salivary Glands

Clavicle

Last fixed rib
Liver
Floating Ribs
Pancreas

Colon

Cœcum
Appendix

Pharynx

Oesophagus

Stomach

Duodenum
Small Intestine
Colon

Rectum

FIG. 450.—Showing the digestive system in place in the body.

these possess a much bigger surface than large lumps and, since the digestive juice can only get at the surface of food, chewing makes it far more easily digestible. The salivary glands deserve a word, for all glands which "secrete" a liquid are somewhat alike. They are masses of tissue consisting of a "tree" of fine tubes (Fig. 451). The outer "twigs" of these tubes are lined with cells which build up the enzyme amylase. The gland has also cells which secrete slippery mucus which assists in the swallowing of food. When a nerve message informs it that saliva is required, the cells send quantities of water and dissolved amylase down the "branches" into the larger "trunks" or ducts which open into your mouth.

Swallowing food is an intricate business. Between your mouth and your gullet is your windpipe and it is most undesirable that food should get into this. Quite a complicated series of movements are needed. First, the chewed food is rolled into a ball and by lifting the front of the tongue, the ball is shifted to the back of it and then thrown back, so that it hits the back of the throat, which has a nerve connection which sets a number of different actions going. The nose is closed by the soft palate, so

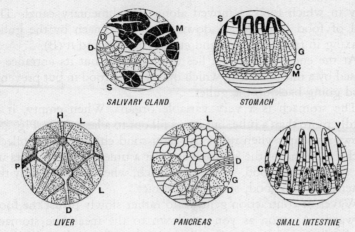

FIG. 451.—The microscopic structure of some parts of the digestive
system.
SALIVARY GLAND. M, mucus-secreting cells; S, enzyme secreting
cells; D, D, ducts.
STOMACH. S, mucus-secreting membrane; G, tubes lined with cells
secreting enzymes (pepsin); C, layer of circularly disposed muscle fibres;
M, layer of longitudinally disposed muscle fibres.
LIVER. P, branch of portal vein; H, branch of hepatic vein; L, lobule
of liver cells; D, branch of bile duct.
PANCREAS. G, cells secreting enzymes; D, branch of duct; L, islet of
Langerhans producing insulin.
SMALL INTESTINE. V, villi absorbing food products; C, cells
secreting enzymes; black dots, mucus-secreting cells.

that food cannot get into it. The soft front part of the throat in
front of the tonsils closes round the food like a pair of curtains
and so prevents it going back to the mouth. The voice-box is
closed and breathing prevented, so that food cannot enter the
lungs. The epiglottis (visible in Fig. 459), a flap of tissue behind
the tongue, which forms the front edge of the beginning of the
gullet, is pulled over the windpipe and so guides the ball of
food into the top of the gullet (œsophagus). This is a muscular
tube which automatically swallows
anything that touches it. Swallowing
is a "peristaltic" wave which should
be understood because it is the only

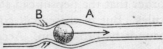

FIG. 452.—Peristaltic motion.

way in which food is moved along the alimentary canal. The ball of food is propelled down to the stomach by the gullet relaxing in front of it (A) and contracting behind it (B).

At the end of the gullet lies the stomach, but its entrance is closed by a muscular ring which opens to let food in but prevents food going back up the gullet.

The stomach is a very variable organ. When empty, it is hardly more than a tube, but it can fill out to a large bag. Fig. 449 shows its shape when full. The semi-solid chewed food collects in the near end of the stomach and for a time the saliva splits up the starch in the food. But the stomach, when stimulated by the distension with food, starts to contract.

Waves of contraction gently and rather slowly thrust the food forward. As soon as you sat down to the meal, the stomach received news from the brain of an impending job and started to produce its own secretion "gastric juice." It is lined with cells, which are illustrated in Fig. 451, and which produce gastric juice and mucus. The gastric juice is mostly water but contains, firstly, two enzymes, pepsin and rennin and about $\frac{1}{2}$% of hydrochloric acid, without which pepsin will not do its job of splitting protein molecules into smaller but still quite large fragments. Rennin's task is to coagulate milk. The "rennet" used to coagulate milk for making junket is an extract of calves' stomachs! The food is churned in the stomach for a long time—two to five hours. At the end of this time, most of the insoluble protein of the meat has been changed into a solution of somewhat simpler molecules (peptones). About a half of the potato-starch has been changed to malt sugar. The fat has been melted and has been churned into small droplets, but otherwise not affected. The stomach then forces this liquid through another "gateway" —the pylorus—into the small intestine.

In the stomach, the food is made very acid, presumably, in order that the pepsin can start the breaking up of protein molecules. But in these acid conditions, the fats, starch and sugars cannot be broken up. Accordingly, when the food passes into the 20 foot tube of the small intestine, a new type of digestion is started. The wall of the intestine pours out an alkaline liquid containing several enzymes. The large gland, called the pancreas, also discharges an alkaline liquid containing enzymes. This neutralises the acid from the stomach and starts a new type of digestion. At the same time , the liver sends a supply of the greenish or yellowish liquid "bile." Bile is produced by the liver, partly as a way of getting rid of waste products which the liver removes from the blood: but it has a most useful function in digestion. It lowers the surface tension (p. 90) of fats tremendously and so allows the watery liquid digestive juices to wet the fatty surface and so digest it more quickly.

The result of the action of water, aided by the enzymes, is to turn all the carbohydrates into glucose and simple sugars like it, all the fats into glycerine and fatty acids, which in presence of bile are appreciable soluble in water. The proteins give soluble amino-acids. So, everything in the food is dissolved in water except what cannot be digested. The chief thing which we cannot digest to any appreciable extent is cellulose, the cell-walls of plants. This passes on unchanged.

All this time, the intestine has been actively moving. Either it sends peristaltic waves (Fig. 452) to push the liquid along or it churns it by "segmenting." A length of intestine, divides itself into lengths, like a string of very plump short sausages. Ten seconds later, it unsegments and then constricts itself again, so that the narrow places come where the wide ones were before. This stirs the liquid.

All the while digestion is going on, the cells lining the small intestine have been absorbing the liquid digested material. The small intestine, in order to do this more efficiently, has its surface lined with tiny fingers called "villi" (Fig. 451) which give it a velvety appearance. This obviously makes the surface much greater and allows more cells to join in the work. Let us leave for a moment the remarkable way in which they dispose of their captives!

The material, robbed of nearly all the soluble products of food stuffs, gets to the end of the small intestine in some three-and-a-half hours from the time it left the stomach. Here, it meets a valve which opens at short intervals, letting the liquid into the large intestine.

The large intestine runs up the right side of the body, across the front and down the left side to the exit. It does almost nothing in the way of digestion except to recover the water from the material that enters it. The large intestine is also a vast city of bacteria. These are not present in the stomach, which is too acid for them. They are present to some extent in the small intestine, but the large intestine abounds in them! We discharge daily from our intestines about 4×10^{13} bacteria—twenty thousand times as many bacteria as there are people in the world. It is a disputed point whether the products of these bacteria are harmful to us; they certainly produce poisonous substances and these pass into the blood: however, those chemical watch-dogs, the liver and kidneys, seem to get rid of them easily. A few individuals are apparently free from these bacteria. They do not seem to be the better for it: they are, in fact, usually constipated.

Return to the small intestine. It has gathered, by means of the cells which line it, a supply of the amino-acids, sugars and fatty acids from the digested food. Everything the cells pick up (except the products of fat which are differently dealt with), goes into the capillaries and is thus carried by the blood stream to that remarkable organ, the liver.

The liver receives all the blood from the intestines *via* the portal vein. This breaks into very fine capillaries which ramify through the liver cells and rejoin to form the hepatic vein which carries the much-altered blood to the heart. The liver, in addition to transforming the digested foodstuffs, secretes bile and so it is permeated by branches of the bile duct which leads to the intestine.

The meal we have digested contained carbohydrates—starch, sugar, etc. Digestion broke these down into the simplest kinds of sugars, glucose, fructose, and galactose (all with six carbon atoms). These are absorbed and sent to the liver. The liver does the remarkable chemical feat of turning all these into glucose, which it transforms into the "animal starch" glycogen.

This is stored up in the liver until a supply of glucose is wanted for energy production (p. 836). The liver keeps the glucose in the blood-stream always at about 0.1%. If there is more glucose in the blood, the liver turns it into glycogen. If there is less glucose, the liver makes it from its glycogen store.

Glycogen is absolutely necessary for the work of the body: the liver can make it from proteins if the food does not contain carbohydrates: in starvation, it can actually make sugar from the body's own proteins. In order that sugar shall be turned into glycogen minute quantities of a chemical substance which we call *insulin* must be present in the blood. This is made in the islets of Langerhans, little patches of tissue scattered about the substance of the pancreas (Figs. 451, 454). The diabetic patient either produces little or no insulin or requires exceptional quantities of it. Consequently, glucose is not turned by him into glycogen, but accumulates in his blood until his kidneys remove it. He therefore passes sugar in his urine instead of storing it as glycogen. One of the greatest medical discoveries of the century was that diabetes can be largely controlled by injections of insulin, extracted from these "islets." Unfortunately, it is expensive—for the manufacture of it is difficult—and patients dislike having injections at intervals of a day or so. But instead of dying of diabetes, most of those who have the disease and take the trouble to carry out the treatment can live.

The proteins in the meal were all turned to amino-acids which dissolve and also pass *via* the cells of the intestinal wall to the blood stream and so to the liver. Some of these are turned into glucose in the liver. Their nitrogen is changed to urea and is excreted by the kidneys and the carbon and hydrogen and oxygen portion is changed into glucose. The rest of the amino-acids continue to circulate in the blood and are built up once more into the proteins of the body's cells.

It used to be a complete mystery as to how the various cells built up amino-acids into proteins. It is still very difficult to understand: it appears that a protein molecule contains several hundred amino-acid molecules linked together. Probably each

28*

animal has a different linkage-arrangement for each of its proteins. The cell, then, must have some arrangement for ensuring that the amino-acid molecules link into chains in the right sequence.

The interesting discovery has recently been made that digestive enzymes work both ways—that with *much* water present, they split proteins into amino-acids, but with less water present, they will turn amino-acids into proteins. Pepsin will turn thousands of times its weight of egg-white into a mixture of simpler soluble compounds: if this mixture is concentrated by evaporating some of the water, pepsin will then turn it back into a protein "plastein" very much like egg-white.

Plastein, however, is not egg-white, and probably some other enzyme than pepsin is used by the cells which build up egg-white in the hen. It is remarkable that the body does nearly all its complicated chemical changes by means of enzymes. We have not yet found out what an enzyme is: we have really no idea why it works, and the lack of this knowledge is our chief obstacle to understanding the working of the body.

Carbohydrates in the diet, then, go to make glycogen for energy purposes: proteins partly to make glycogen and partly to build up tissue proteins. Fats, like carbohydrates, are energy producers.

We left fats in the intestine split into glycerol and fatty acids, which in presence of bile dissolve appreciably in water. The fatty acids and glycerol diffuse into the cells of the intestine's wall; there they combine again and form tiny drops of fat. These are taken up by white corpuscles (lymphocytes) which transport them through the cell into tubes called lacteals. The lymphocytes then break up and liberate the fat, which appears as a sort of milk of fine droplets suspended in lymph. This liquid "chyle" travels through a network of tubes and finally passes into the great veins at the bottom of the neck and so enters the bloodstream. The fat in the blood is partly deposited in the tissues generally, and also in special deposits of fat-cells.

Fat is the chief storage-material in the body. When the reserve is drawn upon, fat is oxidised like sugar, to produce energy, but it is not well understood how this is done.

DIET AND VITAMINS

Any ordinary mixed diet contains sufficient protein, carbohydrate and fat for ordinary needs. It also will usually supply the mineral salts which the cells of the body require—common salt, calcium salts, iron salts, etc.: of these, calcium is the most likely to be lacking.

One of the most interesting discoveries of recent years is that the body cannot continue to nourish itself without very minute amounts of certain substances which it cannot make for itself. These substances have been named vitamins. The story of the disease scurvy very well illustrates the effect of the lack of a vitamin. In the time before steam shortened sea voyages, it was not uncommon to be six months at sea. The food of sailors was salt meat and biscuit—often very bad, but none the less, containing the necessary protein, carbohydrate and fat. On very long voyages, the remarkable disease of scurvy very frequently developed. Pains in the bones of the leg about the knee joint, bleeding from the gums and from the intestine and bleeding under the skin (giving rise to spots) reduced the men to the condition when they could no longer work, and even caused death. It was discovered that lemon juice, fresh vegetables, etc., cured it in an absolutely remarkable manner. The disease is now only found in babies who have either been fed on artificial foods of which the vitamins have been destroyed, or on cow's milk in which the vitamin is often deficient. Modern mothers always give babies orange juice as a precaution. Some two hundred years after lemon juice had been in use for this purpose, organic chemists began to try to extract from the juice the stuff that cured the scurvy. They succeeded and called it vitamin C. Later, they found out exactly what the stuff was, and the pure vitamin was actually made artificially.

The structure of its molecule is shown in Fig. 453: this shows it as related to the sugars. It is believed that this vitamin is required in order that the red blood-corpuscles should be formed

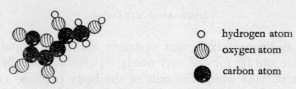

FIG. 453.—The molecule of Vitamin C (ascorbic acid): note
the general likeness to a sugar molecule (Fig. 367).

in the marrow, but *how* it causes this, no one can conjecture. The
amount of vitamin C, and indeed, of any vitamin required by the
body is extremely minute.

There are certainly five and probably more of these vitamins, all
of which we need if we are to develop properly and be properly
nourished.

Vitamin A is found in minute proportion in animal fats, milk,
butter, cream, beef-fat and particularly cod-liver and halibut-
liver oil. It is not found in vegetable fats. A diet which lacks this
substance causes changes in the eyes. Tears are no longer produced and the outer surface of the eye becomes dry and inflamed:
complete blindness may be the result. Changes in the membranes
of the intestines and lungs also occur. This disease xerophthalmia
(or "dry-eye") is almost unheard-of in Europe. But in Japan,
where very little fat is eaten, it is not uncommon. Denmark in
the war of 1914—1918 sold her butter and fats at famine prices to
the combatants, while her own people lived on margarine and
skimmed milk. The result was outbreaks of xerophthalmia. The
molecule of Vitamin A is practically a half-molecule of carotene
(the orange pigment found in carrots and in many red and
yellow flowers) with a hydroxyl group on the broken end.
Compare its formula given below with the formula of carotene.
(p. 602). Its action seems to be to protect delicate areas like the
lungs and eyes from infection.

Vitamin B is probably a mixture. It is found in most foodstuffs, but particularly in yeast. It is present in the husk and the
germ of seeds like rice and wheat but not in the starchy portion.

$$\begin{array}{c}
H_3C \quad CH_3 \\
\diagdown \diagup \\
C \qquad\qquad CH_3 \qquad\qquad CH_3 \\
\diagup \diagdown \quad H\ H \quad | \quad H\ H\ H \quad | \quad H \\
H_2C \qquad C{-}C{=}C{-}C{=}C{-}C{=}C{-}C{=}C{-}CH_2{-}OH \\
| \qquad\qquad \| \\
H_2C \qquad C{-}CH_3 \\
\diagdown \diagup \\
C \\
H_2 \qquad\qquad\qquad\qquad \text{Vitamin A.}
\end{array}$$

Now, many people prefer food which looks nice to food which is valuable: they like their bread or rice very white! In countries where polished rice without husk or germ is almost the whole diet, the disease beri-beri occurs. This is a nerve disease with weakness and tenderness in most parts of the body. In other countries where maize is the staple cereal another unpleasant disease, pellagra, occurs which can be cured by the use of yeast or plenty of lean meat. In England, where meat and milk are part of most dietaries, neither pellagra or beri-beri are anything but rarities.

Vitamin C prevents scurvy—we have already discussed it.

Vitamin D is necessary for the proper formation of bone. The disease of rickets used to be very common. It affected children only. To-day, it is hard to find a well-developed case of rickets, although the early stages are common enough, a fact much to the discredit of our social system.

Vitamin D is found in most fats—except vegetable ones— cod-liver oil is rich in it. The pure vitamin can be made by exposing ergosterol, a substance found in many fats, to ultra-violet light. It had been noticed that rickets was a town disease and was worse in winter than in summer: this suggested that light had something to do with it, and sure enough, exposure to ultra-violet light or to country sunshine (in big towns, the smoky air filters out all the ultra-violet light) cured the disease entirely. It was thus discovered that ultra-violet light acting on the skin, turns the ergosterol[1] in the fat of the skin into vitamin D. It seems that vitamin D is needed in order that the calcium and phosphorus needed to build bones shall be taken up by the bowel from food.

"Vitamin E," contained in wheat germ and in many plant tissues, is necessary in order that rats shall be able to breed. That its presence is needed for the breeding of man, is at least probable.

These vitamins are quite as much of a puzzle as the rest of the chemistry of the body. Probably they are "catalysts" which speed up some chemical process. They seem to be much simpler substances than enzymes, which are also catalysts. It may seem odd that the body has not learnt to make these vital substances, but it would seem that only the unnatural diet of mankind could be seriously lacking in them.

Enzymes and vitamins are alike in that a very minute amount of them will cause a great deal of work to be done. Rennin will coagulate two million times its weight of milk; vitamin D will keep a thousand million times its weight of children from getting rickets (daily dose about 0.03 milligrams).

DUCTLESS GLANDS

There is a third class of substances of which minute quantities are required for the working of the body. This includes the substances produced in the ductless glands and called "hormones." The best-known glands, like the salivary glands, pancreas and liver, have an exit tube which carries the stuff they produce to the place where it is required. The ductless glands simply discharge the substance they make into the bloodstream. They are to be regarded as small chemical factories where one or two special substances are made.

There are at least six kinds of these glands. Fig. 454 shows where they are. The thyroid and parathyroids in the neck, the the adrenals (above the kidney) often known as suprarenals,

[1] Recent work indicates that some other substance than ergosterol may be concerned.

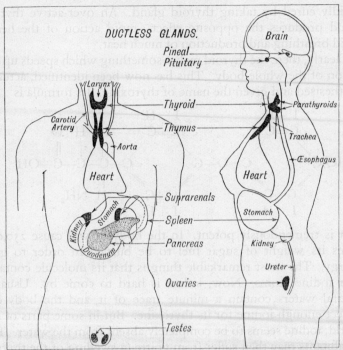

FIG. 454.—Where the ductless glands are to be found. The ductless glands are shown in black: the other organs indicate their position. It is not certain whether the pineal and thymus glands are true ductless glands. The pancreas is partly a ductless gland: (Islets of Langerhans, p. 872).

the pituitary body at the base of the brain, certain parts of the pancreas and the ovaries and testes all certainly act in this way. One or two other organs such as the thymus and pineal glands are suspected of doing so.

Let us start with the thyroid gland, which is H-shaped, and lies on each side of the windpipe (Fig. 454). If the thyroid gland is completely taken away, the patient becomes sluggish and slow in speech, his temperature is low, and the tissue beneath his skin becomes thickened and swollen. He becomes almost unrecognisable. This condition is called myxoedema. It is completely and rapidly cured by taking thyroid gland. An over-active thyroid gland produces the opposite effect—rapid action of the heart, rapid breathing and production of much heat.

Clearly, then, the thyroid makes something which speeds up the action of the whole body. This has now been identified, actually synthesised and given the name of thyroxine. Its formula is

$$
\text{HO.C}
\begin{array}{c}
\text{I}\quad\text{H} \\
\text{C}=\text{C} \\
\diagdown \\
\end{array}
\text{C}-\text{O}-\text{C}
\begin{array}{c}
\text{I}\quad\text{H} \\
\text{C}=\text{C} \\
\diagdown \\
\text{C}-\text{C} \\
\text{I}\quad\text{H}
\end{array}
\begin{array}{c}
\text{H}\ \ \text{H}\ \ \text{O} \\
|\quad|\quad\| \\
\text{C}-\text{C}-\text{C}-\text{C}-\text{OH} \\
|\quad| \\
\text{H}\ \ \text{NH}_2
\end{array}
$$

It is tremendously potent. In the body, it will cause 250,000 times its weight of sugar fuel to be burned in order to give energy. The most remarkable thing is that its molecule contains four iodine atoms. Now, iodine is hard to come by. Usually, natural waters contain a minute trace of it, and the body can collect enough iodine for its thyroxine. But in some parts of the world, iodine seems to be completely absent from the water. The inhabitants may then suffer from goitre (a swelling of the thyroid which enlarges in order to do its best) or much worse from cretinism. If a child has a defective thyroid gland or no iodine to make its thyroxine with, it becomes very backward and dwarfed, repulsive in appearance and often quite idiotic. These "cretins" can be cured completely by thyroid extract if the child is treated soon enough, but once the damage is done, the treatment is less successful.

Close to the thyroids are the parathyroids, two small glands which for years were only anatomical curiosities, but which are now known to be essential to life. These produce a substance which has not been identified, but is called parathormone. Its task seems to be to keep the proportion of the calcium in the blood correct; though how it does this is not known. If these glands are not working or have been removed, the amount of the calcium in the blood drops and nervous twitchings and spasms develop which may have fatal results. If the parathyroid glands are over-active—a rare disease—the calcium in the blood is increased, being taken from the bones which become softened and terribly deformed.

The adrenal glands are two small bodies shaped like a cocked hat, and lying close to the kidney. Each is really composed of two glands. The adrenal gland has an outer coat or cortex, and an inner portion or medulla. The cortex is absolutely necessary to life, though it is not known what it produces. An overgrown and presumably over-active adrenal cortex causes precocious growth and sexual maturity.

A great deal, however, is known about the "core" or medulla of the adrenal gland. It produces minute quantities of a substance called adrenine (adrenaline) which is quite a simple chemical compound—for a product of the body. It is a benzene derivative and can quite easily be made in the laboratory. Its object is simple—*to prepare the body to meet an emergency*, and it is only in emergencies that it is poured out from the gland in appreciable quantities.

It seems to act directly on the organs without the mediation of the nerves, and produces a remarkable set of symptoms which may roughly be called the symptoms of the rage and fear which an animal may be supposed to feel when confronted with an enemy.

The eyes protrude and are widely opened; the pupils are dilated. The heart beats more strongly and rapidly. Digestion ceases—so releasing blood for the muscles which may be needed for combat or flight. The skin becomes pale because tiny capillaries have contracted and also sent their blood to the muscles. The spleen, which is a sort of reservoir of blood corpuscles, contracts and sends more blood

$$
\begin{array}{c}
\text{OH} \\
| \\
\text{C} \\
\diagup \quad \diagdown \\
\text{HC} \qquad \text{C.OH} \\
\| \qquad\qquad | \\
\text{HC} \qquad \text{CH} \\
\diagdown \quad \diagup \\
\text{C} \\
| \\
\text{H.C.OH} \\
| \\
\text{H.C.H} \\
| \\
\text{H.N—CH}_3
\end{array}
$$

Formula of adrenine.

into circulation. The liver turns some of its glycogen into glucose which the muscles will need in the expected violent exercise. The peculiar physical sensation of "losing one's temper" is probably the effect of adrenine.

Adrenine is used in medicine. Its most important use is to make the capillaries contract. The dentist, when he injects a local anæsthetic, mixes it with a little adrenine. This contracts the blood-vessels in the tissue round the injection: consequently, the local circulation almost ceases and the anæsthetic is not carried away. Incidentally, it is most effective in preventing bleeding.

Another gland—the pituitary—the most complicated chemical factory of all, lies at the base of the brain. Like the adrenals, it is two glands in one. The "anterior lobe" produces minute quantities of at least three substances. One of these influences the growth of the bones. If the anterior lobe of the pituitary is over-active while the "long bones" of the legs and arms are growing, the unfortunate subject grows into a giant—from seven to ten feet high. These giants are usually feeble, for their bodies cannot produce enough muscle to make their huge frame effective. They usually die in middle life or earlier,the reason being that their disordered pituitaries cease to produce sufficient secretion for their needs.

Giant rats, two-and-a-half times the normal size, can be grown by injecting anterior lobe extract into young normal animals. If the overgrowth of the gland sets in after growth has finished, a most strange disorder, acromegaly, sets in. The bones of the lower part of the face and of the hands and the feet grow enormously, and the appearance of the patient is strangely and utterly changed. Both gigantism and acromegaly are fortunately very rare.

The anterior lobe also produces minute quantities of one or more substances called prolans which are essential in regulating the formation of ova in the female and in maintaining normal pregnancy. They are the foundation of the only test for pregnancy which is reliable from the earliest stages. The urine of a pregnant woman contains traces of these prolans. If small quantities of urine are injected into immature mice, they become sexually mature if it is derived from a pregnant woman.

The pituitary gland exerts its effects not only by the direct agency of its own hormones, but also by its action on other glands. Thus the prolans made by it seem to be the substances which at puberty stimulate the testes and ovaries to grow and produce their own hormones, which cause the obvious bodily and mental changes which occur at this period. The pituitary also seems to produce substance which regulates the thyroid gland's activity and it is likely that it has other and unknown functions, perhaps exerting a direct influence on the brain-centres that surround it.

The posterior lobe also seems to produce minute quantities of several very active principles. The extract "pituitrin" which contains all of them is used in medicine. It causes a rise in blood-pressure (which may be valuable for curing the shock which occurs after surgical operations, etc.) It also seems to control fat-production (the gigantically fat often seem to have disordered pituitaries) and also the water-content of the body.

The sex-glands, ovary and testis, also elaborate substances of this kind: we will speak of them again in our discussion of reproduction.

The chief subject we have still left untouched is the working of the nerves.

NERVES AND THE NERVE-IMPULSE

The body is continually adapting and readapting itself to its environment. In order to do this, it is necessary for the organism as a whole to be informed swiftly and accurately of any alteration in its external world, and to be able to alter itself to fit it as swiftly as possible. The nervous system plays the most important part in this process: it has indeed been called the telephone system of the body, and if this analogy is not pressed too far, it is an apt one, as will be seen.

The unit of the nervous system is the neurone, the nerve cell with its processes (Plate XLIV). This cell has developed to an exceptional degree the properties of excitability and conductivity:

that is to say that the neurone is especially sensitive to stimulation, whether it be by the application of an electric shock or by the liberation in the body of some chemical substance, and that it responds to stimulation by conducting an impulse. The nerve impulse is a disturbance propagated along the whole length of the neurone.

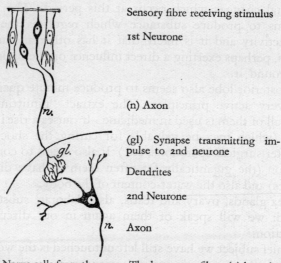

Sensory fibre receiving stimulus

1st Neurone

(n) Axon

(gl) Synapse transmitting impulse to 2nd neurone

Dendrites

2nd Neurone

Axon

FIG. 455.—Nerve cells from the nose. The long axon-fibres (n) branches at the end and the branches intermesh (gl) with those of a second nerve cell. This intertwining of branches is called a synapse and is the means of transmitting the impulse from one neurone to the next. (Courtesy of Messrs. Longmans, Green & Co., Ltd., from Schäfer's *Essentials of Histology*.)

The neurone consists of the nerve cell proper, a process called the axon emerging from one end of it, and other processes called dendrites which emerge from the other end (Fig. 455). The axon is, as a rule, much longer than the dendrites and is known as the nerve fibre. The length which a single nerve fibre can attain is shown by the fact that the nerve fibres which reach the skin in a man's foot are the axons of nerve cells situated in his spinal cord at about the level of his kidneys: these single nerve fibres, then, are several feet long.

The nerve fibre cannot live for long after it has been separated from its cell: the cell contains the nucleus and the nucleus is essential for the life of the cell and its processes: a cut nerve therefore dies, and though a new fibre may grow out from the cell, this takes a long time. A nerve fibre separated from its cell is, however, useful for studying the properties of nerve fibres. If the sciatic nerve of a frog is removed from its body, it can be kept alive for several hours. The nerve of a mammal is more difficult to keep alive.

To demonstrate the properties of the nerve fibre, the main nerve of a frog's leg, the sciatic nerve, is dissected out. The action of the nerves can be shown by the fact that when this sciatic nerve is stimulated, the disturbance propagated down its fibres leads in some way to the contraction of the gastrocnemius (calf) muscle. It is possible that the arrival of the nervous impulse at the junction between the muscle and nerve (see Fig. 438) causes the liberation of a chemical substance, perhaps acetylcholine, which in its turn causes the contraction of the muscle. Possibly however, the impulse of the nerve discussed on p. 887 is continued into the muscle. For our purpose, it is enough that when the living nerve is stimulated, the muscle contracts. It is useful to attach the tendon of the muscle to the lever of a myograph so that every twitch of the muscle may be recorded on a smoked cylinder, a process illustrated in Fig. 456 and explained on p. 396 and below.

The nerve may be stimulated artificially by snipping with scissors or by thermal or chemical stimuli, but such methods injure the nerve, and are not to be recommended. It is better to stimulate electrically, using an induction coil with a short-circuiting key in the secondary circuit. Two needle electrodes are arranged, touching the nerve (Fig. 456).

The sciatic nerve is, of course, not a single nerve fibre, but a large number of fibres bound up within a common sheath. This experiment, however, gives a great deal of information about the single nerve fibre. The secondary coil is first arranged so that a very feeble current is given. There is no contraction of the muscle: such a stimulus which is too light to excite the nerve

FIG. 456.—A myograph as used for the study of nerve impulses. The timing arrangements (left) are described on page 396. The induction coil supplying the stimulating current is at the right-hand bottom corner. The muscle and nerve are mounted on the block at the top right-hand corner. (Courtesy of Messrs. C. F. Palmer (London), Ltd.)

fibre is said to be below threshold. On gradually increasing the strength of the current, a strength is reached at which the muscle responds with a faint contraction. This is the threshold of stimulation or rheobase. The time during which the current is allowed to act also determines whether or not it will stimulate the nerve. However strong the stimulus, it must be applied for a definite time if it is to be effective. The chronaxie of a nerve is the minimum time during which a current twice the strength of the rheobase must be applied if the nerve is to be excited. For a frog's nerve it is about 0.003 secs.

If the strength of the stimulus is increased, the contractions of the muscle become stronger until a level is reached at which no increase of the current will alter the extent of the contraction. The stimulus is now said to be maximal.

The threshold stimulus excited one or a very few fibres in the big nerve trunk. An increasing stimulus excited an increasing number of fibres until at last the stimulus was sufficient to excite every fibre in the trunk: this gave the maximum contraction. If a single nerve fibre had been used, there would have been no such increase of contraction with single shocks of increasing strength; for the single nerve fibre follows what is called the all-or-none law. If a stimulus is sufficient to excite it at all, it responds to the best of its ability, no more and no less, just as the force with which a bullet leaves the muzzle of a rifle has nothing to do with the strength applied to the trigger. Either the force applied to the trigger is great enough to fire off the gun or it is not great enough: there are no half-way measures. The only way in which the stimulus can affect a single fibre is by determining the number of the impulses passing along it in a given time: but these factors, too, are limited by what is known as the refractory period of the nerve fibre.

It has been shown that single nerve fibres follow the all-or-none law for a single impulse. The speed of the impulse, which may be as great as 100 yards per second in the nerve of a mammal, depends on the character of the fibre: the thicker this is, the more rapidly the impulse travels. Now a single nerve fibre follows the all-or-none law, so if our sense organs and our muscles were supplied by a single nerve fibre each we could not grade our actions: we could only hit a violent blow or none. Consequently, every organ is supplied by a big bundle of nerve fibres and the power of the reaction is accurately graded and controlled by the number of these that are working at a given time, and the number of impulses that pass along each nerve fibre in a given time.

The nerve impulse can only be transmitted by a living nerve

fibre. It is probable that the cell-membrane of the fibre is a film
with a neutral layer separating layers of positive and negative
ions and that the trans-
mission of the impulse is
brought about by a suc-
cessive disturbance of the
layer, allowing the posi-
tive and negative ions to
meet. This disturbance
first occurs where the
nerve is stimulated. A
wave of depolarisation—breaking down of the layer—travels
along the whole length of the fibre. When the layer is quite
broken down, the nerve is absolutely refractory and quite
inexcitable; the return of excitability is due to the rebuilding of
the polarised film; when that film has been rebuilt, the process
of breaking down can occur again.

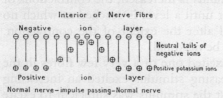

FIG. 457.—A method by which the nerve-
impulse may be transmitted.

The transmission of the nerve impulse, then, is a vital process,
demanding the use of energy for its rebuilding: nerve that is
transmitting impulses uses more oxygen than an inactive nerve.
Thus, while the nervous system may be compared to a telephone
system, a strict comparison of nerve fibres to telephone wires is
quite unjustified, for the nerve fibre conducts the impulse at the
expense of a breaking down of its own structure: not until that
structure is restored can it transmit another impulse.

The nerve fibre normally receives the stimulus which sends the
wave of depolarisation along it from another nerve-cell or from
an *end-organ*.

THE SENSES: TOUCH, TASTE AND SMELL

We usually speak of *five senses*, touch, taste, smell, hearing and
sight. Each of these is experienced by an organ, the sensitive
part of which is the end of a nerve. This classification into five
senses is not enough. Under touch, we really group several
senses. We can feel a thing in several different ways. Actually,

the light touch of a feather, the sensation of heat, the sensation of cold, the sensation of pressure (as when a finger is firmly pressed on the skin), the sensation of pain, are all felt by different organs. Moreover, we have a sense which tells us how our limbs are arranged. If your eyes are shut, you can tell whether your elbow is bent or straight. It is this same sense that enables you to touch your nose with your eyes shut, a faculty which disappears in certain diseases! There is a sense, too, which tells us whether our muscles are pulling or slack; one can feel how hard one is pulling on a rope. Finally, there are a number of vague sensations of well-being or ill-being which come from our internal organs.

Fig. 458 shows some of the touch organs. The simplest of all are nerve fibres which branch and wind among the cells of the deeper layers of the skin. These feel pain only. They are found all over the skin so close together, that it is difficult though not impossible to thrust a fine needle into the skin without causing pain. The inside lining of the eyelids has these end-organs only. Consequently, it cannot feel touch but only pain. Most membranes have these endings but solid organs have not. Thus, it is possible to cut the liver or even the greater part of the brain without causing any pain. Pain, from a disordered organ, is felt only in the membrane of the organ or the outer skin, either over the organ or supplied by nerves communicating with its nerves. Thus stomach pain may be felt in the shoulder-blade and heart-pain in the left arm! Light touches are felt by special organs, the Meissner's corpuscles which have nerve-endings spirally coiled round a bulb. Hairs, though quite insensitive, act as very delicate touch organs.

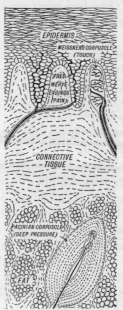

FIG. 458.—The organs of "touch" in the skin.

Round their roots ramify nerve fibres which detect the faintest motion. A cat's whisker is a long strong hair equipped with specially elaborate nerve-endings.

One naturally thinks that all one's skin is equally sensitive to touch, heat and cold. Actually, by searching its surface with a fine hair or a hot or cold needle, it is found that it is a mosaic of spots, some sensitive to touch, others to heat, others to cold. The heat and cold feeling organs have not been certainly identified.

The Pacinian corpuscles feel pressure. They are bulbs very like an onion with a nerve fibre in the middle. They are found in the skin and also in the membrane of the joints and elsewhere. They feel pressure and, in the joints, this sensation of pressure tells us where our limbs are.

The muscles have nerve-endings in them branching along the fibres. Tendons have rather similar organs. These tell us whether our muscles are contracted or extended, and whether they are tense or loose. The muscles which execute most delicate and controlled movements—eye, tongue and hand—have the greatest number.

Touch and its allied senses are very delicate. Put your hand in your pocket and pick out a halfpenny from a penny or a shilling. A complicated mixture of feelings of smoothness (true touch), weight (Pacinian corpuscle), shape (position and movements of the fingers run over it), give us a very good picture of it. To realise what touch can do, read about Helen Keller, who, with almost no other sense, was educated to do far more than hold her own with those who had the sight and hearing she lacked.

Taste is a chemical sense which resides in peculiar end-organs, "taste-buds," in the tongue. There are only four kinds of taste, sweet, bitter, sour and salt. The taste of roast mutton or asparagus is almost purely a smell. The best witness of this is the fact that a really bad cold makes food tasteless. A man whose nose is closed cannot tell a piece of onion from a piece of apple, by taste, as long as he does not see it. Substances must be dissolved in water to be tasted. Taste is chiefly useful as a warning against poisonous but odourless materials.

Smell is very poorly represented in man. It is a commonplace that a dog can guide itself and recognise its master's belongings by smells which we cannot even begin to detect. None the less,

even Man's sense of smell is very delicate. A piece of musk will scent a room and it is said that a chemical balance will not detect the weight it loses in a day. Perhaps, then, it loses 10^{-4} gms. a day. The nose detects the smell in about 5 ccs. of air the room contains 75,000,000 ccs. One therefore can smell 6×10^{-12} gms., six billionths of a gram of musk. No chemical test would detect this quantity, though it represents a goodly number of molecules. The organs of smell are the nerve endings of nerve cells which send fibres through pores in the bone of the roof of the nose-cavity into the brain.

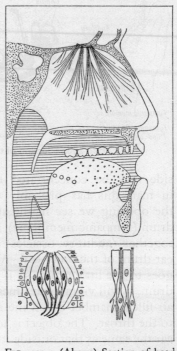

THE EAR

Human beings have specialised in delicacy of touch, hearing, and above all sight, though probably some animal excels us in each of these. Our hearing is probably not nearly so acute as that of many animals, but we have developed

FIG. 459.—(Above) Section of head showing olfactory nerves passing through perforation in the bottom of the "brain-box" and ending in the lining membrane of the nose. (Below) Left, organ of taste in the tongue, nerve fibres represented in heavier line. Right, organ of smell (*cf.* Fig. 455).

discrimination between and understanding of sound signals in the form of words and music to such an extent that our brains have had to develop a large auditory and speech-receiving centre (Fig. 480) to cope with the use we make of our ears.

The ear is a combination of two organs, a sound-detector and a balancing organ.

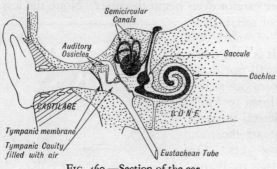

FIG. 460.—Section of the ear.

The sound detector consists of an amplifier and a detector provided with hundreds of "detector units," each sensitive to a particular note. Look at Fig. 460. A compression wave from the air outside may be concentrated by the outer ear (pinna), though in man this has probably very little effect. It travels down the opening we see in the side of the head and drives the eardrum (tympanic membrane) inwards. Three small bones hinged together (auditory ossicles) transmit this push to the smaller ear-drum of the inner ear. All the energy given to the big drum goes to the little drum, so if its area is a tenth of that of the big drum, it will vibrate ten times as strongly. The bones work in an air-filled chamber called the middle-ear. This has a tube leading to the throat. The object is to keep the air pressure in the middle ear the same as that outside it. If one goes down a deep lift-shaft, one feels a fullness in the ears. The pressure outside has risen and is forcing the drum inward. If one then swallows, the eustachian tube opens and the air passes in and equalises the pressure.

The little drum is a window in a chamber full of fluid and hollowed out of the bone of the skull. The vibrations of the drum set the fluid vibrating too. The chamber contains a bag of fluid (black in the diagram) which is coiled at one end like a snail's shell. This is the essential organ of hearing. In Fig. 461 you see this enlarged. The parts marked *scala vestibuli* and *scala tympani* are filled with the outer fluid: the part marked cochlear canal is a continuation of the inner "bag." Now the cochlear canal has a sort of spiral piano-keyboard of nerve fibres (organ of Corti). There are five or six thousand of these nerve fibres only one of which appears in the lower part of Fig. 461; probably each is so arranged that it responds to a particular rate of vibration. Physiologists are not agreed about this: however, it is certain that the sound throws the fluid in the cochlea into vibration and that the nerve fibres in the cochlea detect these.

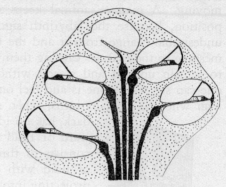

The ear is, in fact, a very sensitive and accurate scientific instrument. A really trained ear will detect, it is said, a difference of $\frac{1}{64}$ semitone in pitch. If the note was C′, this would represent the difference between 512 and 512.75 vibrations a second. Even if we doubt this degree of accuracy, the ear remains wonderfully delicate. Its power of analysing complicated vibrations is extraordinary. That it can pick out a violin or flute from the hundred or so different simultaneous vibrations of an orchestra is extra-

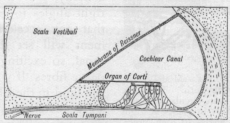

FIG. 461.—(Above) Vertical section of the cochlea. Bone is shown dotted; auditory nerve black; white spaces are filled with fluid. (Below) a portion further magnified.

ordinary and not explained. The perception of direction of sound by the ear is also not easy to understand. Actually, sounds straight in front of one are easily confused with sounds from behind. The direction of a sound is perhaps spotted by the difference in the loudness of the sound in each ear. I have a left ear which cannot hear the faint ticking of a watch. In the dark, I hear my watch ticking on my right, though it is actually on a table at the foot of the bed. It has also been thought that the direction is detected by the fact that a sound wave (e.g. on the right), reaches the right ear before the left.

The inner ear contains a totally different organ—the labyrinth—which tells the brain the position of the head and the way it is moving. A man or animal keeps itself in the usual upright position, because the labyrinth signals the beginning of any undesirable change from it and the brain-centres send a nerve-message to the muscles causing them to correct it. It is possible to remain upright and steady without a labyrinth as long as one can see where one is and feel one's feet on the floor, but a man who has no labyrinths, when supported in water in the dark, has no idea whether he is head up-ward or head downward! The labyrinth consists of three semi-circular tubes full of fluid with a bunch of nerve fibres projecting into each. One tube runs horizontally, the other two vertically and at right angles to each other (Fig. 462), so that any acceleration or turning move-ment will set the fluid moving in one canal, so exciting one of the bunches of nerve fibres. If you spin round and round, the fluid in the labyrinth turns with you to a great extent; if you then stop the fluid goes on turning. This violently and unnaturally stimulates the nerves and the posture muscles are sent a disturbed and confused message: equilibrium is lost, you feel giddy and may fall. The queerest experiment—a very unpleasant one—is to inject cold water into the outer ear. This cools the bone and sets up convection currents (p. 108) in the fluid in the labyrinths. Instantly, all the symptoms of giddiness and nausea set in and the subject may fall helpless. The "saccule" (Fig. 462) contains

FIG. 462.—Model of the labyrinth. The three semi-circular canals C are in planes at right angles to each other. The otolith is at the bottom of the saccule at O. The flat surfaces are, of course, imaginary!

another organ, the otolith, which tells which way gravity is pulling. The otolith is simply a small mass of gelatinous stuff, containing a good deal of chalk, with nerve hairs embedded in it. If you are upside-down, the otoliths pull on the nerve-hairs: if you are rightway up, they press on them. In this way, the brain is informed how the head is situated even when it is kept still.

These otoliths are possessed by fish and by simpler creatures such as shrimps. Some shrimps have a simple cavity with nerve-endings and a loose grain or two of sand to act as an otolith. But they moult the skin of their balancing organs with the rest of their shell and skin, and they then put another grain of sand into the new empty cavity. An ingenious biologist provided the newly moulted shrimps with iron filings instead of sand. He then suspended a powerful magnet over the tank. The iron filings were drawn upward instead of falling downward, and the shrimps consequently all swam upside down!

THE EYE

The eye is for man at least the chief avenue by which impressions reach his brain. The blind are more handicapped than the deaf, while the few people lacking taste or smell can conduct their lives without their friends noticing the difference. The various touch-senses are hardly ever lost except in paralysis.

The eye is a camera. It has a lens, a stop and a sensitive screen, and an arrangement for focussing objects at various distances.

As an optical instrument, it is imperfect, for it only focusses a sharp picture on one small area. The rest of the picture is blurred and indistinct. Fix your eye on a word in the middle of this page. *If you keep your eye still* you can only read the two or three lines above and below it—the rest is blurred. When you scan a whole landscape, you unconsciously move your eyes so that each piece is focussed in turn on the "yellow spot" where focussing is sharpest and sensitiveness is greatest. None the less, the eye is a marvellous production, when it is considered that it is made from jelly-like proteins, not rigid metal and glass. The outer case

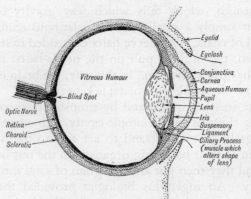

Eyelid

Eyelash

Conjunctiva
Cornea
Aqueous Humour
Pupil
Lens
Iris
Suspensory
Ligament
Ciliary Process
(muscle which
alters shape
of lens)

Vitreous Humour

Blind Spot

Optic Nerve
Retina
Choroid
Sclerotic

FIG. 463.—The eye in vertical section.

of the eye is a ball about an inch in diameter with a small rounded projection at the front, the cornea. The "case" is made up of three layers; outermost is the *sclerotic* or "white of the eye" with the transparent *cornea* let into it like a window. Lining the sclerotic is the *choroid*, a layer of nourishing blood-vessels and pigment cells which give a dark background: this is prolonged into the ringshaped iris, the coloured part of the eye. This has muscle fibres in it, and so can make the hole in it, the pupil, contract to a pin-point or expand widely. This happens automatically: a bright light makes it contract and darkness makes it expand. The iris corresponds to the stop of the camera. The back of the iris is black. This, showing through the muscular part, gives the curious dark grey-blue colour of a new-born European baby's eyes. As the child grows up, much or little white, yellow or brown pigment deposits in the front and middle of the iris. There is no blue pigment in a blue eye. Blue-eyed people have very little pigment and their eye colour is chiefly due to the black showing through and perhaps to a light-scattering by tiny granules of light pigment; as more and more pigment is deposited, the eye may become hazel or brown.

The innermost coating of the eyeball is the retina—the sensitive membrane; this we will discuss again.

The focussing of the light is done to a small extent by the curved cornea, but much more by the crystalline lens, a beautifully transparent little lens of clear elastic jelly. It is attached to the eye by a ring of muscle fibres. When these contract the ring narrows: the lens is thus caused to become thicker and more nearly a

PLATE XLIII

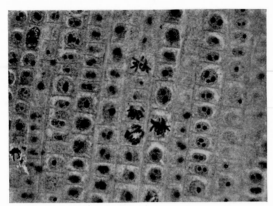

Microphotograph of cell division in the root of a plant.

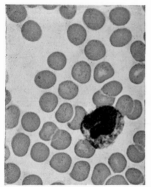

Blood. The corpuscles are somewhat distorted by the process of staining. The larger darkly stained object is a white corpuscle ($\times$ 1250).

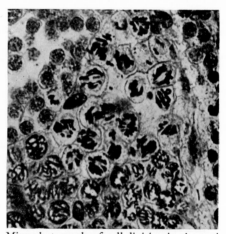

Microphotograph of cell division in the testis of an amphibian.

PLATE XLIV

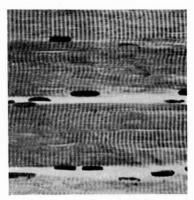

Striated Muscle from rabbit
($\times$ 420).

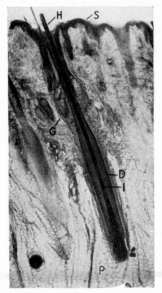

Human scalp ($\times$ 20) H, hair; S,
epidermis; G, sebaceous gland;
D, outer root sheath; I, inner
root sheath; P, panniculus adiposus
(loose fatty tissue).

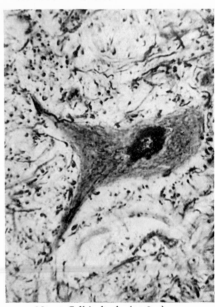

Nerve Cell in brain ($\times$ 875).

sphere. Its focal length (p. 475) becomes less and it therefore focusses near objects on the retina. When the muscle fibres relax, the lens springs back to its more flattened form and so focusses distant objects. The ordinary camera is focussed for near objects by lengthening it (p. 479): the eye is focussed for near objects by increasing the magnification of the lens. In old age, the lens usually loses much of its elasticity: it cannot be compressed and so focusses distant objects clearly, but cannot focus near objects. This causes the long sight of old age.

The eye is filled with clear fluid between the cornea and lens, and with a very thin transparent jelly between the lens and retina. The retina is naturally quite different from any other nerve ending for it has to be sensitive, not to touch or motion, like the skin or the nerve endings of the ear, nor to chemical actions like the tongue and nose, but to light which has little effect on most chemical substances.

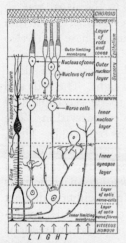

FIG. 464.—The retina or sensitive screen of the eye. The *bottom* is the side on which the light impinges.

The trick seems to be done by manufacturing a purple-coloured substance which absorbs light, and is at once decomposed by it. This chemical decomposition is detected by the nerve fibres and an impulse is sent to the brain.

Fig. 464 gives an idea of the structure of the retina. The oddest thing is that the part sensitive to light is on the side of the retina distant from the light: no human designer would have arranged it so. Actually, the whole retina is only $\frac{1}{10}$ to $\frac{1}{2}$ a millimetre thick and very fairly transparent, so that light reaches the back of it almost unaltered.

In the middle of the retina appears the optic nerve from the brain. This spot where the nerve emerges is blind. Shut your left eye, look *fixedly* at the cross in Fig. 465, holding it some 10 inches away. With a little practice, you will find a position

FIG. 465.—Illustrating the blind spot. Shut the left
eye and gaze at the cross: on moving the book
backwards and forwards about six inches from
the eye the spot will disappear.

where the spot on it disappears entirely. You have now directed
your eye so that the picture of the spot falls on the optic nerve,
which, since it is a carrier of impulses, not a detector of light, is
blind. From this spot radiate fine nerve fibres (Fig. 464)
which end in nerve cells; these connect up in the usual way to
another layer of nerve cells which themselves connect to a thin
layer of nerve cells specialised as light-detectors. These are of two
kinds, cells bearing rods and cells bearing cones. Each has a
nucleus and an end piece, the cone or rod. These latter alone
contain the visual purple which is affected by light. The rods and
cones differ in function. The cones seem to be the organs of
delicate and discriminating vision and of colour-vision. The
"yellow-spot" in the centre of the eye contains only cones. Here,
we have the most sharp and distinct sight—you are reading this
with your yellow spot. The rods are the sensitive organs. In
faint light—as at night—the cones will not function. The rods
alone receive the faint image. They do not give either a distinct
and sharp image nor do they perceive colour. After dark, everything is seen in a faintly blurred monotone. The impressions
from each rod or cone or at least from each two or three travel
back along a separate fibre of the optic nerve. The optic nerves
meet and cross in a peculiar way inside the brain: their fibres end
in a large area at the back of the head, where in a wholly
mysterious fashion their impulses are perceived as sight and
registered as "memory."

Incidentally, it may be noted that the image on the retina is
upside down as in a camera! We have, however, got so used to
this that it appears to us the right way up.

The eye is set in a hollow in the skull. The hollow is filled
with loose fatty tissue. Fig. 466 shows how the eye is pointed

at any object. It is easy to see that the eye can be rotated in any direction by combined pulls from the muscle-bands, shown in black.

It is not for nothing that we have two eyes. Our two eyes receive nearly, but not quite the same impression, and from these slightly different views we get our ideas of distance and "solidity." The action of our eye-muscles in controlling the direction in which our eyes point, is usually unconscious (though, of course we can move our eyes at will) and is very delicate.

First, let us see how we judge the distance of an object. We can judge the distance of an object using only one eye. Thus we can guess the distance of a building by the slight haziness which the air interposes between us and it. Nearer objects can be placed by their size. We know how big a cow is and by unconsciously comparing our image of it with past images in our memory, we can judge its distance.

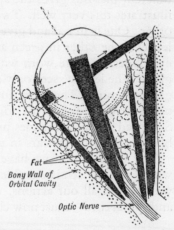

Fig. 466.—The manner in which the eye is rotated by the pull of bands of muscle.

Fat

Bony Wall of Orbital Cavity

Optic Nerve

One-eyed people, however, are definitely worse than two-eyed, in judging distances. A one-eyed hostess occasionally pours the tea behind the cup instead of into it!

The perspective of a landscape, too, tells us something of the distances. An artist's picture on a flat canvas is to be compared with the image in a single human eye. It is very interesting to see how he gets the effect of distance by colour, haze and perspective.

The two-eyed person judges short distances by feeling the amount he has to make his eyes turn inward towards each other to focus the object. Bring your finger from arm's-length slowly to the bridge of your nose. Your eyes turn slowly inward till, at a few inches from your nose, you can converge them no further, and you see two images of your finger.

Sight with two eyes gives a solid effect. The right eye sees a little more of the right side of an object and the left eye sees a little more of the left side. The combination of two slightly different pictures gives the appearance of solidity. The anaglyph illustrates this very well. Two pictures are printed on top of each other. One is in red and gives the view as it would be seen by the left eye: the other in green and as it would be seen by the right eye. Spectacles are worn with a red left-glass and a green right-glass. The left eye sees only the red picture and the right eye the green picture. These are fused by the brain and give the impression of solidity. This principle has been used for stereo-films. Since red and green shades properly chosen combine to a grey or black, the image appears in monotone like a photograph.

The sense organs we have studied send impulses to the brain which in turn sends suitable impulses to the muscles by which we perform all our actions. The central nervous system—brain and spinal cord—must now claim our attention.

THE CENTRAL NERVOUS SYSTEM

No organ which does the work which the brain performs could possibly be simple, but we cannot survey our world without trying to understand something about the brain which perceives it.

The nerve cells of the finger you burn on a hot stove do not send a *direct* message to your arm muscles to take it away and only very seldom in the nervous system does the same neurone or nerve cell receive the stimulus from the environment and carry the impulse directly to the muscle or other "effector" organ by which the organism responds to the stimulus. Ordinarily, two or more nerve cells are concerned. The impulse is passed on from the neurone, which receives the stimulus, to another which carries it to the effector organ. Very often, one or more neurones are interposed between these two. The point at which the impulse is passed from one neurone to another is called a synapse, and may be compared to a telegraphic relay (Figs. 455, 467). Passage of the impulse across the synapse is brought about not, it seems, by direct conduction of the impulse as electricity is conducted, but probably by the liberation of a definite chemical substance at the nerve endings of the first neurone, this chemical substance stimulating the second neurone. The synapse is a one-way conductor: for although a nerve fibre will, on suitable stimulation, conduct an impulse in either direction, an impulse can only pass a synapse in one direction, from the axon of one nerve, in by way of the dendrites of the other, and thence out by way of its axon. (Fig. 455.)

The synapse then provides a means by which the impulse passing up the long fibre (neurone) of any given nerve cell is transferred to another nerve cell. These synapses are then the connections by which the incoming impulse, as of a burn, is steered to the motor nerve fibre which causes an action, as of withdrawing the arm. The synapses are in four main regions, the spinal cord, the brain-stem, the cerebellum and the cerebrum.

The spinal synapses provide for the simplest functions, simple movements and the like. The brain-stem regulates many important bodily functions of which we are usually unconscious, such as respiration, temperature regulation, circulation. The cerebellum is concerned with maintaining posture and balance. The cerebrum or brain proper is responsible for all the higher functions. The complicated associations of sense impressions, past and present, which we call thought, is the highest of these; but a very great part of the brain is concerned in regulating all our skilled movements, walking, cycling, buttoning a coat—everything in fact that we have learned to do since we were babies. It has also powers of control over all the lower centres. The spinal reflex makes us withdraw a finger from the flame, but a cerebral order made Mucius Scaevola hold his hand in the flame till it was consumed.

With certain exceptions then, the synapses by which nerve cells are connected are in some part of the central nervous system, which consists of the brain, brain-stem and the spinal cord. Impulses (generally sense-impressions) from the skin, the muscles and from all the organs of the body are collected in the central nervous system. The neurones that carry these *incoming* impulses are described as "afferent" nerves. From the spinal cord, impulses are sent outward by other "efferent" nerves to the muscles and other organs, causing various movements to take place. The central nervous system then may be compared to a telephone exchange at the G.H.Q. of an army. It collects messages and reports from the sense organs by its afferent fibres and sends out instructions to the different parts of the organism by the efferent ones. Such a process may involve only a few neurones or it may involve a great many: the simplest instances involve the spinal cord alone; it is, therefore, simplest first to describe the spinal cord and to consider a simple spinal reflex.

The spinal cord is a mass of nervous tissue lying in the vertebral canal. From it issue the nerves which bring and carry back impulses, in pairs at fairly regular intervals. Each of these spinal nerves is attached to the cord by two roots, a posterior or afferent root, and an anterior or motor root. The two roots soon join to make up a mixed nerve with both incoming and outgoing fibres.

A cross-section of the spinal cord shows a central mass of grey matter and an outer mass of white matter surrounding it. The grey matter (which has, on either side, an anterior and posterior horn) consists of *nerve cells*, while the white matter consists of *nerve fibres*. The nerve cells of the efferent nerve lie in the anterior horn of grey matter while those of the afferent nerve lie in the posterior root ganglion. The axons of these afferent nerves end in small swellings close to the bodies of the motor nerve cells, although branches of the afferent axons pass up and down the cord into other situations. If a nerve-ending (N) is stimulated by a prick or burn (Fig. 467), an impulse travels up the afferent fibre A: the afferent neurone (P) is stimulated; an impulse passes from it across a synapse to the efferent neurones and thence to the efferent nerves (E, E), causing the arm muscle which those nerves supply, to contract and withdraw the finger. Here is the spinal reflex at its simplest, causing a motor response to a stimulus applied to a nerve.

It is rather doubtful whether such a simple spinal reflex exists. Probably all spinal reflexes involve a third neurone interposed between the afferent neurone and the efferent: but reflexes in which very few neurones take part, are many. If the legs are crossed and the patella and tendon of the upper knee is given a sharp tap with the edge of the hand, the foot gives a brisk kick and falls more slowly than it rose. This reflex is of obvious usefulness. Most of us have trodden on "the stair which was not there," and but for the reflex stretching of the leg in response to the bending of the knee we should have fallen. This reflex is very powerful, so powerful that there have been cases of patients who have sustained a broken patella owing to its strength: it is also very swift. The reflex straightening of the leg and recovery of the subject occurs before he even realises that he has been in

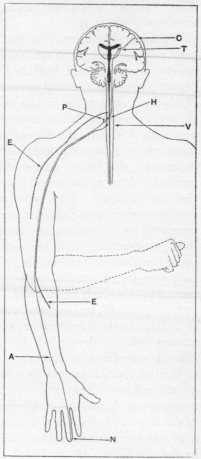

FIG. 467.—Illustrating the manner in which a stimulus causes an action. N, nerve ending; A, afferent nerve fibre; P, nerve cell (neurone) in posterior root ganglion; E, E, motor nerve fibres from efferent neurones in anterior root of nerve; V, spinal column; H, synapse; T, thalamus; C, cortex.

danger of falling. The simplest spinal reflex is valuable on account of this swiftness of action which saves the subject from disaster before he is aware of danger, let alone before he can take any steps to avert it.

We have seen, then, that the motor nerve-cells in the spinal cord may be excited to activity by direct action of the sensory nerves from without: but they can also be influenced by the higher parts of the central nervous system, the cerebrum and the cerebellum, which lie in the skull, and the brain stem which connects the higher brain centres with the spinal cord. Incoming nerve fibres run to the higher centre as well as directly to the motor nerve cells: and other nerve fibres run from these higher centres to the motor nerves. The higher centres receive information from all the sensory mechanisms, from the eye, the ear, the labyrinths, etc.: they *collect* and *synthesise* this, and the instructions they send out are the result of all the external factors operating on the organism. An action in response to such combined instructions will be better suited to the needs of the organism than will the single spinal reflex which can answer to only one set of conditions: but since the distance the impulse must travel is much greater and a larger number of synapses have to be negotiated, action follows more slowly on the stimulus than in the case of the simple reflex, which therefore is valuable for the instant actions demanded by sudden dangers. The higher centres, apart from the cerebrum, regulate all the normal functions of the body which are not, as a rule, within the conscious control of the subject. They regulate the position of the body, the temperature of the blood, the ventilation of the lungs, the rate of the heart and all those activities of the body which tend to keep it in adaptation to its environment and to prevent gross changes in the conditions under which the living cells must exist. Of course, many of these functions can be controlled by the conscious effort of the subject. The rate of breathing can be altered at will: nevertheless, the ventilation rate of the lungs is normally regulated very nicely without any conscious effort provided that the brain stem and its connections with the spinal cord are intact.

The individual properties of the so-called lower centres of the brain and of the cerebellum need not be discussed. It is enough to say that between them they collect impressions from every sense organ at the disposal of the body and that with the help of these impressions they control the relation of the organism to its environment with great accuracy. The possession of a cerebrum, or brain, is not at all necessary for such a comparatively complicated process as that by which a falling cat rights itself in the air and falls on its feet. As long as only a small number of rather ordinary things happened to it, the organism could do well enough without any cerebral hemispheres at all: but the reflexes of the spinal cord, the brain-stem and the cerebellum become inadequate when it is a question of searching for food, of protecting the body against even moderate alterations of temperature, or of escaping from an enemy.

Before considering the true brain or cerebrum and "voluntary" activity, a distinction must be made between two different parts of the nervous system. In the first place, there is the nervous system whose activity is expressed by the movements of the voluntary muscles even though the movements are brought about without conscious activity. The muscles that serve the knee jerk reflex are voluntary muscles. The activity of the nerve cell which leads to the contraction of those muscles, may, however, be brought about either by a direct reflex through the spinal cord, by a reflex through the brain-stem for the purpose of maintaining the standing posture of the body, or by voluntary activity of the cerebrum, as when we kick a football.

There is, however, another nervous system, the autonomic system, hardly connected at all with the main system we have described. This system is concerned with regulating the activities of organs over which we have no control, such as the heart, the muscular coats of the blood vessels, the iris of the eye, the sweat-glands, the hair follicles and of the muscular coats of the alimentary canal as well as of the other various organs whose activity is beyond the control of the voluntary nervous system. The autonomic system has a system of incoming and outgoing impulses: but its behaviour may also be determined by chemical stimuli, such as the acidity of the blood reaching the respiratory centre, or thermal stimuli, such as the temperature of blood reaching the hypothalamus, a portion of the lower brain in which the centre regulating the whole autonomic system is thought to lie. Certain sections which are essentially regulated by this autonomic system of nerves use the voluntary muscles for their own ends. If, for instance, the body is subjected to conditions of external cold, the motion of the voluntary muscles called shivering is used for the production of extra heat.

The heat regulating mechanism may well be used as an illustration of the use of the nervous system to regulate the environment of the cells. A warm-blooded animal like man, regulates his temperature within very narrow limits irrespective of the temperature of his environment. Apart from such voluntary activity as the wearing of clothes in cold weather or the eating of ice-cream when the weather is hot, the regulation is beyond voluntary control, although it is interesting to note that when the activity of the higher parts of the nervous system is depressed by sleep or by narcotics, heat regulation is imperfect. The intolerable heat under which surgeons work is not dictated by a distaste for fresh air but by the needs of the unconscious patient whose body temperature might fall disastrously were he not kept in a warm room and well supplied with blankets and bottles.

If the subject is in a cold environment, the general response of the body is directed towards the conservation of heat. The blood vessels to the skin are constricted, to prevent as far as possible, the loss of heat from the surface of the body. If necessary, extra heat has to be produced and this is done by increasing the amount of glycogen "burned" to produce energy: the voluntary muscles are excited into the quite involuntary activity of shivering, the thyroid gland pours its secretion into the circulation in increased amount and the general activity of the cells is raised. In this way, great extremes of cold can be withstood, but if the regulation is imperfect, as when, for instance, a man caught out of doors in very cold weather yields to the temptation to sleep; once the general temperature of the body begins to fall, the organism is involved in a vicious circle from which it will not readily escape; for at a lowered temperature the activity of the cells is lowered, and as it is this very activity which causes the production of heat, the temperature of the body must tend to fall again.

Adaptation to external heat is also very perfect. In this case, the vessels of the skin are dilated in order that the blood may be cooled readily by the external air. At rest, this mechanism may be sufficient: but if work is done or if the external temperature is very high, such a process cannot be effective and sweating occurs; in sweating, there is active secretion of a watery fluid by the sweat glands and the latent heat of evaporation of this fluid is lost to the body which is cooled. Since sweating is a very important mechanism for the loss of unwanted heat, it is possible for the body to withstand very high temperatures, temperatures that are well above the boiling point of water, as long as the atmosphere is dry and evaporation is rapid; but a high temperature is not easily withstood when the air is moist, and the subject is overcome by a temperature that approaches 37° C., the normal temperature of the body, if the air is totally saturated with moisture. Water vapour may also be lost by the lungs, and, if the air is not too moist, another mechanism is here available for the loss of unwanted heat.

THE CEREBRUM

The motor unit consisting of the muscle (or gland) and its motor nerve cell is merely the final path by which movement is carried out: as far as the final effect is concerned it is immaterial in what way the motor unit is excited, whether by a direct reflex through the spinal cord, or by a fibre from the cortex of the cerebrum itself: for there are fibres, axons of cells lying in the grey matter of the cerebrum (which lies outside the white matter, not, as in the cord, enclosed by it) and passing down to end at various levels near the nerve cells—relay centres—of the motor units. Destruction of these brain fibres or of the brain-cells from which they arise, abolishes the faculty of voluntary movement: that is to say, a subject deprived of them could not straighten his knee of his own accord, but his knee-joint reflex could still be elicited. If the motor-neurone itself were cut, there could be no movement of the knee of any kind: destruction of the nerves in the brain only abolishes voluntary activity. The cells giving rise to these fibres controlling voluntary movement are strictly localised in a definite motor area of the brain, there being more closely localised areas for the arm, the leg, the toes and other parts. The left side of the brain controls the right side of the body and *vice versa*, although certain muscles, such as those of respiration, which normally act in co-operation with those of the opposite side are represented on both sides of the brain. There are, moreover, areas of the cerebrum which receive sensory impressions from all the different sense organs of the body.

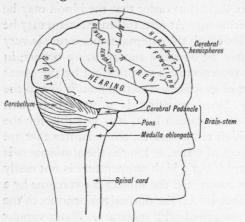

Fig. 468.—The main portions of the central nervous system. The *spinal cord* transmits impulses to the brain and operates simple reflexes. The *brain-stem* regulates the basic bodily functions. The *cerebellum* co-ordinates active and delicate movements of muscle required for maintaining posture and balance. The *cerebrum* is responsible for all the higher activities, the functions that a man has and such a creature as a frog has not.

It is in the cerebrum that these sensations reach consciousness. If, for instance, a man touches a hot plate with his finger, the finger is swiftly withdrawn, and this withdrawal would take place reflexly through the spinal cord without the cerebrum being called into action at all. Only in the cerebrum (Fig. 467), however, does the sensation reach consciousness: the cerebrum may even prevent the withdrawal of the hand if we have a powerful wish to keep it there.

In the cerebrum, every kind of sensory impression is collected and remembered. Conscious memory is only a small part of the memory. The cerebrum forgets nothing, but becomes the storehouse of all the accumulated experience of the invididual. The possession of a cerebrum is necessary for education, for profiting by experience: and the possession of great areas of association, of fibres linking up the storehouses of sensory impression, makes the brain capable of synthesising the whole experience of the individual. The missing link, however, as regards our knowledge of cerebral activity, is the link between experience and action. It has been argued and is still being argued that the so-called voluntary activity of the brain is merely reflex activity of a very complicated kind: that when a man acts in a certain way, he does so in response, not to the urge of some mysterious free-will but under compulsion, in response to a very complicated pattern of sensory impulses received by his cerebrum at different times and stored there for ever. As new sensory impressions reach the cerebrum, the pattern of accumulated experience is constantly changing but the conduct of the individual depends on the state of his accumulated experience at any given time. Such a theory is widely favoured, and its acceptance has, perhaps, been helped by the fact that its opponents cite no alternative theory supported by demonstrable facts: they talk rather of a "something" called "free-will." The behaviourist theory of the brain is still far from being accepted: it is improbable that it will be accepted for a very long time, and one may perhaps be permitted to abandon for a moment the strictly scientific attitude of unbiased enquiry and express the hope that we shall never be compelled to accept it.

The nervous system, then, may be considered as a complex arrangement of neurones, collecting and synthesising sensory impressions and sending out instructions to the mobile organs. It has been seen that in some cases only a few neurones are involved, and in these cases the anatomical connections of the different neurones are sufficient to account for the whole sequence of events from the stimulation of the sensory nerve-ending to the firing off of the muscle contraction. Other more complicated reflexes use more neurones, but may still be regarded as reflexes: the important question that has been left unanswered is, however, as to whether mere anatomical relations of nerve cells and nerve fibres are sufficient to account for conscious sensation, for the storing up of impressions called memory, and for the activity which we are pleased to call voluntary.

Our study, then, of the working of a Man gives us a picture of a system of instruments—limbs, jaws, etc.—for causing motion in themselves and other objects. These are worked by chemical motors (muscles) which are stopped, started and controlled by impulse-carriers (the nerves) in response to the sum of our sense impressions brought by these nerves from receiving instruments, both at the present and in the past. The brain is the organ which converts these manifold and related sense-impressions into motor impulses. All the instruments of the body operate by slow chemical changes of their substance, and they contain in themselves chemical means of repairing wastage and damage. A pump, the heart, circulates through the whole body a fluid (blood) which brings materials for energy production (glucose and oxygen) and for tissue building (amino acids). This fluid also carries away waste products, to be removed by the lungs and the elaborate filter of the kidneys. A chemical laboratory in the form of the digestive canal converts miscellaneous organic compounds— food—into such substances as the blood can profitably carry to the tissues. All these instruments or organs are dependent on each other: changes in one influence the others through the bloodstream and nervous system they all share: thus Man is not a collection of instruments, like a wireless set or a chemical works, but is a whole whose parts co-operate under the brain as organiser.

This summary takes no account of thought, memory and free will: it views man externally. Science has no answer to our question as to the possibility of explaining these except "Wait and See."

This chapter has treated a man as an isolated unit: we have now to consider how men make men.

CHAPTER XXXIX

REPRODUCTION

HEREDITY

THERE are two ways in which an individual creature can reproduce itself. The manner in which a single cell divides into two has already been noticed (p. 820). An animal or plant may simply multiply its cells in this fashion and then split off a portion of itself: the single-celled paramecium (Fig. 504) may divide in two: the many-celled sea anemone may bud off another from its side: even as high a creature as an aphis can bring forth young aphids without the co-operation of a male. This asexual reproduction is the exception, though it is the ancient and primitive method. Most animals and plants propagate themselves by two individuals, male and female, contributing a portion of themselves to make a new individual. This process is termed sexual reproduction.

The male produces an active, freely-swimming cell called a sperm; the female produces a larger but passive cell, an ovum. The sperm enters the ovum. Their nuclei join and the cell so formed grows into a new individual. This formation and fusion of sperm and ovum is common to plants, insects, fishes, birds, mammals and men: to every creature which has sex.

It is best then to study this before we consider the details of the way fertilisation is brought about and the young fertilised ovum is nourished: for these latter are accomplished in very different ways by different living things.

It will be remembered that every cell has a nucleus containing a material called chromatin, and that when the cell divides, the

911

chromatin gathers itself first into long threads (the spireme) which then split into shorter lengths called chromosomes. These split lengthwise in half, and one half of each chromosome goes to each half of the dividing cell. Both the new cells get replicas of all the chromosomes of the old. The chromosomes join again to a spireme which breaks again into knots and threads of chromatin.

This is the process of asexual reproduction. In sexual reproduction a different arrangement ensures that the new cell from which the young is to develop gets a complete set of chromosomes. Man has 48 chromosomes in each of his cells: the essential process is much more easily represented in the case of an animal which has only a few. The stone-fly is such a creature, but the process is essentially the same in man or sparrow or daffodil.

The male of every species has germ-cells which produce spermatozoa. In man and higher animals these are in the testes. The chromosomes are usually in pairs alike in shape. Thus, in

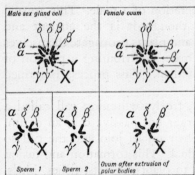

FIG. 469.—How the offspring receives equal contributions of chromosomes from its parents. Above are shown the complete outfit of 10 chromosomes for the male and female stone-fly. Below are shown the sperm and ovum each with a half set of 5 chromosomes. These fuse to a fertilised ovum which thus has a full set of 10 chromosomes.

Fig. 469 the complete cell of the male animal has ten chromosomes, two rod-like ones a and a', two thick V-shaped ones β and β', two smaller V-shaped ones γ and γ', two little dot-like ones δ and δ' and finally, a single long one X and a little short one Y. When a cell like this divides in the ordinary way, the two new cells each get the same equipment of chromosomes. But the male makes its spermatozoa by halving the cells of its sex gland. This division is different from all others because the chromosomes are not *halved* but *shared*, half going to each spermatozoon. Thus, one sex gland cell makes two sperms; of these, one sperm may get chromosomes α, β, γ, δ' and Y, while the other gets α', β', γ', δ and X; but they may divide up in any way as long as the sperm gets *one* of each of the α, β, γ and δ pair, and *either* X or Y. There are in this case thirty-two ways in which this sharing can be done. The more chromosomes there are the more ways of sharing them are possible. Man has 48; he can divide a gland cell into two sperms in 2^{24}, about 17,000,000 different ways. These two spermatozoa then divide once more but this time split their chromosomes and so keep the same outfit as they had before.

The unfertilised female ovum has a complete outfit of chromosomes $\alpha\alpha'$, $\beta\beta'$, $\gamma\gamma'$, $\delta\delta'$, but instead of X and Y, a pair of the long X's. Females[1] have a pair of chromosomes XX where males have an odd couple XY. When the male sperm enters the female ovum this halves its chromosomes too, and throws out half as a "polar" body. It would then have, say, chromosomes α, β', γ', δ' and X, but of course, it can have any selection from the ten as long as it has *one* of each pair. The ovum divides again, throwing out another polar body but keeps its previous set of chromosomes.

Now, the fertilisation of the egg occurs by the male sperm cell swimming to the female ovum and penetrating into it. Suppose the first sperm we mentioned was successful in doing this. The nuclei of the sperm and ovum combine. The fertilised egg will have chromosomes α, β, γ, δ' and X from the male, and α, β', γ, δ' and X from the female: so its cell will have the chromosomes $\alpha\alpha$, $\beta\beta'$, $\gamma\gamma$, $\delta'\delta'$ and XX. It will be a female, for it has the pair of chromosomes XX. Suppose the other sperm had been the one to fertilise the egg. The fertilised egg would have chromosomes $\alpha\alpha'$, $\beta'\beta'$, $\gamma'\gamma'$, $\delta\delta'$, and X and Y. This would be a male with the odd pair of chromosomes XY.

Now, we have reason to suppose that each of these chromosomes is a string of "genes" each carrying a factor which gives its owner some quality, and it is evident that the way in which

Except with birds and butterflies, where affairs are reversed.

characters are inherited from the father and mother depends on the "*genes*" which are in the chromosomes they both contribute. The male and female, both being of the same species, have the same number of chromosomes but their chromosomes may contain many different genes. Thus, a colour-blind man has a gene which a normal man or woman lacks, though he has the same set of chromosomes. A great number of human characters are inherited: but many of them are difficult to study. Some inherited characters are however obvious and easy to trace. As a first example, we may take brachydactyly, a deformity consisting of there being only two bones in the fingers instead of three. Suppose a normal woman marries a brachydactylous man. The man has the gene for brachydactyly in one of his chromosomes. His spermatozoa each have a half set of chromosomes taken at random, so half his spermatozoa will have the gene for brachydactyly and the other half will not. The ovum from the normal woman will have a normal gene: it is equally likely to be fertilised by any of the millions of spermatozoa which have access to it in the act of fertilisation.

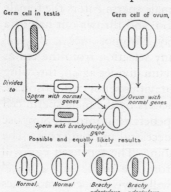

Fig. 470.—Diagram illustrating the manner in which a dominant characteristic such as brachydactyly is inherited. A brachydactylous man is supposed here to have married a normal woman. Only the pair of chromosomes which may contain the brachydactyly gene are illustrated. The normal chromosomes are shown as white rods, those containing the brachydactyly gene as shaded rods.

Now, brachydactyly is what we call a dominant, that is to say, if its gene is present with the normal gene, the former overcomes the latter. If the child is the product of a normal ovum, fertilised by a sperm with the gene for the deformity, it will have shortened fingers; if by the sperm without the gene, the child will be normal. Consequently, on an average, half the children of the brachydactylous man and normal woman will be brachydactylous. Fig. 471 is a pedigree (due to Farabee). The usual signs ♂ for male and ♀ for female, are used, the brachy-dactylous are black, and the normal, white.

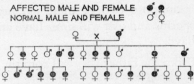

It should of course be realised that it is only *probable* that half the offspring will be brachydactylous, in the same sense that it is probable that of ten playing cards, taken at random, five will be red.

FIG. 471.—Pedigree of a family descended from a parent having the brachydactyly gene. (After Farabee.)

The more cases we examine, the more nearly we are likely to find equal totals of normal and abnormal children. But, in an individual family it might easily happen that there were nine normal to three abnormals or *vice versa*. There will be equal numbers of sperms with and without the brachydactyly gene; it is simply a question of luck which single one of the millions of sperms concerned in a single act of fertilisation happens to reach the ovum first.

One brachydactyly gene is enough to give the owner the deformity. In very many cases a quality is inherited only if *both* chromosomes of a pair possess the gene. We may take the case of the inheritance of blue-eyes as an example, though it is probably rather more complicated than appears below. Here, the gene for blue-eyes or grey-eyes is a recessive; that is to say, the gene for brown or hazel eyes overcomes it. Suppose we call the blue-eye gene *a* and the brown-eye gene *b*. Suppose a blue-eyed man and a brown-eyed woman marry. The blue-eyed man will have an *a* gene in each of the particular pair of chromosomes concerned with eye-colour. We can call him *aa* then. All of his spermatozoa will have one of the pair of chromosomes and therefore one of these *a* genes. The brown-eyed person will have two *b* genes, *bb*, of which one will remain in her fertilised ovum. Then the offspring will have both factors, and its chromosomes will contain both genes, *ab*, and since *b* overcomes *a*, all the children will be brown-eyed. But, they will only in appearance be the same as their brown-eyed parent who has two *b* genes.

Suppose two of these *ab*, brown-eyed people marry. Their sperms and ova will *either* have an *a* or a *b*. So their offspring may have,

From the father.	From the mother.	Child's eyes.
a	*a*	*aa* blue.
a	*b*	*ab* brown.
b	*a*	*ab* brown.
b	*b*	*bb* brown.

So, since all four possibilities are equally probable, on an average, such a marriage would produce one blue-eyed child to every three brown-eyed, of which three, only one would be a pure brown with no blue gene. This case is a very common one.

Here are some examples of it. In each case the dominant *b* behaves like the brown-eye factor and the recessive *a* like the blue-eyed factor.

Dominant	Recessive
Blackness in rabbits.	Blue colour in rabbits.
Tallness in peas.	Dwarfness in peas.
Short hair in rabbits.	Angora fur in rabbits.
Rough hair in guinea pigs.	Smooth hair in guinea pigs.
Web-fingers.	Normal fingers.
Mongolian "slant-eye."	European eye.
Normal pigmentation in man.	Albinism.

In a number of cases the *ab* offspring have a different appearance from that of the *aa* or *bb* offspring. A simple case is that of the crossing of ivory-coloured and red antirrhinums. If we call the gene for red (*a*) and that for ivory (*b*), then *aa* plants are red, *bb* plants ivory, while *ab* plants are pink.

A third interesting type of inheritance is the "sex-linked" which is well illustrated by hæmophilia, the defect, already mentioned on p. 840, by which the blood of the sufferer from it does not easily coagulate. Fig. 472 shows a pedigree of an affected family. It is easily seen that only males[1] suffer from the

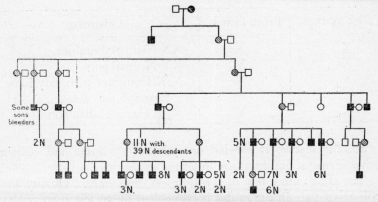

FIG. 472.—Seven generations of hæmophiliacs (bleeders). White circles or squares or the letter N indicate normal persons. Black squares indicate males who suffered from hæmophilia. Shaded circles indicate females who, though unaffected themselves, carried the gene in one of their X-chromosomes and so transmitted the disease. (After Davenport.)

condition, and that it is only inherited through the mother.

Hæmophilia is a recessive, like blue-eyes, and its gene (*b*) is contained in the X chromosome of which a man has only one (p. 912) and a woman two. Now, suppose a man with hæmophilia marries a normal woman. His sperms have either an X chromosome with the hæmophilia gene X_h or a Y chromosome.

An ovum from a normal woman will have one X chromosome. So, the result of the mating will be either a child with chromosomes X and X_h—a daughter—or a child with chromosomes XY—

[1] If both partners came from an affected family, the daughters might suffer from the disease. If one partner is normal, this cannot happen.

a son. The son will be perfectly normal and neither has the disease nor hands it on. The daughter will not have the disease, for her normal X chromosome overpowers the recessive abnormal X_h one with the hæmophilia gene. Now, suppose she marries a normal man. Her fertilised ova will *either* have the X or X_h chromosomes. The father's sperms will have X or Y chromosomes. So, the possibilities are

From mother	From father	Offspring
X	X	XX Normal daughter.
X	Y	XY Normal son.
X_h	X	X_hX Daughter who may have hæmophiliac sons.
X_h	Y	X_hY Hæmophiliac son.

So, the disease is handed on. Colour-blindness and certain other forms of blindness are inherited in this way.

The above are a few of the simplest cases only. Quality and colour of hair in the rabbit is controlled by no less than twelve different genes, and the number of possible variations is therefore very large. Very few cases of human heredity have been completely worked out. Human beings are particularly difficult to study from the point of view of heredity, first because they breed slowly, and long and complete pedigrees are very difficult to trace; secondly because human beings are so interbred that a pure stock is nowhere to be found.

HUMAN REPRODUCTION

This combination of two half-sets of chromosomes from a sperm and ovum respectively occurs in every species which has two sexes. The means by which the sperm and ovum are brought together, and the way, if any, in which the fertilised ovum is cared for until it can look after itself varies enormously. Among almost all land-animals, the male introduces his sperm into the body of the female. Amphibians and fish often shed their sperm and ova into the water, where they meet. The very curious method adopted by plants is mentioned on p. 994 ff.

Let us trace the complete course of reproduction of a human being. A new-born baby is either male or female. This depends on whether its original cell and, therefore, all the cells which grew from it by the ordinary process of division (p. 820), had two equal X-chromosomes, in which case it is a girl, or an X and a Y chromosome, in which case it is a boy. In the first case, the female sex-organs are developed (p. 922), in the second case, the male organs. These organs have no function at first and remain small and undeveloped until the age of puberty, which may be between 9 or 15, varying greatly in different races, and in individuals of the same race. At this age, the anterior lobe of the pituitary gland sends out a substance which stimulates the ovary or the testes to grow. These again send out hormones which cause all the changes of puberty.

The result of these changes is, then, firstly to make the sex-organs develop and become capable of doing their work of creating offspring, and next to develop secondary sexual characters, such as beard and deep voice in a man, and the body hair of a woman. Mental changes also occur: notably an emotionally-coloured attitude to the other sex, and perhaps not unconnected with this a feeling for beauty, bodily or spiritual. From the time when puberty is well advanced until old age, the male sex system steadily produces millions of spermatozoa which are always ready for the act of generation. The male organs are shown in Fig. 920. The testes consist of nests of tubes, the walls of which are lined with cells which grow and divide into spermatozoa as already described. The spaces between the tubes are packed with interstitial cells which produce minute quantities of a most potent hormone, androsterone, which brings about the changes at puberty and continues to exert influence thereafter.

We all know the difference between the savage and powerful stallion and the docile gelding: the active, lean and enterprising tom-cat and the heavy and indolent neuter: the ferocious bull and the mild ox. The removal of the testes, in general, makes an animal fat, lazy and docile. There is a general belief that the changes of old age are due to the dwindling and loss of function in the ovary and testis. Attempts have been made to graft testes, usually from an ape, into old men: the operation often succeeds in restoring vigour and a feeling of well-being, but it does not restore the worn-out tissues and hardened arteries of old age.

The chief task of the testes is to make spermatozoa. The human spermatozoon is a minute cell consisting of four parts, a sharp point which can penetrate the ovum, a flat shovel-shaped head which contains the nucleus and genes, a middle piece which contains the apparatus causing the first division of the egg, and a long whip-like tail. By lashing this tail, the spermatozoon can swim—not very rapidly. The spermatozoa of almost every creature are of this shape, having a head and swimming freely by means of their whip-like tail (Plate XLII).

The spermatozoa pass through a long coiled tube, the epididymis, along the spermatic duct. The only remaining part which the male takes in reproduction is to introduce his sperm into the female. This is done by means of the exterior male organ. Some forty million sperms, mixed with the secretion of the seminal vesicles and of the prostate gland, are forced into the passage leading to the interior of the female

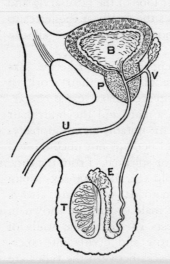

FIG. 473.—The male organs of reproduction, slightly modified so as to appear in a single vertical section. T, testis; E, epididymis; V, seminal vesicle; B, bladder; P, prostate; U, urethra.

sex-organs. Here they swim upward through the uterus and the uterine tube towards the ovary.

Now, let us turn to the much more complicated processes in the female. From puberty onwards, a remarkable cycle of events have been repeating themselves over a period of some twenty-eight days: the object of these is to supply an ovum to be fertilised by the spermatozoon and to provide a means by which the fertilised ovum can be nourished while it grows.

The essential sex organ of the female is the ovary (Fig. 474) in which is secreted a hormone which causes the changes at puberty, but which also contains a great number of ova or egg-cells each contained in a little bag, or Graafian follicle (Plate XLVl). They gradually mature and finally project from the wall of the ovary.

For the first few days of the 28-day cycle, that remarkable gland, the pituitary, produces a hormone called prolan A which stimulates the ovary to produce another hormone, œstrin, which is known to be a complicated chemical substance, œstrone, with formula as shown below. It is interesting to note the likeness between the male and female sex-hormones.

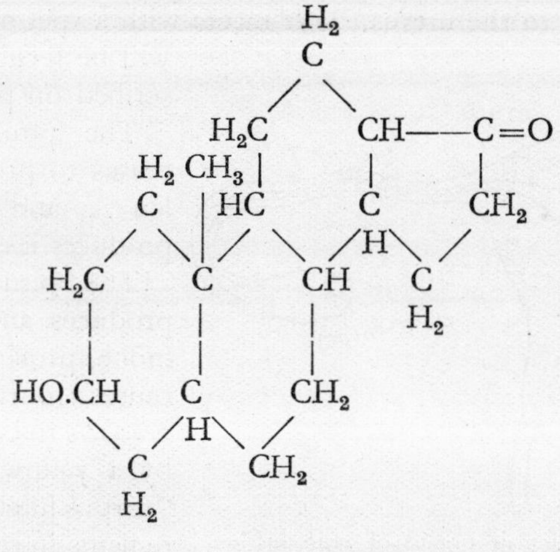

The male sex-hormone: androsterone.

$$
\begin{array}{c}
\text{H}_2 \quad \text{CH}_2 \\
\text{C} \quad | \\
\diagup \quad \diagdown | \\
\text{H}_2\text{C} \qquad \text{C} \text{---} \text{C}=\text{O} \\
\text{H} \qquad | \qquad | \\
\text{C} \quad \text{HC} \quad \text{C} \qquad \text{CH}_2 \\
\diagup\diagup \quad \diagdown\diagup \quad \diagdown\diagup\text{H}\diagdown\diagup \\
\text{HC} \qquad \text{C} \qquad \text{C} \qquad \text{CH}_2 \\
| \qquad \| \qquad | \\
\text{HO.C} \qquad \text{C} \qquad \text{CH}_2 \\
\diagdown\diagup \quad \diagdown\diagup \\
\text{C} \qquad \text{C} \\
\text{H} \qquad \text{H}_2
\end{array}
$$

The female sex hormone: oestrone.

The œstrone passes into the blood stream and reaches the uterus (Fig. 474), where it causes the inner wall, whose function is to house and nourish the developing child, to grow and become full of blood vessels. A follicle then bursts in the ovary and an ovum is liberated: this is pushed by cilia (p. 977) down a tube (the uterine tube) to the uterus. If it meets with a spermatozoon, it will be fertilised as described on p. 913.

The pituitary then ceases to produce prolan A, and the ovary produces less œstrin.

The pituitary then produces another hormone, prolan B, which causes a fourth hormone *progestin* to be produced by a yellow body the "corpus luteum," which remains in the ovary in the place from which

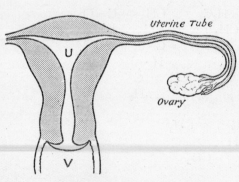

Fig. 474.—The female organs of reproduction. U = uterus; V = vagina.

the ovum emerged. Progestin prepares the wall of the uterus to receive a fertilised ovum. But if the ovum is not fertilised, as in general is the case, progestin ceases to be secreted. The enlarged wall of the uterus breaks down and escapes to the exterior as blood and cell-debris. The cycle then starts over again, the pituitary producing prolan A which makes the ovary produce œstrin which makes the wall of the uterus grow again. The whole cycle repeats itself at intervals of about 28 days.

If the ovum is fertilised, the corpus luteum in the ovary persists all through pregnancy: its function may be to stimulate the uterus to growth.

Let us suppose, however, that the ovum has met a spermatozoon in the uterine tube, and that their nuclei have fused into a single nucleus, and let us glance at the series of changes which turn this single cell into a human being.

The fertilised egg, which is a single cell so minute that it would be only visible as a speck some $\frac{1}{130}$th inch in diameter, is carried down the uterine tube into the uterus and embeds itself in its wall which has become thickened and full of blood vessels. Now, it is obviously impossible to observe the development of a single microscopic cell within the uterus, so our knowledge of the first few days of development is chiefly drawn from observations on other animals. Even before the fertilised ovum reaches the uterus, it begins to divide in the usual manner described on pp. 820–821, first into two, then into four, then into eight (Fig. 475, 1–4), till it becomes a ball of rounded cells which becomes hollow like a tennis ball (5), but with a thicker mass of cells projecting into its interior. The form of a hollow cup (6) is next taken. Meanwhile, the ovum has embedded itself deeply in the wall of the uterus. It next develops a set of organs which are designed to attach it to its mother's uterus and supply it with nourishment. These are discussed on p. 925. The cup then becomes internally closed (7) and then folded on itself (8). Its external appearance in now rather like Fig. 475, B.1. The groove so formed develops into the backbone. The most interesting changes occur between the third and eighth week. When a human embryo is about four weeks old, it is about an eighth of an inch long. It is then hardly possible to distinguish it from the embryo of any other large mammal and indeed, it is very little different from the embryo of a bird or a fish. It has a long and large tail rather like a fish's. It has a single-chambered heart like a fish's and a circulation with loops to four gill-arches (p. 954) like those of a fish. It does not use these rudiments of gills, but for some reason the single cell can only become a man by first organising itself on the plan of a fish and then altering this to the plan of a man. It is clear that there is some connection between the way the primeval cell of a thousand million years ago evolved into a man and the way the primitive single cell of the fertilised ovum develops into each one of us: but what this connection is, is unknown. Fig. 475 gives an idea of the way the primitive fish-like embryo gradually evolves into a recognisable man.

Nearly all creatures other than mammals provide their fertilised egg-cell with a large supply of food "yolk" to sustain it until it can fend

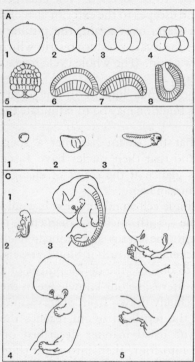

FIG. 475.—Development of fertilised ovum A1–8 earliest stages. 1–4 are views, 5–8 are sections. B1–3 Infolding of the cup-shaped mass of cells forming a groove B1 which is the rudiment of the backbone. These stages are taken from the development of the tadpole, but are closely similar to those occurring in man. C. 1. Fish-like stage with rudimentary gill-arches and long stout tail. 3–5 later stages. Age of embryos shown. A. 1–8 up to *c*. 10 days. C1 about 4 weeks. C3 about 6 weeks. C4 about 7 weeks. C5 about 8 weeks. Figs. A 1–8 are much magnified. C1–5 are about twice natural size.

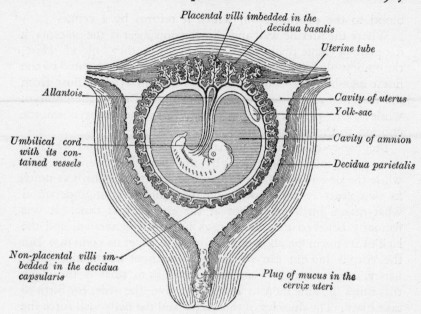

Placental villi imbedded in the decidua basalis

Uterine tube

Allantois

Cavity of uterus

Yolk-sac

Umbilical cord with its contained vessels

Cavity of amnion

Decidua parietalis

Non-placental villi imbedded in the decidua capsularis

Plug of mucus in the cervix uteri

FIG. 476.—The uterus in the third month of pregnancy. Note the circulation of blood from the embryo through the umbilical cord and the chorion (white). The latter is in intimate contact with the *decidua placentalis* (shaded) which is richly supplied with the mother's blood. The embryo hangs in the liquid contained in the *amnion*. Note also the remains of the yolk-sac from which the embryo gained its early nourishment. As the foetus enlarges the *uterine cavity* disappears. (Courtesy of Messrs. Longmans, Green & Co., Ltd., from Gray's *Anatomy*.)

for itself. The hen's egg contains enough food to turn a fertilised germ-cell into an active bird. The mammals have adopted the plan of supplying nourishment from the mother's blood. The egg-cell has a little yolk: this serves to sustain the developing egg until it has its own system of nourishment. Fig. 476 shows how a mammal is supplied with food while it is in the mother's body. The uterus develops its thickened wall (*decidua placentalis*, Fig. 476): ramifying into this are the *villi* of the chorion which is developed from the embryo. The chorion contains a sac of liquid in which the embryo hangs by a sort of stalk. This stalk contains an artery through which the heart of the embryo pumps its own blood to the chorion from which it returns by a vein.

Where the uterine wall and the chorion meet is the placenta, a flat plate of tissue richly supplied with the mother's blood. Here, the embryonic blood and maternal blood are only separated by the finest membranes. Consequently, food and oxygen diffuse from the maternal capillaries into the chorion and so to the embryo: while waste products diffuse back from the embryo *via* the chorion to the mother's blood.

Pregnancy ends in the human being after a period which is very nearly nine months. Why this period is found in man while the dog requires but nine weeks and the elephant as much as two years is not understood, nor indeed is it understood what makes birth take place at the end of that time. It was formerly believed that the corpus luteum degenerated, and the lack of its hormone allowed the uterus to expel its contents. But the corpus luteum can be removed without terminating pregnancy; consequently, we are in the dark as to what is the clock that times the nine months and how it gives the order for birth to take place. The muscles of the uterus and the belly-wall force the baby through the vagina to the outer world: the placenta and membranes follow shortly after.

The child has now to fend for itself as far as air supply, digestion and excretion are concerned. It has lungs, intestines and kidneys which it has not yet used, and these promptly set to work. A new-born chick can eat much the same food as a hen: the mammals are distinguished by elaborating milk in the breasts or mammary glands as a food which nourishes the young for the first few weeks or months.

The mammary glands vary in number in different animals. The human being has the minimum number, two. They are a mass of ramifying tubes lined with secreting cells. The tubes all meet and deliver the milk to the central opening.

Milk is an emulsion of fat-droplets in a weak solution of certain solids. It is a very complete food. It contains everything that the young of the species require—fat, proteins, carbohydrates, salts and vitamins. It contains some 87% water, 3.75% fat, 4.7%

of lactose (milk sugar), 3.4% of caseinogen and lactalbumen—proteins—and 0.75% of salts. It does not follow, of course, that the milk of one creature is the right food for the young of another. Thus, cow's milk contains rather too little vitamin C for the human infant: moreover, since the calf grows more quickly than a baby it contains too much protein and salt. It has rather too little sugar and, interestingly, too little lecithin. Lecithin is a material which is needed for brain development, which does not trouble the calf as much as the human being. The milk which the child sucks from its mother's breast is completely free from bacteria: ordinary milk after storage and delivery may swarm not only with the lactic bacilli which finally make it go sour, but also with the germs of bovine tuberculosis, and any others that may have been introduced by those who have handled it. It is considered too that maternal milk carries with it the anti-bodies (p. 1014) from the mother's blood and is, therefore, capable of conferring on the baby some immunity from infection. It is an odd fact that milk contains almost no iron and apparently the child stores before birth enough iron—which it must have for its red blood pigment —to last it until it is weaned.

CHAPTER XL

The Classes of Animals

SPECIES

WE have now looked into the workings of one animal—
man. We have seen that the body is a community of cells,
separate yet dependent on each other for life. We have seen how
some cells are specialised for strength, others for motion, others
for sensitivity, others for the production of chemical substances.
Every living creature is either a single cell or a collection of such
cells and it is almost certain that from the chemical and physical
make-up of the individual cell arise all the differences between the
kinds of living creatures.

Our next problem should be, then, to see how living creatures
differ from man and from each other. One of the earliest facts we
learn is that there are different kinds of living creatures, cows,
horses, sparrows, herrings, oysters, turnips and whatnot: and that
these mate with their own kind and reproduce their own kind.
We may term these different kinds of animals, *species*. Now no
two animals are exactly alike, but any two sparrows resemble
each other more closely than any sparrow resembles any bullfinch
or chaffinch. Thus, surveying all the single animals and vegetables
we can observe that they can be grouped as species whose
members are more like each other than they are like the members
of any other species. A few cases of difficulty arise when the
differences are small. It would be wrong to say that the Chinese
and European races of men are different species, for the likenesses
between them are so much greater than the differences. We should
call them "races" or "varieties" of the same species. But, there is

PLATE XLV

Deep-sea diving dress. (By courtesy of Mr. David Scott, Chief Paris Correspondent of *The Times*.)

PLATE XLVI

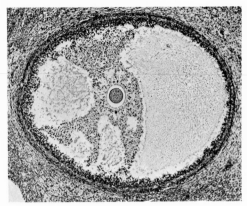

Graafian follicle containing unfertilised ovum
(× 40)

Section of the compound eye of a dragon-fly.

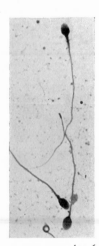

Human spermatozoa (× 600).

no really certain criterion which enables us to say whether two groups of individuals belong to different species or different varieties of the same species.

The biologist says he will give the name *species* to a group of creatures which have the following characteristics. First, they should be more like each other than like the members of other groups: secondly, they must breed offspring which remain equally like their parents and each other: thirdly, they must readily breed with each other, and less readily or not at all with animals of another group: fourthly, the group must not be distinguished by some temporary characteristics due only to outside influences like food or climate.

Thus, take as example the dandelion. Dandelion plants are more like each other than they are like hawkweeds or chicory or any allied plant: dandelion seed produces dandelions just like the parents. They are much more readily fertilised by dandelion pollen than the pollen of any other plant: in natural conditions they never cross with other flowers. Finally, we do not call the small dwarf dandelions of high and rocky places and the large luxuriant dandelions of the meadows two different species, for, if we plant the former in the meadows and the latter in the rocks, they soon become just like their neighbours.

We do not call Chinese, negroes and Europeans different species because, apart from racial prejudices, they breed freely with each other. But it must not be forgotten that this classification into species and races is an artificial one. Probably, a "race" is the first stage in the formation of a new species. Hardly any species, as fossils show us, has remained unchanged over periods of tens of millions of years. It is quite likely that if Chinese, negroes and Europeans were to be isolated for ten or twenty million years, they would evolve in different ways and become so unlike as to be truly different species and no longer able to interbreed.

There are nearly a million known species of animals and plants: new ones are frequently being described. It is clearly unwieldy to classify living creatures into a million groups: accordingly,

30

the classification into species is inadequate for practical purposes. These species can be further classified into *genera*, all the species in which are more like each other than they are like any species outside the genus.

Thus, the species of plants, charlock, cabbage, cauliflower, mustard, turnip, brussel-sprout are put in the genus *Brassica*, for to the eye of the botanist they are more like each other than they are like the wallflower or radish or water-cress which are their nearest common relations. Again, the various species of domestic mouse are classed in the genus *Mus*, for they all are more like each other than any of them are like their nearest allies the rats, field mice, etc.

In what is this likeness found? One will look for it in characters which do not vary much within the species. Thus, colour and markings are poor criteria of a species. A conformation, depending on the bones or fleshy parts is a sounder test and perhaps the best test of all is the chemical one which is described a little later. These genera are further grouped into larger divisions, which are again combined into twenty or so phyla, each of which represents a totally different *pattern* of animal or plant.

Finally, these phyla are grouped into the two Kingdoms of Animals and Plants.

For an example let us return to our mouse. The house-mouse is the SPECIES *Mus musculus*. It belongs to the GENUS *Mus*, which also includes various foreign mice. This genus is grouped with the rats, harvest mice, field-mice, etc., to make a SUBFAMILY *Murinæ* which is grouped with the subfamilies of Gerbils and certain foreign water-rats to make the FAMILY of *Muridæ*. This family with the Dormice, Hamsters, Voles, Lemmings and Jerboas are grouped into the SECTION of *Myomorpha* or mouse-like creatures.

This section joins with the Squirrels, Prairie-dogs, Flying-squirrels, Beavers, Porcupines, Guinea-pigs, to make up a SUB-ORDER of *Simplicidentata* which with the sub-order of rabbits and hares (*Duplicidentata*), make the ORDER of *Rodentia*. The rodents differ from the other mammals in having a peculiar chisel-like pair of front teeth; these are adapted for gnawing and grow all the time the animal is alive. Most rodents have five toes and are vegetable feeders. A good many other characteristics are shared by this order.

The rodents are a group in the SUB-CLASS of *placental mammals*, distinguished by having a placenta (p. 926) as a means of nourishing the unborn young. The placental mammals with the much less important marsupials (kangaroos, etc.), and the egg-laying monotremes (like the platypus) form a very well-marked CLASS of *Mammals*.

Mammals are warm-blooded, hairy, and suckle their young. The mammals, birds, reptiles, amphibians, fishes and cyclostomes (a primitive kind of fish) together make the SUBPHYLUM of *Craniata* or creatures with skulls. This, with a few primitive creatures (e.g., sea-squirts, lancelets) make up the PHYLUM of *Chordates* or *Vertebrates*, distinguished by having a central nervous system (brain and spinal cord) lying all on one side of the digestive system. Now, this whole phylum of vertebrates may be thought of as having a structure and working, something like that which we have studied in man. The other eighteen phyla of animals are built on a completely different pattern. Thus, in a starfish (phylum of Echinodermata) you cannot find any organ that you can also find in man. A frog, on the other hand, has nearly all the important organs found in a man.

This phylum of vertebrates is then grouped with eighteen other phyla, among which may be mentioned the arthropods (crustaceans, spiders, insects, etc.), the molluscs (snails, bivalves, cuttlefish, etc.), the cœlenterata (jelly-fish), to make the GRADE of *Metazoa* or many celled animals. The metazoa with the other grade of *Protozoa*, single celled creatures, make up the KINGDOM of *Animals*. These, with the kingdom of plants (itself divided into grades, phyla, etc.), complete the total of living things.

This classification may seem very cumbrous, but if you have a million things to classify, you must have a pretty complex system.

It is obviously hopeless to do more than try to illustrate the working of a few of the creatures of the main phyla, and to show how widely or otherwise, they differ from the pattern we have discussed.

MAMMALS

Apart from his brain, Man is a rather unspecialised mammal. He has not spun his fingers out into a wing like a bat, nor his nose into a trunk like an elephant. He has kept all his five fingers or toes on each limb. In fact, apart from his naked skin, his lack of a tail, the peculiar shape of his head and his erect position, it is not unfair to regard him as a typical mammal, and such creatures as bats, elephants and horses as divergents from the type. It is worth while, however, to spend a little time in seeing how the unspecialised type we have described in Man is adapted to suit the lives of the various mammals without losing or gaining any important part. All the mammals could be made out of the simple type by *modifying* it: enlarging this bone, bending that one, using an old organ for a new purpose or letting a useless one dwindle away.

One of the strongest pieces of evidence for the theory that mammals have been derived from a common stock, is that all their varied shapes and abilities are the result of variations on the single theme of the vertebrate body.

The bony structures show this admirably. In Figs. 477–8 are shown the skeleton of a man and a dog. Look first at the limbs and feet. All the main bones are not only there, but are roughly the same shape. The dog walks on his fingers and has lost his big toe and reduced his thumb to a small size. His pelvis is decidedly different because he is four-legged. Consequently, it is not a cup to support his organs but is rather a means of transmitting the thrust of his back legs to his body. The difference in the skulls is interesting. A dog has not much brain to house, but his diet requires powerful jaws. In our skull, the jaw bones are small, and the frontal and parietal and occipital bones which

TWO MAMMALS:　DOG and MAN (Brit. Mus.)

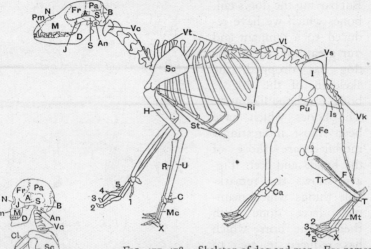

FIG. 477–478.—Skeleton of dog and man. For names of bones in these and in Figs. 482–485 see list below.

A, Alisphenoid; An, Angular (=Tympanic); Ar, Articular (=Malleus). B, Occipitals; Br, Branchiostegal rays. C, Carpals; Ca, Calcaneum; Cl, Clavicle; Co, Coracoid. D, Dentary. E, sub-orbitals. F, Fibula; Fe, Femur; Fr. frontal. G, Pterygoid. H, Humerus; Hm, Hyomandibular (=Columella= Stapes). I, Ilium; Io, Interopercular; Is, Ischium. J, Jugal. K, Symplictic; Kh, Ceratohyal; Ko, Coronoid. L, Lachrymal; Lc, Cleithrum; Ls, supra-Cleithrum; Lt, Lepidotrichal. M, Maxilla; Mc, Metacarpals; Mp, Parasphenoid; Ms, Mesethmoid; Mt, Metatarsals. N, Nasal. O, Opercular; Op, Preopercular. P, Palatine; Pa, Parietal; Pm, Premaxilla; Pu, Pubis. Q, Quadrate. R, Radius; Ra, Radials; Ri, Ribs. S, Squamosal; Sc, Scapula; St, Sternum. T, Tarsals; Ti, Tibia. U, Ulna; Us, sub opercular. V, Splenial; Va, Abdominal vertebrae; Vc, Cervical vertebrae; Vk, Caudal vertebræ; Vl, Lumbar vertebræ; Vs, Sacral vertebræ; Vt, Thoracic vertebræ. W, Prefrontal. X, Phalanges; Y, Parasphenoid. Z, Supra angular; Zt, Supra temporal. Numbers 1–5—digits.

NOTE.—In human anatomy somewhat different names are given.

contain the brain are huge. But barring the dog's tail bones which we have reduced to a remnant and our great toe which the dog has dropped, the skeleton of the dog is bone for bone like ours. The bones which have been most interestingly modified are those of the hands and feet. Fig. 479 shows the remarkable things which mammals have done with them. The horse which has reduced its toes to one useful one, and rudiments of the others, and the bat which has extended its fingers to make a wing, show the extremes.

The skin and hair, being next to the outer world, are organs which are pretty extensively modified. Man is very exceptional in having a thin naked skin. The typical mammalian arrangement is a fairly thin skin well covered with hair, the

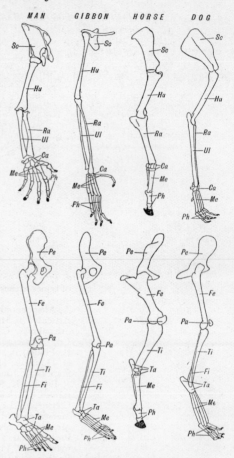

FIG. 479.—The limbs of mammals. Above, scapula; Hu, humerus; Ra, radius; Ul, ulna; Ph, phalanges or fingers; Pe, pelvis; Fe, femur; or ankle bones; Me, metatarsals; Ph, toes.

function of which is to entrap air and so make a layer which does not conduct heat to the exterior. Hair is incidentally a protection against injury. No creature, except a mammal, has any true hair growing from a root—the anatomy of the hair root appears in

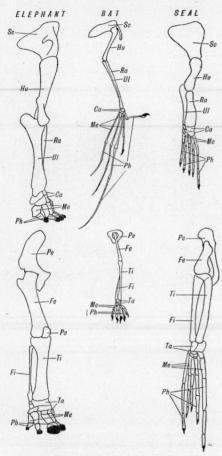

ELEPHANT BAT SEAL

fore-limbs; below, hind limbs. Bones: Sc, Ca, carpal or wrist bones; Me, metatarsals; Pa, patella; Ti, tibia.; Fi, fibula; Ta, tarsal.

Plate LXIV—and every mammal, except whales and dugongs, has some hair. Horns (but not antlers) are really a kind of hair cemented into a solid mass. The quills of hedgehogs and porcupines are modified hairs also.

A few mammals have scales, which is not surprising since our reptilian ancestors were probably scaly. Most interesting is the fact that hairs on mammals with scales are grouped in threes or fives behind each scale, and that mammals who have lost their scales often show the same arrangement of groups. The fine hair on the human fœtus shows this memory of a far distant scaly past!

The nervous system, apart from the brain, is not widely different in mammals generally and in man. The brain, however, shows enormous differences in development, which are mentioned again apropos of the evolution of man (p. 1036); though the brains of rabbit and man are recognisably built on the same plan. Fig. 480 shows the brains of dogfish, frog and pigeon (which of course are not mammals), and of rabbit, dog, monkey and man.

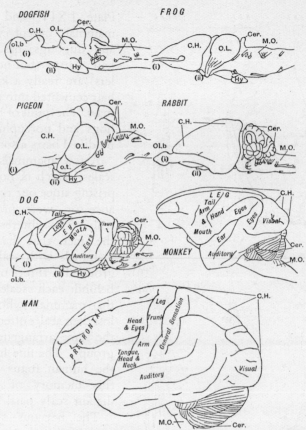

FIG. 480.—The brains of a few vertebrates drawn as if the
bases of each were the same length. Ol.b., Olfactory bulb,
C.H., cerebral hemispheres; O.L., optic lobe; Cer, Cerebellum;
Hy, Pituitary gland; M.O., medulla oblongata (brain-stem);
o.t., optic tract (i) olfactory nerve, (ii) optic nerve. Note
that the huge cerebrum of man hides much of the lower
centres of his brain.

The sizes are drawn as if the bases of the brains of all the
animals in question were of the same length. The cerebral
hemispheres, which deal with registering and recording of sense
impressions and the making of skilled movements in response,

are negligible in the dogfish, better in the frog and better still in the pigeon, which shows the dawn of intelligence. The rabbit shows little or no advance: its life needs, if anything, less skill of movement than the strongly and skilfully flying bird. Its organ of smell is well developed, which is characteristic of the mammal. The dog has a far better brain. In order to give it more surface (the active portion), it is crumpled up into folds. The dog is very teachable: he has consequently a large area where he can store his sense impressions or memories. His visual area and his prefrontal area (see pp. 1036 ff), and his auditory area are small, for he does not depend on his eyes or reasoning or speech, but his olfactory region is huge. A dog can recognise his master doubtfully by sight, but certainly by the smell of his trousers—a state of affairs that we, who could not tell our own wives from other women by their smell, find it hard to imagine. The monkey's brain is larger still, for he is a creature leading a highly skilled life swinging among the branches and needs very complete and accurate control of his muscles. The olfactory region is reduced to very small proportions while the visual and auditory parts are much increased, for a life in the trees gives little scope for smell and much for sight and sound. Man's brain finally is hugely enlarged. It will be seen that the chief enlargement is in the auditory region—concerned largely with word-images and speech: in the region between the visual and the motor region, where, probably the registering of sense impressions goes on, and most of all in the prefrontal region which probably deals with visual images registered in memory, and the association of these. Probably in the prefrontal region the highest mental processes of ingenuity, reasoning and intuition have their seat.

In the sense organs of the mammals, the differences are smaller. Many mammals have special touch-hairs like the cat's whiskers. These are most highly developed in the night-flying bat tribe. The organs of taste in mammals are not very different from those in man, but as might be expected, the organs of smell in the nose are much more elaborated. Instead of the small area devoted to smell in man, the dog has in its nose a most elaborate system of folds of thin bone covered with a membrane in which are the nerve endings

30*

of the sense of smell. The other extreme of having very little sense of smell is reached in the primates—men, apes and monkeys—and in sea-beasts, seals and whales. The sperm-whale has not even an olfactory nerve.

Nearly all mammals have efficient eyes built on the same principle as the eye of man. The pupils of some form a slit instead of a circular hole—the cat is a good example. The moles have poor eyes—sometimes their eyelids are joined though there is an eye beneath. An eye, easily irritated by earthy particles, is a hindrance to the mole in his dark tunnels. One beast, the Australian marsupial mole *Notoryctes*, has only a rudiment of an eye with no lens and no rods and cones!

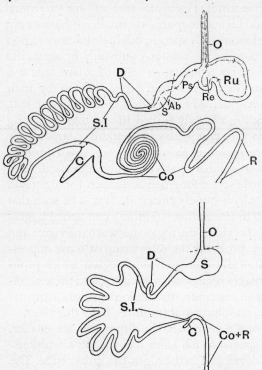

The organs of digestion are of the same general pattern in mammals but their details vary greatly according to whether the food needs little digestion or much. The ruminants —e.g., the cow— are examples of the first type and carnivores such as the dog, of the

FIG. 481.—The digestive system of a herbivorous mammal (above) and of a carnivorous mammal (below). The course of the food in the upper figure is shown by dotted lines and arrows. O, œsophagus (gullet); Ru, rumen; Re, reticulum; Ps, psalterium; Ab, abomasum; S, stomach; D, duodenum; S.I., small intestine; C, cæcum; Co, colon; R, rectum.

second. Man's digestive system is more like the dog's than the cow's. The mouth is much alike—the mammals, by the way, are the only creatures with true movable lips. A few creatures (such as the prairie dog), have cheek pouches which they can fill with food. The teeth vary enormously according to whether they are cutters, crushers or grinders. The tusks of walruses and hogs are simply huge canine teeth used as weapons. Those of elephants are exaggerated upper incisors. The tongue is of various shapes, but the only important modification in it is the horny tongue of the cat tribe adapted for rasping flesh from bones. The gullet is again similar in most mammals. The stomach of the mammals is normally very like the human, but in the ruminants who feed on herbage and chew the cud, the true stomach is preceded by three compartments formed out of the gullet. When a cow eats grass, it goes in to the rumen (Ru) thence to the reticulum or honeycomb (Re). These are simple storage places. It is then "swallowed upwards" and chewed and then returned to the "psalterium" (Ps), and the "abomasum" (Ab) for true digestion. The intestine of a herbivorous creature has to be very long. It usually has a big blind pouch, the cæcum, where food is stored before it passes to the large intestine, and the large intestine is very long and coiled. All this gives the bacteria in the intestine a chance to turn the cellulose in the grass, etc., into valuable sugar, a trick the mammalian digestive enzymes cannot perform.

BIRDS

The considerable likeness we have seen among mammals, extends to some extent to birds. A bird "works" very much as a man does, but there are certain differences between any bird and any mammal.

Every bird and no mammal has the combination of feathers, wings[1] based on an "arm" (not like a bat's wings which are stretched on fingers) and two feet. Were it not for those most remarkable beasts, Echidna and the Duckbilled Platypus, we

---

[1] All birds have wings, though some (e.g., penguins and ostriches) no longer fly with them.

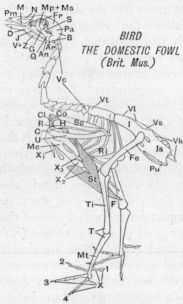

BIRD
THE DOMESTIC FOWL
(Brit. Mus.)

FIG. 482.—The fowl's skeleton. (For names of bones see p. 933.)

could say that no mammals had beaks and laid eggs and that all birds did so!

The bird is most beautifully adapted for flight; indeed, the feat of sustaining a heavy body in the air is so great that without wide adaptations it could never have taken place. We believe that birds evolved from reptiles specialised as runners and leapers: the Australian collared lizard runs on two legs to-day. These reptiles probably first parachuted by folds of skin as do the flying foxes to-day, and gradually evolved their arms into wings. It should be noted that birds did not evolve from Pterodactyls which had wings of skin stretched between a finger, an arm and a leg. The bird's flight is founded on feathers. These are, like hairs, developments of the scales of reptiles, but no one has found any intermediate stages between feathers and scales. The first fossil bird, the famous Archæopteryx whose remains are shown in Fig. 483, had definite feathers, though its reptilian ancestry is obvious in its tail and toothed jaws.

In order to work its wings and accomplish flight, the bird must be able to maintain a rapid output of energy, and must be light in weight, and must have relatively huge muscles to work its wing. To obtain the energy, the birds have developed a high temperature: the swallow keeps itself at 110° F. It can do this by eating tremendously—an owl may eat an average of six whole mice a night—and by having a very good non-conducting coat of feathers. Its heart is of the efficient four-chambered type, and its blood is very rich in oxygen.

The bird gets its light weight by cutting its bones down to the lightest. Its bones are built like girders, and often are filled with air-containing sacs which join its lungs. In the albatross, every bone but two is air-filled. Finally, the pectoral muscles (shown in man in Fig. 437) are developed till they may be half the weight of the bird. They are, of course, "the breast" of a bird which we eat. To give these muscles a direct pull, the sternum, which is the breastbone which joins the ribs in front, grows out into a great keel on which the muscles haul. All this has had its effect on other parts of the bird. In order that it should be able to execute the

K.Sch.gez.

$\frac{2}{1}$

Fig. 483.—The fossilized remains of *Archaeopteryx*, the most primitive fossil bird. Compare the skeleton with that of bird (Fig. 482) and lizard (Fig. 485). Among primitive features note the clawed front limbs, presence of teeth and absence of large keeled breastbone (reduced $3\frac{1}{2}$ times). (Courtesy of Messrs. Macmillan & Co., Ltd., from Parker and Haswell's *Textbook of Zoology*.)

FIG. 483a.—*Draco volans* (⅔ natural size). An animal which has evolved a limited power of flight. The "wing" unlike those of any other creature is stretched on elongated ribs. It is used only as a plane and cannot be flapped. (Courtesy of Messrs. Macmillan & Co., Ltd., from Gadow's *Amphibia and Reptiles* in the *Cambridge Natural History*.)

delicate feats of balancing needed for flight in the air and for walking on two legs, it develops the cerebellum in its brain which is one of the organs for co-ordinating bodily movements. Contrast the cerebellum of the frog's brain and the pigeon's (Fig. 480).

The best bird's brain is poor beside an average mammal's. Birds seem to have strongly emotional feelings and great instinctive powers, shown in their nest building and migrations. But they do not seem to have much power of learning by experience. The hawk can be trained, but the acts it will perform are very few compared to those of a dog or a horse. A bird, in flying, probably uses the air-currents just as does a man in a glider, but does so in the same sort of instinctive way as we adjust our walk to irregularities in the ground. Flight makes the bird enormously the most rapid traveller of the animal kingdom. There is every reason to believe that the most rapid fliers can travel at 100 miles an hour. It is obvious that this enables birds to find safe nesting-places and to avoid the rigor and starvation of winter by migration.

It is not obvious why birds should always have beaks, which are really horny immovable lips fastened on to the toothless jaw-bones! This organ has developed in very numerous ways. The hawk and eagle have a short, sharp beak designed to cut and tear. The strong broad bills of the finches are made to deal with hard seeds. The snipe's is made for probing mud in search of food, while the duck's bill is adapted to take up mud and search it for food.

The internal organs of the bird differ in many respects from ours. Since it does not chew its food, it has usually a pouch in its gullet, "the crop," to store it in, and a part of its stomach specialised into a gizzard. This is a strong muscular bag with a hard lining. The bird swallows pebbles which, when rubbed against the food by the muscles of the gizzard, reduce it to pulp. A bird has no bladder. Its urine is passed to the equivalent of man's rectum. It does not excrete its waste as urea, but as salts of uric acid.

$$
\begin{array}{ll}
\underset{\text{Urea}}{OC\!\!\begin{array}{l} \diagup NH_2 \\ \diagdown NH_2 \end{array}}
&
\underset{\text{Uric acid}}{
\begin{array}{l}
NH\!-\!CO \\
\;|\qquad|\;\; H \\
CO\quad C\!-\!N \\
\;|\qquad\|\quad\;\;\diagdown CO \\
NH\!-\!C\!-\!N \diagup \\
\qquad\quad H
\end{array}}
\end{array}
$$

The whitish excretion of birds mainly consists of these urates, and is a most valuable manure.

Far the most important of the senses which birds depend on is sight. Their sight is very acute, but since they have monocular vision, seeing different pictures with each eye, their world-view must be less informative than ours. Their hearing is acute but they probably depend on it but little. Smell is unimportant and taste slight. Covered as they are with feathers, they probably have no acute sense of touch.

The breeding and nesting of birds is a fascinating study for which we here have no space: it is perhaps well, however, to explain something of the reproductive system of the bird.

The fertilisation of birds is like that of man in essentials. The egg is formed in the ovary as in the human being, but instead of being a tiny object, $\frac{1}{130}$ inch in diameter, it may be an inch or more across. The egg, as formed in the ovary, consists of the germ cell which is tiny and the yolk which is relatively enormous. At intervals, the ovary discharges an ovum which travels down the oviduct (the uterine tube in man), the walls of which secrete the white of the egg. It is fertilised in the oviduct and then passes into the shell-gland—the equivalent of the human uterus—where a hard shell of calcium carbonate is deposited on it. From this it is expelled to the exterior. The germ-cell develops in the egg very much as a human germ-cell does, but instead of being nourished by products diffused from the mother's blood, it develops a set of vessels which absorb the yolk and white of the egg for nourishment.

REPTILES

The reptiles, amphibians and fish complete the vertebrates. We have only space for a brief survey of their main features. The living orders of reptiles are the crocodiles and alligators; the lizards and snakes; the tortoises and turtles; and, in an order of its own, that archaic beast the Tuatera lizard of New Zealand, remarkable for having a third eye on the top of its head. What is a reptile, then? It is an air-breathing vertebrate and is cold-blooded. It has a scaly skin and lays shelled eggs with yolk and white. Its brain has a very small cerebrum, the region concerned with thought and conscious action in general. These points distinguish a reptile from an amphibian like a newt (which lays soft jelly-covered eggs and has a soft skin), and from birds and mammals which are warm-blooded.

The skeleton of the reptile is not so very widely different from that of a bird or mammal. The most notable difference is the small and feeble pelvis and scapula, which could only belong to

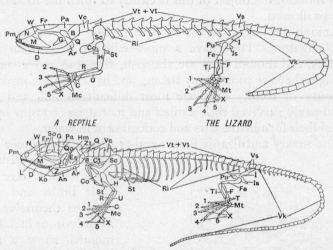

FIGS. 484–485.—The skeletons of an amphibian and of a reptile. (Names of bones, p. 933).

creatures which made no great use of their limbs. Many reptiles drag themselves on their bellies: the snakes have discarded their limbs though they keep an internal vestige of them. The reptile's brain-case is small, the head being mainly jaws. Its internal organs are much like the bird's, but the heart is quite notably different (Fig. 491). The typical reptilian heart is in between the mammal-and-bird type D, and the amphibian type C, there being an incomplete separation of the ventricles.

The result of this is that all the blood does not go through the lungs at every circulation. Consequently, the reptile has worse aerated blood than the bird or mammal, and since it is cold-blooded too, it is a creature which cannot keep up a sustained effort though it may move in swift dashes.

The senses of reptiles are probably not over-acute. Their horny skins are provided with touch corpuscles. Taste certainly exists. Hearing is probably moderate to poor. Their eyes are quite efficient and their sense of smell, good. Some have also a peculiar scent-organ closed off from their noses and opening into their mouths: the object of this is clearly to smell the food before it is swallowed.

Among the largest of the modern reptiles are the crocodiles and alligators: They have a more efficient heart than most reptiles, and though they are sluggish, they can move quickly enough: they are enormously strong, and have a most formidable armoury of teeth. They are most difficult to kill, and have presumably survived their extinct and monstrous cousins by the use of their formidable jaws and concealment in water.

The snakes and lizards form another class. The former have some interesting adaptations. They have lost their limbs and have adapted themselves for a carnivorous life. Their mouths show a most complete adaptation to this. A snake kills its prey by swallowing it alive, as a grass-snake swallows a frog, or by crushing it to death, as does a boa, or by poison. A snake, in any event, swallows its prey whole and in order to do this,

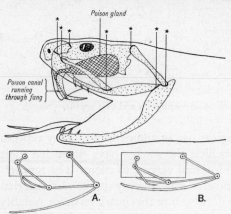

Poison gland

Poison canal running through fang

A.   B.

FIG. 486.—Jaws and poison apparatus of a snake. Below, the hinge-joints of the jaw which allow an enormous gape.

its lower jaw is hinged on to a bone which is itself hinged on to the skull, making its gape enormous. Its teeth are set backwards and the lower jaw is in two halves linked by an elastic ligament at the "chin." It hooks its teeth into the victim, pushes the right half of its lower jaw forward, holding the prey with the left half meanwhile. It then hooks the right half into the victim again and pulls him further into the throat. The process is then repeated with the other half! The poison fangs possessed by many snakes are in the upper jaw. Fig. 486 shows how they work. The gland injects the poison through a long sharp tooth grooved or hollowed to receive it.

Snake poison is a mixture of proteins. One destroys the blood-cells, another paralyses the nerves. There are two possibilities of saving a patient bitten by a deadly snake. First, the limb should be tightly bound on the heart side of the bite, and the punctures opened up widely with a knife, and if possible washed out with bleaching powder solution or potassium permanganate. This may make the difference between death and a serious illness only. The complete cure is an *antivenine*, which is a protein which combines with snake venom and renders it harmless. It is made by injecting snake poison into horses, first in tiny doses, then in larger ones. The horse becomes immune to the snake poison, i.e., develops a substance in its blood which combines with venom and destroys it. The horse is then bled, the serum of the blood is separated from the corpuscles, sterilised and sealed up for use. The antivenine is a perfect cure for the bite of the snake whose venom was used to immunise the horse and also for the bite of similar snakes, but two or three antivenines are usually needed to treat the bites of all the common snakes of a country.

Tortoises and turtles are among the few surviving creatures which depend on armour for protection. Armour is a very unsafe thing. It is a great hindrance to active movement, and once a dangerous enemy finds the way in, the race is doomed. The reptiles have always had a tendency to develop armour, probably as a result of carrying too far the tendency which made them develop the soft amphibian skin of their ancestors into horny scales.

The most interesting of reptiles are, however, the extinct ones. In the Jurassic period some 130 million years ago, the reptiles were the highest animals in existence, and the world lay open to them. They developed in every direction. Some took to a vegetable diet and some became carnivorous, some took to the water and some to the air. All alike had the poorest type of brain. One of the chief groups of these creatures was the Saurischia, who walked or ran on two legs. One such creature developed much like an ostrich with powerful hind-legs, a long slender neck

FIG. 487.—Extinct Reptiles. Left, Triceratops. Centre, Diplodocus. Right foreground Stegosaurus. Right background, Struthiomimus. (From material contained in Dr. W. E. Swinton's *The Dinosaurs* (Murby)).

and a beak, though instead of an ostrich's flightless wings, it had small arms and hands. Others developed into huge carnivores. Tyrannosaurus is an example—built something like a vast powerful kangaroo, it was some forty feet from nose to tail, and stood as high as the eaves of a two-storey house. To this group of Saurischia also belonged the Diplodocus (Fig. 487), sixty-five feet from the nose to the whip-like tail. It probably lived in swamps and fed on water-plants, for its teeth were so feeble as to be unsuited for any but the sloppiest diet. Iguanodon was a feeder on tree-boughs, and like Tyrannosaurus, was kangaroo-like. The most extraordinary creatures of this kind were the armoured Dinosaurs. Stegosaurus is the strangest of these. Triceratops (Fig. 487) is the culmination of a series of similar creatures, rather resembling the rhinoceros.

The extinct flying reptiles called Pterodactyls deserve notice, for they developed a curious similarity to birds. The wing was neither that of bat—(skin stretched on fingers) nor of bird (feathers on arm and fingers), but had skin stretched between the arm, an elongated finger and the hind-leg. Like birds, they developed a large sternum, and, curiously, a beak. It is difficult to see how the sluggish cold-blooded reptile with its imperfect circulation gathered the great energy needed for flight.

FIG. 487*b*.—A species of Pterodactyl, one-seventh natural size. Note the wing stretched between arm, finger, leg and tail. (Courtesy of Messrs. Macmillan & Co., Ltd., from Gadow's *Amphibia and Reptiles* in the *Cambridge Natural History*

These reptiles died out more than a hundred million years ago. The cause was probably a great change of climate and perhaps the development of efficient carnivorous mammals.

AMPHIBIANS

The amphibians are still of the vertebrate pattern, but simpler than the reptiles. The chief modern amphibia are frogs and toads, newts and salamanders. They have a thin moist skin without scales. They can breathe to a great extent through this skin. They usually lay in water eggs without a shell, which develop into a "larva" quite different in structure from the adult. The larva— e.g., the tadpole of a frog—has gills and lives a vegetarian existence in water: at a certain stage, its thyroid gland produces its iodine-containing secretion which makes it lose its gills, develop lungs, grow legs and change into a carnivorous land-dwelling creature. Tadpoles kept in water containing no iodine grow larger and larger but do not change into frogs, while tadpoles fed on thyroid gland metamorphose very early into minute frogs. The larval method of growth seems curious to us, but the mammals, birds and reptiles are actually exceptional in not having larvæ. Amphibians, fish, insects, crustaceans, molluscs, all start out as creatures wholly different from the adults. Part of the significance of this seems to be a sort of recapitulation of the race's history, such as we see in the young human embryo with its fish's heart and its tail. Amphibians evolved from fish, their tadpoles are fish-like. Insects evolved from worms, their larvæ—maggots and caterpillars—are wormlike. But the practical utility of the larval life is that the larva is generally wholly adapted for feeding and so for quick growth and has to spend no energy on maintaining the sexual outfit which the adult needs.

Some creatures, as frogs, have a short larval existence of weeks, and an adult life of years. Other amphibia such as the axolotl, often kept in aquaria, live and breed in the larval state, and only change into the adult form if the water dries up. Many insects have a long life in the larval form, and a very short one as an adult.

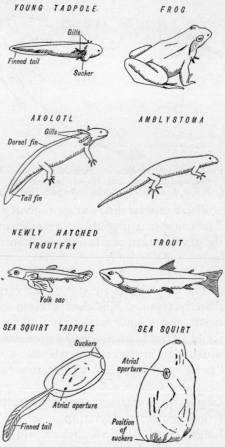

FIGS. 488, 489.—Some larvæ (left) and the scale is adopted, for it would not be possible larva on the same scale.

The mayfly feeds for a year as a somewhat wormlike water creature. It lives as an adult only for a few hours: long enough to be fertilised and lay its eggs. One American cicada—a grasshopper-like creature—spends 17 years underground as a "nymph," and then emerges for a life of a few weeks as an adult.

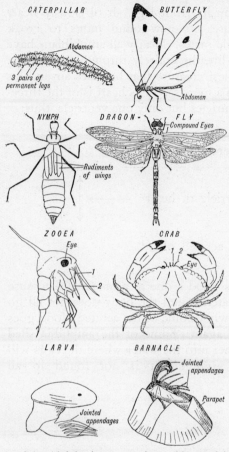

CATERPILLAR

Abdomen

3 pairs of
permanent legs

BUTTERFLY

Abdomen

NYMPH

DRAGON-FLY

Compound Eyes

Rudiments
of wings

ZOOEA

Eye

1

2

CRAB

1 2

Eye

LARVA

BARNACLE

Jointed
appendages

Parapet

Jointed
appendages

adults (right), they grow into. No special
to show the adult crab and the minute zooea

The relative time spent as larva and adult depends roughly on the advantage to the creature. A tadpole is much more vulnerable than a frog—every carnivorous aquatic creature feasts on them. So the aquatic life of the frog tends to be short and some toads cut out this phase by letting the larvæ metamorphose in eggs carried on the female's back. On the other hand, the cicada larva is safer underground than chirping on a bush—it therefore tends to dwell longer beneath the earth in safety.

In the skeleton of the newt shown in Fig. 484 the very small ribs and the very feeble pelvis are notable. The first feature means that the mechanical system of breathing by lungs has not yet been perfected, the second that walking is as yet clumsy.

The senses of amphibia are quite acute. They have efficient eyes. Their ears are very peculiar, however. There is no outer ear-drum, but a muscle fibre connects the innermost ear-bone (*stapes*) with the shoulder girdle! In this way the frog is adapted for hearing ground-vibration, as of the tread of someone approaching, transmitted by its front legs. It obviously hears ordinary sounds, for it uses its new-found lungs to croak vigorously to attract possible mates. Nearly all amphibians have lungs, though one or two breathe entirely through their skins. The amphibian is the simplest creature that breathes air and his lung is a simple affair, often a mere sac. His heart is of the three-chambered type with two auricles but only one ventricle, thus:

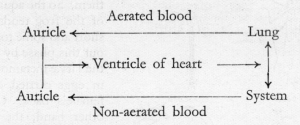

This circulation is not as good a one as a mammal's because the blood which has circulated round the body does not all go to the lungs to be aerated, while some of the aerated blood goes straight back to the lungs again. Some of the amphibia shed their eggs and sperm together into the water where the eggs will develop. This primitive arrangement is not found in all amphibia.

FISH

Fish are more primitive than amphibians. They have no lungs and therefore no voices. They have no legs, though their fins are the primitive origins of limbs. There are two classes commonly called fishes; besides the true bony fish (Teleosts) there are "Selachians," which include dogfish, sharks, etc. These have no true bones but only cartilages; they lack true scales and also lack the swim-bladder or air-sac. None the less, much of what we say of fish is true of selachians also.

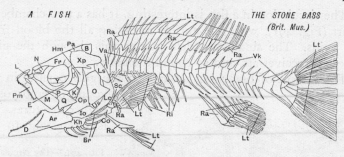

FIG. 490.—The skeleton of a fish. (For names of bones, see p. 933.)

Fig. 490 shows a fish's skeleton which is obviously very different from any other vertebrate's. The skull is a very complicated system of bony plates covering a sort of gristly box. This elaborate skull has been simplified by all the other vertebrates which have originated from fish. There is a well-developed vertebral column and ribs. The paired fins, the pectoral and pelvic (Fig. 490) correspond to the legs of amphibians and higher creatures, and as Fig. 485 shows, they have something of the same structure.

The digestive arrangements are not unlike those in other vertebrates. Fish have very small brains with generally a good cerebellum which deals with the posture and activities concerned in swimming, but almost no cerebrum which is concerned with sense impressions and thought. The goggle-eyed mud-hopper fish *Periophthalmus*, which have largely abandoned swimming in favour of a life on the surface of the mud of swamps have, on the other hand, a fair cerebrum and little cerebellum, for such a life demands the alert use of the eyes. Fish have a sense of smell, and also of hearing, probably neither very acute. Their labyrinth and semi-circular canals are very well developed, for a sense of position is urgently needed by a creature surrounded on all sides by water. Their eyes are probably not really capable of acute vision. Fish have an organ which no other vertebrate has—the "lateral line"— which is a system of water-tubes communicating with the exterior and provided with nerve-endings; its object is to detect water movements.

The circulation in a fish is interesting. It has a two-chambered heart (Fig. 491), with one auricle receiving all the blood from the veins. The single ventricle pumps this through the gills, where it receives air, and so round the body.

The system of branching arteries to the gills persists in the young of embryos of higher creatures. It is interesting to see

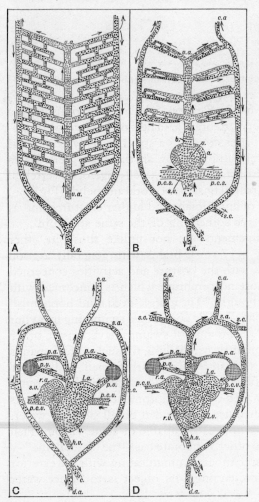

FIG. 491.—The circulation in (A) amphioxus; (B) a fish; (C) an amphibian; (D) a mammal. Oxygenated blood is shown as black dots, de-oxygenated blood as circles. (A) blood passes up the central vessel, through the gill-arches and thence to the rest of the body. There is no heart, but the central vessel can contract. (B) there is a true heart. The gill arches are fewer. (C) the heart has two auricles and one ventricle. The system of blood vessels is based on the gill arches of the fish. (D) there are two auricles and two ventricles. The likeness of the circulation to the fish's is further reduced.

Names of vessels, etc.: a, auricle; b, bulbus arteriosus; c, cœliac artery; ca, carotid artery; da, dorsal aorta; hs, hepatic sinus; hv, hepatic vein; la, left auricle; lv, left ventricle; pa, pulmonary artery; pv, pulmonary vein; pcs, precaval sinus; pcv, precaval vein; ra, right auricle; rv, right ventricle; sc, subclavian artery; sv, sinus venosus; v, ventricle; va, ventral aorta.

how the branchings are reduced from (A) amphioxus, the most primitive fish through ordinary bony fish (B), to amphibia (C), which retain some of the branches to mammals (D), which have dropped all but one.

Gills are comb-like structures of tissue permeated with blood-vessels; their function is to bring the blood as close as possible to the water, the dissolved air of which aerates the blood. They are fed with water which enters by the mouth, passes through slits in the back of the throat over the gill filaments and out by the gill slits just behind the head.

Every rapidly swimming creature has developed a bluntly pointed head and a long tapering body, the true streamlined form (p. 101). It is perfectly seen in herrings, cod and other ocean fish. Even bottom-dwelling fish adopt this shape, flattening themselves out in addition. The flat-fish is a curious adaptation. On the fishmonger's stall the plaice looks absurd, but go and watch him in the aquarium at the Zoo. On the bottom he is almost invisible and a nimble swimmer as well. These flat-fish are not lying on their bellies but on their sides. Consequently one eye, in order not to remain useless, has migrated to the other side. The young flat-fish still repeats his past. The fry have normal eyes, which only gradually shift to the same side of the body.

The world of the sea is almost wholly a carnivorous one. The majority of mammals live peacefully on plants, but the plants in the open sea are mostly microscopic single-celled creatures like diatoms. These green plants take their sustenance from carbon dioxide and water and the rather scanty nitrates of the ocean. Being green plants, they flourish only on the ocean's surface where light abounds. They are too small for any fish to eat, but tiny crustaceans—such as copepods, a sort of water flea—eat them. Herrings and such fish devour the copepods, and larger carnivorous fish, such as tunny, devour the herrings. In the depths of the sea, where the water is cold, slowly moving and pitch dark, dwell incredible creatures which get their living from the rain of dead which sink from above. They are extraordinarily

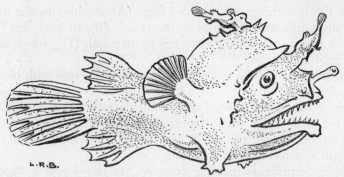

L·R·B·

FIG. 492.—A deep-sea angler fish with parasitic males. (Courtesy of Messrs. Gerald Duckworth & Co., Ltd., from Boulenger's *A Natural History of the Sea;* artist, L. R. Brightwell.)

specialised. They have huge jaws, for food is rare in those depths and once seized must not be lost. Some have enormous eyes to catch the faint glimpses of light from above. Most of them are illuminated by phosphorescent organs, the object being probably to enable the female and male to find each other. This is a real difficulty in these black, sparsely inhabited depths. One extraordinary way of solving it is that of the parasitic male. The tiny male attaches himself to the female's body and his jaws become continuous with her tissues so that, like an embryo, he is nourished by her blood stream. His organs, other than his organs of sex, atrophy, but when the female sheds her eggs, he can shed his sperm into the water at the same time.

The swimming of a fish is accomplished partly by fin-motions, but mostly by the tail propelled by the powerful body muscles. The economy of movement is beautiful to watch and well repays half an hour at the Zoo aquarium.

Fish are the simplest of the important vertebrates. A simpler family still, allied to the vertebrates, deserves notice. The sea-squirt hatches into a well-organised creature with a simple nervous system, a notochord or primitive backbone and a swimming tail very like a tadpole (Fig. 488). But the "tadpole" attaches a sucker to a rock, his tail dwindles, most of his organs disappear and he ends as a bag, looking very much like a simple seaweed.

Now all these Vertebrates—Mammals, Birds, Reptiles, Amphibians and Fish—are quite recognisably built on the same plan, while the rest of the animal kingdom is entirely different in construction. All the Vertebrates have bones arranged on the same plan of a skull, backbone and limbs or fins. All of them have a heart which pumps blood round their body in a closed circuit: their blood is red. They have a mouth with jaws (except in the case of a few of the simplest fish), their digestive equipment includes stomach, small intestine, large intestine, liver and pancreas. They have only two functional eyes, each with a lens and retina. Extraordinary as it may seem, none of these familiar features is reproduced in the other phyla of animals. We do not have much opportunity of inspecting the interiors of other creatures than mammals or birds, but if you are dressing a crab or eating an oyster, you find nothing in it which is obviously to be identified with what you find when gutting a rabbit.

ARTHROPODS

The most important phylum after the chordates—as far as number and economic importance goes—is that of the arthropods of which the chief members are the crustaceans, the insects and the spider and scorpion tribe. Fig. 493 shows how a crayfish—a typical crustacean—is arranged. First of all, he has no bones, but in place of them a hard shell of a material called chitin—somewhat akin to cellulose.

Instead of moving his limbs by muscles pulling on bones, he moves them by muscles pulling on his body shell, which is, in fact, an outside skeleton. This is a quite efficient arrangement, as anyone who has been nipped by a lobster will agree, but it has the grave disadvantage that the shell does not grow, and when the lobster inside finds it too tight he must moult. He discards his whole shell, claws and all, and is then perfectly soft and defenceless for a day or two while a new shell is forming.

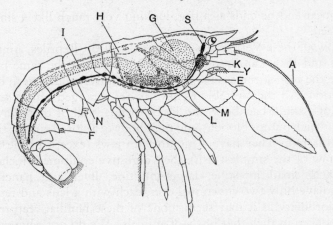

FIG. 493.—The internal arrangements of a crayfish—a typical arthropod.

S = "Brain"	A = antenna
K = kidney (green gland)	N = Ventral nerve-cord
M = mouth	F = Swimmerets
E = gullet	Y = Maxillipede (limb acting as
L = digestive gland ("liver")	mouth parts
G = gizzard	Dotted lines represent blood-
H = heart	vessels
I = intestine	

All arthropods have a shell or skin of chitin and all have to moult. It is not disadvantageous to a soft creature to moult, but a shelly one is put in great danger by it.

The crayfish's limbs are quite unlike a mammal's. He has a large number of appendages (nineteen pairs), some of which are specialised into feelers—antennæ—some into jaws of a kind, others into claws, others into legs, others into swimmers. All arthropods have these or some of these "appendages," but turn them to very different uses. Internally the crayfish is quite unlike a vertebrate. His main nerve runs from tail to head along the front instead of the back. It has numerous ganglia like little brains all along it and a bigger one at the top which serves the eye. There is little space for the storing of impressions. This nerve system—judging from the equipment of a vertebrate—will do little or no more than our spinal cord. It will enable the creature to co-ordinate its bodily movements, for all nerves join up to it, and it will provide a system of reflexes by which certain stimuli produce certain results.

The senses of a crayfish must be very different from ours. Its hard shell has probably little or no touch sense. Its organs of hearing are very primitive and are more important as balancers (p. 895) than as sound receivers. The eyes are rather like those of insects (p. 960), but poorly developed, and its vision must be wholly unlike ours. The crayfish's antennæ are undoubtedly delicate sense organs, both of touch and probably of some "chemical sense" like smell or taste.

The blood circulation of the crustacean is, by vertebrate standards, very poor; we must remember, though, that a small cold-blooded animal needs less circulation. A small warm-blooded animal, by the way, needs a very rapid circulation, for it cools so quickly that its heat-producing chemical reactions must proceed very rapidly. A mouse's pulse beats at the rate of 600 to the minute. The crustacean heart is a bag with inlet valves like a bellows. It forces the blood through arteries, which end in openings so that the blood pours into the spaces between the organs and finds its way back as best it can. Some crustacea dispense with a heart and circulation and trust to their movements to keep their blood going. The blood is usually colourless and its oxygen-carrying power is poor.

Crustacea generally breathe by gills and have a peculiar "baler" organ which pumps water over them.

The digestive arrangement is unlike ours. The food is cut up by mouth-parts which are really modified legs and sent to a large muscular gizzard, sometimes with teeth in it. Instead of our liver and pancreas, one large digestive gland does the work of both.

Crustacea lay eggs, but they do not always hatch into recognisable crustacea. They commonly start as a larva and change into a crustacean. Fig. 489 shows two stages of the ordinary crab.

The crustacea are found as far back as the Silurian period; they have held their own then for some 400,000,000 years. They are chiefly water-dwellers. Lobsters, crabs, prawns, shrimps, barnacles and water-fleas and hosts of minor and unfamiliar creatures make up the water crustacea. Woodlice are the most familiar of land-crustaceans.

The other main division of the arthropods is the insects. Just as the crustaceans have not done much to colonise the land, so the insects are not at home in the water. An insect is fundamentally like a crustacean. It has no bones, but instead a shell or skin of chitin on which its muscles pull. Its mouth parts, too, are modified legs. Its circulation is like the lobster's, and the chief internal difference between the two is the breathing system. An insect is permeated by air-tubes or tracheæ, which branch into most of the organs. An insect at rest is usually seen to be expanding and contracting its body—an action well seen in a wasp. By doing this, it is drawing in and squeezing out air from the tracheæ. An insect's extraordinary compound eyes are worth notice. The eye of a fly or bee consists of hundreds or thousands of tiny eyelets, each focussing the light in front of it on to a sensitive end organ (Plate XLVI). It is not correct to suppose that each of these eyelets forms a complete picture of the landscape; each focusses on to its nerve-end an image of the piece of the field of view immediately in front of it. In this way, a whole picture—probably indistinct, is built up. Insects are very quick to detect a moving object, as you see if you try to catch a fly, but they seem to have little perception of the shape of things. Their antennæ contain very sensitive organs, probably of touch and smell.

The insect in nearly all cases lays eggs, and these are usually fertilised, though not always. The drone (male) bee comes from an unfertilised egg and unfertilised green-fly produce living young. In all insects, however, sexual generation sometimes occurs. The newly hatched insect may be exactly like the adult, but this is rare. The egg may hatch into a "nymph," which is much like the adult insect, but lacks wings and sexual parts. Cockroaches and dragon-flies illustrate this. But usually the

PLATE XLVII

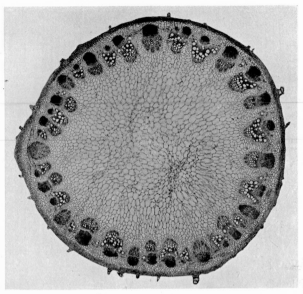

Stem of Sunflower ($\times$ 12) (compare figures 507, and 511).

Section of leaf of
Cycas ($\times$ 15) show-
ing epidermis,
palisade-cells, etc.

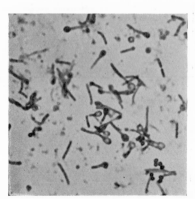

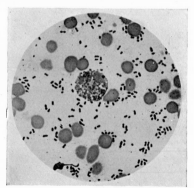

Tetanus bacteria ($\times$ 660).

Pneumococcus in blood. Note the
white cell which has engulfed a
number of bacteria ($\times$ 660).

PLATE XLVIII

A

B

Fossil remains.
   A—Trilobite, a very ancient
     crustacean
   B—Plant of Carboniferous Age
   C—Primitive fish

(By courtesy of the Trustees of the
British Museum [Natural History]
from their Guide to Fossil Plants.)
(Crown Copyright: by courtesy of
the Controller of H.M. Stationery
Office.)

C

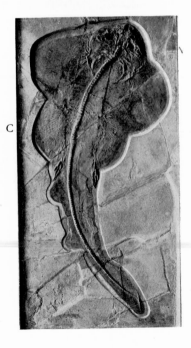

The Spectral Tarsier. (By courtesy
of Professor W. E. Le Gros Clark
and the *Illustrated London News*).

creature which appears from the egg is worm-like. A caterpillar is a good example of a well-developed larva which can walk and find its food; a fly-maggot is the simplest type of larva, which is only able to exist in a rich food supply.

The larva's function is to eat and grow and its body contains little else but digestive organs. It grows and moults; and, when fully grown, it becomes a pupa, a passive creature which neither moves nor feeds. The chrysalis of a butterfly is a pupa, as is also what is incorrectly called an ant's egg. A most extraordinary change takes place within the pupa. Inside the caterpillar, before it pupates, buds, destined to form the legs, wings, etc., of the perfect insect, have formed. In the pupa the organs of the larva break down and lose their form and practically digest themselves, acting as food for these buds, which grow into the organs of the perfect insect. This, then, splits the pupa and emerges. The wings of an insect are limp and tiny when it leaves the pupa. Blood is pumped into them from the body: they enlarge, dry and harden. The growth and hardening of a butterfly's wings is a most impressive sight.

There are just on half a million kinds of insect known. They must outnumber all other creatures except the single-celled microscopic ones. Think of the cockroaches, grasshoppers, locusts, earwigs, mayflies, dragon-flies, termites, lice, aphids, beetles, moths, butterflies, houseflies, bluebottles, fleas, ants, bees and wasps. They are an ancient family and seem to have been among the first land creatures to be evolved. They were the first living creatures to conquer the air. Even in the remote periods when the first coal-swamps were storing power for us to squander, great dragon-flies winged their way over the desolate marshes.

The insect wing is not a modified limb, as are all the types of vertebrate wing, but a completely new structure. Also it is not muscular; in nearly all insects the wings are moved by means of muscles, which alter the shape of the thorax or chest; only in dragon-flies are the chief muscles attached directly to the base of the wing; and no insect has muscles in its wings as the flying vertebrates have. An insect has typically two pairs of wings, but for efficiency in flight there is a tendency either to link them together as in bees, or to lose one pair, as in flies whose hind wings are represented by mere knobs.

The great success of the insect tribe is probably due to this early conquest of the air, to their extreme fertility and to their small size, all of which features have combined to make the race survive. They have little or no power to learn, it would seem, but they have instincts—inborn nerve mechanisms—which make them perform the right actions for survival, and they are so fertile that the race is none the worse if the vast majority die before maturity. Insects get a living in almost all of the recognised ways. A great number devour vegetation, locusts and caterpillars, for example; others, as aphids, suck its juices, other insects, such as bees, gather nectar from plants and benefit then by fertilising them. A good many insects are scavengers: the common housefly is a good example. Objectionable as it is in bringing dirt from rubbish heaps and latrines on to food, its natural function of removing decaying animal matter is harmless enough. Some insects, like wasps, are largely carnivorous, preying on other insects. Many insects are parasites: the human flea and louse and bug and mosquito are examples of parasites which feed on the exterior of their hosts. Far more unpleasant are those that live within. The ichneumon fly deposits an egg in a caterpillar. A grub hatches and lives on the caterpillar's blood and fat, avoiding its vital organs, for to destroy these would be its own destruction. The full-fed parasites finally kill the caterpillar and emerge.

The most remarkable way of living is the communal one practised by termites, ants, bees and wasps. The great cities of bees and ants seem to have arisen from a family affair where the mother guards her offspring till hatched. All stages from solitariness to complete specialised communities are found among bees.

The wasps have rather simple communities. The queen is fertilised in the autumn and hibernates through the winter. In spring she starts a nest (underground in the case of the common wasp) by lining a cavity in the ground with paper—chewed vegetable fibre. Here she lays a number of eggs and feeds the larvæ which hatch from them with chewed caterpillars or flies. These wasps, in a month or six weeks, are adults. They are not, adults, however, like the queen, but are sterile females, the workers. They take on the task of nest-making and the queen gives up work and devotes herself to egg-laying only. At the end of the season the larvæ are better fed, and for this reason develop into queens instead of workers. These are fertilised by the males and hibernate till next spring.

The bees have a more complicated existence. They live on flowers. The flower secretes a solution of cane-sugar (nectar) to attract the bee. The bee sucks this into its "stomach," where it is digested to glucose and fructose: this it regurgitates as honey. They also gather pollen on their hairy bodies and they carry a sort of basket of hairs on their legs to contain it. Wax is manufactured by the bee and exudes from the joints of the abdomen. There are literally hundreds of kinds of bee, but the common hive-bee is the best studied. The hive-bee colonies are much bigger than wasp-colonies. A strong stock of bees may contain twenty thousand individuals. The bees build their combs of wax and use these for several purposes. In parts honey is stored, in others pollen is kept, and in others the bee larvæ, maggot-like creatures, are reared. The queen-bee is fertilised only once in her life. She stores the sperm and allows a tiny portion to reach each egg as laid and she commonly lays more than a million! These fertilised eggs hatch into larvæ. The workers feed these on a rich food, "royal jelly," secreted by the workers. An ordinary fertilised egg, reared in a specially large cell and fed on royal jelly till it becomes an adult eventually becomes a queen, but the worker bee receives it for only four days and then is fed on honey and digested pollen. The new hatched worker-bee works in a hive for a few days: she then goes out collecting nectar and pollen and in the busy period of the honey-flow dies, exhausted, before two months have elapsed. A bee-colony remains slightly active all the winter. The workers gather into a cluster and so conserve the warmth of their bodies; a bee once chilled to 40° F. will never recover. The male bee or drone is produced from an egg which the queen does not fertilise from her store of sperm. When a new queen has been reared, she may either fight to the death with the old queen, or, if the hive is overcrowded, the old queen departs with a swarm of workers to found a new colony.

Ants may have a more complicated system than bees, for instead of the "castes" of queen, worker and drone, they have more than one "caste" of workers—thus, some may be specialised as soldiers and others as mere storage barrels, who remain with crops hugely distended with honey. The habits of ants are a study in themselves; their tending of aphids for the sake of the honey they exude, their growing of fungi for food, their en-slaving of other ants, are all most curious parallels to human institutions.

Termites or white ants, which are not ants at all, are the most specialised. They live chiefly on wood and cause great damage. They cannot tolerate the light and so they build tunnels of earth running from their nests to their food. The huge nests are conspicuous objects in a tropical landscape. They have a most complicated caste system. They have three castes of egg-laying members and two castes of sterile ones, workers and soldiers. Some of the soldiers have powerful jaws, while the "nasute" soldiers have an extraordinary swollen head containing glands and a projecting tube; they practise a sort of chemical warfare by producing a pungent secretion from these glands. Termites grow fungi in their nests and use them to feed their "royal caste" and also their young.

The spectacle of these insect colonies is a strange one. They are superficially like human colonies, but their behaviour is quite stereotyped. The wasps and ants and bees and termites will go on year after year in an unchanging sequence. They are a State without politics. The worker bee of a certain age is incapable of doing otherwise than gather nectar and pollen and bring it home. She may have feelings of satisfaction—this we can only guess at—but there is no possibility of departure from the round save by the slow processes of evolution.

The molluscs are an ancient and quite successful race. They are not very prominent on land, though snails and slugs are represented by a great number of species. In the sea, very many more forms exist, the most developed being the cuttlefish family, some of which are gigantic in size. In Fig. 494 is a diagram of a snail. The largest part of a snail is the foot-muscle on which it creeps by expanding it and contracting it in waves which are best understood by setting a slug or snail to crawl on a sheet of glass and watching the sole.

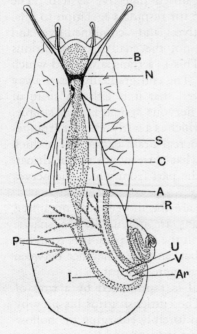

FIG. 494.—The snail, a typical mollusc.

B = buccal mass
N = nerve-ring (nerves as black lines).
S = salivary gland
C = crop
R = rectum
A = anus
U = auricle of heart
V = ventricle of heart
I = intestine
P = veins
Ar = artery

The foot, unlike the muscles we have met hitherto, does not pull on to any hard part: it is a tangle of muscle fibres which just contracts and expands. A snail has a simple heart and circulatory system: in many molluscs, the intestine passes through the middle of the heart! The blood is aerated by gills in water forms and by a simple lung in land forms. Certain molluscs have very curious respiratory pigments like our hæmoglobin, but containing copper or manganese instead of iron.

The hæmocyanin, which carries the air in the water-snail's blood, is distinguished as having the largest known molecule, with a weight about six million times that of an atom of hydrogen. This vast assemblage of atoms may be about $\frac{1}{10000}$ mm. in diameter, and so is not so much smaller than the largest particle a good microscope can see.

The molluscs have a well-organised digestive system. The snail has a horny file in its mouth for rasping vegetation to bits. It has salivary glands and a digestive gland—combined liver and pancreas. Certain molluscs (but not the snail) have a curious organ called a crystalline style. This is a transparent rod which fits into a pouch of the intestine. The end gradually wears away during digestion and it is believed that it is either a store of enzymes or a food reserve. The nervous system is very simple. The chief sense organ is the eye, which is a fairly efficient arrangement with a lens and retina. No real brain exists, but a thick ring of nerve tissue loops round what corresponds to our throat. This resembles a brain in being the part from which the nerves to eyes, tentacles and body diverge.

The cuttlefishes and octopuses are the most highly organised of molluscs. Their internal organs are not unlike the snail's. The cuttlefish and snail are built on the same plan, it is true, but then so are the elephant and the bat, and the difference between the giant squid and the land snail is quite as great.

The muscular foot of the snail is represented by a ring of tentacles studded with suckers. The cuttlefish grips his prey by pressing the sucker against it, then forcibly enlarging the hollow of the sucker. A partial vacuum is produced and the pressure of the water and the air above it holds the prey to the tentacle.

The snail's shell is represented by the well-known cuttlebone which is bedded within the back of the animal. The cuttlefish swims with its tentacles trailing behind; its chief means of movement is to suck water into its body cavity and eject it backwards, so pushing itself forward in the same way as does a sky-rocket

(p. 670). This sucking in and blowing out of water provides a supply of aerated water which passes over its gills. The most interesting possession of the cuttlefish is its ink-gland, which secretes a dark coloured substance at the bottom of a sort of bulb tube. When a cuttlefish is frightened or pursued, it ejects a cloud of deep brown "sepia" into the water and turns sharply aside, thus eluding its not highly intelligent pursuers.

The cuttlefishes, octopuses and squids all have very well-developed eyes, curiously impressive to the human observer. They are carnivorous. The squids are some of the largest creatures known. It seems extraordinary that a vast creature, whose body apart from its tentacles may measure 20 feet in length, is without any proper brain. Little is known of these vast deep-sea squids. Stories are told of tremendous creatures covering as much as an acre, but no doubt the seaman's imagination has been at work.

ANNELIDS

Simpler again than the arthropods or molluscs are the annelids or segmented worms, familiar members of which are the earthworm and the leech. A great many worms exist, but most are inconspicuous water-dwelling creatures. A worm is distinguished by its bristles. Perhaps you have never noticed the bristles on the earthworm, which certainly looks pretty bald, but they can be felt by running the finger over its surface. It has eight bristles on each segment. They are directed backwards and by catching in the earth give the worm a hold by which it can pull itself along. Its nervous system is a cord running down the front of the belly. There is no real heart, only two vessels which run down front and back and intercommunicate by passages, some of which are contractile and function as hearts. No digestive gland exists. A worm has no kidneys; instead, it has nephridia, each of which is a long fine coiled tube discharging to the exterior, it probably works like a single tubule of a mammal's kidney. The worm has many of these. Worms live by swallowing earth or decayed leaves and

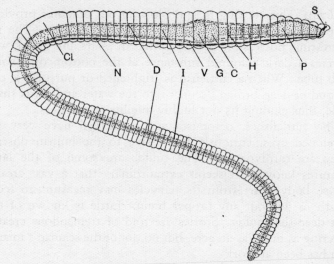

FIG. 495.—An annelid—the earthworm.

S = supra-œsophageal ganglion (nearest equivalent to a brain)	I = intestine
	H = contractile vessels functioning as hearts
P = pharynx	
C = crop	D = dorsal blood vessels
G = gizzard	V = ventral blood vessel
N = nervous system	C = clitellum (site of sex organs)

digesting the organic matter. The worm population may be hundreds to the square yard. Their continual burrowings admit air to the soil and make it more porous, and their vast numbers make the amount of earth they discharge at the surface quite appreciable. Darwin, in his fascinating book, *The Formation of Vegetable Mould Through the Action of Worms with Observations on Their Habits*, calculates than in ten years earthworms bring up enough earth to cover the ground one or two inches thick.

ECHINODERMATA

The echinodermata—the starfish is the one we know best—are extraordinarily unlike any other set of creatures. They have been

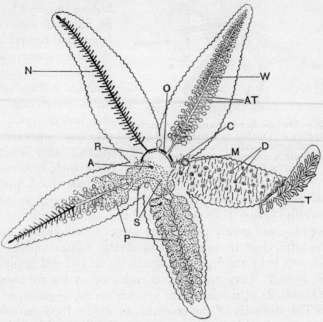

Fig. 496.—An echinoderm, the starfish. The five rays are identical, but different structures are illustrated in each. Starting from top left ray (nerve-system). N=radial nerve; R=nerve-ring. Top right ray. Water system, W=radial water-vessel; AT=ampullæ operating tube feet; O=water ring canal; M=madreporite (sieve plate admitting water). Middle right ray. External appearance. D= plates of calcium carbonate; T=tube feet. Lower right ray. Digestive system. P=gut; S=stomach; A=anus. Lower left-ray, relation of above to each other.

evolving for some 400,000,000 years and have established their place and hold it.

The starfish is one of the commonest sea-shore creatures and can become a very great nuisance by opening and eating oysters! All the creatures we have studied have at least had a front and and back end, but the starfish has none. Any of its five rays can lead the way. Its most characteristic organ is its water system. A ring-shaped canal runs round its centre and sends branches into each of the rays. From the underside of the rays pass out

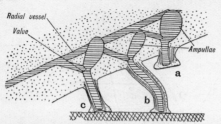

FIG. 497.—The tube-feet of a starfish; (a) retracted; (b) applied to a surface by contracting the ampulla and forcing water into the tube; (c) the ampulla partly expanded, withdrawing water and causing the foot to act as a sucker.

hollow fingers which can be inflated with water from the central canal. When the water is drawn from them again by muscles acting on the bulbs projecting from the central canal, they act like suckers. The starfish uses them to walk with, he uses them to pass food into his mouth and, astonishingly, he uses them to open an oyster. The starfish grips both valves of the oyster with its rays and steadily and gently pulls. The oyster's shell-closing muscle is powerful, but it soon tires and the oyster opens. The starfish eats it by turning its stomach inside out and applying it to the oyster! They are great enemies of oyster fisheries and cause hundreds of thousands of pounds' worth of damage in the year. The stomach of the starfish can digest food outside the creature, but it also has a gut (Fig. 496). It has blood but no circulating system and no lungs or gills. The blood just occupies the spaces between its organs. A ring of nerve surrounds the mouth and sends branches into each ray. The top of a starfish is armoured with little plates of calcium carbonate buried in the skin. It has on it very odd organs called pedicellariæ—little pincers. These are used for defence. Other creatures allied to the starfish are the sea-urchins, sea-lilies and sea-cucumbers—all built on the radiating plan. But this phylum of Radiata are evolved from ordinary creatures with "left-and-right" symmetry, for their larvæ only develop their radiating form some time after hatching.

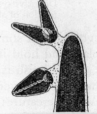

FIG. 498.—The tiny pincers which the starfish can use as a means of defence.

THE FLATWORMS

The phyla simpler than those we have mentioned contain very simple creatures indeed. Thus, the flatworms are just a digestive tube, ramifying like a tree to the farthest corners of the body, and a reproductive system. Some have simple sense organs, a primitive eye and touch organ. These lowly creatures are worth a mention because they include some of the worst of parasites and because they have such extraordinary life histories. They are without blood or circulation, consequently the alimentary canal has to branch into every part of the animal to feed it. Their only organs are, first, the mouth and gut (many have no posterior opening at all); secondly, a simple excretory system; thirdly, a very complete and large set of reproductive organs. There are nerve cords and a small enlargement on them which might be called a brain. The parasitic kinds have no eyes, but have usually suckers with which to keep their hold on their hosts.

The really interesting thing about the parasitic worms is the way many of them have to find two hosts to support them. The liver-fluke which causes a disease of sheep called "liver-rot" is a good example of this strange way of living. The grown-up liver-fluke inhabits the bile-ducts which lead from the liver of a sheep to its intestine. These forms lay eggs which pass out of the sheep with its droppings.

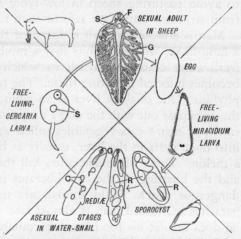

FIG. 499.—The life history of the liver-fluke. The different stages are not on the same scale. The adult fluke is natural size, the other stages are microscopic objects.

These eggs hatch if suitably moist and warm surroundings are to be found; but they hatch into a minute larva (miracidium) which can swim by cilia (Fig. 504, p. 977). This quests around until it finds a water-snail of a particular species and bores through its skin, where it changes and grows into a sac (sporocyst) in which arise by budding simple creatures called rediæ which have a sucker and an intestine.

These rediæ bud internally into minute free-swimming larvæ called cercaria. These escape from the snail and swim to some solid object like a blade of grass. Here they attach themselves, lose their tails and settle down to be passive cysts and wait till a sheep swallows them. They then grow up to liver-flukes once more! One might think it was impossible for the creature to complete its life-history if it had to wait for the co-operation of a sheep and a water-snail. But the fluke lays thousands of eggs; only one egg need reach the water-snail. Once there, it produces many rediæ, which each produce many cercariæ, only one of which need reach a sheep. The remedy for this disease is simply to avoid pasturing sheep in low-lying fields which are flooded from streams. Cattle are safe in such fields, however.

Man is attacked by half a dozen of these creatures, including a lung-fluke, which inhabits first a mollusc as a cercaria, then a fresh-water crab or crayfish in which it forms a cyst. Man becomes infected by eating these. The tapeworms belong to this phylum. One of these lives as an adult in a dog's intestine and the eggs pass out with the dog's droppings. If an animal—sheep cattle, or man—eats vegetables soiled with these, the eggs grow into huge cysts in the liver, usually as big as an orange or even a melon. These of course often kill the host by mere pressure and the bursting of the cyst liberates poisons which can cause dangerous shock. Wild animals are terribly infested by these parasites . Civilised man is almost free of them, chiefly because he does not let his food become contaminated with dirty water or animal droppings, and moreover, does not let untreated sewage, which may possibly contain eggs of parasites, enter his rivers. A terrible scourge of the tropics is a "round-worm" known as the hook-worm, a parasite which fortunately for us cannot complete its life-cycle in cool climates, but which infests 500,000,000 people who dwell in tropical countries and causes a wretched state of anæmia and weakness. This creature dwells in the small intestine of man and sucks blood from its walls. It lays eggs which pass out with the fæces. In communities whose lavatory is the world at large, this means that the ground is widely sown with hookworm eggs. These hatch into larvæ which inhabit the soil and bore through the sole of a bare foot walking on it. The blood carries them to the lungs and they bore their way to the air passages. Like every foreign substance in the lung, they are coughed up and then swallowed and so reach the small intestine and start life again as hookworms. The cycle could be interrupted by making natives adopt civilised sanitary habits—which seems impossible—or by killing all the hookworms in all the people of a community, so that egg infection ceases.

The hookworm is tough—what will kill him is apt to kill you; but doses of 3 cc. of carbon tetrachloride in a capsule which is digested in the small intestine is an efficient though rather a dangerous cure. Thymol is safer.

These simple but sinister creatures are almost unknown to us dwellers in cool, civilised and highly sanitary countries; those who advocate a "return to nature" should not forget the hookworm, the tapeworm, the lung-fluke and a host of other bringers of misery.

CŒLENTERATA

The Cœlenterates are (except for the sponges) the simplest of all the many-celled creatures. Fig. 500 shows a very simple creature, the hydra which grows to $\frac{1}{4}$ or $\frac{1}{2}$ inch in length and clings to bits of weed in ponds. Its organs are simply a mouth, the rudiment of a gut and hollow tentacles which are armed with stinging cells which can disable their prey—infusoria or water-fleas. It has muscle fibres for movement, but no true nerves—far less a brain. A sort of network of nerve fibres spreads all

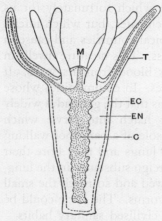

FIG. 500.—The hydra, a coelenterate about 15 times magnified.

M = mouth
C = coelenteron (body cavity)
EN = endoderm (inner layer)
EC = ectoderm (outer skin)
T = tentacle

over the creature and transmits a stimulus such as a touch from one part to another. Hydra is not always easy to find and needs a microscope to discover its structure, but the sea-anemone and the jelly-fish are well-known representatives of the class. Sea anemones are, in principle, very like hydra, but the jelly-fish require a little more explanation. It may be regarded as a bell. The mouth is in between the four clappers. On the oval arms are tentacles which first kill the prey by poisoning it; the arms then transfer it to the creature's mouth, whence it passes to a stomach and to numerous radiating food canals. Many people have been made quite ill by the

sting of a jelly-fish; this is how it works. A cell containing the poison has a very fine hair-like hollow thread coiled up in it. The thread is part of the cell-wall, like a glove-finger turned inside out and pulled inside the glove. The cell has a fine hair at the end. When this is touched, the cell bursts and shoots out the fine thread by turning it inside out (as one might pull an inside-out glove-finger from a glove). The thread point

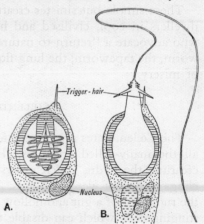

FIG. 501.—The nematocyst or poison cell of a jelly-fish. (A) before, (B) after discharge (much magnified).

buries itself in the prey and injects the charge of poison.

These cœlenterates— hydra, sea-anemones and jelly-fish can reproduce by budding like a plant as well as by sperms and eggs, therein showing themselves more primitive than any creature we have yet studied.

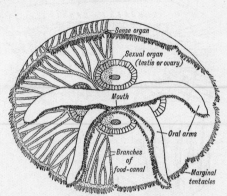

JELLYFISH

Fig. 502.—A cœlenterate—the jelly-fish.

SPONGES

Simplest of all many-celled animals are the sponges; indeed, there was for a long time doubt as to whether they were to be called animals or plants. The sponge we use in the bathroom is the skeleton only of a sponge. This skeleton is of *spongin*, which is not a carbohydrate like the cellulose of a plant, but a protein like hair or silk—a reason for thinking the sponges are not plants. The skeleton of fibres is usually supplemented by beautiful microscopic "spicules" of silica or of calcium carbonate (Fig. 503). Living sponges of the size of the top of a little finger are common in British waters, but the sponges of commerce are the skeletons of those living in the Mediterranean or tropical seas.

A sponge has some sort of root attaching it to the sea-bottom. For the rest, it is a network of fibres supporting a mass of jelly which is honeycombed by fine tubes. On the outside of the living sponge open invisibly fine tubes which branch into capillaries finer than a hair. These open into little chambers lined with cells which have delicate whiplashes (cilia). The cells ply their lashes so as to drive the water through the chambers

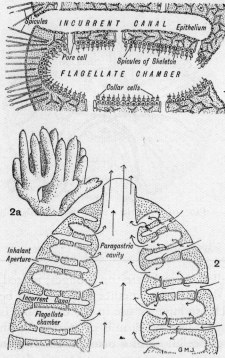

FIG. 503.—A sponge. (1) Illustrating the chambers lined with "collar-cells" which by lashing their cilia cause the water to circulate; and the skeleton of spongin strengthened by spicules. (2a) The growing sponge. (2) The water-circulation in a single branch.

and out by tubes which combine to make the wide tubes, the track of which can be traced in the big holes in a bath sponge. So the sponge continually sucks water through its skin and ejects it through the large holes with some force. The separate living cells feed on the organic matter in the sea-water and breathe its oxygen.

The sponge is hardly more than a colony of cells which have combined to keep house within a skeleton they have erected. Sponges can reproduce asexually by throwing off little balls of cells. Sexual reproduction sometimes occurs, but very little is known about it.

PROTOZOA

Life is perhaps reduced to its lowest terms in the single-celled creatures. These can be highly organised or may be almost without visible evidence of structure. The viruses alone, which are not certainly known to be living, may be simpler than a single cell. Let us look at a fairly complicated free-swimming single cell; the infusorian *Paramœcium*, common in stagnant pools

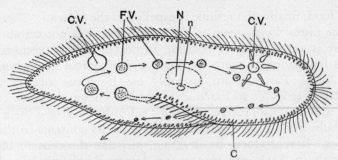

FIG. 504.—A single-celled animal, Paramœcium.

C = cilium   CV = contractile vacuoles
F.V. = food vacuoles   N = nucleus
n = micronucleus

and large enough to be just visible as a speck, is a good example.

It is a single cell with nucleus, cytoplasm and cell-wall, and these are organised. The many-celled animals usually specialise certain cells to form an organ such as a muscle, nerve or gland. The protozoon makes the equivalent of these out of its one cell. Naturally, then, it is a more complicated but less specialised cell than any in a many-celled animal or plant.

Externally, paramœcium has a profile like a bedroom slipper. The outside of the animal is clothed with very fine hair-like structures known as cilia. Their fineness is well appreciated when it is remembered that a human hair is thicker than the whole animal is long. These cilia are practically oars; they bend and straighten themselves and so lash the water backward—this has the effect of propelling the animal forward.

Cilia move successively in waves like the stalks of a corn-field when a gusty wind blows; probably the motion of each cilium gives an impulse to the next. Cilia are not the exclusive property of protozoa. Even in man, ciliated cells line the wind-pipe and the uterine tube. The paramœcium has a hole (C) into which the cilia can waft food particles, e.g. bacteria. This food is taken up in vacuoles which are hollow, bubble-like spaces in the cytoplasm and act as a sort of primitive stomach. Into these the cell substance pours out enzymes which digest the food; finally, the residue is expelled to the exterior. There are some fibres which seem to act as muscles; it is not certain that there is anything corresponding to nerves in paramœcium, but in a few protozoa there are fibres which control the lashing of the cilia. Paramœcium probably has no sense organs: it is certainly sensitive to touch and light and chemical substances in the water. Waste products are got rid of by excreting them into a "bubble," which at intervals discharges its contents to the exterior. It reproduces by dividing, just like the cells of higher animals (p. 820), and may go on doing so indefinitely and for ever. Thus a Paramœcium has the chance of immortality. It divides into two, which are in a sense both part of the original animal. These are *young*; they grow up again and again divide; so there is no reason why a paramœcium should ever grow old and die, if it can avoid the accidents of being eaten, dried up, poisoned, etc., which dispose of the vast majority

The higher animal specialises its cells; the germ cells are potentially immortal, for they divide into sperms or ova which make new individuals; all other cells must die altogether.

Even protozoa sometimes reproduce sexually by two individuals combining into one and forming a cell which divides again into individuals, but many protozoa appear to be able to reproduce for indefinite periods without sexual reproduction.

Paramœcium is only one of thousands of kinds of protozoa utterly different in shape and habits. Ciliated free-swimming forms are called infusoria. A drop of stagnant water is sure to show hundreds or thousands. Other protozoa have no cilia but drift in the currents of sea-water. Examples of these are foraminifera (Plate XXXII), which secrete a tiny but beautiful shell, through pores in which they thrust long processes to help to prevent them from sinking. Other protozoa have the green pigment chlorophyll; these can make their own food; they colour the sea and some fresh water green. Protozoa abound in ordinary surface soil. A tablespoonful of earth may contain a million! Some are infusoria, swimming in the film of water that surrounds the soil grains, others are flagellates, propelling themselves by a whip-like tail. Others are amœbæ (Plate XLII), protozoa with an apparently naked surface; these can change their shape indefinitely, thus making tentacles to secure their prey or drag themselves along. This huge soil population feeds on the far more numerous soil bacteria. A good many protozoa are parasites. Some are quite harmless; the white ant cannot digest its woody diet without the help of protozoa living in its gut. Protozoa are the cause of sleeping sickness, tropical dysentery and malaria.

The malaria parasite deserves our notice, for its discovery has been one of the greatest benefits science has given to man. The malaria parasite has a complicated life cycle.

It lives and breed more or less permanently in a man, but they can only get to one man from another *via* a mosquito. Let us start with the infected mosquito's bite. It injects its saliva into the wound and with it malarial parasites in the form called sporozoites. These bore into the red blood corpuscles of the man and develop into forms called trophozoites. These divide into merozoites, and in doing so burst the blood corpuscles. The merozoites then bore into fresh blood corpuscles and develop into new trophozoites. This may continue for years, and naturally causes serious illness from the destruction of blood corpuscles. At intervals some of the merozoites can turn into sexual forms (gametocytes), which die unless a mosquito bites the victim and sucks them into its body. In this case the gametocytes form sperms and ova which unite, forming a fertilised cell (zygote). This bores into

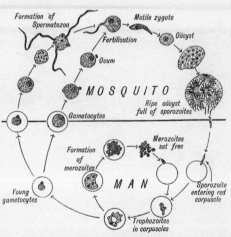

FIG. 505.—The life-cycle of the malaria parasite.

the stomach wall of the mosquito and divides many times. It migrates to the salivary glands and forms "sporozoites" once more. If the mosquito now bites a man, he will receive these sporozoites and the story will start again.

The only way to break the chain is to destroy the mosquito. This has been done in many parts of the world. The standard method is to pour a film of oil on every puddle or pool in the district. The mosquito larva lives in water and must breathe through its tail. The oil film prevents the tail being protruded through the surface. Water tanks in houses are each supplied with a live fish; this eats the larvæ. As tropical mosquitoes also carry the germ of the deadly yellow fever, it has proved possible to make places like the Isthmus of Panama—formerly so deadly that men could hardly dwell there—into healthy countries.

The only creatures simpler than protozoa are the bacteria and viruses. These are treated under the heading of Plants.

CHAPTER XLI

Plants and Bacteria

WHAT IS A PLANT

BETWEEN plants and animals there seems at first to be little in common. Plants do not appear to move or feel or feed—at least in the same sense as an animal. Though their general outline and the form of their leaves, flowers, etc., are so typical that it is as easy to tell a lily from an iris as a cow from a horse, yet they have no fixed shape. No two apple trees have the same number of branches and twigs, though every rabbit has four legs. Moreover, there is only the smallest likeness in function and behaviour between animals and plants. Despite all this, plants and animals have in common the fact that they are built of cells of the same pattern with nucleus, chromosomes, cytoplasm, etc., which divide in the same way by splitting their chromosome outfit. Plants, too, reproduce sexually by sperm and ovum as well as asexually. Moreover, a complete chain can be traced from specialised plants like dandelions or irises down through ferns, mosses, seaweeds, single green cells like those which cover damp tree-trunks, through free-swimming green cells to the simple single cell whence we can trace the upward line through sponges, jelly-fish, worms, fish, amphibians and reptiles to mammals. The kingdoms of Plants and Animals are the great twin trunks of the evolutionary tree.

It is not altogether simple to define a plant. It may roughly be defined as an organism which can nourish itself on simple inorganic compounds. Animals must have proteins, carbohydrates, fats and the like as their diet. Green plants can live on carbon dioxide, nitrates, mineral salts and water. Such plants as moulds and fungi, which have no green colouring matter, cannot get their carbon from carbon dioxide, but must feed on organic matter like animals, but their general form and method of growth shows them clearly to be plants. A few creatures like bacteria are on the border-line, and indeed there is a doubt whether they are animals, plants or a third kingdom.

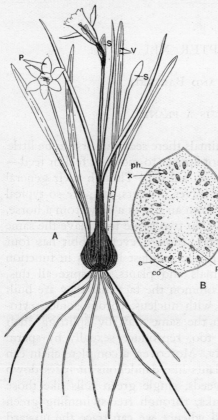

FIG. 506.—The Daffodil—a monocotyledon. Note long narrow leaves with *parallel* veining (V). There are 6 perianth leaves (P) a multiple of three. These are not differentiated into a calyx and a corolla (*cf*. Fig. 507). The bud is protected by a spathe (S). On the left is a section of the flower stem. Note numerous scattered bundles of conducting tissue. e= epidermis (skin); x=xylem (water-carrying vessels); co=cortex; pi=pith; ph=phloem (vessels carrying food products).

Before we discuss the way in which a plant works, it is as well to understand what are the main groups of plants.

We divide plants into those which do not flower, CRYPTO-GAMS and those which do so, PHANERO-GAMS. The CRYP-TOGAMS include (1) the *Algæ* — seaweeds and diatoms and various very simple water plants: the *Fungi, Bacteria* and *Lichens;* (2) the *Mosses* and *Liverworts.* (3) *The Ferns* and *Horsetails* and *Clubmosses.*

The PHANEROGAMS—seed plants—are divided into (1) the *Gymnosperms*, which do not have an ovary to cover the seeds and which all have separate male and female "flowers"; the conifers —pines, firs, etc.—are chief of these; and (2) the *Angiosperms*, which have an ovary for the seeds. There are two chief types of these. The Monocotyledons show but one tiny leaf when the seed sprouts; their flowers usually have parts grouped in threes. Their leaves usually have their veins roughly parallel, stretching from stalk to tip. Examples of these are Grasses, Palms, Lilies, Irises, Reeds, Orchids; and almost all "bulbs" belong to this group.

The Dicotyledons are the plants whose seeds throw up two tiny leaves when they germinate. Their flowers usually have their parts grouped in fours or fives. Their leaves usually have veins branching from a central vein. In this group are

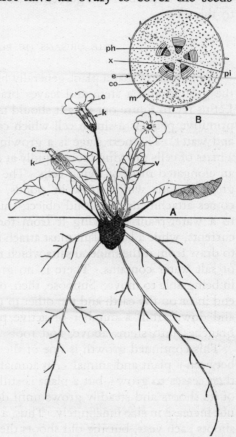

Fig. 507.—The Primrose, a dicotyledon. A. Note wide leaves, with net veining V, narrowed at the base to a stalk. The perianth is differentiated into a corolla *c*, and a calyx *k*. The flower parts are in *fives*. B. Section of flower stem, showing few and regularly-arranged bundles of vascular tissue with cambium separating the phlœm and xylem. Lettering as in Fig. 506. M=cambium (tissue from which phlœm and xylem grows).

most of our ordinary weeds and all the common trees. Most of our trees, vegetables and garden flowers other than bulbs belong to this class.

THE ORGANS OF PLANTS

We all realise that a plant generally has roots branching below the ground and a stem and leaves branching in the air above. Let us try to figure out why it should take this shape. The most primitive plant is a single cell which can nourish itself from air and water. The next stage is a growing mass of cells; the next a mass of cells growing more rapidly at one end, which will make an elongated mass of living cells. The simple algæ, such as the green threads which grow in ponds, are at this stage. Next comes attachment to a solid object; this is clearly an advantage to a water-plant as saving it from the troubles of waves and currents, while a land-plant must attach itself to some solid object to draw from it the mineral salts which rain lacks but which fresh or salt water contains. There is no great advantage to a plant in being able to move. Suppose, then, our plant is fixed with one end in or on the earth and the other in the air. It grows both up and down from a number of active points and so necessarily branches into stems above, and roots below.

This continued growth is one of the most striking differences between a plant and animal. An animal grows to maturity—and then ceases to grow—but a plant is still "embryonic" at the tips of its shoots and steadily grows until death overtakes it. It will not increase in size indefinitely. Thus, a wild rose throws up new shoots each year, but the old shoots die after a few years. Trees decay and fall as they grow old. The great Californian red-woods grow to 300 feet high—enormously the largest of living things—but unless some material stronger than wood were evolved, they could grow no larger without breaking by their own weight.

As we surveyed the working of a man, let us now survey the way a plant works. First, let us consider one of the higher plants at a season when it is growing but not yet flowering.

SECTION OF COLOURLESS PLANT CELL

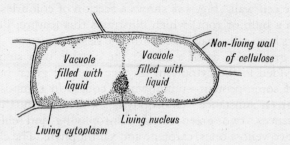

Non-living wall of cellulose

Vacuole filled with liquid

Vacuole filled with liquid

Living nucleus

Living cytoplasm

SECTION OF GREEN PLANT CELL

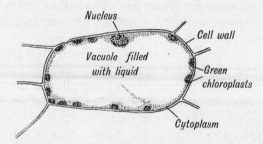

Nucleus

Cell wall

Vacuole filled with liquid

Green chloroplasts

Cytoplasm

FIG. 508.—Typical plant cells. The living cytoplasm and nucleus occupy comparatively little of the cell to which they often form a mere lining. The greater part is commonly filled with fluid.

The obvious "organs" of the growing plant are its leaves, its stem and its roots. Each of these is composed of living cells, usually much too small to be seen by the naked eye.

The plant cell is like the animal cell in containing a nucleus and its apparatus of chromosomes and cytoplasm surrounding it. This has, outside it, a cell membrane and a strong cell wall. Unlike that of the animal cell, the cytoplasm usually has large spaces (vacuoles) filled with liquid. Often the cell is almost filled with liquid, the living cytoplasm and nucleus forming a mere lining to the cell wall. Fig. 508 shows a section of colourless plant cell (as in a bulb or root) which illustrates this feature; Plate XLVII shows how cells coalesce to form the tissue of a stem.

A green cell, as of a leaf or the outside of a stem, contains embedded in the cytoplasm tiny lens-shaped green bodies made up of some protein—unknown of course in composition—and the green substance "chlorophyll," which is a mixture of four substances, two green ones, chlorophyll-*a* and chlorophyll-*b*, and two yellow ones, carotene and xanthophyll. The chlorophylls are very complicated substances curiously like hæmatin—the non-protein part of hæmoglobin, the red blood pigment of animals. Chlorophyll contains nitrogen, of which a plant finds it hard to collect enough from the soil. Consequently, in the autumn, before the leaves fall, the tree destroys its chlorophyll and takes back the nitrogen for future use. The yellow leaf is coloured by the carotene and xanthophyll, which the tree does not bother to break down, since they contain no nitrogen.

A plant's job is like an animal's, to keep itself alive and reproduce its kind. To nourish itself, it has got to make its protoplasm, its skeleton of cellulose, its chlorophyll and anything else it contains, from the contents of the soil and the air, aided by the energy of light. The air can be relied upon for carbon dioxide and oxygen; and the soil for water, nitrates (pp. 643 *ff*) and phosphates (pp. 654 *ff*) and all the salts a plant requires. The plant is the chemist which builds these simple molecules into the vastly complex proteins, cellulose, chlorophyll, etc. Animals cannot do it: they are the pensioners of plants. Every bit of every animal started as a plant. Either it feeds on plants or on other animals which fed on plants.

The leaf is concerned in making the carbon compounds in the plant, the root with gathering water and salts (nitrates, phosphates, etc.) from the soil. Fig. 509 and Plate XLVII show sections of typical leaves. Even a thin leaf is six or seven cells thick. The outer skin of a leaf, which is easily peeled off a thick leaf like that

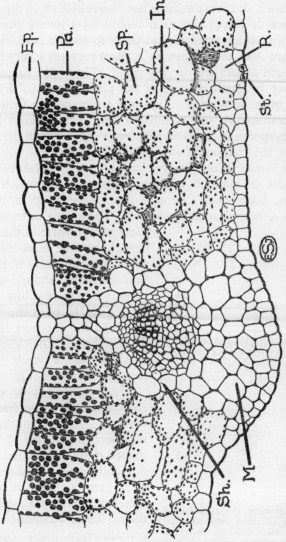

FIG. 509.—Section of a leaf through a vein. Ep, epidermis or skin; Pa, palisade cells; Sp, spongy tissue of cells with air-spaces; In; St, stoma; R, cavity containing air; Sh, sheath surrounding bundle of conducting tissue; M, midrib. In the centre is the conducting tissue of the vein. (Courtesy of Messrs. G. Bell & Sons, and of Prof. F. S. Fritsch, and Prof. E. J. Salisbury, from their *Introduction to the Structure and Reproduction of Plants*.)

of a laurel, is a pavement of cells. It is usually impregnated with
a waxy substance. It is very notable how water collects in droplets
on the surface of leaves just as it would on a greasy surface.
The object of this thin impervious skin is to restrict evaporation
when the plant does not require it. A plant presents a very large
surface exposed to sun and drying wind. The water supply to
the roots may be small, and so if the plant is not to dry up
evaporation must be limited. A plant's leaves remain firm and
stiff only because each cell is inflated with water, like a little
balloon. If evaporation removes this water quicker than the root
can replace it, the "balloons" sag and the leaf wilts.

The upper surface of most leaves has only a few entrances, but
the under-sides are studded with openings (stomata) which can
close or open. Each is like a mouth. Just below the opening, on
each side, is a bean-shaped guard-cell. These two cells, when
the water pressure in the leaf
is high, become more curved
and open the pore; if evaporation is rapid and the water
pressure becomes low, the
guard-cells become less
stretched and the pore shuts.
The action is rather like that
of inflating a cycle tube
hanging on a nail (Fig. 510).

These stomata allow air to
enter and leave the interior of
the leaf. The leaf under its
top skin has a layer of cells
shaped more or less like jam-
pots and packed together so as
to be just touching; there are
therefore air spaces between
them. These "palisade cells"
contain very many chloro-
plasts and are the place where

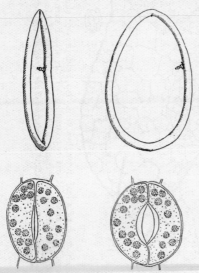

FIG. 510.—Illustrating the opening of
the stoma by increased water pressure
in its guard-cells. (Above) the effect
illustrated by inflation of a cycle-tyre
hanging on a nail.

carbon dioxide from the air-spaces and water from the cells meet with light coming through the leaf-skin. From these materials (p. 614) the chloroplast mysteriously makes starch, sugar probably being an intermediate stage. This starch is only temporary; it is soon broken down to sugar again. Under the palisade cells is a loose spongy tissue of irregular cells which touch each other but leave large air spaces between. Air can filter through these. Every living cell must breathe, and so a system of fine tubes carries air to the deeper parts of the plant (stems), etc. This spongy tissue also serves to carry the sugar from the palisade cells to the veins of the leaf, which are truly veins in the sense of being arrangements for carrying liquids. Solutions can pass from one cell to the next, for very fine strands of cytoplasm pierce the walls and link the cells in a living network.

The leaf, then, when working, is making starch and sugar as described above. The sugary solution can pass from cell to cell and can reach the veins of the leaf which conduct it to any part of the plant which needs it. Proteins are probably also formed in the leaf-cell though nothing is really known about the way this is done. Since proteins cannot diffuse through a cell-wall—their molecules are too big—they are digested to amino-acids, just as in the intestine of an animal, and sent to parts of the plant—e.g., seeds—where they may be wanted. The leaf of the plant, then, corresponds very roughly to an animal's digestive system.

A plant, like an animal, requires some vessels which can carry the food made in the leaf to the parts of the plant which need it. A system of cells adapted to carrying liquids traverses the whole plant from root to leaf *via* the stem. Some are long cells set end to end with a sort of sieve separating them. This "sieve plate" is lined with living cytoplasm and so is not a mere sieve or filter. The function of these cells (bast or phloem) is to carry food products. For water-carrying, there are long fine tubes which started as cells set end to end (Fig. 511); the intervening cell-walls break down and leave tubes (xylem) which carry water from the roots to the leaves. Besides these, there are usually hollow air spaces.

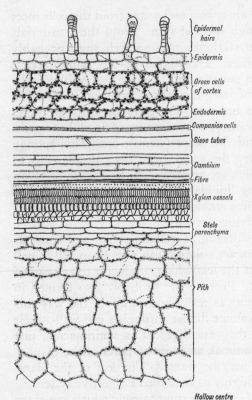

Epidermal hairs

Epidermis

Green cells of cortex

Endodermis

Companion cells

Sieve tubes

Cambium

Fibre

Xylem vessels

Stele parenchyma

Pith

Hollow centre

FIG. 511.—A section of a marigold stem cut along its length. Successively from the outside appear hairs and protective skin; a green layer capable of photosynthesis (p. 989); an inner skin (endodermis); phloem conducting food through sieve-tubes; cambium, the actively growing cells which become, as they mature, either phloem or xylem; fibre giving strength; xylem vessels carrying water; "stele parenchyma" cells—supporting tissues; and pith.

The stems of plants have not only to act as pipe-lines but also as supports. Consequently, in a large plant they must be strong. This is provided for by long tapering pointed cells which lay down strong woody tissue on their walls and finally die, leaving a strong woody fibre.

The root is the collecting organ for water and salts. Only the part of the young root near the growing tip is able to take up water and the salts dissolved in it from the surrounding soil; the older part has a more or less waterproof coating and acts as pipeline. This part of the root near the tip is covered with tiny hairs, very well seen in mustard and cress. These hairs are the organs which take in water from the soil. Now a tree may lose many gallons of water a day by evaporation, which loss is all supplied by water from the roots travelling upwards through the fine xylem tubes. It seems that the cells of the leafy shoots *draw* the water out of these fine tubes. But, you object, a pump can only draw water 30 feet and some trees are 300 feet high: why does the column of water not break and leave a vacuum? The water column must be broken to produce a vacuum. The molecules of water attract each other, and it can be shown that if the water develops no gas bubbles, it needs a big force, actually 3000 lbs. or more per square inch, to break a column of it. A very fine thread of water is much less likely to develop such bubbles of gas. The leaves, then, draw up a thread of water from the root. This theory is generally established, but has some difficulties. It would seem that the root tips exert a pressure, while the leaves exert a tension and that both effects operate together. The root takes in, not only water but dissolved salts which travel with the water to the leaves. The liquid in the soil may contain from $\frac{1}{4}$ to 1 part of salts per 1,000 of water. The plant requires potassium ions, calcium ions, magnesium ions, iron ions, nitrate ions, phosphate ions and sulphate ions and possibly traces of many other elements. The cell has an unexplained power of collecting these ions. The soil water may have one part per five thousand of potassium ion. But the cell can collect that potassium ion out of the water and leave behind other salts. It is not well understood how this is done.

The plant from its air, light and water and salts may make far more material than it requires for present needs. It very often stores this in some convenient form, which can be turned back to plant food when required. Thus, the potato plant lays down tubers full of starch grains. These give the potato a quick start in spring: it does not wait to make its new stem and leaf from carbon dioxide and water, but builds them from its stored starch and protein. Most roots store starch, but some like the beetroot store sugar. The dahlia and artichoke store inulin, a kind of starch made from fructose. Bulbs are not roots but large modified buds! They are also storage organs: thus an onion stores sugar and protein. Seeds always have a store of nutriment, protein, starch and often fat, to send them on their way. The fact that they contain much more protein than the rest of the plant makes them

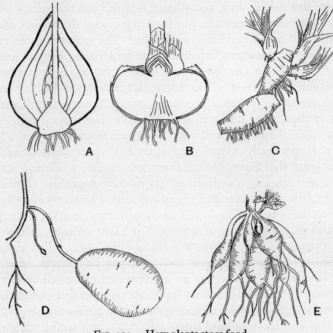

FIG. 512.—How plants store food.

A. Tulip bulb   B. Crocus corm
C. Iris rhizome   D. Potato: stem-tuber
E. Dahlia: root-tuber

the chief food of mankind. Wheat, maize, rice, beans, etc., are complete enough foods to form the staple of a diet.

THE SENSES OF PLANTS

Plants appear to be motionless and irresponsive. This is far from true. They are slow moving, but they move purposefully just as does an animal. The primitive cell has the property of irritability. Like a nerve, it can be influenced by outside interference: the nerve cell is one which has specialised in irritability. Very little is known about the mechanism of a plant's response to stimuli. A plant's chief response is a change of position. If a plant is to flourish, it must get its roots into the ground and its leaves into the light, and it has a mechanism for doing this. Plant a bulb upside down. The roots will travel down round the bulb and the shoot will travel up to the surface. Arrange some flowering lupin heads in a vase. The tips will all bend upward so that they point straight to the ceiling.

These effects are a response to gravity. If no other stimulus interferes, a plant's shoots will grow up and its roots down. This has been very prettily proved by growing seedlings on a rapidly rotating turntable, so that the centrifugal force makes artificial gravity pulling in the direction of the rim. The shoots of the seeds all grow towards the axle and the roots towards the rim! The gravity response helps an underground plant to send its shoots to the air and its roots to the deeper and moister soil. But what the shoot most needs is light: so it has the power of growing towards the light. It has no eyes to see the light, but probably all primitive cells are sensitive to light, the retina being a collection of cells specialised for light reception. Obviously, the gravity-response and the light-response may clash. But the latter is the stronger. The light-response is easily seen in pot plants grown in a window: these almost always curve over to the light. Strangely enough, if only the tip of a shoot finds the light, the whole shoot will grow towards it. This would be easy to understand in an animal with nerves: the plant has no nerves and so it sends a "hormone"—some soluble growth-causing substance back—through the shoot diffusing from cell to cell. But how the growth-causing substance tells the plant which way to grow seems very difficult to explain.

Light has another very interesting effect. The length of the day indicates to many plants when their flowering time has arrived. Chrysanthemums will not flower till the day is reduced to some fixed length, say 12 hours, e.g., after the third week in September. But if these are put in a dark room at four o'clock every afternoon in July, they will flower within a few days.

Some plants are responsive to touch. A good example is the

32

well-known sensitive plant, the leaves of which fold when touched. Climbing plants also respond to touch, as anyone knows who has grown peas or any plant with tendrils.

PROPAGATION OF PLANTS

We have seen how the plant feeds itself: now let us see how one plant makes another. Plants have a curious rule of alternation of generations. A sperm fertilises an ovum. The fertilised cell grows into a plant of one type. This produces a spore which grows into a wholly different type of plant which produces the sperms and ova. "Well," you may say, "I never noticed this going on in the garden. I find a pea plant produces a seed which produces another pea plant." This is quite true, but as we shall see, it is not the whole story.

The simplest way of making a new plant is by division. A portion of a plant if suitably treated will grow into a whole one. Bits broken away from water-weeds put out fresh roots and become whole plants; bits of dandelion root or twitch rhizomes develop new stems and shoots. Yet no plant depends on this method entirely. For some reason, sexual reproduction is a necessity if a plant is to thrive. Man propagates many of his plants by division. All the King Edward potatoes are the same plant, and spring from the same original seed. They all arise from tubers which were budded off by cell-division from other tubers. Every King Edward potato plant has the same genes.

If you were to let the King Edward potato flower and set seed, the result would be to re-sort the genes, losing some and duplicating others, and you would get from your seed a collection of quite different potatoes, good and bad—mostly the latter. Unfortunately, the higher animals have lost this power of reproduction by simple division. What an excellent thing it would be if we could take a hundred cuttings off Darwin or Sir Isaac Newton or Shakespeare and "grow them on" into human beings as like the originals as their twin brothers. We can do this

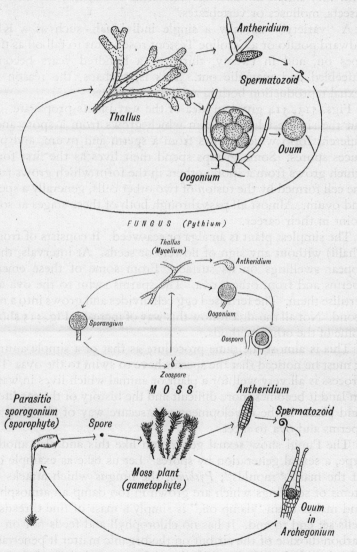

FIG. 513.—Sexual and asexual generation in seaweed, fungus and moss.

with very simple animals like flatworms or starfish, but not with insects, molluscs or vertebrates.

A "variety"—actually a single individual—such as a King Edward potato or a Caroline Testout rose seems to fall off as time goes on, and in twenty, thirty or a hundred years becomes enfeebled and may die out. This is, perhaps, the reason for sexual reproduction both in animals and plants.

Figs. 513, 514 gives an idea of the way plants propagate. All but the simplest have a form which grows from a spore and a different form which grows from a sperm and ovum, and produces spores. Some groups spend their lives as the first form, which grows from a spore: others in the form which grows from the cell formed by the fusion of two other cells, generally a sperm and ovum. Almost all pass through both of these stages at some point in their career.

The simplest plant is an alga or sea-weed. It consists of fronds (thalli) without any sign of flowers or seeds. At intervals, there appear swellings on its surface. From some of these emerge sperms and from others ova. The sperms swim to the ova and fertilise them. The fertilised egg cell divides and grows into a new frond. Not all the algæ follow this way of increase: Fig. 515 shows some of the other methods.

This is almost the same procedure as that of a simple animal. It must be noticed that the sperms have to swim to the ova. This process is all very well for a plant or animal which lives in water: on land it becomes more difficult and the history of the sex life of land plants is the development of a secure way of allowing the sperms and ova to meet.

The Fungi show sexual generation like this and also another type, a sexual generation by spores. Let us take as example one of the many "moulds"; *Pythium*, the fungus which attacks the stems of seedlings which are grown in too damp an atmosphere and makes them "damp off," is simply a mass of fine threads of cells set end to end. It has no chlorophyll and feeds not on the carbon dioxide of the air but on the organic matter it penetrates. The threads (*mycelium*) ramify through or over their food stuff and

F E R N

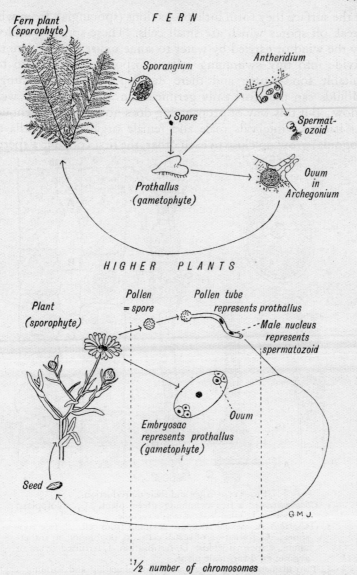

Fern plant
(sporophyte)

Sporangium

Spore

Antheridium

Spermat-
ozoid

Prothallus
(gametophyte)

Ovum
in
Archegonium

H I G H E R   P L A N T S

Plant
(sporophyte)

Pollen
= spore

Pollen tube
represents prothallus

Male nucleus
represents
spermatozoid

Embryosac
represents prothallus
(gametophyte)

Ovum

Seed

G M J.

½ number of chromosomes

FIG. 514.—Sexual and asexual generation in Ferns and in higher plants.

at the surface they form little projections (sporangia), from which break off spores which are small cells. These spores are blown by the wind or carried by water to some moist place. Here they divide into tiny swimming cells, zoospores, which swim to a suitable food-source and there develop into a fresh fungus. Moulds can therefore only germinate in a wet place, as we all know. But this way of propagating does not seem to be enough. At irregular intervals male and female organs (antheridia and oogonia) grow up close to each other, the first contains a sperma-

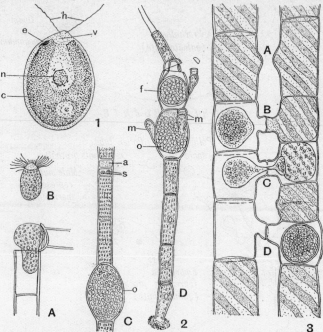

Fig. 515.—Algæ and their reproduction.

1. *Chlamydomonas*, a free swimming green plant. C, chloroplast; n, nucleus; L, cilia; V, contractile vacuole.
2. *Oedogonium* A. asexual zoospore ecsaping from cell. B, free zoospore; C, formation of sexual cells; o, oogonium; a, antheridium; s, spermatozoids; D, fertilization; f, fertilised ovum or zygote; m, dwarf male plant.
3. Two filaments of the alga *Spirogyra* conjugating and forming a zygote D. A, B, C, D show successive stages in conjugation.

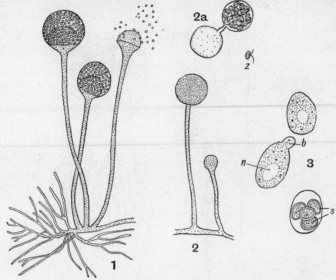

FIG. 516.—Spore formation of simple fungi.

1. Grey mould (Rhizopus nigrans), showing three sporangia, one shedding its spores.

2. Sporangia of "damping-off fungus (Pythium). 2a formation of zoospores from sporangium. z, escaped zoospore.

3. Yeast showing an ordinary cell; a cell reproducing by a bud, b, and a cell which has divided to four spores s. n, nucleus.

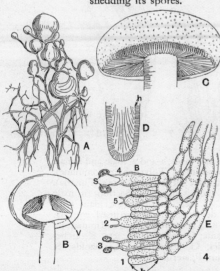

FIGS. 517.—Reproduction of a Mushroom.

A. Formation of young mushrooms on underground mycelium.

B. Mushroom with veil, v, bending back to expose gills.

C. Mushroom cut to show arrangement of gills.

D. Section of single gill, showing spore-bearing outer layer, h.

E. Formation of spores. on exterior of gill; 1–4, successive stages in formation of spores, S; 5, basidium from which spores have escaped; B, basidium.

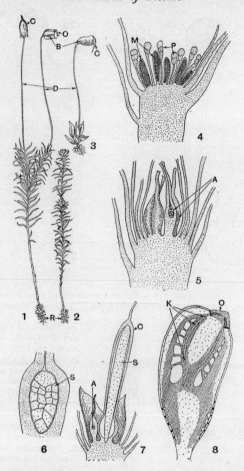

FIG. 518.—Reproduction in a moss, 1 and 2, male and female
plants of a common heath-moss (Polytrichum commune).
The remaining drawings are of another moss (Funaria).
3. Female plant with sporogonium. 4. Section of male
plant with antheridia. 5. Section of female plant with
archegonia. 6. Early development of fertilised egg. 7.
Further development. 8. The sporogonium, still immature.
A, archegonia; B, capsule; C, calyptra, D, seta; K, arche-
sporium; M, antheridia; O, operculum; R, rhizoids; S,
developing sporogonium; P, sterile hairs.

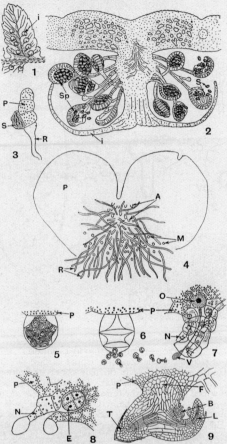

FIG. 519.—Reproduction of a fern. (1) Underside
of leaf showing the sori. (2) A sorus in section
and enlarged (i) cover of the sorus (Sp) sporangia;
S, spores. (3) A spore germinating and forming.
(4) A prothallus with rhizoids (roots) R, having
archegonia A and antheridia M on it. (5) An
antheridium full of spermatozoids. (6) Spermatozoids escaping and (7) Entering the archegonium in which is the ovum O. This when
fertilised (8) E, grows into a fern (9) F, foot of
fern still in prothallus; P, prothallus; T, root of
young fern; B shoot of young fern; L leaf of same.

32*

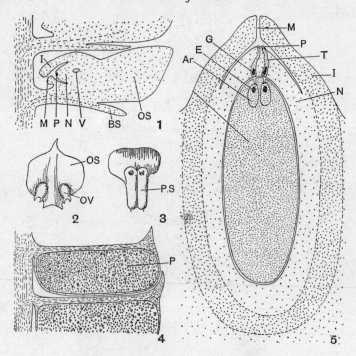

FIG. 520.—Reproduction in a conifer.
1. Section of part of female cone.   2. Upper surface of scale of female
cone.   3. Under surface of scale of male cone.   4. Section of part of
male cone.   5. The act of fertilisation. The pollen grains send out their
male nuclei which unite with the female nuclei E.
P.S. pollen-sac.   T pollen-tube.   G male nuclei.   E nucleus of
female ovum. Ar Archegonium. BS, OS. parts of scale carrying the
ovule. V Embryo-sac. P pollen grains. M micropyle. N, nucellus.

tozoid, the second an ovum. The male organ touches the female,
a passage opens and the male sperm swims through and fertilises
the egg. The fertilised egg (oospore) may remain dormant like a
seed, and at a suitable time germinate, producing free swimming
zoospores which grow into a fungus again. Moulds and fungi
show many variations on the reproduction theme. Many fungi
(mushrooms among them) do not appear to have any sexual stage
and generate only by spores.

The next stage is represented by Mosses, which are definitely
land-plants, but which must be wet to propagate themselves,
though they can stand much drought. A moss is quite recognisably a plant with leaves and stem and fine hairs which play
the parts of roots. Most mosses can be seen to bear cup- or vase-
shaped objects on a slender stem. The moss at certain seasons,
grows antheridia, which produce sperms, and the cup-shaped
objects already mentioned, which contain ova (Fig. 513, also in
more detail, Fig. 518). The sperms swim through the film of
moisture on the wet moss, enter the cups and fertilise the ovum.
The fertilised egg cell grows into a tiny new plant inside the cup!
This plant only lives to produce spores which blow away and
germinate in moist places, forming a network of green threads
from which the new moss grows. The moss thus gets the
advantage of re-assorting its chromosomes by a sexual generation,
and dispersing its offspring by spores to conquer new fields.

The fern does much the same thing as the moss: here the big
plant we call the fern is the part that grows from the fertilised
egg: the part that grows from the spore is inconspicuous. Start
with the full-grown fern. The underneath of its leaf is covered
with dark-brown organs which shed millions of dust-like spores.
A spore which finds a suitable damp place grows into a flat green
leaf-like object, rooted by root-hairs into the ground. This
"prothallus" developes sex-organs, male and female. In wet
weather the male organs open, the sperms swim to the female
organs and fertilise the ovum. This, still in the prothallus, grows
into a fern. At first, the prothallus gives it nourishment, but it
soon develops its roots, whereupon the prothallus withers
away. Fig. 514 shows the principle. Fig. 519 gives more detail.

The sexual stage still needs water in which the sperms can
swim to the ova. This limits ferns to moist places. The flowering
plants escape this limitation by having the sexual generation
inside their own bodies. A flowering plant produces spores—
pollen—from its anthers (Fig. 514). These settle on the stigma
of another flower and germinate. A pollen tube, representing the
prothallus of the fern, grows down into the ovary of the flower and

there liberates a couple of sperms which fertilise a single-celled ovum in the ovary. This ovum develops to some extent and then becomes dry and goes to rest as a seed which later develops into a plant. Fig. 514 shows the principle. Figs. 520, 521 give details for conifers and flowering plants respectively.

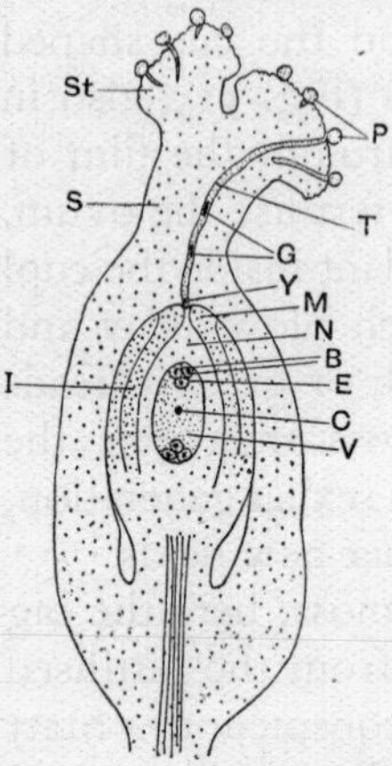

FIG. 521.—Fertilisation in a flower. S, style; St, Stigma with pollen-grains one of which P has sent its pollen tube T into the style; G, nuclei, one of which represents the spermatozoid from the pollen. Y; tube-nucleus; M, micropyle (opening to ovary; N, nucellus; B, egg-apparatus; E, ovum; C nucleus of embryo-sac V; I, integument of ovary. In fertilisation the nuclei of G and E will fuse.

It is a mistake to compare the pollen with the sperm of an animal, and the seed with the animal's ovum. The pollen is a spore which produces a minute "body" which emits sperms. The ovum of the plant is in the ovary of the flower. The seed is a young plant in a resting state.

The chromosomes in the male cells come from the pollen. Those in the female cells come from the plant which bears the flower. If a mixing and reshuffling of chromosomes is to occur, it is desirable that the pollen should come from a different plant from that which bears the ovum. Plants have evolved numerous devices to ensure this. Pollen can be carried by the wind or by insects. The first is a primitive method. For success it requires so much pollen to be produced that some of it cannot fail to hit the stigma of a female flower. Clearly the pollen is most likely to reach the stamens of the flower which produces it, which is just what is *not* required. So the anthers and stamens usually ripen at different times and prevent this. The Grasses are a good example of wind-pollinated plants. Their flowers are inconspicuous and scentless, for they have no need to attract insects.

Most forest trees are wind-pollinated. The male and female flowers are often separate. Catkins are male flowers designed to let the wind shake the pollen out of them very easily.

The insect-pollinated flowers are much more interesting. They have evolved in the direction of being conspicuous to the insect's eye by their bright colours and conspicuous to its scent organs by the smell. They attract insects by offering a bait of sugary liquid, and often arrange some mechanism which will ensure that the insect takes pollen with him to the next flower.

Flower colours are of two kinds. The yellows and oranges are usually fat-soluble substances like carotene (p. 602). The red and blue pigments are anthocyanins, compounds of glucose with dyes having a structure rather like that shown below.

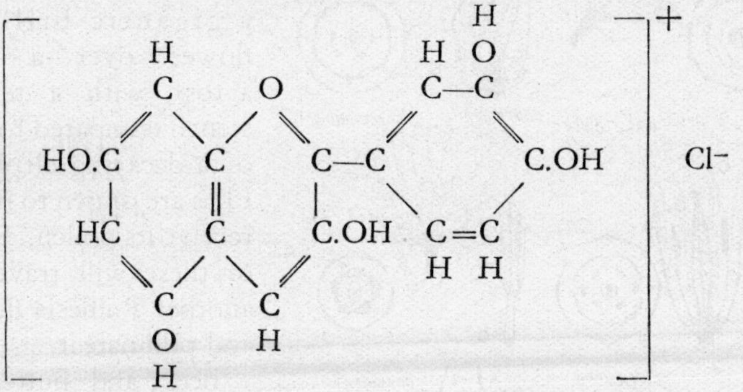

This compound combined with glucose gives
the red colour to the rose.

These dyes can exist as salts—compounds with acids—or as free dyes. In the first case they are red, in the second, blue. Thus a great many flowers can be red or blue according to whether their sap is more or less acid. Cornflowers can be blue or pink. Larkspurs range from pure blue through mauves to pure pinks, blue-bells are known in blue and pink varieties. So flowers in general belong to a blue-pink range or a yellow-orange range.

Their scents are usually delightful to the human nose. Most of the perfumes are fairly simple substances which the chemist can make in his laboratory (p. 604). Some flowers, however, are pollinated by flies. The extraordinary Rafflesia is an example.

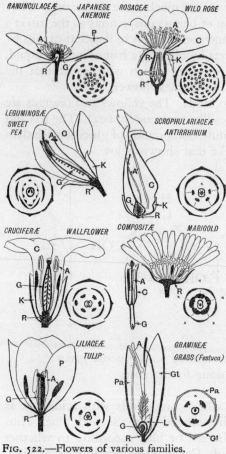

RANUNCULACEÆ — JAPANESE ANEMONE — ROSACEÆ — WILD ROSE

LEGUMINOSÆ SWEET PEA — SCROPHULARIACEÆ ANTIRRHINUM

CRUCIFERÆ — WALLFLOWER — COMPOSITÆ — MARIGOLD

LILIACEÆ TULIP — GRAMINEÆ GRASS (Festuca)

FIG. 522.—Flowers of various families.
A. Stamens. C. Petals. G. Pistil. K. Sepals. L. Lodicule = perianth leaf. R. Receptacle. Gl. glume. Pa. Palea.

This plant, which hails from the East Indies, is a parasite, and takes its nourishment from the trees in whose substance it burrows. It grows no leaves or stems, only burrowing parasitic roots. But at intervals it produces from the base of an infested tree a gigantic brilliant flower over a yard across, with a terrific stench compared to that of a decaying elephant. Flies are drawn to it and receive its pollen. Some of these will travel to another Rafflesia flower and pollinate it.

Bees and butterflies are the chief pollinators. They have long sucking mouth parts. The flower conceals its nectar somewhere at the base where an insect, to get it, has to brush past the anthers and receive a dusting of pollen to be deposited on the stamens of the next flower.

The seed once formed must be transferred to some place where it can germinate. Fig. 523 sums up a few of the methods plants have adopted to spread their seeds over new ground where they will not compete with each other or the parent plant.

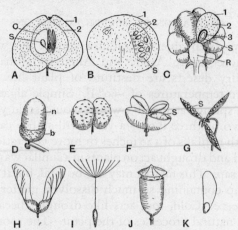

FIG. 523.—How plants disperse their seed.

Fleshy fruits eaten by birds (and men).

A—Apple; a pome—a false fruit.
 1—bright outer skin   } Developed receptacle
 2—fleshy layer
 c—core = true fruit (the developed ovary); s—seed

B—Tomato—a berry—a true fruit.
 1—bright outer skin } pericarp
 2—fleshy layer
 S—seed

C—Blackberry; an aggregate fruit—a collection of drupes.
 1—bright outer skin ⎫
 2—fleshy layer   ⎬ pericarp
 3—hard woody layer ⎭
 S—seed; R—receptacle

Other cases of Animal Distribution.

D—Acorn—a nut, distributed by squirrels.
 n—nut; a single seed in a woody pericarp; b—cupule formed of fused bracts.

E—Goosegrass or cleavers; a fruit with hooks by which it becomes attached to furry or woolly animals. Two fruits grow together but separate when ripe.

F—Spindle—a capsule which opens to display seeds enclosed in a bright orange fleshy aril (an extra seed-coat). Here the attraction to birds is the seeds, not the fruit.

G—Pansy—a capsule which splits to three boat-shaped valves. The sides of these then come together shooting the seeds to some distance. The seeds are enclosed in an oily aril which is attractive to ants and these complete the distribution.

Wind Dispersal.

H—Sycamore, a winged fruit. Two achenes grow together, and in each an out-growth of the pericarp forms a wing. When ripe they separate and blow away.

I—Dandelion—a fruit with a parachute. The parachute is formed from the developed pappus (a reduced calyx).

J—Poppy capsule. A pepper-pot arrangement. The seeds, which are very fine and light, are blown out through pores round the top.

K—A winged seed of Pine. Here the wing is an outgrowth of the seed-coat.

ADAPTATION TO SEVERE CONDITIONS

Plants have been able to colonise almost the whole world. Only the more severe Arctic and Antarctic climates and the completely dry deserts are destitute of plant life. In Siberia, plants endure temperatures of –90° F. Simple algae can live in water of hot springs at 120° F., which would scald your hand. A rainfall of two or three inches a year, will suffice cacti, while in countries with rainfalls of 120 inches or more vegetation flourishes hugely. Cold and drought act on plants in a similar way. Cold tends to freeze the sap. This may or may not be fatal, but it is countered by having sap containing so much dissolved matter that it does not easily freeze. Cold, too, acts like drought, because it slows down all the natural processes of the plant. The roots can gather moisture but slowly, while dry cold winds evaporate it from the leaves. A cold-resisting plant should then have small tough leathery leaves and a concentrated sap. Alternatively, it may be of a low type which can freeze solid and thaw, dry out and soak up water again without dying. In the very cold regions, the tundras, there flourish only mosses, lichens, small-leafed heather-like plants and dwarf birches. Conifers are well adapted to resist cold and moisture because of their small leaves impregnated with water-proof resin. Accordingly, a great belt of pine and fir forest stretches round the Arctic Circle.

Adaptations to drought are interesting. The plant which is to stand dry conditions has many resources. First of all it may develop a small surface. A given mass of plant stuff has least surface when it is in a lump like a football, but most when it spreads into leaves and shoots. Drought-resisting plants have spiny or lumpy leaves (gorse, heather), or in extreme cases are reduced to squat stumpy forms like cacti. They grow a tough waxy skin from which water does not easily escape, and sometimes coat this with dense hairs to shade it from the drying sun and wind. The interior of the thickened leaves or stems is filled with cells, which contain a sap so concentrated that water will hardly evaporate from it.

Some plants develop large underground roots or bulbs which store water from one wet season to the next. Others send tremendously long roots to depths where water still exists. The Cacti and Euphorbias (spurges), actually quite unrelated groups, have specialised in drought-resisting and have thus become so alike that they are hard to distinguish. Both of them, seemingly shrivelled and distorted masses of vegetation, break out into glorious vivid flowers. A walk round the cactus-house at Kew gives a remarkable notion of the drought-resisting devices of plants.

BACTERIA

The Bacteria are difficult to place: they are usually called plants chiefly because their cells seem to have a definite wall, a fact which classes them with the simplest of plants—diatoms, fungi, yeasts and seaweeds.

Bacteria have got a bad name because some of them cause disease. This is quite as unreasonable as condemning animals in general because lions, tigers, and cobras are unpleasant companions. Life would be almost impossible without bacteria, which do the very necessary task of turning organic refuse of all kinds into the simple food materials which plants can use. Bacteria are extremely small living cells. They may be from .0005 cm. to .005cm. in length. A mass of bacteria the size of a mustard seed might contain a thousand million of them. Some of them are stationary, others have fine threads of tissue by which they can propel themselves. Not much is known about their anatomy because they are so small, but granules suggesting a fragmentary kind of nucleus have been seen. They multiply by division, and apparently never combine in any sort of sexual reproduction: this division may be extraordinarily rapid, taking place as often as every twenty minutes. A single bacterium would at this rate produce a thousand million in ten hours, so we must not be surprised to find a liquid apparently free from bacteria one day and swarming with them the next.

The really interesting thing about bacteria is the extraordinary diets they can feed on and the remarkable products they excrete. We get our energy chiefly by turning glucose into carbon dioxide and water. Some bacteria can generate energy for their life processes by turning milk sugar into lactic acid: others turn ammonium salts into nitrates: starch into butyl alcohol and acetone: cellulose into methane: hydrogen sulphide into sulphuric acid: sugar into glycerine or butyric acid or lactic acid or citric acid: urea into ammonium carbonate, etc.

Obviously their chemical make-up must be very different from any animal or plant except perhaps the mould-fungi which have the same sort of omnivorous appetite. Moulds can live happily in such unpromising materials as tanned leather or paper. They seem to have a regular tool-box of enzymes by which they can break up almost anything into something they can live on.

Though no bacterium can be seen by the naked eye, we are all familiar with their behaviour *en masse*. Putrefaction is simply the alteration of some material by bacteria. When milk goes sour overnight, it is because one of the lactic acid bacteria has multiplied until there are a hundred million or more bacteria in every drop. These turn the milk sugar into the sour-tasting lactic acid. When meat putrefies a bacterium has broken the proteins into various evil-smelling simpler compounds. When butter goes rancid, bacteria have split its fat into glycerine and the sour-smelling butyric acid. All these activities of bacteria we could do without. Others are more beneficent. Throw a big heap of mown grass on the ground. In a few hours it will be hot and may get hot enough to scald your hand. Bacteria have multiplied in it, and the chemical changes due to their life and growth are producing heat. Other bacteria will work on the mass, and finally it will become a brown disintegrated mass rather like farmyard manure, and will be a most valuable fertiliser. The masses of leaves which fall in the forests are rotted down by countless bacteria and ultimately become carbon dioxide, water, nitrates, etc. A rich brown residue of leaf mould accumulates. Bacteria break down the proteins and urea of farmyard manure and animal refuse in general to ammonium salts: other bacteria convert these to nitrates which enter the life stream once more *via* the roots of plants.

Bacteria can even perform the extraordinary feat of turning the nitrogen of the air into nitrogen compounds. The soil teems with bacteria, a teaspoonful of soil containing millions. Some of these live by feeding on the plant-fibre, etc., in the soil, but a few have the power of building up the nitrogen of the air in the soil into their own body-proteins. More highly organised creatures such as soil-amoebæ devour these bacteria: when these amoebæ die, other bacteria break their proteins down to nitrates which feed plants. It has long been known that a field left without growing plants becomes more fertile, the reason being the activities of these bacteria. The leguminous plants, peas, beans, vetches, lupins, etc., strike up a partnership with nitrogen-fixing bacteria. The bacteria invade their roots and the plants form nodules (easily seen in a scarlet-runner root) containing the bacteria. These make nitrogen into body-proteins. As the bacteria die, the plant uses their nitrogen.

Perhaps the strangest bacteria of all are the anærobic ones, which can live without oxygen. Every creature except these few bacteria must breathe to get its energy. These get it by breaking down unstable chemical compounds. The black mud at the bottom of a pond contains some of these bacteria. Other anærobic forms are among our most sinister enemies. The bacillus botulinus, among others, can thrive in food which has been hermetically sealed or potted, but which has not been fully sterilised: it produces a fearfully deadly poison. A whole family has died after eating botulinus-infected potted meat in which there was probably only a minute percentage of the poison. The bacteria which cause tetanus are anærobic, which is the reason why lock-jaw follows deep lacerated wounds, where there can be lurking places free from air, more frequently than superficial cuts. It has been stated that the poison secreted by this bacterium is so powerful that a drop would kill 300 men. This would be several thousand times as poisonous as arsenic.

Disease bacteria form only an insignificant proportion of the vast bacterial population of the world. They are very important to us; and by an understanding of their habits, man has vastly increased his expectation of life. All the diseases formerly classed as "fevers" and several others are due to invasion of the body by bacteria (or in some cases the bacterium-like, but still smaller, viruses). Consumption, typhoid fever, tetanus, typhus fever, diphtheria, anthrax, the fevers resulting from infected wounds, the venereal diseases, etc., are all due to the growth of bacteria in the body (Plate XLVII). These bacteria rarely do any direct harm, but produce poisons which cause the symptoms of the disease. A bacterium in the body is in a strong position. You cannot easily poison it without poisoning the patient. We shall see later that methods of preparing antitoxins, poisonous to certain bacteria but not to man, have been worked out.

The greatest boon to man resulting from the discovery of bacteria, is the way to get rid of them. Before bacteria were discovered, nothing was known about the origins of infections and diseases. Surgeons went straight from the dissection of decomposing bodies swarming with bacteria to the maternity wards: in some of these four out of five mothers died. Instruments were not cleaned: surgeons wore coats crusted with decomposed blood and pus. Any major operation like cutting off a leg was more likely than not to cause death, for the hospitals were full of every kind of disease germ. The surgeon did not dare to open the belly cavity or brain: death was almost inevitable. Outside the hospitals, no serious precautions were taken to keep the sewage from percolating into wells. Anyone with typhoid fever—then a very common disease—discharges millions of bacteria from his infected bowels. They found their way to rivers or cesspits, thence often to wells, and epidemics of typhoid resulted. This disease was a most common incident in 1850; rich and poor alike died of it, and it was one of the main causes why parents produced ten children and reared five.

We have learned to associate disease with bacteria. We realise that bacteria must abound everywhere, but we also realise that the bacteria of dangerous infective diseases need not do so. We compel our builders to send sewage through waterproof pipes to sewers. We make local authorities treat the sewage before they send it into rivers. If a town has to drink impure river water, we filter it to remove nearly all bacteria and, if possible, store it for a few weeks, for very few dangerous bacteria live for long outside the body. We still allow highly contaminated milk to be sold, but the public can buy tuberculin-tested milk which is reasonably certain to be free from the bacteria which cause consumption.

The specific for destroying bacteria is heat. A liquid which has been boiled for twenty minutes is certainly free from living matter, and very much less heating will destroy most creatures. Surgical instruments are boiled to remove germs; dressings, gowns, masks, etc., are heated in live steam. There is no space here to describe the technique which has made it possible for surgeons to enter the brain itself without fear of carrying infection with them. More homely instances of removing bacteria are found in the preserving of food. The oldest ways of preserving food are drying, salting and smoking. Bacteria need some moisture for life, and they cannot live in strong brine, which abstracts the water from their bodies. Smoking impregnates the food with chemicals allied to carbolic acid (though less poisonous): these also kill bacteria. The preserving of food by refrigeration is effective up to periods of many months. Bacteria do not grow below the freezing point of water and only very slowly at temperatures a few degrees above. On this depends the bringing of chilled meat from distant countries. But canning is the chief method of preservation, and is now a gigantic industry. The canning of food is accomplished by sealing it up in containers, usually tins, and then heating these to a temperature which will kill all bacteria and spores. The importance of the industry may be judged from the fact that the U.S.A. produces in a year about a hundred and seventy-five million pounds'-worth of canned goods. Other countries, all put together, are far behind the U.S.A.

If canned food is properly sterilised and sealed, it cannot decay or produce food-poisons. Insufficient heating is the cause of bad tinned food. The objection to a diet of tinned food is the objection to a diet of cooked food—that the vitamins present in the food are largely destroyed by boiling. There is a strong instinct that fresh food is more nutritious than canned food, but apart from the vitamin content, there seems to be no evidence that it is in any way deficient or harmful.

Bacteria are readily poisoned by disinfectants. The best of these are hypochlorites such as chloride of lime, metallic salts like copper sulphate, phenolic compounds like lysol and carbolic acid. But their use is limited: for local disinfection (as of drains) and for emergencies, they have their value; but most of them are too poisonous for use in food or water, and disinfection of sewage is generally too expensive. One of the best disinfectants is sun-light. Bacteria succumb rapidly to ultraviolet light, they flourish exceedingly in dark and damp.

These methods of destroying bacteria are crude compared with those employed by the body.

The body has two resources in killing bacteria. It has first a general resource against all types. The white cells of the blood seem to elaborate a substance which has the power of destroying bacteria in general. It will be remembered that the white cells deal with foreign bacteria by killing and eating them. But the white cell has only limited possibilities: its chief weakness as a defence is that it cannot deal with the poison a bacterium produces.

Look at page 1025 where the precipitin reaction is dealt with, and again at p. 947 where we considered the antivenines which cure snake-poisoning. In each case an animal has made a substance capable of destroying a complicated foreign substance. The body, it would seem, has the power of making and sending out substances each of which will destroy a particular complicated organic poison, and that poison alone. It seems very extraordinary that a South American guinea-pig should be able to produce in its blood an antidote which can destroy an African poison which neither it nor its ancestors can ever have met: but such is the fact. The Ehrlich side-chain theory suggests that the huge protein molecules which make up guinea-pig tissue have some part which *combines* with the poison: if they had not, the poison would not affect them, and so would not be a poison. The guinea-pig, then, is believed to make a supply of these molecule-parts and to send them out into its blood to combine with the poison before it reaches the tissue-molecules themselves which are the vital parts of the animal.

This process will destroy bacterial poisons and, it would appear, can destroy bacteria themselves. The result of inoculating an animal or man with living or dead bacteria is to provoke the body to produce an *agglutinin* which causes the bacteria to clump together and to be destroyed.

The animal, then, can attack an invading army of bacteria with its white cells, destroy the bacterial poisons with its specially made antidote (antitoxin) and cause the bacteria to clump together and die by a specially made agglutinin. But the special making of antitoxins and agglutinins takes time. In infection by a bacterium, as in typhoid fever, it may be many weeks before the body has made enough antitoxins and agglutinins to destroy the invader: and in some rapid and deadly diseases, like tetanus, it hardly ever has time to do so.

This is where man can assist in two ways. If we inoculate a sheep or horse with diphtheria germs, it will develop an antitoxin which destroys them and their poisons. The sheep's blood-serum can be drawn off and injected into the diphtheria patient, on whom the effect is quite magical. Diphtheria has thus been transformed from a deadly disease to a fairly harmless one.

Another method of immunising is the "vaccine" method. A charge of *dead* disease bacteria, or a mild and harmless strain of living bacteria, is introduced into the body. These provoke the body to elaborate a quantity of the right antitoxins, and so to be armed against the attacks of any wandering bacteria of the same kind. Vaccination is an example. Here cow-pox—a mild ailment—provokes the body to produce an antitoxin which also destroys the small-pox virus. The troops in France in 1914—1918 were protected against typhoid fever by injecting into them two doses of dead typhoid bacteria before they embarked. The use of the dead bacteria is the ideal method. They contain the same proteins and toxins as living ones, and therefore provoke the body to produce the right antitoxin, but, being dead, they cannot multiply and cause the disease they are intended to ward off.

VIRUSES

It would seem that there exist living things even simpler than bacteria. We have learned to expect that a disease which is highly infective is so because minute living bacteria or protozoa are transferred from the sick to the healthy. Now a number of diseases such as measles and small-pox are known which run the same sort of course as bacterial diseases, such as diphtheria or typhoid fever, but for which no bacterium can be found. In many of these diseases the cells of the animal or plant affected are invaded by very minute bodies, too small for us to be able to discover their structure. These bodies seem to be masses of even minuter particles so small that, when the juices of the diseased creature are filtered though porous earthenware, they are able to pass. When we find that a disease is not caused by a bacterium, but that the fluids of the diseased animal or plant after filtration through porous earthenware still can infect another animal or plant, we say the disease is caused by a virus. Diseases caused in this way include small-pox, foot-and-mouth disease, hydrophobia, distemper, yellow fever, mosaic disease of tobacco, and many others.

Why should we consider the virus to be alive? The chief reason is that it multiplies. If you inject a lifeless poison such as morphine into an animal you will get no more back from the animal than you put in, but if you inject a drop of foot-and-mouth virus into a cow it contracts the disease, and you may get a gallon of the same virus back from it. Viruses, unlike bacteria, can only multiply in living creatures. Perhaps "alive" and "lifeless" are not absolutely definite terms. A virus might well be "alive" in the sense that it multiplies and reproduces its kind, but "lifeless" in lacking sensitiveness and response to environment. Actually, the particles of virus are so small that almost nothing is known about them except that they multiply and cause diseases. The diameter of the particles vary from 0.00002 cm. (200 $m\mu$) for cow-pox to 0.0000008 cm. (8 $m\mu$) for foot-and-mouth disease.

Now a molecule of a simple protein like egg white is about $4\frac{1}{3}$ $m\mu$ in diameter. It would seem then that a particle of foot-and-mouth virus can only contain about seven protein molecules! The only functions we can conceive as being possessed by such a simple particle are the chemical reactions of multiplication and production of toxins. An object consisting of only seven molecules could hardly be thought to undergo any important physical changes as of shape, etc. The virus is perhaps the first stage in the progress from dead to living: the stage of the simplest kind of matter which has the power of multiplication.

CHAPTER XLII

EVOLUTION

THE PROBLEM OF SPECIES

MAN has thought from the earliest times about the problems presented by the different types of creature. The general solution he reached was that an intelligent Deity created all the living species: that on Creation Day there were men, horses, dogs, snakes, elms, oaks, and radishes just as there are now. If any evidence other than that of his religious books was needed, he adduced the marvellous fitness of creatures for the part they had to play. He instanced the beautiful adaptation to flight of birds, with their hollow bones, their huge breastbone and pectoral muscles, or the ingenious methods by which an unconscious plant disperses its seeds, and said that these were obviously creations of an Intelligent Being.

This view, that the species were created as they now are, is no longer held by those who have studied the evidence with an open mind. The scientific world is agreed that all the millions of species of animals and plants have become what they are now by slow changes, and that in all probability all are descended from a common and very simple and very remote ancestor.

Let us see just what we mean by this. We mean that if you could examine your direct ancestors and the direct ancestors of the gorillas in the Zoo, you would find that as you examined more and more remote ancestors, you would finally come to a time when the gorilla's ancestors and yours were the same species of creature. This would be perhaps 50 million years ago, two million or so of generations having passed.

If you could do the same with your dog's ancestors and your own, you would again find a far distant common set of ancestors, queer creatures, half-reptiles, half-mammals, living in early Jurassic times 150 million years ago. Your chickens and you would have a race of almost brainless reptiles as common ancestors in the Permian period perhaps 200 million years back. The fly on the window and you are even more distant relations, for his stock and yours were certainly different as far back as 500 million years ago. Finally, the grass in the field and you may have had a common ancestor in the form of a single cell floating in primæval seas more than a thousand million years ago.

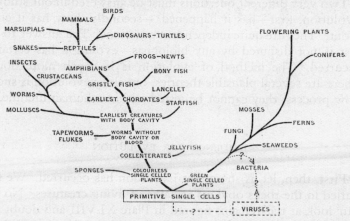

Fig. 524.—The tree of life. A scheme illustrating the way in which all living things may have been evolved from the single cell as common ancestor.

If all species can be regarded as having come into existence by gradual change, no new species having been created from dead matter, we can picture the evolution of all creatures as a sort of tree. Fig. 524 gives the broad outlines of the evolution of the species as we believe it to have occurred—with this in our minds, we can better appreciate the evidence for this view of the world's living creatures.

In the diagram, the ends of the branches represent living

species; the intermediate stages have died out. Thus, birds and snakes are both descended from some ancient and extinct reptilian ancestor, not from any living type of reptile. Man is not descended from any living type of monkey, but both he and living monkeys are descended from an extinct monkey-like creature.

In this diagram, the early stages are the least certain. They must have occurred about a thousand million years ago, and the simplest creatures, being soft and jelly-like, have left little impression on the rocks. As we near the top of the tree, the evidence becomes ever stronger.

Two very different questions must be answered in our study of Evolution, first—has it happened?—secondly, how has it come about? They are quite independent questions. The answer to the first is not disputed by any biologists—evolution has certainly occurred. The method of evolution is in much more doubt. There are several plausible theories, but since evolution is such a slow process, they cannot be tested within a human lifetime.

EVIDENCE FOR EVOLUTION

First, then, let us show that Evolution has occurred. We find buried in the rocks obvious remains of living creatures. No one can look at the remains figured in Plate XLVIII and doubt that they are the remains of creatures that once lived.

We can date the rocks fairly accurately by the uranium method (page 741) and by the order in which we find them, the deepest being the oldest unless they have been disturbed. The result of the examination of the rocks is roughly set out in the table on p. 743. The youngest rocks contain mammals, the next youngest contain no mammals but show birds and reptiles; older rocks still contain no trace of these, but display plentiful remains of fish; still older rocks show only simple creatures like feather-stars and corals while the earliest show no recognisable forms of life. It is quite clear that the simple forms of life existed before the complicated ones and so, if we do not believe that continual new creations have been going on, we must conclude that the complicated forms are offshoots of the simple ones. No one has ever found a bird's bone in the Cambrian slates or a mammal's bone in the Old Red Sandstone. There is an orderly progression from simple forms to complex ones. By simple forms, we mean forms of creatures with fewer and less efficient organs: by complex forms, we mean creatures with an elaborate organisation. As time has passed, so animals have become more capable of defence and attack and better able to resist adverse conditions.

There is no doubt that if a lost continent, peopled only with giant reptiles of the Jurassic age, were to be discovered and a fauna of modern mammals were to be introduced, the latter would very soon exterminate the former, monsters as they were. They were strong, but they were almost without brain: probably they were very slow to respond to any stimulus. The general tendency among the larger creatures has been, judging from our fossils, for creatures with little nervous organisation to be replaced by those with more. The smaller and less intelligent creatures have survived, probably, rather by fertility and resistance to adverse conditions than by increased cunning.

The rocks, then, tell us that simple creatures appeared first, and as time went on, more complex forms appeared. If, as the theory of evolution states, the more complex forms were the direct descendants of the simpler, it should be possible to find a succession of fossils to prove this. If, let us say, a small tapir-like creature evolved into an elephant, it should be possible to find in the rocks a succession of bones becoming less tapir-like and more elephant-like as we near the surface.

It is not possible to illustrate every stage of such a change, for of the creatures that die very few are fossilised, and of the enormous masses of fossil-bearing rock, not a ten-millionth part has been examined.

Many bones were devoured, others rotted, others were scattered by floods or eroded away in rivers or on sea-beaches. None the less, it is possible to show almost every stage in the

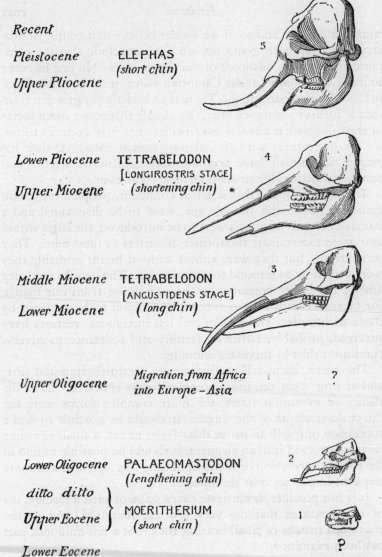

Recent

Pleistocene   ELEPHAS   5
                (short chin)

Upper Pliocene

Lower Pliocene   TETRABELODON   4
                [LONGIROSTRIS STAGE]

Upper Miocene   *(shortening chin)*

Middle Miocene   TETRABELODON   3
                 [ANGUSTIDENS STAGE]

Lower Miocene   *(long chin)*

Upper Oligocene   *Migration from Africa*   ?
                into Europe – Asia

Lower Oligocene   PALAEOMASTODON   2
                (lengthening chin)

ditto ditto ⎫
           ⎬   MOERITHERIUM   1
Upper Eocene ⎭   *(short chin)*

Lower Eocene   ?

FIG. 525.—A series of skulls showing a gradual change from the tapir-like mœritherium to the modern elephant. The earliest skull may be seventy million years old. The whole change would be spread over two million generations, even assuming that the breeding rate was as slow as that of the modern elephant. (Courtesy of the Trustees of the British Museum.)

F ɪG. 526.—Reconstructions of the animals believed to be ancestors of the modern
elephant (left to right), mœritherium, palæomastodon, tetrabelodon, 6 foot man
(to indicate size), African elephant.

evolution of the elephant from the mœritherium (Figs. 525, 526),
or of the horse from the small deer-like eohippus. In a few
cases where creatures were plentiful and well preserved, every
detail can be shown. We do not know the rate at which chalk
was deposited, but it certainly represents the deposit laid down
over some millions of years. If we collect sea-urchin shells from
the different levels, we find that the shells from the bottom differ
quite considerably from those at the top, but that every stage in the
change from the bottom-type to the top-type can be found in the intermediate levels. This really proves that these sea-urchins evolved.

A consideration of the creatures at present living almost forces
the notion of evolution on us. Look back to Figs. 477, 478, 482,
484, 485. Why should man, dog, fowl, lizard and newt, be built
on the same bone-plan if they are not all derived from a common
ancestor with this plan? Look at the limbs of man, gibbon, dog,
horse, elephant, bat and seal (Fig. 478), and of the fowl, lizard
and newt (Figs. 482–485). They are all the same limb modified
by lengthening one bone here and omitting another there, but
never introducing a new structure. It is as if the wheel of a car,
the oar of a boat and the wing of an aeroplane were all found to
be built of the same pieces, distorted to suitable shapes. This
common plan is easily understood if we suppose that all vertebrates have a common ancestor whose descendants gradually
changed their bodies by tiny steps, each generation being no more
different from the last than a parent is different from his children.

If Evolution occurs, we can easily see that it must sometimes
lead to disuse of an organ. If a whale has evolved from a land
creature, as we believe, we should expect to find in it somewhere

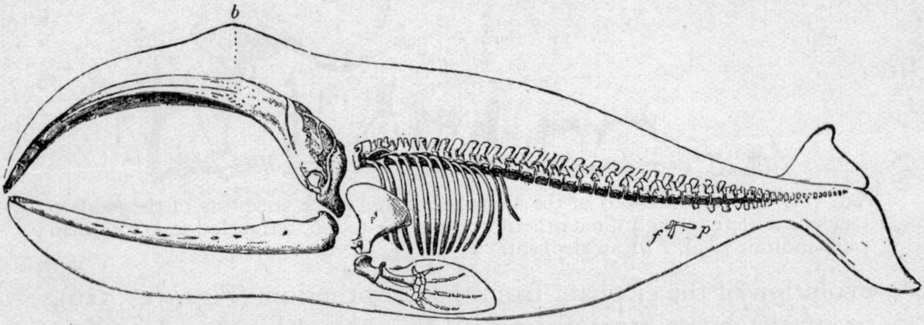

FIG. 527.—Skeleton of Greenland Right Whale. Note vestige of hip-bone or pelvis (*p*), and of thigh-bone or femur (*f*). Compare with Figs. 477 and 490. It will be readily seen that the whale is a mammal and not a fish. (Courtesy of the Trustees of British Museum (Natural History), from *A Guide to the Whales, Porpoises and Dolphins*.)

traces of the legs it needed on land. We find these (Fig. 527). If man descended from a monkey-like ancestor with a tail, we should find remains of this tail he has lost. We find it (Fig. 434, coccyx). When the theory of Evolution leads us to believe that an organ has been lost "recently" (in the geological sense!) we usually find vestiges of it. Now, the whale's rudimentary leg-bones and man's tail are quite useless. If the species had been separately created or had been made in *any* way except by modifying another species, their presence would be inexplicable. Such vestiges of older structures are commonly found in the very young animal and are later lost. The human embryo has at a very early period the same system of great blood vessels as a fish (compare Fig. 491 B and D). It has later a well-marked tail and, later still, a coating of fine hair which it loses. The reason why the embryo has to develop in some respects in the same way as its race has developed is not known.

Another set of facts, very hard to explain except by a theory of Evolution, is the geographical distribution of living creatures. The marsupials—pouched mammals such as the kangaroo and opossum—are found only in Australia and South America. The only reasonable explanation seems to be that (as fossils indicate), the world was peopled with marsupials at a date when there was communication between these continents: that the more efficient placental mammals then evolved and exterminated them everywhere except in Australia and South America, which by then were isolated from Europe, Asia and Africa.

Finally, we have reason to believe that there has been a chemical evolution as well as an evolution of shape. The proteins of the blood of a dog are different from those of a horse. We have found a way of measuring the degree of likeness between the proteins of the blood of two creatures, and we find that the results show that creatures which for other reasons we believe to be recently derived from a common stock, are chemically alike, while those which we suppose to have only remote common ancestors have very different blood-proteins. There are three or four ways of testing the relationship between proteins. The most important of these is the "precipitin" test. If we inject the solution of a protein—say the serum of human blood—into an animal in a series of small doses, the animal's blood develops an antibody (p. 1014) and so acquires the property of combining with the human proteins and turning them into a cloud of insoluble matter. The serum of an animal treated like this will then, if mixed with human blood-serum, give a dense cloudy precipitate. It will not, however, give any precipitate with the serum of a horse or an antelope or a pig. But it will give a precipitate with the blood of a monkey.

Thus in a certain series of experiments animals were sensitised with human blood-serum, and to their serum the serum of various apes and monkeys was added with the following result:

Type of blood-serum added to the sensitised serum.	Intensity of reaction as showed by quantity of precipitate.
Human	100
Anthropoid apes	100
Old-world monkeys	92
New-world monkeys	78
Marmosets	50
Lemurs	0
Other animals	0

33

So we have here a proof that human beings are *chemically* almost identical with apes, very like monkeys, allied to marmosets and quite unlike other animals. Tests of this kind can be done both with animal and with plant proteins, and they show that the animals and plants we believe for other reasons to be derived from a near common ancestor are chemically much more alike than those which have only a remote ancestor.

THE CAUSE OF EVOLUTION

All biologists are convinced of the fact of Evolution. Those who reject it have argued their case very fully, but they have not succeeded in convincing professional biologists, who, after all, are the people with a first-hand knowledge of the evidence.

It is another matter when we come to discuss the way in which Evolution is accomplished. The Darwinian theory is based upon natural selection, and this is clearly one agency at work. The principle is simple enough. Animals of a given species vary slightly and some of these variations can be inherited by their offspring. The animals who are least well able to get their food and escape their enemies are the most likely to die. They are thus less likely to be parents of offspring than are the better equipped members of their species. Thus, the succeeding generation will be chiefly the offspring of the parents who are best at getting their living. *If* the offspring inherit the qualities of their parents, they will be themselves more efficient than the average of the generation before. The whole race will therefore change steadily in the direction which will enable them to survive. This progress may be towards greater strength and size, as with the horse and elephant and the great dinosaurs long before: it may be in the direction of greater protection, as in the case of the tortoises—evolved from lizard-like creatures: it may be in the direction of brain as with men and apes: it may be in the direction of an easy vegetative life and an efficient reproductive system as in the case of an intestinal parasite. All that is necessary is that the change, whatever it is, shall increase the chance of the changed individual having more surviving offspring than his fellows.

No one disputes that Natural Selection is going on: the objectors to Darwin's theory consider that, though natural selection takes place, the inherited changes are so slight that they would have no appreciable effect in saving the lives of their possessors. They maintain, too, that most variations are harmful and would not assist the creature that inherited them.

However, it is generally thought that these objections are not sufficiently strong. Small inheritable variations do occur. The creature whose breeding has been best studied is the fruit-fly *Drosophila*. Some 400 small inheritable variations have been noticed; these are certainly real alterations in the genes. It seems unjustifiable to say that most variations of this kind must be harmful. There is no reason why a dandelion might not as well vary in the direction of having a longer plume on its seed, so getting better dispersion of its seeds, as in the direction of having a shorter plume.

It was thought at one time that a new and favourable character such as a thicker coat of hair, a longer claw or stronger tooth, would not be inherited appreciably, because by breeding with normal individuals the new quality would be diluted to nothing. But from what has already been said about heredity, it should be clear that a new dominant gene will be transmitted to half the offspring who will transmit it to half their offspring. If any of these survive, it will thus become a permanent part of the race.

The Lamarckian theory is founded on the belief that the use or disuse of an organ causes it to develop or dwindle and that this alteration is to some extent inherited. The Lamarckian would say that the giraffe's ancestors stretched their necks in nibbling leaves from trees: their offspring were born with longer necks and the process continued till the giraffe reached its present proportions. There is no real evidence for this theory. The obvious evidence against it is that the Jews have circumcised their children for perhaps 4,000 years and the Jewish baby is still born quite complete like any other. The Lamarckians object that a mere mutilation of this kind will not affect the germ-cells: while the more intimate chemical mechanism of developing or atrophying an organ might do so. There is however little evidence for their view.

A third belief is that the "germ-plasm" (chromosomes and genes) of a species has a particular tendency to alter in certain directions: that a stock tends to vary in certain ways. Thus, the reptiles show a tendency to develop heavy armour—a tendency which led to the extinction of many races. The ammonites, molluscs of the ancient seas tended to produce more and more complicated patterns in the partitions between their chambered cells. It seems unlikely that these variations can have had any advantage to the creatures and it looks as if the ammonites' chromosomes had some "kink" which made them develop genes for "complication of septum." This view is known as the theory of Orthogenesis.

All these theories have their difficulties, but the Darwinian in its modern form is at least an intelligible theory which cannot be shown to be seriously unlikely. When scientific men have been working on the breeding of animals for another fifty years, we shall have a clearer idea of its possibilities.

Evolution is exceedingly slow. It may take a million generations to alter a stock enough to cause it to be classed as a new species. The only creatures which might have gone through a million generations since the date at which the Darwinian theory was first put forward are bacteria. They are an unfavourable case, for they are so small and simple that it is difficult to tell whether they have undergone any evolutionary changes.

Whether the Darwinist or Lamarckian or neither is correct, Evolution remains. A thousand fascinating instances of its working could be given: in our short space, we can go into details of but one—the Evolution of Man.

THE EVOLUTION OF MAMMALS

It seems possible that life originated spontaneously in the primæval ocean. The newly cooled earth was lifeless: but the sea contained the mineral salts needed for life. It contained nitrates and probably ammonium compounds—for ammonia is present in the atmosphere of Jupiter and Saturn, and since it dissolves in water and combines with it and carbon dioxide to give ammonium carbonate, the sea would soon contain whatever quantity of ammonia there was in the atmosphere. There were present then, as simple compounds, all the elements needed for life. There is very fair evidence that, by the action of ultra-violet light from the sun's rays, carbon dioxide and water would form first formaldehyde, then sugars, and that the ammonium compounds, nitrates, sugars, etc., would build up organic nitrogen compounds. There being no bacteria to cause decay, these compounds would accumulate till the sea was a solution of various organic compounds. Reactions which are negligible in the hour or two we give them in the chemical laboratory would in countless millennia build up quantities of highly complicated compounds.

Now comes the difficult step. We can believe all this, but can we believe that a chance assembly of the right molecules might form a living particle capable of nourishing and reproducing itself? Think of a virus particle made up of only a dozen protein molecules, and probably some sugars and salts and certainly a good deal of water. If you could put a set of the right molecules —dead matter—into the exact positions occupied by the same molecules in a living particle, would this not make a living thing? If we believe that a living thing is simply very complicated molecules arranged in certain positions, it is difficult to escape this conclusion. The chance assembly of the right molecules, from a primæval sea containing them, may seem hugely unlikely, but so vast a crowd of molecules are present even in a drop of solution, that, given millions of years of collisions of billions of molecules

33*

occurring billions of times a second in every drop of liquid of which there are billions of billions of drops in the sea, the formation of a living particle seems less unlikely. It is really impossible to estimate the probability of the formation of such a living particle: all that can be said is that few of those well acquainted with the subject believe it to be impossible. Once formed, the living particle would have no competitors. It could feed and divide and flourish without chance of extinction. There is one reason to think that from one such chance encounter of molecules sprang all life. Many of the molecules of living things are unsymmetrical and exist in two forms; like a right and left-hand glove. Only the right-handers are found in living things, though the left-handers are absolutely identical in their behaviour except that their crystals are mirror-reflections of the crystals of the right-handers. All processes for making these unsymmetrical forms from the simple molecules, which are all symmetrical, give *equal* proportions of right-handers and left-handers. So our primæval sea would contain both kinds in equal proportions. If life had arisen several times, it would very probably have, in some instances, been based on left-handed molecules: but since all living things have right-handed molecules, it seems likely that they came from one single right-handed unit.

There is no fossil evidence of the earliest stages of life. We may suppose that the primitive virus particle developed into a cell with a nucleus by what must have been a very lengthy process. We must believe that at a very early stage some cells developed the power of building chlorophyll and so making their own food like plants. The colourless cells probably developed more efficient means of locomotion and digestion and, like the simple Volvox (Fig. 528) to-day, joined into colonies. Closer association gave the first metazoa, creatures with many cells. These developed, we may think, a division of labour. Some cells digested, others defended, others became sensitive to touch and light, others were contractile and acted as primitive muscles.

The next step was the building of some nerve system, so that a central control could direct the actions of the body. The next

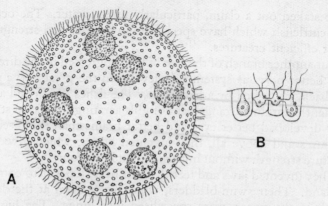

FIG. 528.—Volvox. A colony of cells, representing a stage intermediate between single-celled and many-celled creatures. A. The
whole colony, globular in form and moving as a single unit. It is
about the size of a pin's head. B. The individual cells, identical
but not isolated units, connected by threads of cytoplasm. By
division daughter colonies are formed within the hollow sphere.
The latter, at a certain stage, breaks up and liberates these.
Volvox is intermediate between plant and animal. Like the
former it has chlorophyll and plastids, like the latter flagella and
eyespots.

stage was to develop a body cavity to contain the organs which
before were stretched and distorted by every motion of the body.
Blood was now evolved, making for the possibility of nourishing
a large creature.

At this stage came a great parting of the ways. The starfish family developed its curious water-tube system: it is still a
flourishing concern but has by no means conquered the world.
Another group of animals differentiated into the worms and the
arthropods (insects and crustaceans). These latter were hampered
by the hard shell they developed, necessitating moulting as they
grew. They developed extraordinary instinctive powers, but no
intelligence in the mammalian sense. Insects are to be found in
every corner of the earth: they are one of evolution's successes.
The molluscs have developed successfully too. They have not
apparently developed a high nervous organisation, instinctive or
intelligent. But, largely by the protection of limey shells, they

have staked out a claim, particularly under water. The octopus and cuttlefish which have specialised in activity and strength are most efficient creatures.

But another branch of the tree of life progressed in the direction of a better nervous system and developed the great nerve along the back, protected by a backbone. The fishes developed a very efficient breathing arrangement of gills aerating the blood stream: they developed better eyes and better brains than the insects or molluscs and above all, they invented bones, which give a big creature strength without imprisoning it in armour.

They invented jaws and teeth. Their next step was to come out on land. Their swim-bladders, which keep them at the desired depth in the water, were specialised into lungs. The lung-fish which can breathe under water by gills and also breathe air by means of a primitive lung is still at this stage. Fins were used to drag their bodies about over muddy banks and gradually evolved into legs. The fish turned into clumsy amphibians much like gigantic newts.

The amphibian lays a soft jelly-like egg and so must breed in the water. The next stage was to invent the shelled egg in which the young could develop freely. This invention made animals free of the water. They were now reptiles. Some developed vast size and strength: others developed weighty protective armour: but the successful move was an internal improvement, the development of *warm blood*.

A great many reptiles have survived, but the huge creatures with tiny brains have gone. The modern reptile is, for the most part, a small highly active creature with a very fair nervous organisation. The warm-blooded reptiles evolved, it would seem, first into birds and secondly into mammals. In both cases brain has been improved, though far less in the birds. The mammals and birds have the boon of temperature regulation (p. 905). A reptile is helpless in cold weather. The snakes wound round the music-hall dancer's neck have been put in the ice-box till their reactions are so slow that they are harmless! By developing a constant temperature, mammals became almost independent of weather.

The development of mammals was very rapid. Some specialised for insect-eating, others for vegetarian feeding by gnawing: some, like seals and whales took to the water. Others, like the antelopes and horses, took to grass-eating and specialised in speed, valuable on the open prairie. The stock which was to produce man took to the trees. An arboreal life demands much more complicated and varied motions of the limbs than any other; and these motions can only be executed through a first-class brain. The distinguishing features of man are his brain, his forward-reaching vision and his mobile and sensitive hands. Let us try to see how the tree-climbing creatures developed into men.

THE EVOLUTION OF MAN

That Man is a product of Evolution cannot reasonably be doubted if we accept the evidence that all living creatures have sprung from primitive single cells. None the less, this evolution has been far more difficult to trace than that of the horse or elephant. Of man, since he first lived in communities and buried his dead, there are plentiful remains, but of creatures closely allied to man but sufficiently different to be classed as different species or genera, the remains are very scanty. We shall see that man's forerunners were ape-like, and fossil remains of apes are necessarily very rare. Being tree-dwellers, they are not sunk in bogs or buried by landslides or even drowned and sunk in river mud. They die in the trees or on the ground and are eaten by nature's scavengers. In their attempt to trace the evolution of Man, biologists have depended first on fossil remains, then on comparisons between man as he is and his nearest animal relations as they are.

If a biologist from another planet studied our fauna, he could not help classing man with the apes and monkeys.

Consider the great numbers of points shared by man and the apes and monkeys. Most of these are possessed by no other animals. Man, apes and monkeys—classed together as Primates—

have large brains for their size. Their eyes are directed forward so that they can have stereoscopic vision. They depend on sight for their guidance rather than smell. They have nearly always five digits—fingers and toes—and they can move their thumbs apart from their fingers so that they can grasp an object between finger and thumb. They have flat nails and no claws. Their faces are comparatively flat, they have round domed skulls and small much-convoluted ears. Apart from their brains, they are not highly specialised. A hand is far more like the primitive reptilian foot (as of a lizard) than is the specialised hoof of a horse or cow or pig, or the wing of a bird or bat.

Finally, there is the very strong evidence of the precipitin reaction—detailed on p. 1025. These facts, with others depending on points of anatomy, convince us that Man belongs to the Primates and that they and he probably have evolved from a common stock. We do not believe, of course, that man evolved from any species of monkey or ape identical with those living to-day. If we believed this, we should be asserting that while some of his monkey-ancestors evolved into men others remained wholly unchanged—a most improbable suggestion. We say, rather, that some of the creatures who are our direct ancestors would be classed as apes or monkeys if they were alive to-day.

In the Permian period, some 200 million years ago, reptiles were developing into mammals. In the late Palæocene and Eocene, 60–80 million years ago, the placental mammals had been evolved and were separating into various groups. The Rodents specialised in gnawing, the Carnivores in an equipment of strength and weapons, the Ungulates in speed. A comparatively insignificant group were those who later became the Insectivora—moles, shrews, etc.—and the Primates. The earliest primates were probably like the tree-shrew of to-day. This insignificant creature has, anatomically, much in common with the monkey tribe. The important feature of these early shrew-like Primates was that they took to the trees. A creature that lives an active life in a tree must be agile, that is to say it must execute complicated motions of many different kinds. Running or flying are easily made automatic; much the same stereotyped movements are repeated and a simple organisation of nerves is sufficient to do this. A creature flinging itself about a tree meets branches of all degrees of springiness set at every angle. It must see these and be able to adjust itself to meet them. To do this, a fairly well-developed brain is needed, for every type of motion must have a corresponding relay of nerve-cells in the brain. Moreover, smell and touch are not of much use in the trees, but sight and hearing are particularly valuable. Accordingly, arboreal creatures develop a good brain. An interesting parallel case is the parrot who climbs about the trees with claws and beak much as you may watch him climbing about the bars of an aviary. The parrot has, therefore, developed a better brain than any other bird—which is not saying much. To return to the early Primates, an interesting comparison can be made between the brains of two similar modern creatures, the arboreal tree-shrew and the terrestial jumping-shrew. The bigger brain, specialised on the area which deals with sight images, is interesting.

The simplest modern creatures allied to the monkeys are this tree-shrew and the Tarsier and the Lemurs. These last represent branches which split off from the primates some 70,000,000 years ago. Many Tarsiers have existed but the only one now known is that queer little beast the spectral Tarsier found in the Malay Archipelago (Plate XLVIII).

The interesting thing about him is his face. His huge eyes look forward. His snout is flattened and the face has almost a semblance of humanity. The Lemurs need not detain us: they have definitely evolved away from the human stream. The next milestone in the progress of the Primates is the marmoset type. These have poor brains for monkeys but, compared with other animals of the same size, the neo-pallium is enormous. The neo-pallium is the part of the brain which receives and records all the messages from the nerves of the eyes, ears and skin and also regulates all the voluntary muscles. It is this organ of the brain which enables the mammal to learn by experience—i.e., register sense impressions and let them influence their actions. Fig. 529 shows the progress of the brain from the tree-shrew to the simplest monkey. It must be remembered, of course, that the tree-shrews did not turn into Tarsiers and Tarsiers into marmosets: but there were, on the road from reptile to Man, tree-shrew-like, tarsier-like and marmoset-like stages. Notice the steady increase of visual and acoustic areas and decrease of the olfactory areas—concerned with smell—and the appearance of a prefrontal area which is concerned with co-ordinating the movements of the eyes—leading to "watching," attention, and so to the beginnings of thought. This area is enormous in the

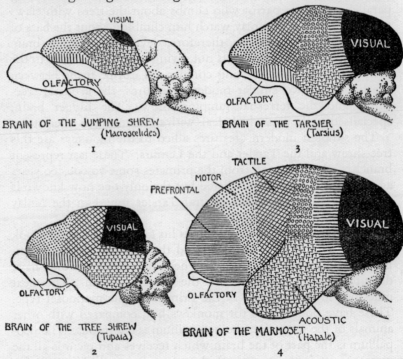

BRAIN OF THE JUMPING SHREW
(Macroscelides)

1

BRAIN OF THE TARSIER
(Tarsius)

3

BRAIN OF THE TREE SHREW
(Tupaia)

2

BRAIN OF THE MARMOSET
(Hapale)

4

FIG. 529.—The brains of the simplest primates. The brain (1) of the terrestial jumping-shrew (2) of the arboreal tree shrew. Note the reduction in the olfactory portion devoted to smell and the increase of the parts devoted to sight (visual). 3 and 4. The brain of the Tarsier and marmoset. Note the increase of the areas representing sight, skilled movements (motor), hearing (acoustic), intelligence (prefrontal). (Courtesy of the Oxford University Press and Professor Elliot Smith, from the latter's *Essays in the Evolution of Man*.

human brain and is regarded as the region where real thought is carried on. Two other important areas, the parietal and temporal, appear in the monkeys: these are concerned with skill of movement (Figs. 480, 529).

The old-world monkeys, then, represent a further stage in development of brain. But a much greater advance is manifest in the apes. The four apes, Gorilla, Chimpanzee, Orang-outang and Gibbon, are classed with Man as Anthropomorpha. All five are alike in having no tail, an erect or semi-erect posture and the best brains yet evolved. The Gibbon is the link between the apes and monkeys. The ape's brain has all the areas of the human brain, but they are much less developed, the great differences being noticed in the prefrontal area concerned with ingenuity and the highest mental functions, and in the temporal and parietal area concerned with skill of movement.

The ape cannot do what man can do because he has not got these huge prefrontal, temporal and parietal areas in which all his sensations and experiences are linked up as memory. An ape cannot talk because this requires a brain with the power to connect sight-images of things, first with the right sequences of complicated tongue, lip and vocal cord movements needed to make the words, and secondly with the ear-impressions of the words spoken by someone else. Thinking is obviously a matter of dealing with sense impressions. We think in terms of pictures blending into each other, or in "words"—records of sounds heard, or sight-images of print. Our mental development is obviously conditioned by the ability to store up huge quantities of sense images and to bring these into connection so as to form a logical sequence. The man-like character of a creature represented by a fossil skull may therefore be fairly judged by the size of the prefrontal, temporal and parietal areas.

An ape, then, cannot do the specifically human act of talking, much less writing or reading. It can only just think out for itself the notion of using an object as a tool—fitting two sticks together to make a longer one in order to reach a banana or putting one box on another to attain the same object of desire. One could never imagine an ape drawing anything or building anything or making any object *of his own accord*, though he can be taught to use a knife and fork or ride a bicycle.

When the ape learned to walk upright—no living ape has attained more than a stooping posture—his hands were freed. Instead of employing them to swing him about trees, he could use them for handling objects—sticks, stones and the like. This must have greatly improved the parts of his brain employed for muscle-skill and so perhaps opened the way to the supreme muscle achievements of speech and writing.

The period during which animals which can fairly be called men have existed must remain very doubtful. There is wide disagreement among authorities. It would not be disputed that man has existed in some form for a million years, but many of the most important remains have been found in strata which are very difficult to date.

The gap between ape and man is spanned by a few fossil skulls. The earliest stage is Pithecanthropus—the Java ape-man.

Pithecanthropus dwelt in Java at a period which is difficult to date but which may be some 150,000 years ago. The bones are very ape-like but it seems clear that the brain, though small for a human being, shows signs that the speech area (in the temporal region) has begun to develop. Pithecanthropus was probably on the verge of being human. Though the actual skull may be 150,000 years old, Pithecanthropus is probably a survivor of a far older period, more than a million years ago. It does not always follow that the most ancient fossils represent the earliest stages in evolution, for it may well be that early types persisted after later ones had evolved. The earliest of truly human remains is probably the *Sinanthropus* skull found in China. From the evidence of the fossil bones found near it, it may be about a million years old. There is evidence that man, as long ago as this, had the use of fire. The next remains are the remarkable Piltdown skull, to the genus of the owner of which the name Eoanthropus has been given. These remains are a good deal later in date than those of Sinanthropus, but belonged probably to a very similar creature. This fragmentary skull has been pieced together with great skill. The jaw is ape-like, and the creature evidently had the powerful bite of the ape. Its skull was very thick. The brain was far larger than an ape's, and not smaller than the smallest human brains. The skull is low and broad and was definitely

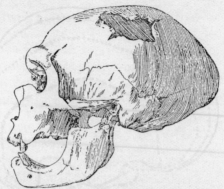

FIG. 530.—The skull of *Homo Neanderthalensis*. (Courtesy of the Trustees of British Museum.)

deficient in the prefrontal area we associate with thought.

The next man-like creature, *Homo Heidelbergensis*, is represented only by a jaw which dates from the lower Pleistocene laid down perhaps two or three hundred thousand years ago. The jaw is less ape-like than that of Eoanthropus.

Of the species of Man most nearly allied to the men living to-day—Neanderthal man—many skulls and bones have been found. He may have existed a quarter of a million years ago: the latest remains are 40,000 years old. The skulls are quite different from modern man's (Fig. 530).

Fig. 532 gives a fair idea of his appearance, far more man-like than any ape, and far more ape-like than any man. His brain was as large or larger than the human, but the development was rather in the region of memory than of thought. He was certainly human, for he made flint implements and in the use of tools showed a definitely human trait. He could draw, and some of his drawings have for realism never been surpassed.

A remarkably complete skull and bones found in Rhodesia (named *Homo Rhodesiensis*), but unfortunately impossible to date, tells us of another distant human relation. His forehead was very low, his nose very flat and his teeth and jaws enormous— though much more human than those of the Piltdown Eoan-

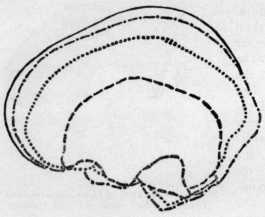

----- Gorilla.

.... Rhodesian.

-.-.-.- La Chapelle aux Saints.

——— Modern European.

FIG. 531.—The profiles of the skulls of Gorilla,
Rhodesian man, Neanderthal man (La Chapelle aux
Saints) and modern European. (Source as for Fig. 529.)

FIG. 532.—A
reconstruction
of *Homo nean-
derthalensis.*
Note the form
of his skull, his
rather long
arms and
stooping pos-
ture.

thropus. The brain was probably inferior to that of the Neanderthal
man, but he may have been superior to him in walking erect.
Neanderthal man seems to have disappeared about 40,000 years
ago, ousted by the Cromagnon race who were, in fact, modern
men. All living men are classed as varieties of the species *Homo
Sapiens.* The Australians are, perhaps, the most primitive, the
negroes, Mongols and European races following.

The scheme in Fig. 533 (reproduced from Prof. Elliott Smith's
Essays on the Evolution of Man) gives the probable Family tree
of Man. Are we to look forward to further evolution? If natural
selection be the cause of evolutionary changes, probably not. The
incompetent, in civilised nations, breed as freely or more freely
than the competent. If we are Lamarckians we may well believe
that Man's effort for knowledge will cause him to develop his

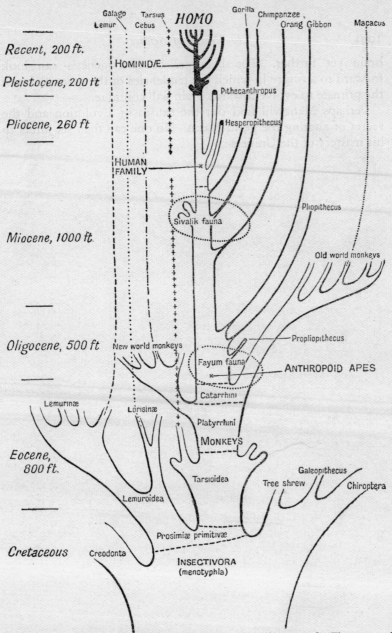

Recent, 200 ft.

Pleistocene, 200 ft

Pliocene, 260 ft

Miocene, 1000 ft.

Oligocene, 500 ft

Eocene, 800 ft.

Cretaceous

Galago   Tarsius
Lemur   Cebus   HOMO   Gorilla Chimpanzee
Orang Gibbon   Macacus

HOMINIDÆ

Pithecanthropus

Hesperopithecus

HUMAN FAMILY

Pliopithecus

Sivalik fauna

Old world monkeys

New world monkeys

Propliopithecus

Fayum fauna   ANTHROPOID APES

Catarrhini

Lemurinæ   Lorisinæ

Platyrrhini

MONKEYS

Tarsioidea   Galeopithecus
Tree shrew   Chiroptera

Lemuroidea

Prosimiæ primitivæ

Creodonta   INSECTIVORA
(menotyphla)

Fig. 533.—A reconstruction of the pedigree of man. (Source as for Figs. 529 and 531).

brain yet further. The believers in Orthogenesis can look forward to a future in which the tendencies of the germ plasm of the primate to evolve towards brain will continue.

Perhaps Man will find out the causes of Evolution and the secret of altering the germ-plasm. No one can then set limits to his mastery of the Universe.

CHAPTER XLIII

LOOKING AHEAD

SCIENCE does not pause for a moment. The picture I have roughly outlined has already shifted since I drew it. Science changes, but not often through its findings being proved false: for this is rare. New facts are discovered, and we look on old knowledge from another point of view. A great discovery, such as that of the electron, does not render the old knowledge untrue: but if we read a work on electricity written in 1870 we are conscious that, while the author says nothing that is not true, he gives a poorer account of the subject because he does not perceive how the phenomena he correctly describes are linked and unified as being almost all the consequence of the moving of electrons. Unquestionably, discoveries will be made in the light of which our science of to-day will look—not untrue—but narrow and impoverished.

What are these discoveries to be? Is it possible to hazard a guess or two as to what the discoveries of the next century or so will concern? Let us glance first at Physics and Engineering. Two kinds of advances can be made: first and least interestingly, the knowledge we already have may be applied. There is very commonly a great lag between the discovery of a fact and its use. The glow of neon was known thirty years ago: the "tubes" have gladdened our streets for but half a dozen. The principle of hydrogenation of oils (p. 235) dates back to 1900, but it did not attain successful commercial use until about 1912. But it is more interesting to guess the new principles which may be discovered. The first large and obvious hole in our physics is our lack of mathematical equipment. When we wish to calculate such matters as the way atoms are likely to vibrate in a lattice, the orbit an electron

1043

would take if it travelled round two positive nuclei, the paths that any three bodies in space attracting each other will assume—we find that the human brain is at fault. The monkey cannot count, the savage often cannot count beyond five; civilised man has made gigantic progress in mathematics, which is really a way of thinking on paper, using letters instead of thoughts: but our understanding of many problems is waiting for new mathematics —for a new technique of thought. The outstanding problem of physics is the nature of electrons, positrons, protons and neutrons and atomic nuclei. Are the first four ultimate particles or are they susceptible of being converted into each other? Can radiation be made into matter and *vice versa*? How is it that an electron can behave like a wave and a train of waves like a particle? How, if at all, do electrons move in the atom? What is the inside of the nucleus like?

These problems are difficult but none would care to say that they will not be solved within 25 years.

The problems of Chemistry hang on those of physics. The chemist's fundamental problem is: Why do atoms combine into some molecule-patterns and not into others? He has some rather crude rules and explanations, but he would like to know, for example, why, though he can get H_2O and H_2O_2, he cannot get H_2O_3: or why cobalt salts form a vast number of complicated compounds with ammonia, while iron salts, otherwise so like them, do nothing of the kind.

The chemist, too, wants a new technique, and it cannot be said that he sees his way towards getting it. His old methods of purifying things by crystallising them and distilling them and identifying them by boiling points and melting points and crystal shapes are almost useless for the largest molecules which are particularly interesting from the biological point of view. Undoubtedly, the chemist, by the use of X-ray pictures and crystal structures, will find out a great deal about the compounds he cannot now tackle. Fresh knowledge about the atom and new methods of handling big molecules may at any future date transform chemistry.

The obvious difficulty of gaining geological knowledge is that much of it is inaccessible in the past, and so cannot be the subject of experiment. No one has indicated any possible method of looking into the past except the method of the detective— that of piecing together small clues. It is probable that the lapse of a very few years will see developed accurate ways of dating specimens of rocks which would do much to clarify their interrupted story. The obvious defects of geology at present are our great ignorance of the bottom of the sea, the upper air, and the crust more than a mile or two below our feet. Deeper borings will probably be made—particularly if a rich country becomes interested in science. If the U.S.S.R. were as wealthy as England, it would soon have some really deep borings. Astronomy depends for its advances on the perfection of instruments to show the material, the directions and sizes of stars; and on mathematics for the reasoning which turns the observed figures into an intelligible world picture. It is not too much to hope that a quarter of a century may bring very strong evidence as to the age of the universe and to the question of its apparent expansion.

Finally, Biology is the real Tom Tiddler's ground of the Sciences. In every direction lie problems to be solved. Whether in working out the problems of heredity or elucidating the causes of Evolution or tracing the mechanism of the working of the body, far more problems are crying for solution than there are workers to tackle them. The outstanding problem, however, is at once biological, physical and chemical. It is— What is happening in the cell? What makes the few hundred molecules in a tiny bacterium or virus alive—able to assimilate and reproduce? If we could know this, we might be able to hazard a guess as to the great question of What is Life? and perhaps draw nearer to that possibly insoluble question—What is Thought?

INDEX

ACKNOWLEDGMENTS

I HAVE much pleasure in expressing my gratitude to a great number of private persons and firms who have assisted me in the preparation of this book.

In the first place I should wish to set the great kindness of Mr. H. Wynne Finch, Mr. J. E. Calthrop and Mr. D. R. Cargill, who have expended their time and expert knowledge in reading the portions of the manuscript which deal with Geology, Astronomy and Human Physiology respectively. I would also wish to acknowledge the help and vigilance of Mr. J. E. Emerson, who read the manuscript of the portion dealing with Physics, and of Miss Grace Jeffree, who not only read the portions dealing with Zoology and Botany, but also drew the majority of the figures illustrating the biological portion. More than a hundred firms and private persons have earned my sincere gratitude by assisting me by providing drawings, photographs and information. These include:

The officials of the Air Ministry.
Messrs. Aiton & Co., Ltd., Derby.
Messrs. W. H. Allen, Sons & Co., Ltd., Bedford.
The Anglo-American Oil Co., Ltd.
Messrs. Armco, Ltd.
Armstrong Siddeley Motors, Limited.
Sir W. G. Armstrong Whitworth & Co. (Engineers), Ltd.
The Askania Werke A.G., Berlin.
The Associated Equipment Company, Ltd.
The Secretary of the Astronomical Society.
Messrs. W. & T. Avery, Ltd.
Baird Television, Ltd.
Messrs. Bass, Ratcliffe and Gretton.

F. C. Bawden, Esq.
Messrs. George Bell & Sons, Ltd.
Messrs. Besson & Co., Ltd.
Messrs. Bird, Norfolk.
Messrs. E. Birkeland.
Professor P. M. S. Blackett.
Messrs. A. Boake, Roberts & Co., Ltd.
The British Aluminium Co., Ltd.
The Officials of the British Museum.
The Dept. of Greek & Roman Antiquities, British Museum.
The British Rema Manufacturing Co., Ltd., Halifax.
The British Rototherm Co., Ltd.
The British Thompson-Houston Co., Ltd.
Messrs. Chance Bros. & Co., Ltd.
The Chesterfield Tube Co., Ltd.
The Chloride Electrical Storage Co., Ltd.
Messrs. Claude-General Neon Lights, Ltd.
Messrs. Cox's Cave, Ltd.
Messrs. A. F. Craig & Co., Ltd., Paisley.
The Cunard White Star Line, Ltd.
The Daimler Co., Ltd.
Dairy Supply Co., Ltd.
Dr. A. H. Davis.
Messrs. John Davis & Son (Derby), Ltd.
Thy Decca Gramophone Co., Ltd.
The De Havilland Aircraft Co., Ltd.
Messrs. Demag, Duisburg.
The Dunlop Rubber Co., Ltd.
Messrs. Dunod et Cie, Paris.
Herbert Edwards, Esq., Flint Knappers, Brandon, Suffolk.
The Engineer.
The English Electric Co., Ltd.
Dr. R. C. Evans, Dept. of Mineralogy and Petrology, Cambridge.
J. Evershed, Esq.
Professor Alan Ferguson.

Messrs. Fox Photos, Ltd.

Frigidaire, Ltd.

Messrs. Frith & Co., Reigate.

The General Electric Co., Ltd.

The Officials of the General Post Office.

Geological Survey and Museum.

Messrs. Glenfield & Kennedy.

Messrs. Charles Griffin & Co., Ltd.

Messrs. Griffin and Tatlock, Ltd.

Hanovia, Ltd.

Messrs. Thomas Hart, Ltd.

Messrs. Adam Hilger, Ltd.

"His Master's Voice," The Gramophone Co., Ltd.

Professor R. H. Hopkins.

Messrs. Henry Hughes & Son, Ltd.

Messrs. Ilford, Ltd.

The Illustrated London News.

Imperial Airways, Ltd.

Imperial Chemical Industries, Ltd.

International Refrigerator Co., Ltd.

Messrs. Kodak, Ltd.

Messrs. Leyland Motors, Ltd.

The L.M.S. Railway Co., Ltd.

The London Aeroplane Club, Hatfield, Herts.

The London Electrotype Agency.

The London Power Co., Ltd.

Dr. Frank W. Martin, M.D., Medico-Legal Dept., The University, Glasgow.

Messrs. Mazda, Ltd.

The McGraw Hill Co.

The Medical Supply Association, Ltd.

Metropolitan-Vickers Electrical Co., Ltd.

Dr. Dayton C. Miller.

The Mineralogical Magazine.

The National Gas & Oil Engine Co., Ltd., Ashton-under-Lyne.

The National Smoke Abatement Society.
Messrs. Newton Chambers & Co., Ltd.
Messrs. L. Oertling, Ltd.
The Oil Well Engineering Co., Ltd.
The Oil Well Supply Co.
The Pacific & Atlantic Photos, Ltd.
Messrs. C. F. Palmer (London), Ltd.
Messrs. W. Parkinson & Co.
Messrs. Philips Lamps, Ltd.
Messrs. Philips Metalix, Ltd.
The Philosophical Magazine.
Messrs. Photopress, Ltd.
Messrs. Pilkington Brothers, Ltd.
The Polish Embassy.
The Polish Travel Office.
Messrs. James Pollock, Sons & Co., Ltd.
The Pyrene Co., Ltd.
Messrs. Philip Quayle, Ohio.
J. H. Reynolds, Esq., Birmingham.
The Rio Tinto Co., Ltd.
Messrs. A. V. Roe & Co., Ltd.
Messrs. Rolls-Royce, Ltd.
Messrs. Ross, Ltd., Optical Works.
The Royal Astronomical Society.
The Royal Institution of Great Britain.
The Royal Observatory, Greenwich.
Messrs. Frederick Sage & Co., Ltd.
St. George's Hospital.
Messrs. Shell-Mex and B.P., Ltd.
Messrs. S. Smith & Sons (Motor Accessories), Ltd.
Smith's English Clocks, Ltd.
Smoke Prevention, Ltd.
The Southern Railway.
The Sperry Gyroscope Co., Ltd.
Messrs. Julius Springer, Berlin.
Messrs. Taylor & Francis.

The Times Publishing Co.
The Vacuum Oil Co., Ltd.
Friedr. Vieweg & Sohn, A.G., Germany.
The Waterless Gas Holder Co., Ltd.
Messrs. W. Watson & Sons, Ltd.
Messrs. G. & J. Weir, Ltd.
The Williams & Wilkins Co., U.S.A.
P. Woodland, Esq.
Dr. L. A. Woodward.
Zeiss-Ikon, A.G.

Acknowledgment of the loan of blocks is made beneath the block in the text. May I ask the indulgence of any whose name has inadvertently been omitted?

My thanks are due to Mr. Wilfred Meynell for permission to quote the poem by Francis Thompson, *To a Snowflake*, appearing on page 42.

I am glad to be able to acknowledge here the great help given me by the professional artists employed by the publishers, namely, Mr. H. Wren (general), Mr. J. G. Turner (engineering), Mr. H. A. Bennett (general), Miss Aileen Watson (musical instruments), and Mr. S. A. Sewell; also by the photographers, namely, Messrs. W. Watson & Sons and Mr. F. Welch (microphotographs), Mr. H. Pocock and the photographers of The Commercial Process Co., Ltd.

I would wish to acknowledge my gratitude to my publishers, and especially to Mr. R. Welldon Finn and his secretary, Miss M. Taylor; I would also mention with gratitude the work of my secretaries and assistants, Mrs. G. M. Keith, Mrs. C. Newall, Miss Grace Jeffree and Miss Lewis.

11, *Gray's Inn Square*,
London, *W.C.* 1.